Greenberg's® Guide To

• 1970 - 1991 •
Lionel Trains

Volume I:
Motive Power and Rolling Stock

By Roland E. LaVoie and
Michael A. Solly, Senior Editor

With the assistance of Andrea L. Kraszewski

Copyright © 1991
by Greenberg Publishing Company, Inc.

Greenberg Publishing Company, Inc.
7566 Main Street
Sykesville, MD 21784
(301) 795-7447

Third Edition
First Printing

Manufactured in the United States of America

Greenberg Publishing Company, Inc. offers the world's largest selection of Lionel, American Flyer, LGB, Marx, Ives, and other toy train publications as well as a selection of books on model and prototype railroading, dollhouse building, and collectible toys. For a complete listing of Greenberg publications, please call or write at the above address and request a current catalogue.

Greenberg Shows, Inc. sponsors *Greenberg's Great Train, Dollhouse and Toy Shows*, the world's largest of its kind. The shows feature extravagant operating train layouts, and a display of magnificent dollhouses. The shows also present a huge marketplace of model and toy trains, for HO, N, and Z Scales; Lionel O and Standard Gauges; and S and 1 Gauges; plus layout accessories and railroadiana. It also offers a large selection of dollhouse miniatures and building materials, and collectible toys. Shows are scheduled along the East Coast each year from Massachusetts to Florida. For a list of our current shows please call or write at the above address and request our current "show schedule."

Greenberg Auctions, a division of Greenberg Shows, Inc., offers nationally advertised auctions of toy trains and toys. Please contact our auction manager at (301) 795-7447 for further information.

ISBN 0-89778-194-5 (hardback)
ISBN 0-89778-189-9 (softback)

Library of Congress Cataloging-in-Publication Data

LaVoie, Roland, 1943-
    Greenberg's guide to Lionel trains, 1970-1991 / by Roland E. LaVoie and Michael A. Solly, senior editor. -- 3rd ed.
        p.   cm.
    Rev. ed of: Greenberg's guide to Lionel trains, 1970-1988. 2nd ed. c1989.
    Includes index.
    Contents: v. 1. Motive power and rolling stock.
    ISBN 0-89778-194-5 (v. 1). -- ISBN 0-89778-189-9 (pbk. : v. 1)
    1. Railroads--Models. 2. Lionel Corporation. I. Solly, Michael A. II. LaVoie, Roland, 1943- Greenberg's guide to Lionel trains, 1970-1988. III. Greenberg Publishing Company.
IV. Title. V. Title: Guide to Lionel trains, 1970-1991. VI. Title: Lionel trains, 1970-1991.
TF197.L22 1991
625.1'9--dc20
                                                                              90-23375
                                                                                  CIP

◆ Table of Contents ◆

ACKNOWLEDGMENTS

*A*ny book of this size and complexity must be a cooperative effort on the part of many people. In this case, an army of Lionel train enthusiasts has applied its expertise to the creation, review and correction of our text. There are a few who should be acknowledged for particularly outstanding help:

First is Texas collector **Cliff Lang**, who extensively edited and corrected nearly the entire text. His intent has been to help make this the most accurate book on Lionel available, and his assistance has certainly helped us approach that goal.

Next are frequent contributors **I.D. Smith** and **Lou Bohn**, two train experts who have continuously supplied the Greenberg offices with updates on new production, previously unknown tidbits on earlier production, and some excellent viewpoints on all subjects related to Lionel. Our book would be incomplete without their substantial help.

Ohio collector **Todd Wagner** supplied us with excellent advance information on Lionel's newest pieces, along with a very useful numerical printout that helped us uncover some never-before-published obscure numbers for pieces which have been listed as "No Number" for years. Todd did an outstanding job double-checking our numbers, prices, dates, and other intricate details.

The first two editions of this book were edited by my good friend **Roland LaVoie**, who is quite possibly the most enthusiastic Lionel train man on the face of the earth. My efforts in editing this third edition pale in comparison to the work he did in creating the book in the first place. He kept me under his wing throughout the project, answering innumerable questions for which I would have had no clue without his expertise. He also brought trains to Sykesville for photography and assisted in organizing the photographic effort.

Glenn Halverson offered his expertise in the areas of sets and variations to enhance our listings.

My frequent consultations with Lionel expert **Clark O'Dell** has avoided many a pitfall and put a more correct slant on some of our descriptions and prices.

We owe great votes of thanks to several collectors and operators who have supplied excellent new information in several specialized areas:

LOTS president **Geoff Swan** supplied an excellent summary of the 9800-series reefer cars and a virtually complete listing of the convention cars for the Lionel Collectors Association of Canada.

Several TCA division members were instrumental in supplying updated information on TCA's special production: **Ted Brahm** of the New England Division, **Chris Rohlfing** of the Midwest Division (also one of our capable manuscript readers, and perhaps the acknowledged expert on prewar Lionel), **Richard Mertes** of the Great Lakes/Detroit-Toledo chapter, and **Ron Artelli** of the Southern Division.

A special thank you to all the TCA Division and Chapter officials who responded to our requests to help improve our coverage of TCA's Special Production Lionel cars.

My thanks also to **Mike Stella** for supplying detailed data on the TTOS production.

LCCA President **Bill Schmeelk** graciously lent us several of his rare cars for photography, supplied details on LCCA's newest production, and gave his permission to reprint an interesting article on the Autolite boxcar which first appeared in LCCA's fine magazine, *The Lion Roars*.

Two good friends from LOTS also deserve special note: **Dick Johnson** rewrote the Automobile Carriers chapter and supplied complete data on LOTS' convention cars. **Bill Meyer** has contributed articles before on the ore cars and the 9090 Minimax car, and this time he contributed many individual details on diesel production, both full scale and O scale.

The many new photographs for this edition was enhanced tremendously by the train collections of **Bill Dyson, Roland LaVoie, Al Rudman,** and **Francis Stem**, and in particular by a gentleman with one of the most complete Lionel collections one can imagine, **Ronald Kaptur**. Bruce Greenberg and Brad Schwab photographed the trains for this edition.

Ronald Kaptur's magnificent collection provided the basis of over half of the trains depicted in this volume. Ron brought hundreds of trains to our studio in Sykesville, Maryland and then assisted us in their photography which required three weekends. The packing and unpacking alone represented hours and hours of effort. Ron also shared his expertise on Lionel trains with us.

Al Rudman, owner of Sidetrack Hobbies in Leonardtown, Maryland made a major contribution to this book by lending hundreds of pieces from his collection for photography. His substantial efforts in lending equipment were critical to producing this comprehensive photographic record. From his perspective as a Lionel train dealer, he was able to offer important insights into Lionel policy.

Francis Stem carefully reviewed his collection and lent us many items that we could not locate elsewhere. He also assisted in the organization of the trains for photography.

Bill Dyson, who operates our 48'-long Lionel layout at our Maryland show, also brought many of his trains to photograph. One chapter in this book, "Tank Cars" contains photographs of cars representing every number. This feat was accomplished in large part because Bill specializes in tank cars and brought his unique collection for photography. Bill also assisted in organizing and transporting the several thousand trains that were gathered together for this book.

Stan Goodman packed and shipped us some most unusual cars for photography. His assistance is very much appreciated.

Dick Johnson lent us his unique collection of auto carriers to photograph, thereby providing a complete photographic record of these cars.

John Newbraugh of Pleasant Valley Process – Newbraugh Brothers Toys worked hard to supply us data on the relationship of PVP-NBT to the Lionel hobby and its contributions to the various areas of Special Production.

Reader and regular contributor **Bill Beatty** provided us with some great detail on diesel lighting and various other interesting facts. **George Romich** sent extensive information about the Berkshires and Hudsons. **John Nowaczyk** and brothers **Robert** and **Ron Hunley** also sent us comprehensive updates and new data. Our thanks to you all.

Our listings would be nowhere near as complete without the willingness of **Joe Bratspis** and the crew at the **Toy Train Station** in Feasterville, Pennsylvania. They tolerated my suspicious wanderings (with my handy tape recorder) mumbling the facts about their huge stock of new and old Lionel products.

It is really our manuscript readers who keep the Greenberg Guide on the narrow path and help verify the accuracy of every fact. We mentioned several before, but all of them deserve our thanks: **Anthony Arpino, Marcel Didier, Neil Fagan, Stan Goodman, Howard Holden, Jim Hunt, Howard Levine, Tom Rollo, Glenn Salamone, Richard Sigurdson**, and **Charles Weber**.

At the Greenberg office in downtown Sykesville, the only word to describe our diligent co-editor at Greenberg's, **Andrea Kraszewski**, is "fabulous." Thanks, Andrea! Andrea was responsible for organizing the text and coordinating communications with the many readers, as well as the supervision of the editorial direction and book compilation. **Donna Dove** assisted Andrea with the design, and numerous additions and corrections to this edition. Donna was responsible for the final layout, editorial direction and book compilation. Without their dedication and skills this book would not have been completed in a timely manner. **Cindy Floyd** assisted with last minute details and corrections. **Maureen Crum** (senior staff artist) was responsible for the design and layout of the covers. **Donna Price** proofread the book for typographical errors, style and consistency. In our photography department, **Brad Schwab** and **Bill Wantz** prepared the many necessary halftones and photostats needed for this edition. **Wendy Burgio** helped size photographs and make photostats. **Rick Andrews, Barbara Frank, Patti Hare**, and **Jan Smith** helped with preliminary typing. **Samuel Baum** supervised production.

Finally, we would also like to thank our many readers and contributors for the data they've supplied over the last two years, all fine Lionel hobbyists and collectors:

A. Arpino, F. Barkshat, P. Bauer, R. Beaulieu, R. Bicknese, M. Blacet, F. Blackwell, J. Brandon, L. Brown, L. Buman, R. Burton, J. Cahill, D. Cousins, P. Crowell, W. Cunningham, P. Czelusta, L. Da Roza, T. DeBord, C. Diaz, J. D'Introno, T. Ellison, R. Eskow, M. Finney, L. Fischer, J. Frangakis, W. Fuller.

Also these fine collectors: L. Gibbs, J. Hailey, H. Hardtke, S. Harrison, W. Howell, D. Hundt, F. Jones, B. Kaiser, J. Koblan, M. Konowich, R. Krenske, J. Kroll, N. Ladd, E. Lazar, C. Letterese, G. Ligon, F. Mace, D. Mareck, P. Mark, C. Massey, A. Menken, J. Michalak, R. Moran, D. Morse.

And these helpful Lionel hobbyists: G. Orrfeo, C. Ostapovicz, G. Petrasek, L. Price, N. Plummer, P. Repka, J. Riemersma, M. Salnick, D. Spiro, R. Stidd, P. Sudhoff, J. Timmerman, R. Weidinger, C. Whiting, E. Whyte, and F. Wilkins.

Mike Solly
March 1991

PUBLISHER'S NOTE:

Mike Solly dauntlessly assumed the enormous task of updating Roland LaVoie's comprehensive history of Modern Era Lionel. Mike subsequently spent all of his spare time for over a year on this project. In the three years since the last edition was published, Lionel has produced hundreds of new items, the most productive period in Lionel's ninety-one year history. In addition, collector knowledge of the Modern Era trains has grown rapidly, due in large part to the very important foundation created by Roland LaVoie's 1988 publication.

Mike also organized the photographic effort for this volume. Over 2000 trains were borrowed, classified, organized and photographed over three weekends. One of seven people involved in this process, Mike's combination of good humor and task orientation made the completion possible.

Bruce Greenberg
March 1991

M<small>ODERN</small> E<small>RA</small> L<small>IONE</small>L
◆ COLLECTING ◆

Greenberg's Guide for Lionel Trains, 1970-1991 – Volume I, is our most comprehensive report on the Modern Era Lionel train marketplace, yet. It provides collectors with a complete listing and current prices of Lionel modern era locomotives and rolling stock, in O and O27 Gauges, produced from 1970 through 1991. Over 1000 items are pictured in full color. In most cases, descriptions of the items have been derived from the actual pieces, however there are some exceptions. Many 1991 items, for example, were not available for viewing and their descriptions are taken from Lionel catalogues. These listings have been marked with an asterisk (*). For the sake of thoroughness, we include not only those variations which have been authenticated, but also those which have been reported, but may need further identification. In these cases we ask our readers for further information where details are missing or doubtful. Values are given for each item where there have been reported sales.

Volume II in this Modern Era series provides completion for the Lionel enthusiast. This volume pays particular attention to significant areas of specialty collecting with chapters on cars made specifically for model railroading clubs, factory errors, boxes, sets and much more. A complete listing of Modern Era accessories also appears in *Volume II*, illustrated with many color photographs.

DETERMINING VALUES

Toy train values vary for a number of reasons. First, consider the **relative knowledge** of the buyer and seller. A seller may be unaware that he has a rare variation and sell it for the price of a common piece. Another source of price variation is **short-term fluctuation** which depends on what is being offered at a given train meet on a given day. If, for example, four 8100s are for sale at a small meet, we would expect that supply would outpace demand and lead to a reduction in price. A related source of variation is the **season** of the year. The train market is slower in the summer and

sellers may at this time be more inclined to reduce prices if they really want to move an item. Another important source of price variation is the relative strength of the seller's **desire to sell** and the buyer's **eagerness to buy**. Clearly a seller in economic distress will be more eager to strike a bargain. Another source of price variation is regional. Not only are trains generally less plentiful in the South and West than they are in the Northeast, but there are regional road name preferences as well. For example, Union Pacific items may be hard to find and expensive in the West due to high collector interest in that road name; yet Reading and Erie, which are more in demand in the East, may be somewhat easier to find in Western regions. A final source of variation is **the personalities** of the seller and buyer. Some sellers like to quickly turn over items and, therefore, price their items to move; others seek a higher price and will bring an item to meet after meet until they find a willing buyer.

Train values in this book are based on *obtained* prices, rather than asking prices. The prices represent a "ready sale," that is, prices most likely to effect a quick sale at most large train meets. They may sometimes appear lower than those seen on trains at meets for two reasons. First, items that readily sell often do so in the first hour of a train meet and, therefore, are no longer visible. (We have observed that a good portion of the action at most meets occurs in the first hour.) The items that do not sell in the first hour have a higher price tag, and this price, although not necessarily representing the actual sale price, is the price found. A related source of pricing discrepancy is the willingness of some sellers to bargain over price.

Another factor which may affect prices is reconditioning done by the dealer. Some dealers take great pains to clean and service their pieces so that they look their best and operate properly. Others sell their items just as they received them, dust and all. Naturally, the more effort the dealer expends in preparing his pieces for sale, the more he can expect to charge for them. This factor may account for significant price differences among dealers selling the same equipment.

From our studies of train prices, it appears that mail order prices for used trains are generally higher than those obtained at train meets. This is appropriate considering the costs and efforts of producing and distributing a price list and packing and shipping items. Mail order items do sell at prices above those listed in this book.

On some items, we have indicated **No Reported Sales (NRS)** in the value column. This does not necessarily indicate that an item is particularly rare. It simply indicates that inadequate information is available for pricing these items.

CONDITION

For each item, we provide four categories: **Good (GD)**, **Very Good(VG)**, **Excellent(EXC)**, and **Mint(MT)**.

GOOD — Scratches, small dents, dirty.

VERY GOOD — Few scratches, exceptionally clean, no dents or rust.

EXCELLENT — Minute scratches or nicks, no dents or rust.

MINT — Brand new, absolutely unmarred with no visible signs of handling, in original box.

In the toy train field there is a great deal of concern with exterior appearance and less concern with operation. If operation is important to you, ask the seller if the train runs. If the seller indicates that he does not know whether the equipment operates, you should test it. Most train meets have test tracks for that purpose.

We include Mint prices in this edition because of the important trade in post-1970 mint items. However, there is substantial confusion in the minds of both sellers and buyers as to what constitutes "Mint" condition. How do we define mint? Among very experienced train enthusiasts, a mint piece means that it is brand new, in its original box, never run, and extremely bright and clean (and the box is, too). An item may have been removed from the box and replaced in it, but it should show no evidence of handling. A piece is not mint if it shows any scratches, fingerprints, or evidence of discoloration. It is the nature of a market for the seller to see his item in a very positive light and to seek to obtain a mint price for an excellent piece. In contrast, a buyer will see the same item in a less favorable light and will attempt to buy a mint piece for the price of one in excellent condition. It is our responsibility to point out this difference in perspective *and* the difference in value implicit in each perspective. Buyers and sellers will need to settle or negotiate their different perspectives.

We do not show values for Fair or Restored. **Fair** items are valued substantially below Good. We have not included **Restored** because such items are not a significant portion of the market for postwar trains.

As we indicated, prices in this book were derived from large train meets or shows. If you have trains to sell and you sell them to a person planning to resell them, you should not expect to obtain the prices reported in this book. Rather, you should expect to achieve about fifty to seventy-five percent of these prices. Basically, for your items to be of interest to a buyer who plans to resell them, he must purchase them for considerably less than the prices listed here.

We receive many inquiries as to whether or not a particular piece is a "good value." This book will help answer that question; but, there is NO substitute for experience in the marketplace. *We strongly recommend that novices do not make major purchases without the assistance of friends who have experience in buying and selling trains.* If you are buying a train and do not know whom to ask about its value, look for the people running the meet or show and discuss with them your need for assistance. Usually they can refer you to an experienced collector who will be willing to examine the piece and offer his opinion.

CATALOGUED OR UNCATALOGUED?

The Lionel train hobby has its own terminology. Two terms — *catalogued* and *uncatalogued* — deserve particular attention.

A *catalogued* item is one that appears in one of Lionel's principal annual consumer catalogues. An *uncatalogued* item is one that either appears in special Lionel publications, such as its Spring or Fall Collector Center brochures, dealer flyers, Stocking Stuffers brochures, Advance catalogues, or does not appear in any Lionel publication. Uncatalogued items produced for clubs, such as TCA or LCCA, are not publicized in Lionel's advertising, but are actively promoted in the respective club's publications. Many uncatalogued items may still be considered regular Lionel production, however certain uncatalogued pieces constitute a subsection, known as *special production*.

In our listings, an item is assumed to be catalogued unless otherwise stated. The dates provided for a catalogued item are the period of years in which the item appeared in the Lionel consumer catalogues. Usually this period corresponds to the item's availability from the Lionel factory to its dealers. However, in some cases, an item catalogued by Lionel in the first year listed did not become available until the second year. On the other hand, Lionel may have made an item only in its first catalogued year, but continued to list and sell remaining inventory of that item in subsequent years. The years noted for catalogued items, therefore, may not necessarily be the years in which the item was actually manufactured. Furthermore, many Lionel pieces are marked with built dates, causing confusion for the collector. For example, a car may be marked, "BLT 1-72," indicating the car was built in January of 1972. Collectors should be cautious of accepting these dates as true indicators of production, as they may or may not correspond to fact.

For uncatalogued items, the years reported are the years in which the item appeared in special Lionel publications, club publications or other advertisements. In the absence of published dates, we have made our best estimates as to an item's availability.

Cases also exist in which an item was uncatalogued in its first year (such as a Service Station set piece), but appeared in the consumer catalogue the next year. Our listings provide both years for these items, with a note indicating where and when the item was advertised.

The pricing of uncatalogued items can be a tricky proposition. Some uncatalogued items are hard to find, while others are quite common. The fact that an item is uncatalogued does not in itself determine the item's value, and many uncatalogued items sell for the same price as similar catalogued items. Collectors should apply the same criteria for determining the value of an uncatalogued item as is used for determining the value of a catalogued item.

SPECIAL PRODUCTION

Special Production is a loosely defined term that generally refers to particular uncatalogued items, which appear unannounced. However, there is not a consensus as to the precise meaning of this term and which items constitute special production.

Some believe that pieces made for special events or people are special production items. The 9467 Tennessee World's Fair boxcar is an example of this. However, others insist that because this car was made by Lionel, it should be considered regular production. Some collectors believe anything made for a particular department or hardware store is special production, since it is not catalogued.

As cataloguers of Lionel production, our difficulty lies in determining clear categories of description, which will best inform and serve the collecting community. The temptation is to create a clear definition of the term, Special Production, and extract those items from the main group of listings for their own special presentation. However, the lack of consensus in defining Special Production makes this difficult. The editors, in attempting to capture as much of Lionel production as possible, have included in this volume such items as store specials, Toy Fair and Season Greetings cars, cars commemorating special events, and even specials made for individuals like the hoppers and engines made for distributor Glen Uhl of Ohio. While these items fall under the definition

of Special Production for many, most of them have been assigned regular catalogue numbers by Lionel. Furthermore, separating them from regular production and leaving them out of this volume would result in confusing holes in the listings. Since all these pieces were produced entirely by Lionel, are available on the open train market, and elicit considerable interest from Lionel fans, they have been listed in this volume with regular production.

However, there is special interest in equipment produced for train clubs, with collectors undertaking to put together complete sets of these club cars. Rather than intersperse these cars with regular listings and dilute their unique story, we have combined them into a comprehensive report in a chapter entitled "Train Club Cars" in *Volume II*. Redecorated Lionel equipment produced by Pleasant Valley Process (PVP) and Newbraugh Brothers Trains (NBT) are also listed in *Volume II*.

The collecting of Lionel trains is a rewarding and fascinating experience. In just the last few years, Lionel has achieved a new renaissance with the production of hundreds of new cars and accessories, including its high-quality and detailed O scale production and particularly the new steam engines. We consider the documentation of Lionel's continuing evolution to be of extreme importance to the hobby, as well as our enjoyable service to the enthusiast. As the saga of Lionel moves toward its hundredth year, the importance of maintaining its history comes into greater focus. Join us in a look at twenty-one years of modern production, even as we anticipate an exciting and expanding future of Lionel trains.

DIESEL LOCOMOTIVES

For this third edition of the Lionel modern era Guide, Diesel Locomotives, Electric Engines, and Motorized Units have been separated into separate chapters. Each chapter has been subdivided for easier reference.

When General Mills' Fundimensions toy division took over production of trains from the Lionel Corporation in 1970, its managers realized that a whole new generation awaited the production and rediscovery of Lionel trains. The firm realized that this new generation did not necessarily share the nostalgia of its elders. Therefore, Fundimensions decided to market its locomotives not just to people with actual memories of steam locomotives, but also to those who would look for imitations of the contemporary world around them. That meant diesel engines, not steamers. The rapid proliferation of diesel engines made economic sense in the early years of Fundimensions, even if it might have been at the expense of the steamers — a new market for toy trains had to be developed.

There were two other highly significant economic advantages to the rapid marketing of many types of diesels. First, diesels had fewer parts and were less costly than steamers and faster to produce. Second, Fundimensions could take advantage of new decorating processes much more easily on the flat plastic surfaces of the diesel cabs than it could on the rounded boilers of the steam locomotives. The postwar decorating techniques were limited to decals, heat stamping, rubber stamping, and some silk-screening. As a subsidiary of General Mills, Fundimensions had access to people knowledgeable in the new and versatile decorating processes known as *electrocal* and *tampo*. By these means, colorful contemporary railroad paint schemes could be applied to Fundimensions' trains — and color sells trains to the public.

Right from the start, Fundimensions made its policy apparent. In its 1970 catalogue only a couple of 2-4-2 Columbia steamers were actually produced. However, the catalogue featured an exceptionally colorful orange and white Illinois Central GP-9, a bright blue Santa Fe NW-2 switcher, and an Alco AA pair of Santa Fe diesels in the famous "war bonnet" paint scheme.

As the years went by, Fundimensions issued many different styles of diesels. Most of these styles have continued under Kenner-Parker and Lionel Trains, Inc. (LTI) management. This chapter discusses and lists them by major styles, including two entirely new diesel types brought out by LTI in the past few years.

Engine Numbering System

The numbering system used for Lionel diesel engines can be somewhat confusing. Prior to the mid-1980s, Lionel's diesel (and steam) engines used a four-digit 8000-series catalogue numbering code. The first digit (8) represents the fact that it is a locomotive. The second digit denotes the year of production, without reference to the decade. This obviously causes much confusion, since it does not explain if an 8370, for example, was made in 1973 or 1983! It also illustrates how one can find an 8365, produced in 1973, listed in a catalogue side-by-side an 8370, produced in 1983. The third and fourth digits in the 8000-series number are simply assigned arbitrarily. Sometimes these third and fourth digits identify a group of diesels within a set, such as the catalogue numbers 8370, 8371 and 8372, which represent the powered New York Central F-3 A and its two matching dummy units.

The four-digit catalogue number was usually identical to the number found on the corresponding engine's cab. However, there are exceptions to this rule. For example, the 8359 Chessie GP-7 (1973) features a "GM 50" on its cab — commemorating General Motors' 50th anniversary — instead of the conventional "8359". Another interesting case is the 7500 Lionel 75th Anniversary U36B (1975-1976). This engine's cab reads "1900-1975", instead of the customary "7500".

---

* *Asterisk found in listings indicates that the information within that listing was derived from Lionel catalogue only.*

After 1986 Lionel switched from its traditional four-digit catalogue numbering system to a five-digit one. For the diesels, Lionel merely placed a "1" before the "8". It is important to note, however, that the engines themselves still bear only the four-digit 8000-series number (the "1" is not included on the cab). The first digit in this new catalogue number — "1" — signifies the engine was issued after 1986. The second digit — "8" — still identifies the item as a powered unit. The third digit no longer identifies the year of production, but rather distinguishes between Collector and Traditional subcategories (see Figure 1.1). And the fourth and fifth digits are sequence numbers. This practice sometimes leads to confusion between the old and new numbering systems: for example, the 18903 Amtrak Alco bears the same "8903" cab number as a small Rio Grande steam engine from 1978! (For an in-depth description of Lionel's complete numbering system, see the "Numbering Systems" article in Chapter 1.)

Lionel's Current Diesel Numbering System

181XX Diesel engines: F-type (Collector)
182XX Diesel engines: SD-type (Collector)
183XX Diesel, Electric engines: FM & GG-1 (Collector)
185XX Diesel engines, switchers: GP-series (Collector)
188XX-189XX Diesel engines (Traditional)

Figure 1.1

Diesel Motor Types

Lionel has produced three basic motor types for its modern era diesels. *Type I* and *Type II* are carry-overs from the hardy postwar motors which have seen so much use and abuse at the hands of Lionel operators for over four decades. *Type III* is a major technological innovation from Fundimensions/Lionel which has drawn rave reviews since its 1982 inception. Actually, there are many sub-variations of the motor, gear and truck assemblies, due to a large variety of ways Lionel arranged the gearing to get one, two or more drive axles. This was also determined by how much space was available and how the motor had to fit within the cab.

Each motor type was developed to achieve a long lifespan, able to withstand tremendous levels of shock, heat and vibration. They are remarkable feats of model engineering.

TYPE I: This is diversely known as a *separate motor and truck assembly*, or the *Pullmor motor* (a description found in the catalogues). This motor type (see Figure 1.2) consists of a single- or double-wound field, depending on the E-unit type, surrounding an armature with a worm gear. The worm gear fits down into the top of the power truck, where it drives either a gear on the main drive axle, or internal spur gearing in the truck which transmits power to more than one geared axle.

The motor is mounted to the truck via a single mounting screw and pivots in a keyhole-shaped opening in the frame.

This arrangement provides excellent pulling power and track operation, since the free-pivoting trucks and wheels can round tight radii and switches more easily than the Type II motor. This drive system is a direct descendant of the system developed for the Fairbanks-Morse Trainmaster in 1954, and modern Lionel has used it in its "premium" diesels and electrics: the F-3s, FMs, EP-5s, and GG-1s. Interestingly, postwar Lionel used this motor in its GP models, but Fundimensions chose the less expensive Type II for the majority of its "Geeps." When mounted in twin-motor configurations (especially with Magnetraction), as in the FMs, the GG-1s and later F-3s, these motors can outpull anything else on tinplate rails.

TYPE II: Known as the *integral truck and motor assembly* (intended to differentiate it from Type I). This drive system is by far the most common motor in the Lionel product line, although the Type III can motor is making rapid gains. The Type II motor (see Figure 1.3) was originally developed during Lionel's downsizing period in 1955 in response to cost-cutting demands. In this system the motor field, drive gears and axle mounting frame (i.e., the main body of the truck) are all one piece. The spur gears are mounted on one side of this piece, driving geared wheels. This drive system rides in a large hole in the frame, suspended from spring-loaded bushings traveling in curved slots fore and aft of the large hole. The integral motor/truck system does not perform as well on switches as its Type I counterpart, because its more rigid wheel base does not conform to the curves as easily. Type II motors are found on modern era Lionel road switchers — GP-7s, GP-9s, GP-20s, Alcos, U36s and smaller SD units. A modified version is used on the large SD-40 diesels.

There are variations in this basic motor type regarding the types of roller pickups. Type IIa was used on the early MPC engines prior to 1972, and consisted of a spring brass wiper pressing down on two hollow roller cylinders. This tended to accumulate dirt and hinder operation, so it was replaced in 1972 with the more common spring-roller arm assemblies using solid rollers. The latter is the Type IIb motor, and is one of the more common motors in the Lionel line.

TYPE III: This is the *can motor,* introduced by Lionel in 1982 (see Figure 1.4). More precisely, it originated on the low-end DC-powered switchers in 1974. The motor itself is DC-powered. In the early 1980s, Lionel was inspired to add a rectifier circuit, thereby allowing it to be used for AC operation as well. Since then, the can motor (and its rectifier) has moved into the higher-end Traditional diesels (those for separate-sale), and even a few Collector engines.

The principal feature of this motor is that it is small and completely enclosed, so maintenance is practically eliminated. The only protrusion is the armature shaft to which the drive gear is attached. The remainder of the truck and geared wheel assemblies are similar to the Type II truck designs. However, in this case, the motor fits down into the truck body rather than riding above inside the cab (which, by the way, is the configuration used in real diesels). This has the additional advantage of permitting more room in the cab for such niceties as the electronic E-Unit, an electronic horn, or even Rail-Sounds.

The can motor is so small and lightweight that the first engines using it were too light to operate well and would jump the track at switches. This problem was solved by adding a weight in the cab, for which there was ample room. Lionel did this on models after 1984, and added a second can motor in the other truck for many newer engines. Engines with these motors run well at the lower voltages which cause the Type I and II motors to stall. The enclosed motor requires little or no lubrication, although the gears do. For all these reasons, and because of the reliability demonstrated by them so far, the Type III motors have been a hit with most Lionel operators — even the die-hard traditionalists. The Type III motors have proven to be excellent runners. Recent SD-series diesels have used a variation on the motor in which it is mounted vertically in the truck, not horizontally.

The can motor is clearly less expensive for Lionel to produce (or subcontract), and so should be expected in more engines as the years go by.

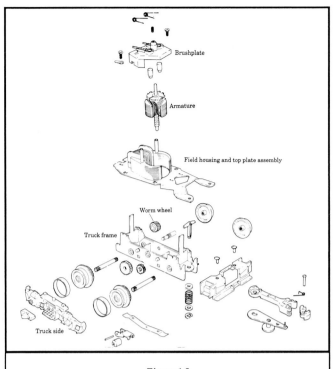

Figure 1.3

Example of Type II Motor/Truck Assembly (GP-series).

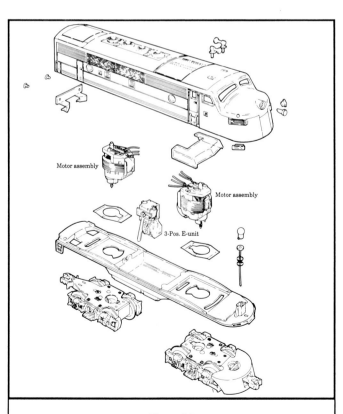

Figure 1.2

Example of Type I Motor (dual-motored F-3).

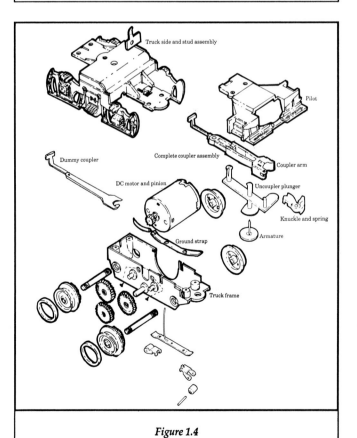

Figure 1.4

Example of Type III Can Motor (Traditional series GPs and Alcos).
Note: Electronic reverse located elsewhere on engine frame.

A spectacular chromed F-3 ABA set. The chromed plastic on this set is difficult to maintain in unblemished condition.   *A. Rudman Colle*
Top shelf: 8054 and 8055 C & S Burlington AA units.
Bottom shelf: Matching 8062 B-unit

GENERAL MOTORS' F-3 DIESELS

In the late 1930s the Electro-Motive Division of General Motors startled the real train world with its FT diesel demonstrator engines. These streamlined locomotives piled up mile after maintenance-free mile, and they routinely pulled trains of six thousand tons, whereas the biggest steam engines could only handle half that much. Following World War II, these freight diesels and their sister passenger units, the E Series, rapidly replaced steam engines all over the country. In 1947 General Motors introduced the F-3 Series, the first truly successful freight diesels. (This story is eloquently told in Robert Carper's book, *American Railroads In Transition: The Passing of the Steam Engines.*)

Despite some personal doubts on the part of Joshua Lionel Cowen, a die-hard steam fan, the Lionel Corporation was quick to incorporate these streamlined beauties. In 1948, just one year after the real locomotives emerged, Lionel produced its Santa Fe and New York Central F-3 locomotives. The Santa Fe model eventually became the best-selling locomotive in Lionel's history because of its dependable performance and its spectacular Santa Fe "war bonnet" paint scheme of red, silver, yellow and black.

Fundimensions did not wait very long to revive this legend of the tinplate rails. In 1973 a special brochure announced the return of the F-3 diesel in Baltimore and Ohio markings (8363 and 8364). By 1978 Fundimensions had reissued many of the scarcest Lionel models. Indeed, some of them, like the Canadian Pacific and Southern F-3 diesels, would become just as scarce as their forebears. In 1976 Fundimensions even reissued the Santa Fe model (8652 and 8653), expecting slow sales because of the presence of so many of the older locomotives within collections. However, the paint scheme was so appealing the firm could not make the Santa Fe locomotives fast enough, and today this model is harder to find than any of its postwar predecessors!

All of the F-3 models produced until 1978 were single-motor locomotives without Magnetraction, horns or some of the intricate trim of the older Lionel pieces. The F-3 disappeared from the catalogue in 1978, but not for long. Another special bulletin announced a twin-motor F-3 (8851) in New Haven markings for late 1978. It was followed in 1979 by a Brunswick green Pennsylvania twin-motored pair (8952 and 8953). On this set, the deluxe trim was at last restored to the F-3. During that same year, collector pressure prompted Lionel to issue a pair of Pennsylvania locomotives in tuscan as well (8970 and 8971), so that the F-3 pair would match the Congressional Limited passenger cars of that year. Since then, all F-3 locomotives have been twin-motored pairs. Also, several new models have appeared, including ones never issued in the postwar era — such as the Southern Pacific (8260, 8261 and 8262), the Union Pacific (8480, 8481 and 8482) and a Burlington Texas Zephyr in chromed plastic (8054, 8055 and 8062). The New York Central F-3 (8370, 8371 and 8372) was revived in 1983, along with an attractive set of passenger cars to create a modern "Twentieth Century Limited." B-units have been available for all of the F-3 locomotives produced, except the 8568 Preamble Express. The B-units were unlighted and came with fixed couplers, except the most recent 18101 Santa Fe, which has two operating couplers.

The F-3 diesels are excellent runners, either as single-motored or double-motored units, thanks to Fundimensions' use of the separate (Type I) motor and power truck instead of the integral (Type II) motor and power truck used on the GP-series diesels. They are usually brisk sellers which command a good premium. Strangely enough, the older postwar Lionel F-3 locomotives have also increased in value, even though they have been reissued. The probable reason for this is the strong appeal of this locomotive as both an operating unit and a historic locomotive. Many operators also say the massive look of the engine gives it a more scaled appearance than other diesels.

The values of the popular F-3 diesels have skyrocketed in the last few years, along with those of their postwar counterparts. Readers will note the sharp price increases reflected in this edition of the modern era Lionel Guide, as compared to the last.

As it turned out, Lionel had something up its sleeve regarding plans for this engine. After a gap in F-3 production following the 1985 and 1987 runs of the Illinois Central (8580, 8581 and 8582), Lionel announced the third revival of the Santa Fe F-3 in 1991 — this time with RailSounds. And there is hope for other road name collectors: while modern Lionel has reissued most of the old postwar favorites, there are still three to go — the Wabash, the Western Pacific, and the Texas Special.

F-3 Body Types

All but one of the modern era Lionel F-3 sets were produced in powered A-dummy B-dummy A combinations, although not all were for sale at the same time. Often, a B-unit would follow a year or two after the powered A-unit was issued.

Six body types for the A-units have been documented, varying with the number of louvers along the side and the three ridges along the lower flanks. The F-3 A-unit body types are shown here in roughly chronological order (see Figure 1.5), starting in 1973 with the *Type I* body for the B & O and Canadian Pacific sets, and the Rio Grande in 1974. *Type II* appeared only for the Milwaukee Road set in 1975, and *Type III* for the Amtrak F-3s in 1974-1975. A *Type IV* appeared briefly for the Southern and Preamble pieces, and the *Type V* for the Santa Fe and New Haven sets. All of these body styles feature molded-in (sealed) porthole windows painted with the rest of the body.

Then in 1979-1980, with the introduction of the Burlington and Pennsylvania sets, Lionel settled on the body style for all later entries — *Type VI*. This style featured two welcome detailing additions — nose grab-irons and the placement of snap-in, clear plastic lenses in the now-opened portholes.

There are only two types of B-unit bodies (not shown). The first, and older, style has closed portholes and one side louver. It is associated with A-styles I-V. The second B-unit has clear plastic opened portholes, like the A-units, and has two side louvers. These are akin to the later Type VI A-unit body style.

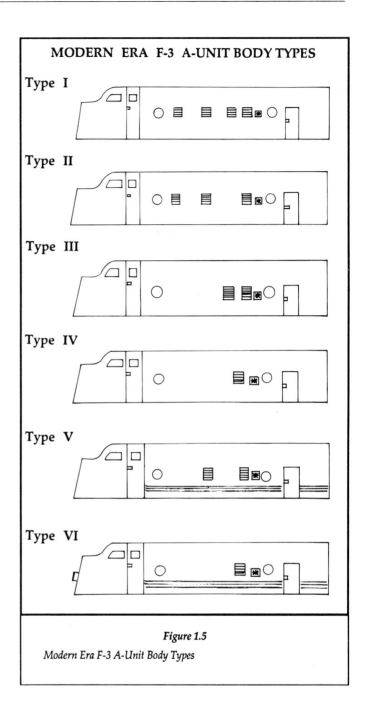

MODERN ERA F-3 A-UNIT BODY TYPES

Type I

Type II

Type III

Type IV

Type V

Type VI

Figure 1.5

Modern Era F-3 A-Unit Body Types

Common Features

All F-3 A-units have a nose light bulb which illuminates the cab and the headlight. Each unit has an operating coupler on the front and a dummy coupler at the rear, until the most recent 18100 Santa Fe engines which have two operating couplers.

A NOTE ON F-3 DIESEL PRICING: The pricing of the F-3 diesels in this section follows usual sales practices. These engines (unlike most other diesels) were often boxed and sold together in A-A or A-B-A combinations. It is extremely rare to find one component of these sets for sale separately. In such cases, this book lists a price as "priced as a set with..." In other cases some F-3s, especially the earlier (prior to 1978) powered units and B-units, were sold separately and boxed separately. Quantities varied. For example, the dummy 8653 Santa Fe F-3 is far more difficult to find than its powered 8652 counterpart. In these instances this book shows individual prices.

A. Rudman, F. Stem, L. Caponi, and R. LaVoie Collection

More of Lionel's handsomest F-3 AA pairs.
Top shelf: **8260 and 8262 Southern Pacific "Daylight."**
Second shelf: **8363 and 8364 Baltimore and Ohio, the first modern era F-3 units.**
Third shelf: **8365 and 8366 Canadian Pacific, available only as part of 1973 Service Station Special set and now very scarce.**
Bottom shelf: **8370 and 8372 New York Central.**

F-3 LISTINGS

	GD	VG	EXC	MT

8054 C & S BURLINGTON: 1980, dual-motored F-3 A- unit; Type VI metallic silver body; black modernistic lettering; red nose markings; lighted; clear plastic portholes; known as the "Texas Zephyr" ("C & S" stands for Colorado and Southern, a railroad acquired by Burlington in 1908 and run as a division). The chromed plastic of this engine is difficult to obtain in unblemished condition. Matching dummy A-unit (8055) and B-unit (8062) available. Six matching passenger cars available separately. *Priced as set with 8055 dummy A- unit.*

— — **350 450**

8055 C & S BURLINGTON: 1980, dummy F-3 A-unit; lighted; matches 8054. *Priced as set with 8054 powered unit.*

— — **350 450**

8059 PENNSYLVANIA: 1980, dummy F-3 B-unit; un-catalogued; Brunswick green with gold stripes and lettering; clear plastic portholes; matches 8952 and 8953 F-3 A-units. Announced only in the Fall 1980 Collector Center brochure. Hard to find.

— — **300 400**

	GD	VG	EXC	MT

8060 PENNSYLVANIA: 1980, dummy F-3 B-unit; un-catalogued; tuscan body; gold stripes and lettering; clear plastic portholes; matches 8970 and 8971 F-3 A-units. Variations exist regarding the intensity of the gold stamping. There are also reports that fakes of this unit have been made. J. Tomczyk comment. Announced only in the Fall 1980 Collector Center brochure. Hard to find.

— — **300 425**

8062 C & S BURLINGTON: 1980, dummy F-3 B-unit; un-catalogued; clear plastic portholes; matches 8054 and 8055 F-3 A-units. Announced only in the Fall 1980 Collector Center brochure.

— — **150 195**

8164 PENNSYLVANIA: 1981, F-3 B-unit; uncatalogued; Brunswick green body; clear plastic portholes; operating horn; matches 8952/8953 AA pair. Distributors were required to purchase nearly $800 worth of goods to acquire three of these units. Very difficult to find. This unit and the 8059 are a match except for the horn. Announced only in the Fall 1981 Collector Center brochure.

— — **400 495**

8260 SOUTHERN PACIFIC: 1982-83, dual-motored F-3 A-unit; Type VI body with distinctive red, orange, white and black "Daylight" paint scheme; three-position reverse unit; one-axle Magnetraction; lighted cab and number boards; clear plastic port-

Some nice splashes of color in these F-3 AA pairs.

A. Rudman, F. Stem, L. Caponi, and R. LaVoie Collections

Top shelf: 8464 and 8465 Rio Grande, available only as part of 1974 Service Station Special set.
Second shelf: 8480 and 8482 Union Pacific. Some of these yellow-painted pairs did not match each other.
Third shelf: 8555 and 8557 The Milwaukee Road, available only as part of 1975 Service Station Special set.
Bottom shelf: 8566 and 8567 Southern "Crescent Limited."

	GD	VG	EXC	MT

holes; one operating coupler on front, dummy coupler on rear. This bright, unique color scheme has become a collector favorite, as has the entire "Daylight" set. Part of 1982 Spring Collector Series as a limited edition, came with matching dummy 8262. Six matching passenger cars available as separate- sale only. *Priced as a set with 8262.* — — 675 795

8261 SOUTHERN PACIFIC: 1982-83, dummy F-3 B-unit; matches 8260. Probably the most difficult of all F-3 B-units to obtain. From 1982 Fall Collector Center brochure.
— — 700 1000

8262 SOUTHERN PACIFIC: 1982-83, dummy F-3 A-unit; matches 8260. *Priced as a set with 8260 powered unit.*
— — 675 795

8363 BALTIMORE AND OHIO: 1973-75, single-motored F-3 A-unit; dark blue plastic body painted light blue; white and gray top; yellow lettering on black stripe; Type I body with sealed portholes; lighted. Reissue of scarce 2368 postwar model.
— 100 250 325

8364 BALTIMORE AND OHIO: 1973-75, dummy F-3 A-unit; lighted; matches 8363. — 60 120 200

8365 CANADIAN PACIFIC: 1973, single-motored F-3 A-unit; uncatalogued; Type I body with sealed portholes; lighted;

reportedly only 2,500 manufactured. Came with set 1350, the 1973 Service Station Special. Reissue of famous 2373 postwar F-3, and now equally scarce. *Priced as a set with 8366.*
(A) Gray plastic body painted brown, maroon and gray with yellow lettering. — 200 500 850
(B) Blue plastic body painted brown, maroon and gray with yellow lettering. — 200 500 850

8366 CANADIAN PACIFIC: 1973, dummy A-unit; lighted. *Priced as a set with 8365.*
(A) Matches 8365(A). — 200 500 850
(B) Matches 8365(B). — 200 500 850

8370 NEW YORK CENTRAL: 1983, dual-motored F-3 A-unit; dark gray Type VI body; light gray lightning bolt pattern; white lettering; two-axle Magnetraction; three-position reverse unit; lighted; clear plastic portholes; operating coupler at front end; matches 8371 and 8372. A reissue of the classic NYC 2333 offered by Lionel in 1948. Six matching passenger cars were available separately. *Priced as a set with 8371 and 8372.*
— — 500 700

8371 NEW YORK CENTRAL: 1983, dummy F-3 B-unit; electronic diesel horn; clear plastic portholes; matches 8370 and 8372. *Priced as a set with 8370 and 8372.*
— — 500 700

More B-units for extending your F-3 AA pairs.
Top shelf: 8469 Canadian Pacific; 8474   Rio Grande.
Second shelf: 8481 Union Pacific; 8575   The Milwaukee Road.
Third shelf: 8581 Illinois Central; 8661   Southern.
Bottom shelf: 8777 Santa Fe; 8864 N H.

A. Rudman, F. Stem, L. Caponi, and R. LaVoie Collection

	GD	VG	EXC	MT

See Factory Errors and Prototypes chapter in Volume II, first edition.

8372 NEW YORK CENTRAL: 1983, dummy F-3 A-unit; lighted; clear plastic portholes; operating couplers at cab end; matches 8370 and 8371. *Priced as a set with 8370 and 8371.*
— — **500 700**

8464 RIO GRANDE: 1974, single-motored F-3 A-unit; uncatalogued; Type I yellow body; black lettering and silver roof; sealed portholes; lighted. Only 3,000 manufactured. Came in uncatalogued 1974 Service Station Special set 1450. Reissue of postwar 2379, but with a brighter yellow body. *Priced as a set with 8465.*
— **150 200 350**

8465 RIO GRANDE: 1974, dummy F-3 A-unit; lighted; matches 8464. *Priced as a set with 8464.*
— **150 200 350**

8466 AMTRAK: 1974-75, single-motored F-3 A-unit; flat silver Type III body and sides; black roof and nose hood; red and blue logo; sealed portholes; lighted.
(A) Price for powered A-unit only. — **100 200 350**
(B) Priced as a set with 8467. — — — **500**

8467 AMTRAK: 1974-75, dummy F-3 A-unit; lighted; matches 8466.
(A) Price for dummy A-unit only. — **60 80 150**
(B) Priced as a set with 8466. — — — **500**

8468 BALTIMORE AND OHIO: 1974, dummy F-3 B-unit; uncatalogued; blue body; yellow lettering; sealed portholes; matches 8363 and 8364 A-units.
(A) Top edge of sides not painted. — — **150 175**
(B) Top edge of sides painted. — — **150 175**

8469 CANADIAN PACIFIC: 1974, dummy F-3 B-unit; uncatalogued; sealed portholes; matches 8365. Hard to find. No individual box. — **100 200 300**

8474 RIO GRANDE: 1975, dummy F-3 B-unit; uncatalogued; yellow and green body; silver roof; sealed portholes; matches 8464 and 8465. — — **125 175**

8475 AMTRAK: 1975, dummy F-3 B-unit; uncatalogued; silver body and sides with black roof; red and blue logo; sealed portholes; matches 8466 and 8467. — — **125 150**

8480 UNION PACIFIC: 1984, dual-motored F-3 A locomotive; Type VI yellow body; red and gray striping and lettering; dark gray roof, nose, frame and trucks; lighted; clear plastic portholes;

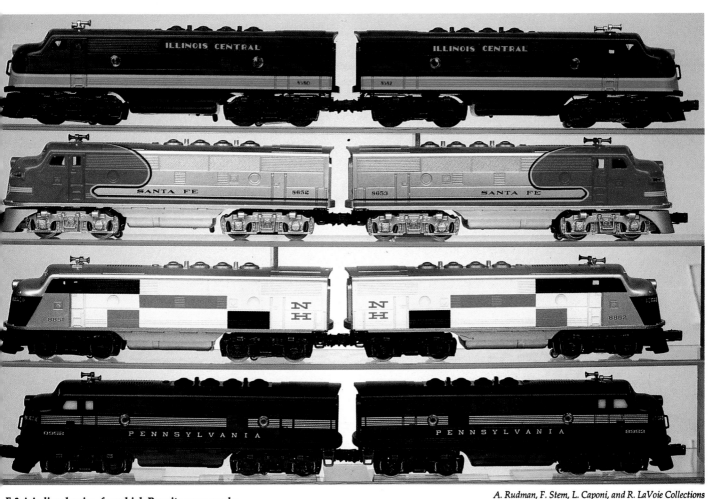

F-3 AA diesel pairs, for which B-units were made.

A. Rudman, F. Stem, L. Caponi, and R. LaVoie Collections

...shelf: 8580 and 8582 Illinois Central.

...d shelf: 8652 and 8653 Santa Fe. The A dummy is extremely hard to find.

...d shelf: 8851 and 8852 N H. This engine, from 1978, was the first twin-motored F-3 produced in the modern era.

...m shelf: 8952 and 8953 Pennsylvania. Note the frosted window inserts, an ordering mistake. There were two B-units made for this pair, one with **and** ...e without a horn.

	GD	VG	EXC	MT

Union Pacific shield-and-wing decal on nose; Magnetraction. Headed the Overland Limited set with six separate-sale matching passenger cars. Collectors have complained that many examples do not match in color: the engine has been found in medium and darker yellow shades, and many boxes have to be examined to find matching colors.

	GD	VG	EXC	MT
(A) Price for powered A-unit only.	—	—	200	300
(B) Priced as a set with 8481 and 8482.	—	—	450	550

8481 UNION PACIFIC: 1984, dummy F-3 B-unit; electronic diesel horn; matches 8480 and 8482.

(A) Price for dummy B-unit only.	—	—	125	175
(B) Priced as a set with 8480 and 8482.	—	—	450	550

8482 UNION PACIFIC: 1984, dummy F-3 A-unit; lighted; matches 8480 and 8481.

(A) Price for dummy A-unit only.	—	—	90	125
(B) Priced as a set with 8480 and 8481.	—	—	450	550

	GD	VG	EXC	MT

8555 THE MILWAUKEE ROAD: 1975, single-motored F-3 A- unit; uncatalogued; gray and orange Type II body; yellow lettering; sealed portholes; lighted. Came in uncatalogued 1975 Service Station Special set 1579. Reissue of postwar 2378.

(A) Price for powered A-unit only.	—	150	200	275
(B) Priced as a set with 8557.	—	—	300	400

8557 THE MILWAUKEE ROAD: 1975, dummy F-3 A-unit; uncatalogued; lighted; matches 8555.

(A) Price for dummy A-unit only.	—	75	100	150
(B) Priced as a set with 8555.	—	—	300	400

8566 SOUTHERN: 1975-77, single-motored F-3 A-unit; green Type IV body with white stripes; the "Crescent Limited" in gold lettering; sealed portholes; lighted.

	—	125	275	400

8567 SOUTHERN: 1975-77, dummy F-3 A-unit; lighted; matches 8566.

	—	60	125	200

8568 PREAMBLE EXPRESS: 1975, single-motored F-3 A-unit; uncatalogued; Type IV red, white and blue body; sealed portholes; lighted. Scheduled to be part of a "Freedom Train" in 1976 with matching passenger cars, which were never produced.

All of Lionel's F-3s are in great demand and hard to find now, especially these shown.
Top shelf: 8970 and 8971 Pennsylvania. These were made when collectors complained that the green 8952 and 8953 did not match the Congressioɴ passenger cars.
Second shelf: 8059 Pennsylvania B-unit, Brunswick green, no horn; 8060 Pennsylvania B-unit, tuscan.
Third shelf: 8164 Pennsylvania B-unit, Brunswick green, with horn; 8261 Southern Pacific B-unit. Both are extremely hard to find.
Bottom shelf: 8371 New York Central B-unit; 8468 Baltimore and Ohio B-unit.

	GD	VG	EXC	MT

No dummy units, either A or B, were issued (the only F-3 to be so made), although some custom-made post-factory engines in this scheme have been found, as well as cab shells placed on dummy chassis. Announced in a late 1975 dealer flyer.

| | — | — | 100 | 150 |

8575 THE MILWAUKEE ROAD: 1975, dummy F-3 B-unit; matches 8555.

| | — | — | 100 | 175 |

8580 ILLINOIS CENTRAL: 1985, 1987, dual-motored F-3 A-unit; medium brown Type VI body (not dark brown as shown in catalogue) with orange and yellow striping; yellow lettering; lighted cab and number boards (which have engine numbers for the first time); clear plastic portholes; black front grab-irons; Magnetraction; black frame and trucks. Reissue of postwar 2363. Separate-sale item from City of New Orleans passenger set. Six matching passenger cars available separately. *Priced as a set with matching 8582 dummy F-3 A-unit.*

| | — | — | 400 | 475 |

8581 ILLINOIS CENTRAL: 1985, 1987, dummy F-3 B-unit; electronic diesel horn; matches 8580 and 8582, but sold separately.

| | — | — | 200 | 250 |

8582 ILLINOIS CENTRAL: 1985, 1987, dummy F-3 A-unit; lighted; matches 8580 and 8581. *Priced as a set with 8580 powered unit.*

| | — | — | 400 | 475 |

8652 SANTA FE: 1976-77, single-motored F-3 A-unit; Type V red and silver body; lighted; sealed portholes. Sold separately. This and the recent 18100/18102 Santa Fe F-3s are the only F-3 sets to have silver trucks.

| | — | 75 | 300 | 400 |

8653 SANTA FE: 1976-77, dummy F-3 A-unit; Type V body; lighted; sealed portholes; matches 8562, but sold separately. Very difficult to find.

| | — | 80 | 225 | 350 |

8661 SOUTHERN: 1976, dummy F-3 B-unit; sealed portholes; matches 8566 and 8567 F-3 A-units. Hard to find.

| | — | — | 125 | 200 |

8777 SANTA FE: 1977-78, dummy F-3 B-unit; matches 8652. This B-unit, like its matching A, is unique in having silver trucks. Difficult to find.

| | — | 85 | 200 | 300 |

8851 N H: 1978-79, (New Haven) dual-motored F-3 A-unit; Type V gray plastic body painted silver-white, orange and black; three ridges run from the cab door to the rear of the side; white "N H" on nose — the "N" has no serifs on the bottom right side

	GD	VG	EXC	MT

(which matches the original 2242 Lionel F-3 New Haven, but differs from the way "N H" is shown on the boxcars); black truck side frames; sealed portholes; lighted; rubber tires; operating front coupler. This model improved upon its predecessor by adding the second motor. *Priced as a set with 8852.*

	—	—	**300**	**400**

8852 N H: 1978-79, (New Haven) dummy F-3 A-unit; Type V body; lighted; matches 8851. Came with 8851 as set. *Priced as a set with 8851.*   — — **300** **400**

8864 N H: 1978, (New Haven) dummy F-3 B-unit; matches 8851 and 8852.   — — **125** **175**

8952 PENNSYLVANIA: 1979, dual-motored F-3 A-unit; gray plastic Type VI body painted Brunswick green; five gold stripes merge on red, black and gold keystone nose decal; gold stripes and lettering are electrocals (note that the areas in which the electrocals are applied have a flat finish readily visible when the train is held on its side); clear plastic portholes; nose grab-irons; lighted; clear number boards without numbers; frosted-white cab windows (result of a parts-ordering error by Lionel); each motor has two geared wheels with rubber tires and a single pickup roller; steps on rear; operating coupler on front, dummy coupler on rear. The engine and its 8970 tuscan-painted twin have proven very popular with collectors, possibly because old Lionel never made P R R F-3s in the postwar era. Came with matching 8953 dummy A-unit. *Priced as a set with 8953.*   — **300** **600** **750**

8953 PENNSYLVANIA: 1979, dummy F-3 A-unit; lighted; matches 8952. *Priced as a set with 8952.*

	—	**300**	**600**	**750**

8970 PENNSYLVANIA: 1979-80, dual-motored F-3 A-unit; tuscan-painted Type VI body; five gold stripes; clear plastic portholes; front nose grab-irons. Made as match to Congressional passenger set. Announced in the 1979 Collector Center brochure and catalogued in 1980. Difficult to obtain now. *Priced as a set with matching 8971 dummy.*   — **225** **400** **500**

8971 PENNSYLVANIA: 1979-80, dummy F-3 A-unit; matches 8970. *Priced as a set with 8970.*   — **225** **400** **500**

18100 SANTA FE*: 1991, dual-motored F-3 A-unit; red, silver, black and yellow "war bonnet" paint scheme; Type VI body; Magnetraction; nose grab-irons; metal silver ladders; three-position E-unit; lighted; printed number boards; die-cast silver-painted trucks; clear plastic portholes; operating couplers at both ends. Lionel billed this engine as a return to the detail design of the original 2333 postwar Santa Fe from 1948, including the mesh screen in the roof vents. Five matching passenger cars sold separately. *Priced as a set with 18101 and 18102.*   — — — **600**

18101 SANTA FE*: 1991, dummy F-3 B-unit; This unit, unlike earlier B-units, has screened roof vents, metal ladders, silver-painted trucks, and operating couplers at both ends; matches 18100 and 18102. *Priced as a set with 18100 and 18102.*   — — — **600**

18102 SANTA FE*: 1991, dummy F-3 A-unit; RailSounds; lighted; screened roof vents; metal ladders; silver-painted trucks; matches 18100. *Priced as a set with 18100 and 18101.*   — — — **600**

AMERICAN LOCOMOTIVE COMPANY (ALCO) UNITS

Among the first diesel locomotives revived by Fundimensions was the little Alco streamlined diesel. The first of these locomotives was a Santa Fe "A-A" pair in 1970 (8020); a "B" ("booster") unit was soon available. The prototype of this locomotive is considered by diesel enthusiasts to be one of the most beautiful locomotives ever made, especially in its six-wheel PA passenger service configuration. Unfortunately, Lionel's shortened model is not to true scale and is not nearly as impressive as the F-3 diesel. Lionel needed an inexpensive diesel model to head the low-cost sets of the early Fundimensions era. Consequently, most of the early ones had two-position reversing units and were somewhat cheaply made. No modern era Alcos have had horns.

In 1975 and 1976, Fundimensions tested the waters to see what reception a deluxe version of the Alco might create. The firm issued a triple Southern Pacific Alco ABA set in one box in "Daylight" colors (8552, 8553 and 8554). Unlike their stablemates, these Alcos had die-cast trucks, three-position reversing units, and two operating couplers. In 1976 Fundimensions issued three Canadian National units, this time for separate-sale (8656, 8657 and 8658). These locomotives came in brilliant orange and black with white zebra stripes, like the prototype. Sales of these triple units were disappointing, so Fundimensions proceeded no further along these marketing lines. Since that time, the Alco has been limited to the lower end of the market.

The number of road names released as Alcos is relatively small, dominated by Santa Fe, Canadian National and Amtrak. This was becasue the Alco was used for several years in a row to head different sets. Oddly enough, neither old Lionel or Fundimensions ever issued Alcos lettered for the railroad that actually owned the most real Alcos — the New York Central!

There was a hiatus in new Alco issues after the popular Texas & Pacific Quicksilver Express set in 1982 (8268 and 8269). Since 1979, Lionel has made no B-units for these sets. From a cost standpoint, Lionel determined it was less expensive to use the same body and frame to create a dummy A-unit than it was to produce a B-unit. Then in 1988 Amtrak (18903 and 18904) and Pennsylvania (18901 and 18902) Alcos with twin can motors were introduced. These came with matching O27-style short passenger cars, even though the FA-2 is a freight engine!

The Alco is a great piece for the beginning locomotive collector to explore. Most of the Alcos are low priced and readily available. Exceptions are the deluxe Alcos mentioned above and an 8022 AA pair made especially for J. C. Penney in 1971. A reasonably complete collection of modern era (or even postwar) Alcos can be acquired in a short time without exorbitant expense.

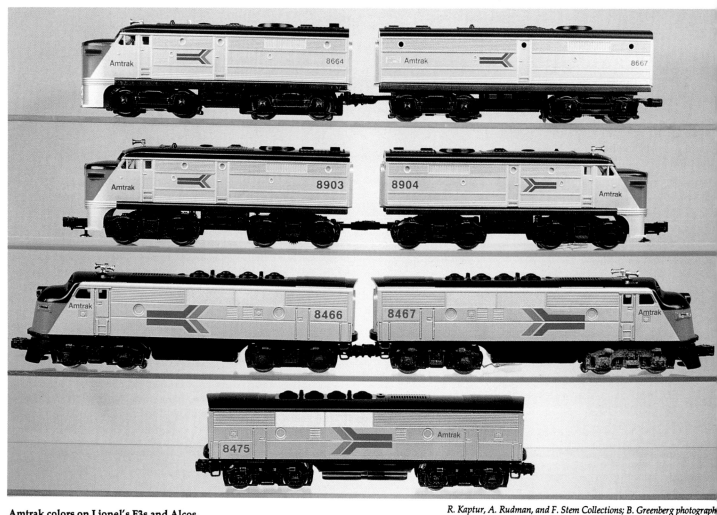

R. Kaptur, A. Rudman, and F. Stem Collections; B. Greenberg photograph

Amtrak colors on Lionel's F3s and Alcos.
Top shelf: **8664 Amtrak FA-2 A-unit Alco; 8667 Amtrak FA-2 B-unit Alco.**
Second shelf: **8903 Amtrak FA-2 A-unit Alco; 8904 Amtrak FA-2 A-unit Alco.**
Third shelf: **8466 Amtrak F-3 A-unit; 8467 Amtrak F-3 A-unit, made in 1974, the first Amtrak models.**
Bottom shelf: **8475 Amtrak F-3 B-unit.**

Common Features

All Alcos are powered by a single Type II integral motor/truck assembly, except the recent 18000-series engines which are powered by dual Type III (can) motors. Lighting in the Alcos follows the pattern of the F-3s: a bulb mounted near the nose illuminates the headlight, cab and number boards, where present. B-units and most dummy A-units are not lighted.

ALCO LISTINGS

8020 SANTA FE: 1970-76, powered Alco FA-2 unit; red and silver body; black lettering; yellow "Santa Fe" nose decals; lighted; came with either 8021 or 8020 dummy A-unit.

	GD	VG	EXC	MT

(A) Powered 8020 Type I body; first of the Alcos made in 1970.

	20	30	75	100

(B) Powered 8020 Type II body.

	20	30	75	100

(C) 1970-71, dummy Alco FA-2 A-unit; red and silver body.

	—	—	50	70

(D) Powered Alco FA-2 unit; blue and silver body. Reportedly part of department store special and, therefore, scarcer then red version. Reader comments requested.

	—	—	100	150

8021 SANTA FE: 1971-72, 1974-76, dummy Alco FA-2 B-unit; red and silver body; two dummy couplers; matches 8020.
(A) "SANTA FE" under vents. W. Eddins Collection.

	—	—	60	75

(B) "8021" under vents. W. Cunningham Collection. We would appreciate reader comments regarding scarcity of this variation.

	—	—	75	100

8022 SANTA FE: 1971, Alco FA-2 twin A-units (one powered, one dummy); uncatalogued; blue body shell with yellow striping and lettering; headlight. All except (D) below have frosted window inserts; some variations have a Santa Fe nose decal in yellow; all examples have the "8" in the number "8022" stamped backwards.

		ALCO BODY STYLES		
Type Designation	Front Pilot Style	Numberboard Slot	Builder's Plate	Year
I	Open for Coupler	Closed	"Lionel MPC" on Lower Rear	1970
II	Open	Open	"Lionel MPC" behind cab door	1971
III	Open	Closed	None	1974
IV	Closed, no Coupler	Open	"Lionel MPC" behind cab door	1972
V	Open	Open	"Lionel" behind cab door	1975
VI	Closed	Open	"Lionel" behind cab door	1982

Figure 1.6

GD   VG   EXC   MT

Made for J. C. Penney uncatalogued set with several different body types and chassis.

(A) As described. There are light blue and dark blue variations of this engine on Type II, III or IV bodies, with and without front couplers, with and without red number board inserts, and with and without nose decals. — **65 125 185**

(B) Powered and dummy A-unit set; numbered "8022"; only 50 sets made for J. C. Penney's Ann Arbor, Michigan store (P. Catalano observation). Powered unit has dark blue Type II body, front coupler, red number boards and nose decal. Dummy unit has gray plastic Type II body painted blue, front coupler, red number boards and nose decal. C. O'Dell Collection.
— — **350 400**

op shelf: **0000 Canadian National prototype.**
ottom shelf: **8025 Canadian National production model.**

GD   VG   EXC   MT

(C) Black plastic Type II cabs painted dark, flat navy blue; no translucent window inserts; no ornamental horns; no Santa Fe decal on nose. Samples observed came mounted on postwar Alco chassis with horn, headlight, red number boards and two-axle Magnetraction; the two chassis also have dummy metal couplers on front and rear. G. Halverson Collection.
— **65 125 185**

8025 CANADIAN NATIONAL: 1971, Alco FA-2 AA-unit (one powered, one dummy); uncatalogued; black Type II body; orange nose and white striping; both units have same number. Parker Brothers' distribution in Canada, imported by United States dealers. Mint condition must include original Parker Brothers' box. Price for both units. — **80 150 225**

8067 TEXAS AND PACIFIC: 1980, powered Alco FA-2 A-unit; blue and white; two-position reverse unit. Illustrated as part of 1051 Texas and Pacific diesel set, but never made.
Not Manufactured

8252 DELAWARE & HUDSON: 1972, powered Alco FA-2 A-unit; dark blue and silver Type IV body; "D & H" decal on side and nose; blank number boards; no front coupler; two position E-unit.
— — **100 125**
See Factory Errors and Prototypes chapter in Volume II, first edition.

8253 DELAWARE & HUDSON: 1972, dummy Alco FA-2 B-unit; matches 8252.
(A) Silver with side decal.   — — **50 75**
(B) Silver without side decal. — — **50 75**
See Factory Errors and Prototypes chapter in Volume II, first edition.

8268 TEXAS AND PACIFIC: 1982-83, powered Alco FA-2 A-unit; dark blue Type VI body; broad silver stripe and lettering; "Quicksilver Express"; light blue eagle decal; blue and silver "T & P" logo on front; red number boards; lighted; AC/DC Type III can motor; electronic three- position reverse; no coupler on front. To solve traction problems in the 1982 production, Lionel made

Some of the more attractive Alco units.
Top shelf: 8268 and 8269 Texas and Pacific "Quicksilver Express," which came with three matching 2400-type passenger cars in 1982.
Middle shelf: 8552 and 8553 Southern Pacific AA units, sold as a set with matching 8554 B-unit below.
Bottom shelf: 8563 Rock Island, from 1975 uncatalogued Sears set; 8554 Southern Pacific B-unit.

	GD	VG	EXC	MT

available two iron weights with a piece of foam with double-sided adhesive for Service Station installation. The 1983 production includes these weights. Part of 1253 Quicksilver Express set, which sold exceptionally well. Price for powered A-unit only.
— — **75** **90**

8269 TEXAS AND PACIFIC: 1982-83, dummy Alco FA-2 A-unit; "Quicksilver Express"; operating coupler; matches 8268.
— — **30** **50**

8351 SANTA FE: 1973-74, powered Alco FA-2 A-unit; blue and silver Type IV body. Part of 1383 Santa Fe freight set and also came in an uncatalogued O27 Sears set. Somewhat hard to find.
— **50** **75** **100**

8361 WESTERN PACIFIC: 1973-74, powered Alco FA-2 A-unit; silver Type IV body; orange stripe; black lettering; red front decal; lighted.
— — **100** **125**

8362 WESTERN PACIFIC: 1973-74, dummy Alco FA-2 B-unit; matches 8361.
— — **50** **75**

8452 ERIE: 1974, powered Alco FA-2 A-unit; lighted.
(A) Black plastic Type III body painted green and gray with yellow lettering; nose decal; no number boards.
— **60** **80** **100**
(B) Same as (A), but Type IV closed pilot, red number boards and no front decal. G. Halverson Collection. **NRS**
(C) Same as (B), but with nose decal. — **60** **80** **100**

8453 ERIE: 1974, dummy Alco FA-2 B-unit; matches 8452 A-unit.
— **40** **50** **75**

8552 SOUTHERN PACIFIC: 1975, powered Alco FA-2 A-unit; light and dark orange Type V body with black roof; silver ends, stripes and lettering; lighted. *Priced as set with 8553 and 8554.*
— **150** **250** **350**

8553 SOUTHERN PACIFIC: 1975, dummy Alco FA-2 B-unit; wheel base altered to accommodate trucks; only Alco B-unit with operating couplers at both ends; matches 8552 and 8554. *Priced as set with 8552 and 8554.* — **150** **250** **350**

8554 SOUTHERN PACIFIC: 1975, dummy Alco FA-2 A-unit; Type V body; lighted; matches 8552. *Priced as set with 8552 and 8553.*
— **150** **250** **350**

8563 ROCK ISLAND: 1975, powered Alco FA-2 A-unit; uncatalogued; red Type IV body; white letters; yellow stripe; closed pilot. Available only in Sears set 1594. — — **75** **100**

8570 LIBERTY SPECIAL: 1975, powered Alco FA-2 A-unit; uncatalogued; white Type IV body; blue top; red nose and stripe; lighted. Came with three 9700-series boxcars and matching unlighted SP-style caboose in uncatalogued 1577 Liberty Special set.
— **50** **75** **100**

8656 CANADIAN NATIONAL: 1976, powered Alco FA-2 A-unit; orange and black Type V body; white diagonal stripes and lettering; lighted; three-position reverse. Much harder to find than is generally realized. — **50** **150** **200**

GD   VG   EXC   MT

8657 CANADIAN NATIONAL: 1976, dummy Alco FA-2 B-unit; two dummy couplers; matches 8656.
— — 75 100

8658 CANADIAN NATIONAL: 1976, dummy Alco FA-2 A-unit; Type V body; matches 8656. Very hard to find because Lionel converted some dummy units into powered ones to boost lagging sales.
— 75 100 200

8664 AMTRAK: 1976-77, powered Alco FA-2 A-unit; Type VI body; black roof and nose top; silver sides and nose skirt; red nose; blue lettering; lighted; one plastic and one die-cast truck; fixed rear coupler. Came with 1663 Lake Shore Limited set, which included four Amtrak short O27 passenger cars. B-unit dummy was available separately, as were three other passenger cars.
— — 100 150

8667 AMTRAK: 1976-77, dummy Alco FA-2 B-unit; matches 8664. Difficult to find.
— 60 75 100

8861 SANTA FE: 1978-79, powered Alco FA-2 A-unit; Type VI body; red and silver "war bonnet" paint scheme; lighted; two-position reverse; two operating couplers. Headed 1864 Santa Fe double-diesel set.
— 25 75 100

8862 SANTA FE: 1978-79, dummy Alco FA-2 B-unit; matches 8861.
— 20 40 50

8901 PENNSYLVANIA: 1988; see 18901.

8902 PENNSYLVANIA: 1988; see 18902.

8903 AMTRAK: 1988; see 18903.

8904 AMTRAK: 1988; see 18904.

18901 PENNSYLVANIA: 1988, powered Alco FA-2 A-unit; dark tuscan-painted Type VII body shell; gold striping along cab sides and front; gold "PENNSYLVANIA" and "8901"; stamped-metal chassis; lighted; twin Type III can motors mounted on trucks; electronic three-position reverse; weight in cab; plastic truck side frames and couplers. Separate-sale item made to match 16000-series Pennsylvania O27 short passenger cars introduced in 1987. *Priced as a set with 18902 dummy unit.*
— — — 125

18902 PENNSYLVANIA: 1988, dummy Alco FA-2 A-unit; numbered "8902"; lighted; matches 18901. *Priced as a set with 18901.*
— — — 125

18903 AMTRAK: 1988, powered Alco FA-2 A-unit; silver-painted Type VII body; black roof; red nose; blue "8903"; red and blue Amtrak arrow logo; blue Amtrak lettering; stamped-metal chassis; lighted; twin Type III can motors mounted on trucks; weight in cab; electronic three-position reverse; plastic truck side frames. Essentially an updated version of the 8664 Amtrak Alco produced in 1976. Part of the top-of-the-line Traditional 11707 Silver Spike passenger set. *Priced as a set with 18904 dummy unit.*
(A) Regular production. — — — 125
(B) Overstamped with "Mopar Express" lettering and logo. This 1989 version of the Silver Spike set was made in very limited quantities (reportedly less than 100) as a special Chrysler promotion. It was won as a prize for matching a ten-digit number. Very hard to find. Follow-up to Mopar Express freight set of 1987-88. *Priced as a set with cars and 18904(B).* M. Salce comment.
— — — 400

18904 AMTRAK: 1988, dummy Alco FA-2 A-unit; blue "8904"; lighted; matches 18903. *Priced as a set with 18903.*
(A) Regular production. — — — 125

GD   VG   EXC   MT

(B) 1989 Mopar Express Special. *Priced as a set with cars and 18903(B).*
— — — 400

AMERICAN LOCOMOTIVE COMPANY (ALCO) RS-3 SERIES

One of Lionel's newest diesel locomotives within its Traditional Series is an excellent model of the highly popular Alco RS-3 diesel switcher. The real RS-3 was a 1600-horsepower locomotive which saw extensive service on many American railroads, particularly in the East, for both freight and passenger service. Lionel's model represented the prototype faithfully. It features an electronic three-position reverse and a twin can-motor chassis.

Because they were developed after 1987, these units possess five-digit catalogue numbers, with only the last four digits appearing on the engine. (See "Engine Numbering System" subhead at beginning of this chapter.) With its Type III can motor mounted in the trucks and electronic reverse circuit board, it is somewhat disconcerting to lift the cab of this engine to find little underneath. However, early reports indicate that the RS-3 is a good runner. These engines seem destined to become the new anchors in the Traditional diesel lines, slowly displacing the older GPs.

Common Features

All RS-3s feature twin Type III can motors and operating couplers. The lighting in the RS-3 diesels is unique. There are two grain-of-wheat headlight bulbs at each end of the engine and one standard bulb mounted inside near the top of the cab. This bulb, if not properly positioned, can burn a hole in the cab roof. Operators are advised to check the position of the lamp. A piece of aluminum foil between the bulb and the cab surface can prevent melting.

RS-3 LISTINGS

8803 SANTA FE: 1988; see 18803.

8804 SOO LINE: 1988; see 18804.

8805 UNION PACIFIC: 1989; see 18805.

8807 LEHIGH VALLEY: 1990; see 18807.

8809 SUSQUEHANNA: 1989; see 18809.

8814 DELAWARE & HUDSON: 1991; see 18814.

8815 AMTRAK: 1991; see 18815.

18551 SUSQUEHANNA: 1989; see 18809.

A. Rudman, F. Stem, L. Caponi, and R. LaVoie Collection

The production of these Geeps spans eleven years.

Top shelf: **8665** Bangor and Aroostook "Jeremiah O'Brien" GP-9, sold with matching porthole caboose in same box as Bicentennial Commemorative 1976; **8559** Norfolk and Western Bicentennial Commemorative GP-9 from catalogued "Spirit of America" set of 1975 (the example shown is a facto error; it is missing a silver circle of stars on the blue nose area).

Middle shelf: Early **8030** Illinois Central GP-9 with heavy Type I railings; **8031** C N GP-7 with later Type II railings. These are the first of Lionel's G diesels.

Bottom shelf: **8064** Florida East Coast; **8158** Duluth, Missabe & Iron Range GP-35, the only GP-35 ever made.

	GD	VG	EXC	MT

18803 SANTA FE: 1988, dual-motored Alco RS-3 diesel; dark blue cab; yellow-painted ends, stripe along upper edge of cab and Santa Fe emblem and cross logo; "8803" on number boards but not on cab; brakewheel directly mounted on cab front end; large crew cab with four windows on each end and two windows on sides; large exhaust stack atop cab; large simulated fan shroud at one cab end; stamped-steel frame and railings; relatively small battery box below frame; twin Type III can motors mounted on trucks; electronic three-position reverse; weight in cab; plastic truck side frames; operating couplers. This is the first of Lionel's RS-3 models. — — — **100**

18804 SOO LINE: 1988, dual-motored Alco RS-3 diesel; general description similar to 18803 entry; has a black plastic cab; yellow-painted ends with black safety striping; yellow lettering and "8804" on cab; stamped-metal frame and railings; lighted at front end; twin Type III can motors mounted on trucks; electronic three-position reverse; weight in cab; plastic truck side frames; operating couplers. — — — **100**

18805 UNION PACIFIC: 1989, dual-motored Alco RS-3 diesel; yellow body with red stripe at top of cab beneath light gray roof; red lettering and painted number board; "The Streamliners" in red on cab; "8805" on cab; rubber tires on drive wheels; stamped-metal frame; twin Type III can motors; electronic three-position reverse; operating couplers. Due to bent-up tabs on the metal frame, the attachment of the body to the frame is often not tight, leaving a noticeable gap. A version of this engine was produced for L O T S in 1989. — — — **105**

	GD	VG	EXC	MT

See Volume II, first edition.

18807 LEHIGH VALLEY: 1990, dual-motored Alco RS-3 diesel; red body; yellow lettering and stripe on lower section of cab; white safety stripes on front and rear; Lehigh Valley diamond logo; painted number boards; "8807" on cab; stamped-metal frame and railings; twin Type III can motors in plastic truck frames; three-position electronic reverse; operating couplers. — — — **110**

See Factory Errors and Prototypes chapter in Volume II, first edition.

18809 SUSQUEHANNA: 1989, dual-motored Alco RS-3 diesel; uncatalogued; gray body; maroon stripe along cab top; gray and maroon "NYSW" and "8809" on cab; stamped-metal frame and handrails; twin Type III can motors; three-position electronic reverse; operating couplers. Came with plexiglass display case, wood base and track section. Special issue for J. C. Penney in its continuing limited edition engine series. Reportedly less than 3,000 made. The engine box is catalogued 18809. The engine and case together are listed as 18551. — — — **225**

18814 DELAWARE & HUDSON*: 1991, dual-motored Alco RS-3 diesel; gray body with blue roof; yellow "lightning" stripe separating gray and blue areas; blue and yellow lettering; "D&H" shield below cab window and on nose; yellow "8814" on nose and on number boards; illuminated cab; operating front and rear headlights; gray-painted stamped-metal frame; gray truck side frames; twin Type III can motors; three-position electronic reverse unit; diesel horn; two operating couplers. This engine headed the

Some chop-nosed GP-20 diesels adapted from the Lionel GP mold.
Top shelf: 8066 T P W from Cross Country Express set of 1980-81; 8160 Burger King from Favorite Foods set of 1981.
Middle shelf: 8352 Santa Fe, one of the first GP-20s; 8369 Erie Lackawanna of 1983 with twin can motor drive system.
Bottom shelf: Limited edition 8463 B&O Chessie System of 1974; 8679 Northern Pacific of 1986 with twin can motor.

	GD	VG	EXC	MT

1991 Service Station Special set, the 11719 Coastal Freight, which was the first time the Service Station set had been catalogued.
— — — **120**

18815 AMTRAK*: 1991, dual-motored Alco RS-3 diesel; silver and black body; Amtrak red, white and blue stripes run completely around body; black lettering outlined in white; "8815" on body and number boards; (shown as "1815" in catalogue); black stamped-metal frame; twin Type III can motors; three-position electronic reverse unit; diesel horn; illuminated cab; operating front and rear headlights; two operating couplers. This engine headed the un-usual 11723 Amtrak Maintenance Train set, the top-of-the-line Traditional set in 1991. Amtrak has become a popular road name for Lionel in recent years.
— — — **130**

General Motors' "General Purpose" (GP) Diesels

General Motors' (GM) "GP" (or Geep) series of diesel road switchers represents the most commonly encountered locomotives on American railroads; so it is not surprising that the GPs also represent the largest group of Lionel's diesels. GM's Electro-Motive Division (EMD) produced more than 6,500 diesels in the GP series in the 1950s. Some units were equipped with steam generators, enabling them to act as both passenger and freight engines.

The only difference between Lionel's GP-7 and GP-9 models was the presence of a snap-on fan shroud atop the roof of the GP-9. It should be noted that the real GP-7 and GP-9 locomotives came both ways. Fundimensions' versions were quite impressive, even if they did lack the separate motor and power trucks (Type I) of the Lionel postwar originals. Until 1984 they were produced without horns or Magnetraction. The first models off the assembly lines were built with hollow pickup rollers which would not bridge the switches. Needless to say, this was an embarrassment for the company. So Fundimensions replaced these rollers with its supply of usable leftover pickup assemblies. This temporary solution worked until the company perfected snap-in solid roller assemblies for the power trucks. It is now understood that Service Stations were to provide the additional pickup assemblies and be reimbursed for the jobs by Lionel.

One GP-7 locomotive became a landmark for Fundimensions because it proved there was a sizable collectors' market for Lionel trains. In 1973, Fundimensions issued a special model of the GM prototype which commemorated the 50th anniversary of the Electro-Motive Division of GM. Fundimensions' 8359 GP-7 Chessie version of this engine, rendered in gold with dark blue Chessie and General Motors markings, sold out rapidly. Since then, Lionel has capitalized upon a collectors' market which eagerly awaits each limited production item.

Over the years Lionel has issued many GP-7 and GP-9 diesels. Some have been entirely original in design, while others have been direct reissues of famous GP-7 and GP-9 locomotives previously issued by the Lionel Corporation in the 1950s. Most of these engines are common, and all levels of

A. Rudman, F. Stem, L. Caponi, and R. LaVoie Collections
From top to bottom: **8353 G T; 8357 Pennsylvania; 8375 Chicago & North Western; 8454 Rio Grande; 8550 Jersey Central.**

collectors can appreciate their relatively low prices. On the whole, the GP-7s and GP-9s give little trouble, and are reliable runners which will pull a medium-sized train well. A few of these engines made in the mid-1970s used a fiber worm gear instead of a brass or nylon one; these fiber gears can strip easily under a heavy load. The rubber traction tires used on these locomotives do not slip if the operator rubber-cements them in place. With normal use and maintenance, they endure operations quite satisfactorily.

The GP-series has seen two Lionel innovations. The first was the use of an AC/DC Type III can motor mounted directly into the power truck. This arrangement was very close to the one found on the prototype. Lionel's first locomotive with this motor, the 8263 Santa Fe GP-7 of 1982, was not entirely successful. The engine was too light, and had used sliding contact shoes instead of the better roller pickups.

Fundimensions improved with its next new GP-7 locomotive, the 8375 Chicago & North Western included in the Northern Freight Flyer of 1983. This locomotive is weighted

and has two can motors, one on each power truck. It also has a fully electronic reversing unit, runs on very low voltage and has excellent hauling capacity. It is also easier to maintain because the motor never needs lubrication (although the gears do). The better roller pickups and twin-motored performance proved a successful formula for the GPs, one which Lionel has followed since then. A dark blue Baltimore & Ohio GP-7 (8662) was produced in 1986. And a green, white and gold Southern GP-7 (8774) headed the Southern Freight Runner Service Station Special set for 1987.

The second innovation in the Geep series was released in late 1984. It was a handsome New York Central (8477) GP-9 with extra detailing such as hand-inserted grab-irons on the front and rear. It used the preferable Type I separate motor and power truck, instead of the integral Type II motor found in most Geeps. It also had twin-axle Magnetraction, lighted number boards and an electronic horn. The locomotive was painted in the very realistic black, gray and white New York Central "lightning bolt" colors which were met with collector enthusiasm. It has become a highly desirable collector's locomotive. A J. C. Penney 8587 Wabash special GP-9 in gray and blue, using the New York Central construction, followed in 1985. In 1987, Lionel put out the handsome 18500 Milwaukee Road GP-9 as part of its Fallen Flags Series No. 2. The deluxe GP-9 made another appearance in 1990 (18502) as the head of Lionel's 90th Anniversary Train.

In 1973 one of Fundimensions' mold and die experts invented a clever die insert for the GP-7 and GP-9 molds. By placing this insert into the die, which "chopped down" the nose of the model, Fundimensions created a new engine — the GP-20. Although this locomotive was not issued in the large quantities like the GP-7s and GP-9s, it does have the distinction of being the locomotive responsible for the introduction of a Fundimensions innovation — the electronic diesel horn.

Unfortunately for Fundimensions, the horn used the same troublesome controller issued with the steam engine

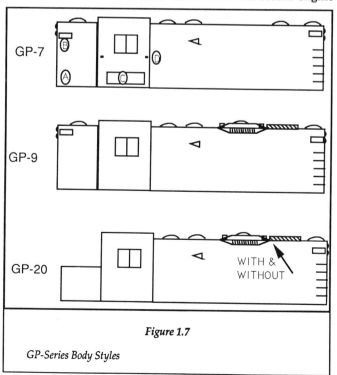

Figure 1.7

GP-Series Body Styles

Type	Body Style	Builder's Plate	Number-boards	Cab Hatch Panel	Railing Indents	Railing Type	Years
					GP-SERIES BODY STYLES		
I	GP-7, GP-9	"Lionel/ MPC"	Numbers	Louvers	No	I & II	1970 Only
II	GP-7, GP-9, GP-20	"Lionel/MPC "or "Lionel"	No Numbers	Louvers	No	II & III	1972
III	GP-7, GP-9, GP-20	"Lionel"	No Numbers	Louvers	Yes	III	1976
IV	GP-7, GP-9, GP-20	"Lionel"	No Numbers	Blank	Yes	III	1978
V	GP-7, GP-9, GP-20	"Lionel"	No Numbers	Blank	No	IV	1978 to Present

Figure 1.9

whistles. This controller had a tendency to get stuck in the closed position, which burned out the diode that changed part of the AC transformer current into DC for the horn. Therefore, the GP-20 was made in limited quantities, and any GP-20 dummy unit which has the electronic horn is quite scarce. It

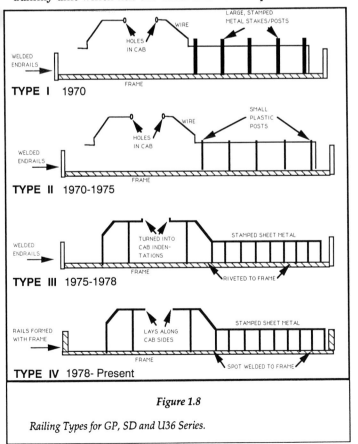

TYPE I 1970

TYPE II 1970-1975

TYPE III 1975-1978

TYPE IV 1978- Present

Figure 1.8

Railing Types for GP, SD and U36 Series.

is a shame that the controller did not work properly, because the horn's sound was excellent. Because it has a muffled sound like a real diesel heard from a distance, some operators actually prefer the Fundimensions diesel horn to the newer electronic one (used after 1981). Some of these diesel horns were used in the Union Pacific U36B dummy locomotive, and the rest were split up between other GP-20s manufactured in 1973 and 1974. The electronic horn was successfully revived in 1981 in the 8157 Santa Fe Fairbanks-Morse locomotive.

A surprise introduction for 1991 was a new GP-38 model in Kansas City Southern markings. This engine altered the GP body mold again by adding side vent details on the body and altering the roof fan arrangement. The cab design was also modified heavily (because this engine is so new, we do not have an illustration).

For the most part, the GP series diesels used the Type II integral motor, except for the New York Central, Wabash, Milwaukee and Lionel 90th Anniversary engines made since 1984. These deluxe diesels used the premium Type I separate motor and also featured Magnetraction. Several of the more recent GPs were made with single or dual Type III can motors.

There are variations in the body styles and railing configurations of the GP locomotives (see Figures 1.7, 1.8, 1.9 and 1.10). Body Style I and railing Style I were only used on the initial 8030 Illinois Central GP-9s and the 8031 Canadian National GP-7s in 1970-1971. Thereafter, all three diesel types varied through the remaining body and railing styles.

Lighting in the GP diesels varies with the body style, motor type and year produced. The earlier single-motored GP-7s and GP-9s have one or two nose lights which illuminate the headlights and the cab. The chopped-nose GP-20 forced the light bulb into the cab itself, where it is fitted into a retainer in the window shell. In this way it illuminates both the cab and number boards. When Lionel converted the GPs

Type	Form	Stakes	End Rail	Attachment To Cab	Years
I	Wire	Large Flatcar -- Metal Posts	Welded to Frame	Front, Rear Holes	1970 Only
II	Wire	Small -- Plastic	Welded to Frame	Front, Rear Holes	1970-1975
III	Stamped Sheet Metal	Stamped Metal	Welded to Frame	Into Side Indentations	1975-1978
IV	Stamped Sheet Metal	Stamped Metal	Formed with Frame	None -- Lays Alongside	1978-Present

RAILING TYPES: GP, SD, U-36

Figure 1.10

(all styles) to can motors, it retained this arrangement and left the light bulb in the cab. The deluxe GPs with the premium Type I motor have lights at both ends. Most, but not all, GP dummy units are not lighted. One other small but interesting difference exists between the postwar and modern versions of the GP diesels: postwar models had three steps on the frame, while the modern versions have two.

Common Features

All GPs feature two operating couplers, stamped-metal frames, plastic steps attached to both trucks and three-position reverse units (on the powered engines), unless otherwise described in the listings.

GP SERIES LISTINGS

	GD	VG	EXC	MT

GM 50 CHESSIE SYSTEM: 1973; see 8359.

484: See 8587.

1776 NORFOLK AND WESTERN: 1976, powered GP-9; Type III body painted red, white and blue; flat gold lettering; nose decal with white circle of thirteen stars; black underframe; Type IIb motor; Type II railings; no power pickup on dummy truck; stamped-metal frames; three-position E-unit; two operating couplers. This model was actually catalogued as 8559 but is listed here for your convenience. Headed 1584 Spirit of America set.
(A) Glossy red paint. — — 100 125
(B) Flat red paint. — — 100 125
See Factory Errors and Prototypes chapter in Volume II, first edition.

1776 BANGOR AND AROOSTOOK: 1976, powered GP-9; uncatalogued; "Jeremiah O'Brien"; red, white and blue Type III body; red, white and blue lettering; nose decal; silver truck side frames; Type III railings; stamped-metal frames; plastic steps attached to both trucks; three-position E-unit; two operating couplers. Catalogued as 8665 (not on engine). Announced only in 1976 dealer flyer. — — 100 160

	GD	VG	EXC	MT

1900 LIONEL LINES: 1990; see 18502.

1980 THE ROCK: 1980; see 8068.

3300 LIONEL LINES: 1988; see 33000.

4000 KANSAS CITY SOUTHERN: 1991; see 18812.

8030 ILLINOIS CENTRAL: 1970-71, powered GP-9; white and orange Type I body; black lettering; lighted; Type IIa motor; pickups on power truck and dummy truck; black frame; lighted at both ends; loop pickup may or may not supplement pickup on dummy truck; stamped-metal frames; three-position E-unit; two operating couplers. Service Stations added leftover Hillside pickups to original hollow roller pickups per Lionel's request. Upon completion of paperwork, Lionel replaced the pickup assembly and allowed the Service Station a $1.00 credit. The first few hundred examples produced with Type I railings were painted too lightly, causing translucence on the locomotive ends which made them glow. This is one of the first diesel engines out of the Mt. Clemens shop. C. Weber comments.
(A) Lighter orange; Type IIa motor (hollow roller pickup); Type I railing; nose decal; loop. The earliest examples of this locomotive came in a plain white box with a red, white and blue label which read "Pulls more than 25 cars". This label was quickly removed! Boxes with this label require a slight premuim.
— 35 85 125
(B) Gray plastic cab painted darker orange; Type II railing; no nose decal; Type IIb motor. White unpainted fan shroud does not quite match white paint on cab. R. LaVoie Collection.
— 35 85 125
(C) Same as (B), but with nose decal and extra set of pickups. C. Rohlfing Collection. — 35 85 125
See Factory Errors and Prototypes chapter in Volume II, first edition.

8031 C N: 1970-71, (Canadian National) powered GP-7; black and orange Type II body; white lettering; no nose decal; lighted at both ends; Type IIa motor; pickup on dummy; "LIONEL/MPC" builder's plate; stamped-metal frames; three-position E-unit; two operating couplers.
(A) Type I railing, Canadian version. Came in Type I plain box with white and black label. Packed with a bilingual edition of instructions and warranty. R. LaVoie Collection.
— 50 70 125
(B) Type II railing. — 50 70 125

p shelf: 8258 C N dummy GP-7; 8266 Norfolk and Western SD-24.

cond shelf: GM50 B&O Chessie System GP-7 (see 8359 listing); 8576 Penn Central GP-7.

ird shelf: 8750 The Rock GP-7; 8800 (18800) Lehigh Valley GP-9.

ttom shelf: 1900 (18502) Lionel Lines GP-9. 1900 celebrates Lionel's first year.

	GD	VG	EXC	MT

(C) Same as (B), but slightly smaller and deeper-stamped "8031" on cab; metal railing ends behind cab. Instead of regular Type II railings, a one-piece black plastic insert is snapped into place along the cab side. The side railing is, therefore, black plastic instead of metal. Pictured with this railing in the 1971 Canadian catalogue. R. LaVoie comment. — 50 70 125

8064 FLORIDA EAST COAST: 1980, powered GP-9; red and yellow Type V body; catalogued with black trucks, but made with silver trucks; Type IIb motor; Type IV railing; stamped-metal frames; three-position E-unit; two operating couplers.
 — — 125 150

8065 FLORIDA EAST COAST: 1980, dummy GP-9; lighted; matches 8064. — — 80 100

8066 T P W: 1980, (Toledo, Peoria & Western) powered GP-20; orange and white Type V body; white-painted frame and Type IV railings; Type IIb motor; lighted; stamped-metal frames; three-position E-unit; two operating couplers. Catalogued with dynamic brake unit on roof, but made without brake unit. Came with 1072 Cross Country Express set. Catalogue shows red color, but actually produced in shades of orange. C. Lang, H. Kaim, G. Halverson and C. Rohlfing comments.

(A) Orange body with white lettering; regular production run.
 — — 100 125

	GD	VG	EXC	MT

(B) Burnt orange with white lettering. G. Halverson Collection.
 — — 125 150
See Factory Errors and Prototypes chapter in Volume II, first edition.

8068 THE ROCK: 1980, GP-20; L C C A; see Volume II, first edition.

8158 DULUTH MISSABE & IRON RANGE: 1981-82, powered GP-35; maroon with yellow middle side band; white numbers and letters; Type IIb motor; Type IV railing. This odd engine is actually an SD-24 body mounted to four-wheel trucks. The only GP-35 made by Lionel. — — 75 125

8159 DULUTH MISSABE & IRON RANGE: 1981-82, dummy GP-35; lighted; matches 8158. — — 60 75

8160 BURGER KING: 1981-82, powered GP-20; yellow Type V body; red top, frame, numbers and letters; Type IIb motor; Type IV railings; stamped-metal frames; three-position E-unit; two operating couplers. From Favorite Foods Freight set, whose components are available only as separate-sale items.
 — — 90 120

8250 SANTA FE: 1972-75, powered GP-9; black and yellow Type II body; yellow lettering; black underframe; nose decal; lighted at both ends; Type IIb motor; Type II railing; power pickup

Some very popular Lionel GP-9 models.

A. Rudman, F. Stem, L. Caponi, and R. LaVoie Collection

Top shelf: 8357 Pennsylvania; 8477 New York Central.
Middle shelf: 8587 Wabash, numbered after its prototype and sold as a J. C. Penney Special; 8654 Boston and Maine.
Bottom shelf: 8757 Conrail (which also came with white-painted frame); 8759 Erie Lackawanna.

	GD	VG	EXC	MT

on dummy truck; "LIONEL/MPC" builder's plate; stamped-metal frames; three-position E-unit; two operating couplers.

— 60 90 120

8254 ILLINOIS CENTRAL: 1972, dummy GP-9; unpainted orange Type II body; white stripe; black lettering; nose decal; not lighted; Type II railings; black frame; "LIONEL/MPC" builder's plate; matches 8030(B) or (C).   — — 60 75

8255 SANTA FE: 1972, dummy GP-9; not lighted; matches 8250.   — — 60 75

8258 C N: 1972, (Canadian National) dummy GP-7; not lighted; no nose decal; matches 8031(B).   — — 65 80

8263 SANTA FE: 1982, powered GP-7; blue and yellow Type V body; single Type III can motor mounted on power truck; Type IV railings; sliding shoe pickups on both trucks; stamped-metal frame; electronic three-position reverse unit; two operating couplers.   — — 75 100

8352 SANTA FE: 1973-75, powered GP-20; dark blue and yellow Type II body with yellow lettering; black underframe; Santa Fe cross logo decal on nose (some pieces were inadvertently issued without it); lighted at both ends; Type IIb motor; Type II railings; stamped-metal frame; three-position E-unit; two operating couplers.   — 40 60 100

8353 G T: 1974-75, (Grand Trunk) powered GP-7; gray plastic Type II body painted blue and orange with white lettering; Type IIb motor; Type II railings; "LIONEL/MPC" builder's plate; stamped-metal frame; three-position E-unit; two operating couplers.   — 40 60 100

8355 SANTA FE: 1973-75, dummy GP-20; pickup on one truck; matches 8352. Sold unlighted, but many have been converted to lighted units because there is a roller pickup.
(A) With electronic diesel horn.   — — 80 125
(B) Without horn; no roller pickups. Some came in boxes that state the unit inside has the horn; buyers should check before purchase. Same comment applies to 8367 Long Island GP-20 dummy units.   — — 5 75

8356 G T: 1974-75, (Grand Trunk) dummy GP-7; not lighted; matches 8353. Somewhat hard to find.   — 30 40 60

8357 PENNSYLVANIA: 1973-75, powered GP-9; gray plastic Type II body painted dark green; gold lettering; lighted; no nose decal; Type IIb motor; Type II railings; black frame; "LIONEL/MPC" builder's plate; stamped-metal frame; three-position E-unit; two operating couplers. Reportedly 9,000 made.   — — 125 150

8358 PENNSYLVANIA: 1973-75, dummy GP-9; not lighted; matches 8357. A few units are known to have been produced with horns. Somewhat hard to find.
(A) No horn.   — — 60 100
(B) With factory-installed horn.   — — 100 125

8359 CHESSIE SYSTEM: 1973, powered GP-7; Type II body with special gold paint for General Motors' 50th anniversary; blue "B & O" and "GM 50" lettering; nose lettering; "8359" not on locomotive; lighted at both ends; Type IIb motor; Type II railings; black frame; stamped-metal frame; three-position E-unit; two operating couplers. Reportedly 9,000 made. W. Mitchell Collection.   — — 100 150

GD   VG   EXC   MT

See Factory Error and Prototypes chapter in Volume II, first edition.

8360 LONG ISLAND: 1973-74, powered GP-20; charcoal gray-painted Type II body; silver lettering; no nose decal; lighted at both ends; Type IIb motor; Type II railings; "LIONEL/MPC" builder's plate; stamped-metal frame; three-position E-unit; two operating couplers. Shown in advance catalogues as light gray with darker gray roof, but not made that way.
(A) Black frame.   —   60   75   100
(B) Black frame with painted red stripe.
                                                        —   60   75   100

8367 LONG ISLAND: 1973, dummy GP-20; electronic diesel horn sounds extremely realistic — its loudspeaker faces upwards in cab (where motor usually goes), and the result is a true "muffled" diesel horn sound. Not lighted, but is easily converted to a lighted dummy; matches 8360.
(A) Plain frame.   —   —   75   90
(B) Red stripe on frame.   —   —   75   90
(C) Same as (A), but no electronic diesel horn. Some came in boxes erroneously stating that horn was included; purchasers should check before buying.   —   —   60   75

8369 ERIE LACKAWANNA: 1983, powered GP-20; Type V body in gray and tuscan Erie Lackawanna colors, although shown in catalogue as blue and tuscan; dual Type III can motors; Type IV railings; plastic truck frames and couplers; electronic three-position reverse unit; one operating coupler, one dummy coupler. Only offered for separate-sale in Traditional Series catalogue. Lionel also made a matching 6425 caboose. These twin-motored locomotives are better than their single-motored counterparts because pickup rollers are used rather than sliding shoes. The interior of this locomotive has a large weight to help traction. R. LaVoie Collection.   —   —   100   125

8375 CHICAGO & NORTH WESTERN: 1983, powered GP-7; yellow and green Type V body; lighted; dual Type III can motors with rectifier for AC or DC operation (the electronic reverse unit); Type IV railings; stamped-metal frame; two operating couplers. Came in 1354 Northern Freight Flyer set. See 8369 for operating comments.   —   60   100   125

8454 RIO GRANDE: 1974-75, powered GP-7; black Type II body; orange lettering; dull yellow hash marks; black frame; Type IIb motor; Type II railings; "LIONEL/MPC" builder's plate; stamped-metal frame; three-position E-unit; two operating couplers.   —   40   100   125

8455 RIO GRANDE: 1974-75, dummy GP-7; not lighted; matches 8454.   —   —   50   80

8463 B & O CHESSIE SYSTEM: 1974, powered GP-20; uncatalogued; blue and yellow Type II body; blue lettering; vermilion stripe; black frame; nose decal; Type IIb motor; Type II railings; "LIONEL" builder's plate; stamped-metal frame; three-position E-unit; two operating couplers. Limited edition of 10,000. Appeared only in a late 1974 dealer flyer.
                                                        —   —   125   150

8477 NEW YORK CENTRAL: 1984, powered GP-9; uncatalogued; black Type V body with large gray stripe edged by smaller white stripes on side (lightning bolt pattern); small "NEW YORK CENTRAL" above gray stripe; gray and white striping on cab ends with New York Central logo; separate plastic grab-irons on front and rear; electronic horn; Type I AC motor; die-cast truck side frames; stamped-steel frame and Type IV handrails; three-position E-unit; two operating headlights and couplers. The

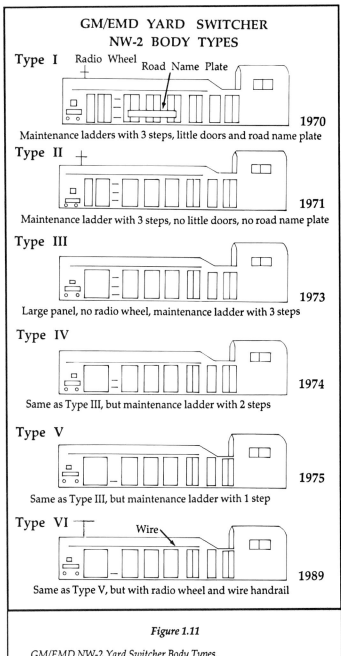

GM/EMD YARD SWITCHER NW-2 BODY TYPES

Type I — Radio Wheel, Road Name Plate — 1970
Maintenance ladders with 3 steps, little doors and road name plate

Type II — 1971
Maintenance ladder with 3 steps, no little doors, no road name plate

Type III — 1973
Large panel, no radio wheel, maintenance ladder with 3 steps

Type IV — 1974
Same as Type III, but maintenance ladder with 2 steps

Type V — 1975
Same as Type III, but maintenance ladder with 1 step

Type VI — Wire — 1989
Same as Type V, but with radio wheel and wire handrail

Figure 1.11

GM/EMD NW-2 Yard Switcher Body Types.

GD   VG   EXC   MT

power truck is similar, but not identical, to the older Lionel power trucks of the Geeps produced in the 1950s. The magnets in this truck are larger, producing stronger Magnetraction. In considerable demand by collectors and appreciating in price. This engine appeared only in a 1984 Spring Collector Center brochure.
                                                        —   175   300   395
See Factory Errors and Prototypes chapter in Volume II, first edition.

8500 MILWAUKEE: GP-9; see 18500.

8504 FRISCO: 1991, GP-7; see 18504.

8550 JERSEY CENTRAL: 1975, powered GP-9; red- and white-painted Type II body; white lettering; black frame; nose decal; Type IIb motor; Type II railings; no pickup on dummy truck;

General Motors GP (General Purpose) road switcher diesels.
Top shelf: 8662 Baltimore & Ohio GP-7 with Lionel's new twin can-motor drive system; 8666 Northern Pacific GP-9 from Northern Pacific Service Station set of 1976.
Middle shelf: 8763 N W GP-9; 8775 Lehigh Valley GP- 9.
Bottom shelf: 8854 CP Rail GP-9 from Great Plains Express set of 1978; 8866 Minneapolis & St. Louis GP-9 from Service Station Special set of 1978.

	GD	VG	EXC	MT

"LIONEL" builder's plate; stamped-metal frame; three-position E-unit; two operating couplers. — **70 100 125**
See Factory Errors and Prototypes chapter in Volume II, first edition.

8559 NORFOLK AND WESTERN: 1975; see 1776 Norfolk and Western.

8561 JERSEY CENTRAL: 1975-76, dummy GP-9; not lighted; matches 8550. — **40 60 80**

8562 MISSOURI PACIFIC: 1975-76, powered GP-20; blue Type II body; white lettering and hash marks; black underframe; Type IIb motor; Type II railings; stamped-metal frame; three-position E-unit; two operating couplers. — **55 100 125**

8565 MISSOURI PACIFIC: 1975-76, dummy GP-20; not lighted; matches 8562. A few with horns are known to exist. Some units without horns are packaged in boxes marked for horn-equipped units — check before purchase.
(A) No horn. — **45 60 75**
(B) With horn. Very hard to find. — **60 100 125**

8576 PENN CENTRAL: 1975-76, powered GP-7; black Type II body; white lettering; Type III railings; stamped-metal frame; three-position E-unit; two operating couplers. This engine appeared first in a late 1975 one-page flyer, then was catalogued in 1976.
(A) Door outline shows through "PENN CENTRAL" lettering; black frame; nose decal; Type IIb motor; "LIONEL/MPC" builder's plate. — **60 125 150**
(B) Same as (A), but door outline painted solid; "LIONEL" builder's plate; Type III body; no nose decal.
— **60 125 150**

	GD	VG	EXC	MT

8587 WABASH: 1985, powered GP-9; uncatalogued; blue and gray Wabash bluebird paint scheme with white lettering and "484" on number boards; made for J. C. Penney, came with display case. This engine was available from train dealers at a lower price than originally listed in the J. C. Penney catalogue. Same construction as 8477 New York Central — Magnetraction, Type IV railings and separately-installed ladders. No. 484 was the first GP-9 delivered to the Wabash. G. Sams comment. R. Sigurdson and N. Banis Collections. — — **300 395**
See the Factory Errors and Prototypes chapter in Volume II, first edition, for a great story of a major factory blunder on this engine!

8654 BOSTON AND MAINE: 1976, powered GP-9; blue, white and black Type III body; white and black lettering; white frame; no nose decal; Type IIb motor; Type III railings.
— **60 115 150**

8655 BOSTON AND MAINE: 1976, dummy GP-9; not lighted; matches 8654. — — **80 100**

8662 BALTIMORE & OHIO: 1986, powered GP-7; dark blue Type V body with yellow-orange stripe; yellow lettering; two Type III can motors mounted on trucks; Type IV railings. Came with 1652 B & O freight set. — — **100 125**

8665 BANGOR AND AROOSTOOK: See 1776 Bangor and Aroostook.

8666 NORTHERN PACIFIC: 1976, powered GP-9; uncatalogued; black and gold Type III body; red stripe; gold and red lettering; gold frame; no nose decal; Type IIb motor; Type III railings; no MPC logo; stamped-metal frame; three-position E-unit; two operating couplers. Came in 1976 Service Station Special set 1672. — — **125 150**

hese are some of Lionel's most interesting NW2s and GP20s.

p shelf: **8153 Reading Lines NW-2; 8354 Erie NW-2.**

cond shelf: **8770 Electromotive Division NW-2; 8501 Western Maryland NW-2.**

ird shelf: **1980 (8068) The Rock GP-20, special addition for the LCCA; 8355 Santa Fe GP-20.**

ttom shelf: **8772 GM&O GP-20.**

	GD	VG	EXC	MT

8668 NORTHERN PACIFIC: 1976, dummy GP-9; matches 8666. Issued as an add-on to the 1976 Service Station set.
— — **100 125**

8679 NORTHERN PACIFIC: 1986, powered GP-20; black and gold Type V body; red stripe separates black from gold areas; red, black and white Northern Pacific Monad (or ying-yang) heralds on cab sides, front and rear; gold lettering and number; headlight; twin Type III can motors mounted on trucks; Type IV railings; stamped-metal frame; three-position electronic reverse unit; two operating couplers. R. LaVoie Collection.
— — **100 125**

8750 THE ROCK: 1977, powered GP-7; blue and white Type III body; white and blue lettering; white frame; nose decal; Type IIb motor; Type III railings; stamped-metal frame; three-position E-unit; two operating couplers.
— — **100 125**

8751 THE ROCK: 1977, dummy GP-7; not lighted; matches 8750.
— — **50 75**

8757 CONRAIL: 1977-78, powered GP-9; gray plastic Type III body painted blue; white lettering; nose decal; Type IIb motor; Type III railing; no pickup on dummy truck; stamped-metal frame; three-position E-unit; two operating couplers.
(A) Black underframe and railings. — **75 100 140**

(B) White underframe and railings. — **75 100 140**

8758 SOUTHERN: 1978, GP-7 dummy; green and white; matches 8774. This unit is unique in that it has a lower engine number than does its 8774 powered unit.
— — **80 100**

8759 ERIE LACKAWANNA: 1977-79, powered GP-9; gray plastic Type III body painted gray, tuscan and yellow; yellow lettering and frame; lighted; nose decal; Type IIb motor; Type III railing; stamped-metal frame; three-position E-unit; two operating couplers. — — **120 150**

8760 ERIE LACKAWANNA: 1977-79, dummy GP-9; matches 8759. — — **100 125**

8763 N W: 1977-78, (Norfolk & Western) powered GP-9; gray plastic Type III body painted black; white lettering; black frame; nose decal; Type IIb motor; Type III railing; stamped-metal frame; three-position E-unit; two operating couplers.
— — **100 125**

See Factory Errors and Prototypes chapter in Volume II, first edition.

8772 G M & O: 1977, (Gulf, Mobile & Ohio) powered GP-20; gray plastic Type III body painted red and white; white frame; nose decal; Type IIb motor; Type III railing; stamped-metal frame;

	GD	VG	EXC	MT

three-position E-unit; two operating couplers. Came with 1764 Heartland Express set. — 55 **100** 120

8774 SOUTHERN: 1977-78, powered GP-7; gray plastic Type III body painted green and white with gold stripe and lettering; Southern decal on front end; black frame; Type IIb motor; Type III railing; small pickup rollers mounted on power truck; stamped-metal frame; three-position E-unit; two operating couplers. — 80 **125** 150

8775 LEHIGH VALLEY: 1977-78, powered GP-9; gray plastic Type III body painted bright red; yellow heat-stamped lettering and stripe; Type IIb motor; Type III railing; stamped-metal frame; three-position E-unit; two operating couplers. — 80 **125** 150

8776 CHICAGO & NORTH WESTERN: 1977-78, powered GP-20; gray plastic Type III body painted yellow and dark green; green lettering; red, white and black decal beneath cab window; black frame; Type IIb motor; Type III railing; stamped-metal frame; three-position E-unit; two operating couplers. — 80 **125** 150

8778 LEHIGH VALLEY: 1977-78, dummy GP-9; not lighted; matches 8775. — — **80** 100

8779 CHICAGO & NORTH WESTERN: 1977-78, dummy GP-20; not lighted; matches 8776. — — **80** 100

8800 LEHIGH VALLEY: GP-9; see 18800.

8802 SOUTHERN: GP-9; see 18802.

8854 C P RAIL: 1978-79, powered GP-9; gray plastic Type V body painted red, white and black; white lettering; white and black C P logo; black truck sides; Type IIb motor; Type IV railing; two geared wheels with rubber tires; stamped-metal frame; three-position E-unit; two operating couplers. Came with 1977 Great Plains Express set. — 75 **85** 125

8866 MINNEAPOLIS & ST. LOUIS: 1978, powered GP-9; uncatalogued; gray plastic Type IV body painted red and white; blue cab roof; white and red lettering; red and white logo beneath cab windows and on hood front; rubber tires on two geared wheels; Type IIb motor; Type III railing. Part of 1868 Service Station Special set sold by Lionel to its Service Stations for their exclusive sale in 1978. This locomotive is the only item not also available for separate-sale in the set, although in reality it was available separately when dealers broke up the sets.
(A) Type III railing. — 80 **100** 125
(B) Type IV railing. — 80 **100** 125

8867 MINNEAPOLIS & ST. LOUIS: 1978, dummy GP-9; lighted; matches 8866, except for Type IV railing. — — **75** 100

8957 BURLINGTON NORTHERN: 1979, powered GP-20; black and green Type V body; white lettering; no stripe; Type IIb motor; Type IV railing; stamped-metal frame; three-position E-unit; two operating couplers. — 70 **100** 125

8958 BURLINGTON NORTHERN: 1979, GP-20 dummy, lighted; matches 8957. — — **80** 100

18500 MILWAUKEE ROAD: 1987, powered GP-9; orange and black Type V body shell (orange color continuous through cab as in rare postwar version); white "8500" on black part of cab; black lettering on sides and ends; red and white Milwaukee logo on cab; Magnetraction; premium Type I motor; Type IV railings; black frame; stamped-metal frame; plastic steps attached to both trucks; three-position E-unit; two operating couplers. Deluxe version GP which came with separate-sale Fallen Flags set No. 2. This engine

was also offered, without modification but with a display case, as a special purchase from J. C. Penney in 1987 as part of its continuing Special Engine series.
(A) As described, no display case. — — **175** 225
(Lest we feel modern era Lionel has ushered in the ultimate in quality, see Factory Errors and Prototypes chapter in Volume II, first edition, for an interesting story.)
(B) J. C. Penney version with display case.
— — — **250**

18502 LIONEL LINES: 1990, powered GP-9; cream Type V body; orange roof; blue cab; gold lettering and "90 YEARS" logo on main body; number on cab is "1900", commemorating Lionel's beginning. Part of 11715 Lionel 90th Anniversary set. This engine continues the deluxe GP-series started by the N Y C 8477: separate nose grab-irons; Magnetraction; Type I motor; electronic horn/bell; three-position reverse unit; and headlights at front and rear. Catalogue states the engine has RailSounds, but it is not made that way. RailSounds circuitry for the set was included in the 19219 boxcar. — — — **275**

18504 FRISCO: 1991, powered GP-7; red Type V body; broad white stripe completely around cab; red lettering and "8504" below cab window. Continues deluxe GP-series: Type I motor; Magnetraction; separately-installed nose grab-irons; lighted at both ends; stamped-metal frames; die-cast trucks; and three-position E-unit. Paint scheme similar to 8571/8572 U36 pair made in 1975. Part of Frisco Fallen Flags Series No. 5, whose components were all sold separately. — — — **245**

18800 LEHIGH VALLEY: 1987, powered GP-9; gray plastic 1Type V body shell painted brick red; yellow "8800", lettering and striping; black and white safety stripes on cab ends; black frame; headlight; twin Type III can motors mounted in trucks; Type IV railings; stamped-metal frame; electronic three-position reverse unit; two operating couplers. Came with 11702 Black Diamond freight set, which has proved one of the more popular Traditional Line sets. — — **100** 125

18802 SOUTHERN: 1987, powered GP-9; uncatalogued; green- and white-painted Type V body; gold stripe separates green and white colors; gold lettering and "8802"; black frame; twin Type III can motors mounted in trucks; Type IV railings; stamped-metal frame; plastic steps attached to both trucks; electronic three-position reverse unit; two operating couplers. Came with 11704 Southern Freight Runner Service Station set for 1987.
— — **100** 125

18812 KANSAS CITY SOUTHERN*: 1991, powered GP-38 diesel; pale- white body; red lettering; "4000" on cab; large "KCS" centered on body; black stamped-metal frame; Type III can motor; three-position electronic reverse unit; diesel horn; single bulb illuminates cab, number boards and headlight; two operating couplers. This is a new GP-series body design introduced in 1991. It differs from earlier GP engines by its added side vent detail and altered fan/roof arrangement. The nose detail has been modified as well. Lionel has never before used Kansas City Southern as a road name for an engine. Came as separate-sale only with a matching 16526 KCS SP-type caboose. — — — **140**

33000 LIONEL LINES: 1988, RailScope GP-9; Type V body with dark gray and black cab; white lettering and "3300"; red, white and blue Lionel logo; twin Type III can motors; Type IV railings. This revolutionary locomotive has a miniature video transmitter inside the cab which projects an "engineer's-eye"-view to a television set. The photo image is sent by electronic pulse through the rails, then through an RF modulator (disguised as a

A. Rudman, F. Stem, L. Caponi, and R. LaVoie Collections

▸ome U36B and U36C locomotives, early and late.

Top shelf: Two 1776 Seaboard Coast Line Bicentennial Specials. The left is the regular production model, part of Bicentennial Spirit of '76 set; the right is the special production for T C A, part of Bicentennial passenger set. Note frame lettering and T C A emblem on red diagonal stripe.

Middle shelf: 7500 Lionel 75th Anniversary Special of 1975; 8050 Delaware & Hudson U36C of 1980. (Note design change on this engine's nose; double headlight of previous models is eliminated.)

Bottom shelf: 8061 W M Chessie System U36C from Royal Limited set of 1980; 8155 Monon of 1981.

	GD	VG	EXC	MT

stack of lumber) to the antenna terminals of a television. The result is a sharp black and white picture of the engine's view, just as if the operator were inside the locomotive. The operator can even videotape his layout from the TV image! Can be used with any television, although a Lionel TV is available separately (see 33002 entry in the Accessories chapter in Volume II, first edition.)

— — — **275**

33004 NEW YORK CENTRAL: 1990, RailScope GP-9. Announced for 1990, but never made. **Not Manufactured**

33005 UNION PACIFIC: 1990, RailScope GP-9. Announced for 1990, but never made. **Not Manufactured**

THE GENERAL ELECTRIC U36 SERIES

The first Fundimensions diesel locomotive not patterned after any postwar design was the U36B, issued in 1974. Except for its not-quite-scale length, Fundimensions' "U-boat" was an accurate representation of the rugged General Electric prototype. The Seaboard Coast Line was the primary owner of the U36B engine type — "U" (universal), "36" (-hundred horsepower), and "B" (four-wheel trucks). The first Lionel models were the aptly-numbered 1776 Seaboard Bicentennial

locomotive and the 8470 Chessie System at the head of Fundimensions' Grand National top-of-the-line freight set. Both these locomotives became very popular. And in rapid succession, Fundimensions issued Union Pacific, Great Northern, Frisco, Burlington Northern, Southern, and Northern Pacific models.

One U36B deserves particular mention because it is one of the most valuable of all Fundimensions products. In 1977, Fundimensions began its Walt Disney series of hi-cube boxcars, and chose the 8773 Mickey Mouse U36B to head it. Because collectors of Disneyana compete with train collectors for it, this locomotive explosively increased in value by 1980. The 7500 Lionel 75th Anniversary locomotive, which headed a string of freight cars with historic Lionel logos, is another U36B which may merit attention and is somewhat hard to find. While many collectors shy away from this set because they feel it is unattractive, some are drawn to the silver and red colors. The 7500 U36B is an excellent "sleeper" candidate because it is not very common, is still reasonably priced and has not yet attracted collector attention.

In 1979, Fundimensions issued a new U36 locomotive, which sported six-wheel locomotive trucks (first seen on the 1978 Milwaukee SD-18). To do this, Fundimensions redesigned and shortened the fuel tank under the frame. Thus, the U36B became a U36C — the "C" is railroad code for six-wheel trucks.

As a class, the U-boats offer more detailing than their GP counterparts, and are slightly higher priced. Dummy units

Six U36B engines. Dummy units were made for all of these but the 8669 Illinois Central Gulf.
Top shelf: 8470 C&O Chessie System from 1974 Grand National set, the first U36B; 8564 Union Pacific (matching 8573 dummy unit had a horn and is extremely scarce).
Middle shelf: 8571 Frisco; 8650 Burlington Northern.
Bottom shelf: 8669 Illinois Central Gulf, available only in Illinois Central Gulf set in 1976; 8755 Santa Fe.

are available for many of these locomotives, including one very scarce 1975 Union Pacific with an electronic horn (8573). The massive appearance of the U36s made them favorites of some Fundimensions collectors. In 1987, Lionel produced a new Santa Fe U36B (18801) with a twin can-motor configuration for the Traditional Series. It appears that all future Traditional diesels will use the twin can-motor powering system, while the Collector Series locomotives will use the older motors and truck frames (which are more expensive to produce).

The "U" series was eventually replaced on the real railroads by the Dash 7 series, and then by the popular Dash 8 in 1988. This appears to be the case in Lionel-land as well. There was a gap in U36 production from 1982 to 1987; and since the Santa Fe in 1987, no further U36 engines have appeared.

U36 Body Types

TYPE I: *Pre-1979*; indentation for handrails; Type III railings; cab light and rear light.

TYPE II: *Post-1979*; no indentation for handrails; nose headlight deleted; Type IV railing; cab light only.

The lighting arrangement for the U36s changed at about the time (1979) the body change from Type I to Type II occurred. Earlier U336Bs have a cab/number board/front headlight bulb mounted to the frame near the back headlight. This arrangement is mounted with the Type I body. The 8955 in 1979 and all later U36Bs and U36Cs used a single-bulb system with a light in the cab window shell. The rear bulb was deleted, but the rear headlight still receives some light from the cab bulb. This arrangement is associated with body Type II. Dummy U36B or U36C units are not lighted.

Common Features

All U36 units feature stamped metal-frames, two operating couplers and three-position mechanical E-units (on the powered diesels). Unlike the GP series, the U36s have no "LIONEL" builder's plate on the motor. All U36s, except the recent 18801 Santa Fe from 1987, have been powered by a single Type II integral motor. The 18801 uses twin Type III can motors. This model also, therefore, uses the electronic reversing unit. For a description of the railing types, see the GP subsection of the Diesels chapter — the U36s use the same frame/railing types.

A. Rudman, F. Stem, L. Caponi, and R. LaVoie Collections

More attractive U-Boats.

Top shelf: 8771 Great Northern U36B from Rocky Mountain Special set of 1977; 8773 Mickey Mouse Express U36B, which has become highly prized by Disney collectors as well as train collectors.

Middle shelf: 8801 (18801) Santa Fe U36B with twin can-motor drive system; 8857 Northern Pacific U36B.

Bottom shelf: 8955 Southern U36B; 8960 Southern Pacific U36C, available with dummy unit only in Southern Pacific Limited set of 1979 which sold out even before it was distributed. This was the first U36C (six-wheel trucks). U36Bs have four-wheel trucks.

U36 LISTINGS

	GD	VG	EXC	MT

1776 SEABOARD COAST LINE: 1976, powered U36B; red, white and blue Type I body; blue lettering; black underframe; lighted; nose decal; United States flag under cab window; no pickup on dummy truck; no MPC logo; stamped-metal frame and railings; three-position E-unit; operating couplers. This locomotive (actually catalogued as "6-1776") was part of the Spirit of '76 set, which included thirteen separate-sale boxcars, each representing one of the original Thirteen Colonies, and a 7600 Frisco N5C caboose. Fundimensions had more ambitious plans to make boxcars for the remaining 37 states, but this was never carried out.

(A) No lettering on frame. — — 100 125

(B) Bright white "SEABOARD COAST LINE" on frame. Later production. — — 100 140

(C) Pale off-white "SEABOARD COAST LINE" on frame. Earlier production — Lionel had great trouble stamping the frame. — — 100 140

1976 SEABOARD COAST LINE: 1976, U36B Bicentennial; made for the Train Collectors Association (T C A). See Volume II, first edition.

7500 LIONEL 75TH ANNIVERSARY: 1975-76, powered U36B; red, silver and black Type I body; black frame; "7500" on box; "1900-1975" on cab; stamped-metal frame; three-position E-unit; operating couplers. Part of the 75th Anniversary set 1505.

	GD	VG	EXC	MT

The set was a slow seller at its issuance and is still available new at a relatively low price, which qualifies the set as a "sleeper" candidate for collectors. R. LaVoie comment.
— — 80 100

8050 DELAWARE & HUDSON: 1980, powered U36C; gray Type 1II body; blue top; yellow striping and lettering; cab light only; silver-painted six-wheel trucks; stamped-metal frame; three-position E-unit; operating couplers. Matching 8051 dummy available separately. The nose piece of this and some later U36 locomotives has been modified to eliminate the molded headlights — this change apparently occurred at the same time as the change to the Type II bodies. — — 125 175

See Factory Errors and Prototypes chapter in Volume II, first edition.

8051 DELAWARE & HUDSON: 1980, dummy U36C; matches 8050. — — 100 125

8061 W M CHESSIE SYSTEM: 1980, (Western Maryland) powered U36C; yellow and orange Type II body; blue roof; dark blue lettering; bright orange-painted frame; silver-painted six-wheel trucks; cab light only; stamped-metal frame; three-position E-unit; operating couplers. Came in 1070 Royal Limited set.
— — 145 175

8155 MONON: 1981-82, powered U36B; Type II body; gold sides and ends; dark blue roof and band running along cab bottom; cab light only; Type IV railings. — — 75 100

8156 MONON: 1981-82, dummy U36B; matches 8155.
— — 60 75

B. Greenberg photograph

8201 (18201) C&O Chessie System SD-40, which powered a unique Chessie System unit train in 1988.

	GD	VG	EXC	MT

8470 C & O CHESSIE SYSTEM: 1974, powered U36B; blue, orange and yellow Type I body; blue lettering; black frame; nose decal; stamped-metal frame; stamped-metal Type III railings; three-position E-unit; operating couplers. Came in 1460 Grand National set. Shown in 1974 catalogue with large emblem and lettering, but not produced that way. This was the first U36B produced. **— 70 100 150**

8560 C & O CHESSIE SYSTEM: 1975, dummy U36B; matches 8470, although some reports stress this does not exactly match the 8470 because the vermilion stripe at the top of the cab is slightly wider than on the powered unit. Sold unlighted, but some units have had pickups and lights added later.
(A) No lights or third-rail pickup. **— — 75 100**
(B) Lighted unit with pickup on one truck.
— — 75 100

8564 UNION PACIFIC: 1975, powered U36B; gray and yellow Type I body; red stripe; black frame; nose decal; Type III railings; stamped-metal frame; three-position E-unit; operating couplers. Came in 1560 North American Express set.
— 75 125 175

8571 FRISCO: 1975-76, powered U36B; white and red Type I body with red lettering; black frame; no nose decal; Type III railings; stamped-metal frame; three-position E-unit; operating couplers. **— 60 75 100**

8572 FRISCO: 1975-76, dummy U36B; matches 8571.
— — 60 75

8573 UNION PACIFIC: 1975, dummy U36B; uncatalogued; diesel horn; pickup on one truck; not lighted; matches 8564. Pictured only in a Fall 1975 dealer flyer.
(A) With horn; reportedly only 1,200 made. Very hard to find.
— — 200 275
(B) Without horn. Purchaser should check boxes before purchase. **— — 125 150**

8650 BURLINGTON NORTHERN: 1976-77, powered U36B; black and green Type I body; white lettering and hash marks; black frame; Type III railings; stamped-metal frame; three-position E- unit; operating couplers. **— — 125 150**

8651 BURLINGTON NORTHERN: 1976-77, dummy U36B; matches 8650. **— — 90 100**

8669 ILLINOIS CENTRAL GULF: 1976, powered U36B; white and orange Type I body; black lettering; black frame; nose decal; Type III railings; stamped-metal frame; three-position E-unit; operating couplers. From 1664 Illinois Central freight set.
— — 125 150

	GD	VG	EXC	MT

8755 SANTA FE: 1977-78, powered U36B; blue and yellow Type I body; blue and yellow lettering; yellow frame; silver metal truck side frame; nose decal; Type III railings; stamped- metal frame; three-position E-unit; operating couplers.
— — 150 200

8756 SANTA FE: 1977-78, dummy U36B; not lighted; matches 8755. **— — 90 100**

8771 GREAT NORTHERN: 1977, powered U36B; gray plastic Type I body painted black, white and blue; white lettering; black frame; Type III railing; stamped-metal frame; three-position E- unit; operating couplers. Came in 1765 Rocky Mountain Special set. **— 80 100 120**

8773 MICKEY MOUSE: 1977-78, powered U36B; gray plastic Type I body painted orange and white with Mickey Mouse, Pluto and Donald Duck; Type III railing; stamped-metal frame; three-position E-unit; operating couplers. Headed the now-scarce Mickey Mouse separate-sale set featuring thirteen Disney hi-cube boxcars and porthole caboose. This item has shown greater appreciation than most modern era engines.
— 300 400 500

8801 SANTA FE: 1987; see 18801.

8857 NORTHERN PACIFIC: 1978-80, powered U36B; gray plastic Type II body painted black; orange band along base; yellow cab end, frame and rails; burnished truck side frames; Monad logo on cab decal; cab light only; five-unit plastic horn on hood roof; Type IV railings; stamped-metal frame; three- position E-unit; operating couplers. **— 60 100 125**

8858 NORTHERN PACIFIC: 1978-80, dummy U36B; not lighted; matches 8857. **— — 55 85**

8955 SOUTHERN: 1979, powered U36B; gray plastic Type II 1body painted green and white; gold lettering; five-horn ornamental cluster on roof; brakewheel on hood near cab; gold stripe runs completely around cab; "SOUTHERN RAILROAD" decal on hood near cab; cab light only; Type IV railings; geared motor wheels with rubber tires; stamped-metal frame; three- position E-unit; operating couplers. **— 75 125 175**

8956 SOUTHERN: 1979, dummy U36B; matches 8955.
— — 70 100

8960 SOUTHERN PACIFIC: 1979, powered U36C; uncatalogued; Type II body; bright red-orange and yellow "Daylight" colors; white lettering; cab light only; Type IV railing; stamped-metal frame; three-position E-unit; operating couplers. Some units have been found with the railings spot- welded off center so that the frame looks bent. This is the first U36C produced: it is a

A. Rudman, F. Stem, L. Caponi, and R. LaVoie Collections

The first of Lionel's big, scale-length SD-40 diesels.
Top shelf: 8265 Santa Fe.
Middle shelf: 8376 Union Pacific. Both of these had single motors.
Bottom shelf: The dual-motored 8458 Erie Lackawanna. A matching E L dummy is available.

	GD	VG	EXC	MT

U36B frame and cab with six-wheel trucks, a shorter fuel tank, and two small marker lights near forward facing hood. This and the 8961 came in the Southern Pacific Limited Set 1970. The engine was pictured in the 1979 advance catalogue, but not in the regular catalogue because the set was a sell-out.

	—	70	80	100

8961 SOUTHERN PACIFIC: 1979, dummy U36C; matches 8960. Came in Southern Pacific Limited set 1970.

	—	—	60	75

8962 READING LINES: 1979, powered U36B; green and yellow Type II body; "BEE LINE SERVICE"; die-cast trucks; metal wheels and Type IV handrails; cab headlight only; illuminated number plates without numbers; stamped-metal frame; three-position E-unit; operating couplers. Came with Quaker City Limited set 1971.

	—	80	150	200

18801 SANTA FE: 1987, powered U36B; Type II body; blue and yellow Santa Fe freight color scheme; yellow "Santa Fe" and blue "8801" on cab; black frame; cab headlight only; twin can Type III motors mounted in trucks; stamped-metal frame; electronic three-position reverse unit; operating couplers.

	—	—	—	85

THE GENERAL MOTORS ELECTRO-MOTIVE DIVISION "SPECIAL DUTY" SD DIESELS

SD-9, SD-18, SD-24 and SD-28

Typically, when Fundimensions introduced a new feature, it used that feature throughout a wide range of its line to help amortize the cost of the tooling. That is certainly true of the handsome six-wheeled trucks in current use on many of its diesels. In 1978 Fundimensions placed the six-wheel trucks under a Milwaukee GP-20 cab, added a fan shroud, and changed the model to the SD-18 (8855). Santa Fe (8872 and 8873) and Ontario Northland (8162 and 8163) models were quick to follow, this time in both powered and dummy units.

As with several other engines, Lionel took liberties in its road name assignments — the above-mentioned railroads did not own SD-18s. Interestingly, Lionel has yet to issue an SD diesel in a road name that did own them!

By changing the SD-18's cab roof from rounded to flat, the model became a "chop-nosed" SD-28. This version was

SD-40 diesels with dual motors.   *A. Rudman, F. Stem, L. Caponi, and R. LaVoie Collections*

Top shelf: 8200 Conrail, which came in the Conrail Limited set with Standard O cars.
Bottom shelf: 8585 Burlington Northern, which came with a unit train of Standard O boxcars.

produced in Burlington (8151) and Lionel Lines (8380) colors. To date, these remain the only two SD-28 units.

Nor were the high-nosed models neglected in the use of the new six-wheel trucks. In 1980 Fundimensions produced a round-roofed Seaboard SD-9 (8063) to head its Mid-Atlantic Limited Collector set. The next year, a high-nosed Geep with a flat roof, the SD-24, was made in attractive Canadian Pacific (8152) markings for the Maple Leaf Limited. This particular locomotive had an electronic horn, as did a Norfolk and Western SD-24 (8266) at the head end of the Continental Limited set. These, again, are the only two locomotives of this type to date.

For some reason, Lionel waited ten years to release another SD-9, and has not issued any more SD-24s or -28s to date. Apparently, it was experimenting with the body styles in the early 1980s (see Figure 1.10) before settling on the SD-18 as the lower-scale six-wheel diesel, and the SD-40 for the higher-scale.

This experimentation also extended to the GPs. In 1981 Lionel placed an SD-24 body decorated in Duluth, Missabe & Iron Range colors on four-wheel trucks and called it a "GP-35"

(8158). This is the only such engine of its type in the Lionel line.

The early models of the six-wheeled diesels had a peculiar operating problem. The blind center wheels of these locomotives (the ones without flanges) were made a little too large, causing the drive wheels to skid under heavy loads. The problem was soon corrected, and the usual answer to the early problem was to file down the blind wheels carefully. The later six-wheelers had traction tires on the blind wheels as well, effectively curing the trouble.

Although these locomotives will run on O27 track, they are far better runners on the wider-radius O Gauge trackage, where their long wheel base shows to better advantage.

SD-40

In 1982 Fundimensions introduced a spectacular new modern era diesel, a model of the brutish but attractive SD-40 so popular with railroads today. Fundimensions' model of this locomotive is scale length and has been considered one of the finest diesel models ever produced. Scale O Gauge model

SD-SERIES BODY STYLES						
Body Style	Nose	Dynam. Brake	Number Of Fans	Shape of Fan Shroud	Horn Location	Roof Shape
SD-9	High	Forward	3	Rounded	Body Side	Round
SD-18	Low	Forward	1	Square	Body Roof	Round
SD-24	High	Aft	2	Square	None	Flat
SD-28	Low	Aft	3	Square	Cab Roof	Flat
SD-40	Low	Center	5	Square	Cab Roof	Flat

Figure 1.12

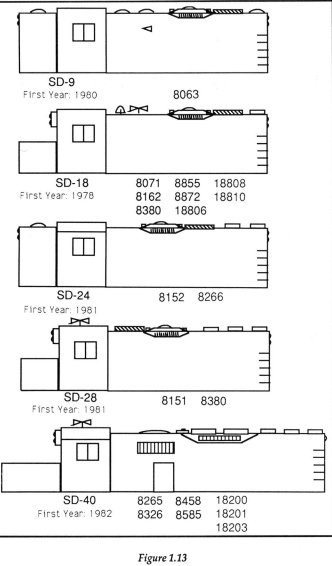

SD-9
First Year: 1980   8063

SD-18   8071   8855   18808
First Year: 1978   8162   8872   18810
                 8380   18806

SD-24   8152   8266
First Year: 1981

SD-28   8151   8380
First Year: 1981

SD-40   8265   8458   18200
First Year: 1982   8326   8585   18201
                             18203

Figure 1.13

SD-Series Body Styles

railroaders have even purchased the body shell and trucks to adapt to their own operational requirements. It was first produced in 1982 in bright Santa Fe blue and yellow freight colors (8265). Since then, successive years have seen this locomotive issued in a new paint scheme. In 1983 a yellow, red and gray Union Pacific (8376) was made. Both the 8265 and the 8376 locomotives were produced only in single-motor configuration, using a heavily modified version of the Type II integral truck/motor drive. Many collectors found this hard to understand, since the locomotive was so large it would easily accommodate an extra motor. But all reports indicated the SD-40 ran well.

The SD-40 produced in 1984 corrected the single-motor oversight. This time the locomotive was a beautiful gray, maroon and yellow Erie-Lackawanna (8458), built with twin Type II motors. Like the Union Pacific, it headed a limited production Collector set. An SD-40 in Burlington Northern Cascade green and black colors (8585) was produced as part

of the Burlington Northern Limited, a unit train of five matching Burlington Northern Standard O boxcars and an extended vision caboose. A sixth boxcar was later produced as part of a 1986 year-end package. A big, blue Conrail SD-40 (18200) headed another limited edition set for 1987. This model was slightly improved by the addition of reinforcers for the screw holes where the body fastens to the frame (cracks had developed in earlier models). One of the latest models of this engine is the 18203 C P Rail model with a bright red and white paint scheme, part of the successful Standard O C P Rail freight set. Lionel even produced dummy SD-40 units to create some truly impressive double-headed train sets.

The SD-40 has been greeted with considerable acclaim by collectors because of its massive size and attractive design. It has many fine body details, including a realistic snowplow attachment on the front truck. In reality, given the differences between the SD-40 and the other SD models, the massive SD-40 engine should be listed in a category of its own.

As popular as the SD-40 is, there is one operating restriction; when using the SD-40 engine, its overhang will not clear O27 switches. (This is also true of Hudsons, the long aluminum passenger cars and other longer rolling stock.) This is unfortunate, given the amount of standard and wide-radius O27 track and switches on layouts around the country. The problem could be resolved with a simple redesign of the switches. Even though these longer items do not look good on the tight-radius O27 tracks, such track is useful in limited-space or yard applications.

It is a little too soon to tell which of these locomotives will become scarcer than others, but the twin-motor units should command a premium. The Burlington Northern has become difficult to find recently, and the C P Rail and Conrail SD-40s have also been very popular.

SD-9, SD-18, SD-24 and SD-28 Common Features

All SD-9s, SD-18s, SD-24s and SD-28s feature a single Type II (integral motor/truck) drive system (through 1989), operating couplers at the ends, six-wheel die-cast trucks, Type IV railings (see GP section for types), and illuminated cabs/number boards/headlights (a single bulb). Dummy units are also lighted. In 1989 and 1990, Lionel departed from its earlier SD-series motoring scheme by placing a heavily modified Type III can motor in the SD-18, which is now being used in the higher-end Traditional Line sets.

SD-40 Common Features

All SD-40s feature a modified Type II motor (single or double), die-cast six-wheel trucks, and operating couplers on both ends. One SD-40, the UP 8376, experimented with the electronic reverse unit. The others have had a standard mechanical E-unit. The cab, number boards and front headlight are illuminated by one bulb in the window shell. There is also a rear light mounted to the frame. The recent dummy SD-40s are also lighted.

A. Rudman, F. Stem, L. Caponi, and R. LaVoie Collecti▮

Some impressive six-drivered diesels. Differences in cab configurations determine the type numbers of these General Motors Special Duty (SD) locomotiv▮
Top shelf: 8063 Seaboard SD-9 from 1980 Mid-Atlantic set; 8071 Virginian SD-18.
Middle shelf: 8151 Burlington SD-28 from Burlington set of 1981; 8152 Canadian Pacific SD-24 from 1981 Maple Leaf Limited set.
Bottom shelf: 8162 Ontario Northland SD-18 (sold with matching dummy unit with horn); 8266 Norfolk and Western SD-24 from Continental Limited
of 1982.

SD LISTINGS

	GD	VG	EXC	MT

8063 SEABOARD: 1980, powered SD-9; black body; yellow band with red trim; yellow frame; six-wheel trucks with blind center wheels and rubber tires on the three wheels on geared side; three-position reverse; Type IV railings; operating couplers at both ends. Came with 1071 Mid-Atlantic set.

| | | — | — | 125 | 175 |

8071 VIRGINIAN: 1980, powered SD-18; uncatalogued; blue and yellow; six-wheel trucks; silver truck sides; Type IV railings; operating couplers at both ends. Shown only in the Fall 1980 Collector Center brochure.

| | | — | — | 100 | 150 |

8072 VIRGINIAN: 1980, dummy SD-18; matches 8071.

| | | — | — | 60 | 75 |

8151 BURLINGTON: 1981, powered SD-28; red; gray top; and white nose stripes; white frame, numbers and lettering; black truck sides; Type IV railings; operating couplers at both ends. Came in 1160 Great Lakes Limited set.

| | | — | — | 125 | 175 |

8152 CANADIAN PACIFIC: 1981, powered SD-24; flat top; maroon and gray; two yellow side stripes; three horizontal nose stripes; white frame; yellow numbers; maroon "Canadian Pacific" in script on gray background; front nose decal is often found cracked or missing; horn; six-wheel trucks; Type IV railings; operating couplers at both ends. From 1158 Maple Leaf set.

| | | — | — | 195 | 250 |

	GD	VG	EXC	MT

8162 ONTARIO NORTHLAND: 1981, powered SD-18; uncatalogued; blue; yellow trim and lettering; "Rail/Services"; silver truck sides; Type IV railings; operating couplers at both ends. Part of the 1981 Fall Collector Center.

| | | — | — | 125 | 150 |

8163 ONTARIO NORTHLAND: 1981, dummy SD-18; matches 8162.

| | | — | — | 100 | 125 |

8200 CONRAIL: 1987, SD-40; see 18200.

8201 C & O CHESSIE SYSTEM: 1988, SD-40; see 18201.

8203 C P RAIL: 1989, SD-40; see 18203.

8204 CHESSIE SYSTEM: 1990, SD-40; see 18204.

8265 SANTA FE: 1982, powered SD-40; blue- and yellow-painted body; illuminated cab and number boards; headlights at both ends; six-wheel die-cast silver-sided trucks; single modified Type II motor with single-wound motor field for mechanical E-unit; motor body housing has integral locator tab; measured pull of 10 ounces; Magnetraction; electronic horn; operating couplers at both ends. First SD-40 diesel, uses new scale cab design.

| | | — | — | 325 | 425 |

8266 NORFOLK AND WESTERN: 1982, powered SD-24; maroon body with yellow trim; die-cast six-wheel trucks; three-position reverse unit; electronic horn; Type IV railings; operating couplers at both ends. Part of 1260 Continental Limited set issued in Spring Collector Series.

| | | — | — | 150 | 200 |

8376 UNION PACIFIC: 1983, powered SD-40; yellow and gray body; red stripe; green hood top; front and rear headlight;

A. Rudman, F. Stem, L. Caponi, and R. LaVoie Collections.

Top shelf: 8380 Lionel Lines SD-28, for which many matching cars have since been issued; 8855 Milwaukee Road SD-18, Lionel's first six-drivered diesel from the 1978 Milwaukee Limited set. Note difference in orange color of these engines.
Middle shelf: 8872 Santa Fe SD-18, which was sold with matching dummy.
Bottom shelf: 8962 Reading Lines U36B from Quaker City Limited set of 1979.

GD VG EXC MT

illuminated cab and number boards; Magnetraction; electronic horn; six-wheel die-cast trucks; single modified Type II motor with a double-wound field for the electronic E-unit; measured pull of 10 ounces (this may vary between locomotives); the motor body housing has a separate stamped-metal locator tab mounted in it; electronic three-position reverse unit (the only SD-40 to date equipped with it); operating couplers at both ends. Part of a special limited edition set, the 1361 Gold Coast Limited. R. Sigurdson and D. Johns comments.   —   —   **450**   **550**

8380 LIONEL LINES: 1983, powered SD-28; uncatalogued; dark blue upper body, upper cab and nose top; black frame; red, white and blue Lionel logo on cab side and nose; blue number is below the logo on the cab; blue "LIONEL LINES" in modern sans-serif lettering below color division; illuminated cab; chromed plastic ornamental five-horn unit atop cab; squared-off cab roof; black six-wheel trucks; Type IV railings; operating couplers at both ends. Announced in Fall 1983 Collector Center brochure. This engine has since become the head of a popular Lionel Lines freight set (all separate-sale) in the bright orange and blue Lionel colors. The set is hard to complete because of the scarcity of the 5712 reefer.
(A) Medium orange lower body and nose.   —   —   **150**   **250**
(B) Darker orange lower body and nose.   —   —   **150**   **250**
See Factory Errors and Prototypes chapter in Volume II, first edition.

GD VG EXC MT

8458 ERIE LACKAWANNA: 1984, powered SD-40; gray cab; maroon and yellow striping; yellow lettering; "RADIO/EQUIPPED"; yellow-painted frame; illuminated cab and number board; die-cast six-wheel trucks; two modified Type II motors; electronic horn; Magnetraction; lights and operating couplers at both ends. Part of 1451 Erie Lackawanna Limited Collector set. A matching dummy unit was made in 1989.   —   —   **375**   **450**

8459 ERIE LACKAWANNA: 1989, dummy SD-40; see 18202. Note that this number is also used for a Rio Grande snowplow from 1984!

8552 DULUTH, MISSABE & IRON RANGE: 1990, SD-18; see 18552.

8585 BURLINGTON NORTHERN: 1985, powered SD-40; Cascade green lower body; black upper body and roof; white number, "BN" logo and safety stripes; lighted cab and number boards; headlights at both ends; black six-wheel die-cast trucks; two modified Type II motors; Magnetraction; electronic horn; green-painted handrails; operating couplers at both ends. Part of 1552 Burlington Northern Limited set.   —   —   **350**   **450**

8806 NEW HAVEN: 1989, SD-18; see 18806.

8808 ATLANTIC COAST LINE: 1990, SD-18; see 18808.

8810 C S X: 1990, SD-18; see 18810.

8811 ALASKA: 1991, SD-9; see 18811.

8660 C P Rail and 8761 G T NW-2 switchers.

	GD	VG	EXC	MT

8813 DULUTH, MISSABE & IRON RANGE: 1990, SD-18; see 18813.

8855 MILWAUKEE ROAD: 1978, powered SD-18; gray plastic body painted dull orange and black; black and white lettering; red and white logo underneath cab window. The first in the SD locomotive series, this engine is a combination of a GP/U36B chassis, Type II motor with six-wheel trucks, and a GP-20 cab unit with added dynamic brake and five-unit ornamental horn cluster. (In real railroad parlance, a "cab" unit is a GM F diesel or an Alco FA diesel, and a "hood" unit is a GP, "U-Boat" or SD diesel. However, in tinplate terms, a "cab" is the plastic shell of any tinplate diesel.) Because of the increased truck size, the "battery box" (which contained a D-cell battery in postwar days, but today only represents a fuel tank) was redesigned shorter and now reads "LIONEL MT. CLEMENS MICHIGAN 28045". Features three-position E-unit, two disc-operating couplers, and rubber tires on end geared wheels (center wheels are blind). Sold only as part of the specially boxed 1867 Milwaukee Limited set and not available for separate-sale.
(A) As described above. — — 115 150
(B) Die-cast six-wheel trucks with Magnetraction, electronic horn and lighted number boards. This appears to be a factory alteration using new trucks similar to those on SD-40s. We would appreciate any reader comments on other examples in existence. H. Hardtke Collection. — — 115 150

8872 SANTA FE: 1978-79, powered SD-18; gray plastic body painted yellow and blue; yellow and blue lettering; Santa Fe decal on nose; illuminated cab; yellow frame (see 8855 for SD-18 background information); six-wheel trucks; three-position reverse unit; Type IV railings; two disc-operating couplers at both ends. — — 100 150

8873 SANTA FE: 1978-79, dummy SD-18; lighted; matches 8872. — — 75 100

18200 CONRAIL: 1987, powered SD-40; bright blue body; white Conrail wheel logo, striping and lettering; "8200" on cab; blue side rails and white end rails; black frame; lighted cab; front and rear headlights; two modified Type II motors; three-position reverse; Magnetraction; electronic horn; operating couplers at both ends. Came with 11700 Conrail Limited set. — — 250 325

18201 C & O CHESSIE SYSTEM: 1988, powered SD-40; yellow, vermilion and dark blue cab; vermilion-painted side and end rails; dark blue Chessie Cat logo and lettering; "8201" on cab; lighted cab; two headlights; six-wheel trucks; two modified Type II motors; three-position E-unit; Magnetraction; electronic horn; operating couplers at both ends. Headed 11705 Chessie System unit train. — — 250 325

18202 ERIE-LACKAWANNA: 1989, dummy SD-40; un-catalogued; "8459" on cab; illuminated cab and headlight; die-cast trucks; matches 8458. First dummy SD-40 produced. From 1989 Holiday Collection. — — — 165

18203 C P RAIL: 1989, powered SD-40; red-painted gray plastic body; white "8203" on cab; large white "CP Rail" on main body; white and black C P logo at rear; diagonal red and white stripe on front; and black and white stripe on rear; headlights at both ends; lighted cab interior and number boards; Type IV handrails; dual modified Type II motors in die-cast six-wheel trucks; three-position reverse; Magnetraction; electronic horn; snowplow attachment on front. This handsome engine headed the unique C P Rail freight set of 1989. — — — 250

18204 CHESSIE SYSTEM: 1990, dummy SD-40; un-catalogued; "8204" on cab; illuminated cab and headlight; metal frame and railings; die-cast trucks; matches 18201. From 1990 Stocking Stuffer package. — — — 180

18552 DULUTH, MISSABE & IRON RANGE: See 18813.

18806 NEW HAVEN: 1989, powered SD-18; dark Brunswick green body; orange-painted cab; orange "N" above white "H"; white "8806" on cab; illuminated cab and number boards without numbers; headlights at both ends; stamped-metal frame and railings; single modified Type III can motor mounted upright in a six-wheel truck — a new scheme for the can motor, which is used here for the first time in an SD- series diesel; rubber tires on drive wheels; three-position electronic reverse unit. — — — 105
See Factory Errors and Prototypes chapter in Volume II, first edition.

18808 ATLANTIC COAST LINE: 1990, powered SD-18; black body; white lettering and "8808" on cab; two yellow stripes on side from cab to rear; illuminated headlights, cab and number boards without numbers; stamped-metal frame and railings painted yellow; single modified Type III can motor in six-wheel trucks; three-position electronic reverse; horn. Catalogue incorrectly shows "8806" on cab. — — — 110

18810 C S X: 1990, powered SD-18; light gray body; blue cab roof, lettering, "8810" on cab, and C S X nose decal; stamped-metal frame and railings painted a matching gray; lighted cab, headlights and number boards without numbers; single modified Type III can motor; blue-painted six-wheel trucks; three-position electronic reverse; horn. Came as part of top-of-the-line 11717 C S X Freight Traditional Series set in 1990. — — — 120

18811 ALASKA*: 1991, powered SD-9; dark blue and yellow Alaska paint scheme; blue main body; yellow cab nose and rear; yellow "ALASKA" and "8811" below cab window; "ARR" decal at rear; red, white and blue nose decal; illuminated cab and number plates with numbers; headlights at both ends; electronic diesel horn; separate grab-irons on nose (a new detail for SD diesels); single modified Type III can motor in black six-wheel die-cast trucks; three-position electronic reverse unit; two operating

GD VG EXC MT

couplers. Catalogued with a Type I (Pullmor) motor, but made with the Type III vertical can motor. Illustrated with a matching 16523 caboose, and should go well with other postwar and modern era Alaska rolling stock.   —   —   —   **125**

18813 DULUTH, MISSABE & IRON RANGE: 1990, powered SD-18; uncatalogued; maroon-tuscan body; yellow stripe along length of body; yellow safety striping on frame; yellow lettering and "8813" on cab; green "D M" logo on lower front; headlights at both ends; illuminated cab and number boards; stamped-metal frame and railings; six-wheel die-cast trucks; modified Type III can motor; three-position electronic reverse unit. Special edition for J. C. Penney in its continuing engine series. Reportedly less than 3,000 made. Catalogue number of engine together with plexiglass display case and board is 18552.   —   —   —   **200**

THE NW-2 SWITCHERS

Since the early postwar era, Lionel has called its switchers "SW-1 models," instead of the "NW-2 diesels" they really are. The firm is perpetuating a Lionel mistake in terminology which dates back to 1950! Regardless of what they are called, Fundimensions' switcher engines have not often been popular with collectors, even though some of them have become quite scarce. They are, however, popular with operators. The development of the switcher, first introduced by postwar Lionel in 1949, parallels that of the Alco — it underwent a cheapening process in 1955 by removing the Magnetraction and stamping the frame rather than casting it.

The modern era series began in 1970 with the 8010 Santa Fe switcher in blue and yellow (most of the early switchers followed the line of the cheaper postwar models). In 1973 Fundimensions revived the black Erie switcher with the 8354; this locomotive had the better three-position reversing E-unit. Subsequent issues included the 8471 Pennsylvania, 8556 Chessie, 8660 C P Rail, 8761 Grand Trunk and 8057 Burlington models.

Fundimensions initially limited its use of NW-2 switchers to the bottom-of-the-line sets, and only a few of these locomotives are truly scarce. These include the 8354 Erie, 8556 Chessie, 8473 Coca-Cola, 8761 Grand Trunk and 8471 Pennsylvania models, plus a special promotional switcher for Nibco Faucet Products (8182) in 1982. The 8374 Burlington

Northern and the 8485 U. S. Marines locomotives feature the innovative Fundimensions AC/DC can motor.

There was a gap in production after 1984. Then, in 1989-1990, Lionel introduced new models of the NW-2 with many upgraded features — die-cast frame, die-cast trucks, a ringing bell, Magnetraction and wire handrails. None of these amenities have been seen on the NW-2 since 1955. And for the first time, an NW-2 switcher is at the head of a Collector set (the 18501 Western Maryland). Like the Alcos, the NW-2 switchers are relatively easy to acquire at good prices and are a great specialization area for the beginning collector.

Common Features

Most early NW-2 switchers feature a single Type II motor (except the 8374 BN and 8485 Marines, which have Type III can motors and altered frames). The two recent deluxe NW-2s from 1989 and 1990 were upgraded to the premium Type I motors. All are lighted and most have two operating couplers. The lighting on the NW-2s consists simply of a nose headlight, until the 1989 and 1990 deluxe models, when a light was added to the cab. The body style variations (see Figure 2.13) follow a roughly chronological order. Only the postwar carry-overs 634 and 8010 had Type I bodies. The style had progressed to Type V by 1975. Most NW-2s used this latter design. Only in 1989 did a new style appear with the Western Maryland 18501.

NW-2 SWITCHER LISTINGS

GD VG EXC MT

634 SANTA FE: Circa 1970, NW-2 yard switcher; uncatalogued; Type I body; chrome-plated plastic bell and radio antenna. These are leftover postwar cabs which were given Fundimensions trim pieces. Thus, this model can be faked by adding trim pieces to a postwar 634 cab and mounting it on an early Fundimensions chassis. Essentially the same as 8010. Rerun of 1965-66 switcher. R. LaVoie comment. **30 40 55 100**

1203 N E T C A BOSTON AND MAINE: 1972, NW-2 switcher; T C A; cab only. See Volume II, first edition.

1983 NABISCO: 1983, NW-2 switcher. See Volume II, first edition.

8010 A T S F: 1970, NW-2 yard switcher; blue with yellow lettering; radio wheel; lighted; stamped-metal frame; builder's plate lettered "Santa Fe" on (A) only; single Type II motor; two operating couplers.
(A) Yellow safety stripes around Santa Fe cross logo and number on cab; flat medium blue unpainted cab; Type I body; two-position E-unit; operating couplers. This was the earliest version, and was offered in catalogued sets and for separate-sale.   —   —   **60 75**
(B) No yellow stripes on cab; bright royal blue unpainted cab; manual reverse switch; dummy couplers. Later production. Sold as part of uncatalogued sets.   —   —   **60 75**

8010 ATSF. This is one of modern Lionel's earliest engines.

Lionel promoted these switchers as SW-1 models, but their correct designation is NW-2.
Top shelf: 8057 Burlington Route; 8374 Burlington Northern with new drive system.
Middle shelf: Scarce 8471 Pennsylvania; 8473 Coca-Cola (note early use of "Catch The Wave" color scheme) from uncatalogued Coke set of 1974.
Bottom shelf: 8485 U. S. Marines in camouflage colors; very scarce 8556 B&O Chessie System.

A. Rudman, F. Stem, L. Caponi, and R. LaVoie Collec

	GD	VG	EXC	MT
8057 BURLINGTON ROUTE:				

8057 BURLINGTON ROUTE: 1980, NW-2 yard switcher; Type V red and gray body; white-enameled frame; white stripes on front; lettered "Way of the Zephyrs"; headlight; single Type II motor; three-position E-unit; two operating couplers. Hard to find. — — **75 150**

8111 D T & I: 1971-74, NW-2 yard switcher; orange Type II body; black lettering; headlight; single Type II motor; two-position manual reverse; two operating couplers. Came with or without silver radio wheel. C. Rohlfing comment. Headed the 1382 Yard Master set.

| (A) Two green marker lights. | — | 20 | 35 | 75 |
| (B) Two red marker lights. | — | 20 | 35 | 75 |

8153 READING LINES: 1981, NW-2 yard switcher; Type V body; dark green front and top; black frame; yellow sides; dark green numbers and logo; one plastic and one die-cast truck with hollow roller pickup; two-position reverse; single Type II motor; headlight; two operating couplers. Came only with 1154 Reading Yard King set. — — **100 125**

8154 ALASKA: 1981-82, NW-2 yard switcher; Type V body; dynamic brake and air tanks atop cab; same paint scheme as postwar Lionel 614; headlight; single Type II motor; two operating couplers. Also offered by Montgomery Ward in 1982 with matching 6441 bay window caboose in display case for $149.99. One of more sought after NW-2s. — — **85 125**

8182 NIBCO: 1982, NW-2 yard switcher; uncatalogued; white Type V body; blue-green "NIBCO" logo and number on the cab; green and blue ribbon runs the length of the cab; above the ribbon is blue "Quality Piping Products". Part of special uncatalogued promotional set 1264 made by Fundimensions for Nibco Plumbing Products, 2,000 made; offered as a premium for plumbers with purchase of faucet sets. See Uncatalogued sets chapter in Volume II, first edition, for description. — — **125 175**

8354 ERIE: 1973-75, NW-2 yard switcher; black plastic body with gold lettering; red or green marker lights; lighted; two die-cast trucks; single Type II motor; two operating couplers.

8473 Coca-Cola Switcher with three steps on the door behind "Coke".

8569 Soo.

	GD	VG	EXC	MT
(A) Type III body.	—	—	90	120
(B) Type IV body.	—	—	90	120

8374 BURLINGTON NORTHERN: 1983, NW-2 yard switcher; green and black Type V body; white lettering and logo; stamped-metal frame with safety stripes; two red indicator lights and operating headlight; AC/DC Type III can motor — first NW produced this way; three-position electronic reversing unit; sliding shoe contacts; two operating couplers. Accommodating the new motor truck forced Lionel to alter the frame — the metal steps were removed in favor of the steps on the truck. This and the 8485 are the only two NW-2s made in this fashion. Lionel also made a matching 6427 B N transfer caboose. — — **90 125**

8460 M K T: 1973-75, NW-2 yard switcher; gray plastic Type IV body painted red with white lettering; headlight; single Type II motor; two-position manual reverse; one dummy coupler.
— — **50 75**
See Factory Errors and Prototypes chapter in Volume II, first edition.

8471 PENNSYLVANIA: 1973-74, NW-2 yard switcher; dark green body; yellow/gold lettering; red keystone on cab sides; headlight; single Type II motor; two operating couplers. Somewhat hard to find.
(A) Type IV body. — — **250 300**
(B) Type V body. J. Nowaczyk Collection.
— — **250 300**

8473 COCA-COLA: 1974-75, NW-2 yard switcher; red body; white lettering; headlight; single Type II motor; two-position reverse; two operating couplers. Headed the 1463 Coca-Cola Special set.
(A) "Three-step" variety, Type III body.
— **100 125 150**
(B) "Two-step" variety, Type IV body.
— **100 125 150**
(C) "One-step" variety, Type V body. — **100 125 150**

8485 U. S. MARINES: 1984, NW-2 switcher; olive camouflage-painted Type V body; black frame and railings; headlight; AC/DC Type III can motor; plastic truck side frames; frame altered as described under 8374; weighted, sliding shoe contacts; three-position electronic reversing unit; two-operating couplers.
— — **75 100**

8501 WESTERN MARYLAND: See 18501.

8503 SOUTHERN PACIFIC: See 18503.

8556 B & O CHESSIE SYSTEM: 1975-76, NW-2 yard switcher; yellow and blue Type V body; headlight; single Type II motor; two operating couplers. Hard to find.
— **110 225 300**
See Factory Errors and Prototypes chapter in Volume II, first edition.

	GD	VG	EXC	MT

8569 SOO: 1975-77, NW-2 yard switcher; red body; white lettering; Soo Line logo on cab; black stamped-metal frame; headlight; single Type II motor; two-position reverse; dummy couplers. Part of the 1582 Yard Chief set. — **30 75 100**

8660 C P RAIL: 1976-77, NW-2 yard switcher; red Type V body with white lettering; large black and white C P logo on cab; stamped-metal frame; headlight; single Type II motor; two operating couplers. — **50 100 125**

8761 G T: 1977-78, (Grand Trunk) NW-2 yard switcher; blue Type V body; orange-painted ends; white lettering; white-enameled stamped-metal frame; headlight; single Type II motor; two operating couplers. — — **125 175**

8770 ELECTROMOTIVE DIVISION: 1977, NW-2 yard switcher; General Motors' Electro-Motive Division factory demonstrator paint scheme — blue and white body with white lettering; headlight; single Type II motor; one plastic truck and one die-cast truck. This engine surprisingly headed a relatively low-level Traditional set in 1977, the 1761 Cargo King.
(A) Two disc-operating couplers; three-position E-unit.
— **80 100 125**
(B) Fixed couplers; two-position reverse unit.
— **30 40 80**

8860 ROCK: 1978-79, NW-2 yard switcher; gray plastic Type V body painted blue; black and white lettering and logo; white-enameled frame; white nose with two red indicator lights; blue paint around headlight; rubber tires on two geared wheels; single Type II motor; three-position E-unit; two operating couplers.
— **50 100 125**

18501 WESTERN MARYLAND: 1989, NW-2 yard switcher; dark gray Type VI body; cream top, lettering, number and logo; Western Maryland wing logo on front reading "Fast Freight Line"; "8501" on cab; operating headlights at both ends, dioded to function in the direction of travel; running lights on front. This engine resurrects deluxe features not seen on the NW-2 since the postwar 6250 in 1955: Type I motor with Magnetraction, die-cast frame and trucks, ringing bell, three-position reverse and wire handrails. Good runner. First modern era NW-2 switcher to head a Collector set, the separate-sale Western Maryland Fallen Flags No. 4. — — — **295**

18503 SOUTHERN PACIFIC: 1990, NW-2 yard switcher; Type VI body painted medium gray; white lettering; "8503" on cab; red stripe on chassis walkway edge; red-painted nose and lower cab rear; two operating headlights, dioded for direction of travel; running lights; electronic bell; die-cast frame and trucks; Magnetraction; Type I motor; three-position reverse; wire handrails. Engine continues the "deluxe" series of NW-2s started by the 18501. Catalogued with RailSounds circuitry, but not produced that way. Came with matching 19707 S P searchlight caboose.
— — — **400**

THE FAIRBANKS-MORSE (FM) TRAINMASTER

It is not easy to reproduce a legendary locomotive. So when news came in 1979 that Fundimensions was about to revive the scale-length Fairbanks-Morse (FM) Trainmaster,

A. Rudman, F. Stem, L. Caponi, and R. LaVoie Collections

Big "bruisers," the Fairbanks-Morse twin-motored giants.
Top shelf: 8056 North Western.
Second shelf: 8157 Santa Fe, which introduced Lionel's new electronic diesel horn.
Third shelf: 8687 Jersey Central Lines "Miss Liberty" Statue of Liberty Centennial commemorative.
Bottom shelf: 8951 Southern Pacific, the "Black Widow." Missing from this assemblage is the first Fairbanks-
Morse, the 8950 Virginian of 1979.

collectors were anxious to see if Fundimensions would do the locomotive justice. Indeed, the firm did — the Fundimensions FM Trainmaster is a nearly exact duplicate of the postwar Lionel model, right down to the six-wheel die-cast trucks, air tanks and battery box/fuel tank. The first models of this magnificent twin-motored diesel were the blue- and yellow-striped 8950 Virginian locomotive (a revival of the postwar 2331) and the stunning 8951 Southern Pacific "Black Widow" locomotive, which had only existed as a Lionel prototype. Both locomotives sold extremely well and are still in great demand, especially the Southern Pacific.

Three more FM locomotives followed in quick succession. The 8056 North Western green and yellow locomotive in 1980 met with only a lukewarm reception, possibly because the paint scheme resembled the Virginian in style a little too much. The next year, Fundimensions produced a beautiful Santa Fe (8157) in blue and yellow freight colors (even though Santa Fe never owned any real Trainmasters; C N W did not, either!). The firm added the icing on the cake with this one with the new electronic diesel horn. Finally, Fundimensions issued a special production for J. C. Penney in 1983, which has become nearly impossible to obtain. This was the 8378

B. Greenberg photograph

The earliest and latest FM Trainmasters.
Top shelf: **8950 Virginian FM with number on ends, obscured by railings. This was Lionel's first FM Trainmaster.**
Bottom shelf: **8301 (18301) Southern FM.**

Wabash FM in gray and blue "bluebird" colors. The new Lionel management commemorated the centennial of the Statue of Liberty by issuing the 8678 Jersey Central "Miss Liberty" FM in 1986 with a matching Standard O boxcar and extended vision caboose. In 1988, Lionel issued the 18301 Southern model with a matching scale high-cupola wood-side caboose. An Erie-Lackawanna may be in the future — it is one of the only postwar FMs the modern firm has not recreated.

All of the Fundimensions FM Trainmaster locomotives are desirable pieces. Operationally, they can only be out-pulled by the die-cast GG-1 electrics. The Wabash and Southern Pacific locomotives are very hard to find. The Virginian, Jersey Central, and Santa Fe locomotives rank a notch below these in scarcity; and the Chicago & North Western seems to be the easiest piece to acquire. It should be noted that locomotives without horns can be retrofitted with the electronic horn, and many FM owners have indeed done just that.

As of yet, there have been no variations in the body style, the heavy-duty stamped-metal frame or the six-wheel die-cast trucks of these engines. The FMs have an unusual truck which, with its blind driver on the innermost wheel, gives an unbalanced look when viewed from the side.

Common Features

All FMs feature two Type I Pullmor motors, a three-position E-unit, operating couplers, stamped-metal frame and railings, die-cast six-wheel trucks, Magnetraction, ornamental horns, and operating headlights at both ends.

FAIRBANKS-MORSE
TRAINMASTER LISTINGS

	GD	VG	EXC	MT

530 WABASH: See 8378.

8056 NORTH WESTERN: 1980, dual-motored Fairbanks-Morse Trainmaster; yellow and dark Brunswick green body; yellow safety striping; "ROUTE OF THE / 400"; operating headlights at both ends; stamped-metal frame and railings; die-cast six-wheel trucks; two Type I Pullmor motors; Magnetraction; three-position E-unit; operating couplers. — — **300 395**

8157 SANTA FE: 1981, dual-motored Fairbanks-Morse Trainmaster; blue with yellow trim, numbers and lettering; yellow safety striping; operating headlights at both ends; stamped-metal frame and railings; die-cast six-wheel trucks; two Type I Pullmor motors; Magnetraction; three-position reverse unit; operating couplers. This was the first engine to use the new diesel electronic horn. — — **400 495**

8301 SOUTHERN: 1988; see 18301.

8378 WABASH: 1983, dual-motored Fairbanks-Morse Trainmaster; uncatalogued; deep blue body; gray and white striping; Wabash flag logo on cab below window; "8378" does not appear on body; "530" appears on body near cab; operating headlights at both ends; stamped-metal frame and railings; die-cast six-wheel trucks; two Type I Pullmor motors; Magnetraction; three-position E-unit, operating couplers. "Bluebird" markings are quite similar to the 2337 and 2339 Geeps made by Lionel in the 1950s, except that this blue color is darker. The carton, marked "8378-203", contained the engine box and a boxed display case marked "GLASS". Despite this marking, the case is plastic; it has an oak base with a piece of Gargraves Phantom track fastened to it. Two plastic bumpers are also supplied. An instruction sheet marked "LIONEL WABASH BLUEBIRD, 09-8378-250" came with the

GD   VG   EXC   MT

box, and a second sheet found with regular production units, 70-8157-250, was also included. Special production for J. C. Penney Christmas special.

A short run of about 800 was made in Mt. Clemens just before the factory moved to Mexico. Thereafter, reports about production conflict. Some say that there was no more production. Others say that Mexican production did occur and can be distinguished from Mt. Clemens production by an aluminized paper sticker attached to the underside of the engine which has "CPG" and "Made In Mexico" information; whereas the pieces made in Mt. Clemens have "MADE IN U.S.A." on their plates. Reportedly, there are slight color differences in the Mexican locomotive. In addition, the Wabash flags on the Mexican models are installed at an angle, and the finish is not as sharp. The Mt. Clemens pieces were made from September to December 1983; when it was discovered there were substantial back orders, Mexican production began in April 1984. Back orders received the Mexican-made pieces. The total production run was supposed to be about 5,000, but it is likely that far fewer were actually made. D. Johns, P. Catalano, R. Shanfeld and R. LaVoie comments; G. Kline, N. Banis, S. Goodman and R. Darasko Collections.

(A) Mt. Clemens production.   —   —   1200   1500
(B) Mexico production.   —   —   1100   1300

8687 JERSEY CENTRAL LINES: 1986, dual-motored Fairbanks-Morse Trainmaster; dark flat olive green body; cream striping, logos and numbers; Jersey Central Statue of Liberty logo on cab; electronic horn (though catalogue makes no mention of this); operating headlights at both ends; stamped-metal frame and railings; die-cast six-wheel trucks; two Type I Pullmor motors; Magnetraction; three-position reverse unit; operating couplers. Issued with companion 7404 Standard O boxcar and 6917 extended vision caboose sold separately. Has reinforced screw holes to prevent cracking of body shell. Commemorative of 100th anniversary of Statue of Liberty.   —   —   360   525

8950 VIRGINIAN: 1979, dual-motored Fairbanks-Morse Trainmaster; no number on the cab sides of this engine, but number is on front and rear, obscured by the railings; operating headlights at both ends; stamped-metal frame and railings; die-cast six-wheel trucks; two Type I Pullmor motors; Magnetraction; three-position reverse unit; operating couplers. Rerun of postwar 2331 locomotive with new catalogue number. This reissue was an exact copy of the yellow and blue original — except for slightly brighter paint — right down to the tendency of the Fairbanks-Morse body shell to crack at the screw holes. Caution is advised when disassembling this and the earlier modern era Fairbanks-Morse locomotives. The 8687 Jersey Central has reinforced screw holes to prevent the problem. R. LaVoie comments.   —   275   350   495

8951 SOUTHERN PACIFIC: 1979, dual-motored Fairbanks-Morse Trainmaster; black body; silver-white lettering and orange stripe on frame; operating headlights at both ends; stamped-metal frame and railings; die-cast six-wheel trucks; two Type I Pullmor motors; Magnetraction; three-position reverse unit; operating couplers. Rerun of prototype Trainmaster shown at 1954 Toy Fair with a different number. Also known as the "Black Widow."   —   500   625   700

18301 SOUTHERN: 1988, dual-motored Fairbanks-Morse Trainmaster; green cab; silver-painted lower sides and ends; white stripe at roofline; gold lettering and numbers; "8301" on cab; electronic diesel horn; stamped-metal frame and black railings; die-cast six-wheel trucks; operating headlights at both ends; two

GD   VG   EXC   MT

Type I Pullmor motors; Magnetraction; three-position reverse unit; operating couplers.   —   —   350   400

THE GENERAL ELECTRIC DASH 8

During its 90-year history, Lionel occasionally was first, or nearly first, to issue models of popular new prototype engines. The best example was the speed Lionel exhibited in bringing out its O Gauge version of the Union Pacific streamlined M-10000 in 1934, only a few months after the real thing crossed the country for the first time.

But the cost of the tooling also meant that other popular engines, such as the RS-3, were not modeled until decades after they first appeared on real railroads. And once created, the tooling for Lionel's models tended to be used for many years, often long after the prototype rolling stock had disappeared. New F-3s roll along Lionel layouts today, more than 20 years after they disappeared from America's railroads.

Happily, in the case of the General Electric (GE) Dash 8, Lionel was quick on the draw after GE created the prototype in the mid-1980s. Lionel has not only developed a new body style (complete with engineer figure), but also a new six-wheel truck frame similar to, but not the same as, those used on the SD-40.

Initial reports on these engines indicate some quality-control problems. The most important of these are the burnt armatures and poor reversing units. And there are some collector complaints about the 18205 that its trucks should have been gray to match the engine, not black. Lionel acknowledges this was a mistake. Despite these defects, the engine has proved a hot seller and appears destined to take over the top-of-the-line Collector diesel sets from the GPs and U36s. Other reports indicate it is a good runner, after initial problems were corrected.

Common Features

So, far, both engines in this series feature the modified Type II motors used on the SD-40 except with a new type of six wheel die-cast truck, Magnetraction, three-position reverse untis, operating couplers at both ends, cab lights, headlights at both ends, and a flashing warning light on the cab roof.

DASH 8 LISTINGS

8206 SANTA FE: 1990; see 18206.
9100 UNION PACIFIC: 1989; see 18205.

GD   VG   EXC   MT

18205 UNION PACIFIC: 1989, Dash 8-40C diesel; gray roof; red numbers and lettering; gray metal handrails and frame with red stripe along frame edge; lighted number boards without numbers; cab lights, headlights and a flashing warning light on the cab roof; black six-wheel die-cast trucks, similar to, but not exactly the same as, those on the SD-40s; dual modified Type II motors; Magnetraction; three-position reverse unit; operating couplers at both ends. This engine is prototypically numbered "9100" on the cab, an unusual departure from Lionel's customary 8000-series numbers. First in the new-style locomotives modeled after the popular GE prototype Dash 8-40C. Union Pacific was the first road to purchase the Dash 8-40C from GE.

     —   —   —   **375**

GD   VG   EXC   MT

18206 SANTA FE: 1990, Dash 8-40B diesel; yellow- and blue-painted cab body; yellow frame, handrails and large "Santa Fe" on cab side; blue Santa Fe nose logo; "8206" on cab; cab lights, headlights and a flashing warning light on the cab roof; electronic bell/horn; dual modified Type II motors; Magnetraction; three-position reverse unit; operating couplers at both ends. Second in the new series of top-of-the-line diesels. This engine differs from its 1989 Union Pacific predecessor in that it has new four-wheel truck frames modeled more precisely after the "Floating Bolster" prototype. Came with 11713 Santa Fe Dash 8 set.

     —   —   —   **375**

E LECTRIC ENGINES

*B*efore we describe Lionel's production of electrics, a note on terminology is necessary. In *prototype* railroading, an electric engine is referred to as a "motor" because it receives its power from overhead wires, and does not generate power internally as do steam and diesel locomotives. But in *model railroading* terms, anything that is powered and can pull a train is considered a "locomotive," whether it is a model steam, diesel or electric engine. Obviously, all Lionel's engines actually operate on third-rail power, and not steam- or diesel-fuel-generated power.

EP-5 ELECTRICS

Fundimensions took quite some time to reissue the famous electric locomotives of the postwar era; but collectors agree it was well worth the wait. The first of the electrics to emerge from the miniature erecting shops of Fundimensions was the "double-end" EP-5 rectifier electric in 1975. Fundimensions has always called this engine "Little Joe," but that is an error; the real "Little Joe" was a quite different locomotive purchased by the Milwaukee Road and the Chicago, South Shore and South Bend Railroad. The name came about because these South Shore locomotives were originally intended for Russian export during World War II; hence, the name "Little Joe" after Joseph Stalin. The real "Little Joe" had a dual-ended cab similar to the EP-5, but was larger and heavier, had a different wheel configuration, and a different shape of cab front. The EP-5, on the other hand, was an electric made for the New Haven Railroad by General Electric. Famous for its rapid acceleration, it consequently earned the nickname "The Jet."

Except for its length and its four-wheel trucks (instead of the six-wheel types used on the real thing), Fundimensions' model of the EP-5 was quite accurate. The two pantographs on Fundimensions' models were modifications of those of the postwar era. Instead of the fragile coil springs of the postwar models, Fundimensions incorporated a strip of spring steel to create upward pressure, thereby enabling these engines to maintain better contact on overhead catenary wires. Some postwar engines have been refitted with Fundimensions pantographs for this reason. But the steel strip can be fragile, too, with a tendency to snap under excessive loads.

The first EP-5, issued in 1975, was an 8551 Pennsylvania tuscan with gold striping and lettering. The 1976 model was an 8558 Milwaukee Road locomotive in maroon, orange and black. In 1977 an attractive Great Northern EP-5 (8762) was made in dark green and orange. A special EP-5 (8272) was made for J. C. Penney in 1982. This engine had Pennsylvania colors and markings like its 8551 predecessor, but the nose and sides were bright gold with tuscan lettering. In 1988, a modified 8762 was resurrected, this time with Magnetraction and a horn, as the 18302 Great Northern at the head of the Fallen Flags No. 3 set.

The EP-5 is a fine runner which looks good with either freight or passenger consists. The EP-5s are relatively common, except for the J. C. Penney locomotive, which is hard to acquire due to its limited production.

Common Features

All EP-5 engines have two operating couplers, headlights at both ends, and two pantographs which can be wired for actual overhead-wire operation. They use a single Type I "Pullmor" motor with three-position E-unit. The headlight bulbs illuminate the cab and number boards.

The earliest and latest EP-5 electrics. *B. Greenberg photograph*
Top shelf: 8551 Pennsylvania EP-5, the first modern era revival of this postwar favorite.
Bottom shelf: 8302 (18302) Great Northern EP-5, the third time Lionel has made this engine.

EP-5 LISTINGS

	GD	VG	EXC	MT

8272 PENNSYLVANIA: 1982, GE EP-5 electric; uncataloged; tuscan body; gold-painted ends; heat dissipater box atop engine; broad gold striping across sides; tuscan lettering and numbering within side striping; single Type I motor; no Magnetraction; headlights at both ends; pantographs which can be wired for actual operation; three-position E-unit; operating couplers. Special edition made for J. C. Penney. Full price includes display board with piece of Gargraves track and plastic display case. C. Darasko and G. Kline Collections.

	—	—	275	350

8302 GREAT NORTHERN: 1988; see 18302.

8551 PENNSYLVANIA: 1975-76, GE EP-5 electric; tuscan body with gold stripes and lettering; single Type I motor; headlights at both ends; pantographs which can be wired for actual operation; three-position E-unit; operating couplers.

	—	150	200	300

	GD	VG	EXC	MT

8558 THE MILWAUKEE ROAD: 1976-77, GE EP-5 electric; maroon, orange and black body; single Type I motor; headlights at both ends; pantographs which can be wired for actual operation; three-position E-unit; operating couplers.

	—	85	175	200

8762 GREAT NORTHERN: 1977-78, GE EP-5 electric; gray plastic body painted dark green and orange; yellow lettering and stripes; four red and white goat logos; two large decals on nose; single Type I motor; headlights at both ends; pantographs which can be wired for actual operation; three-position E-unit; operating couplers.

	—	100	200	275

18302 GREAT NORTHERN: 1988, GE EP-5 electric; orange and dark green cab; yellow striping, numbering and lettering; red, white and green Great Northern goat logos on sides and nose; "8302" on cab; single Type I motor; electronic horn; headlights at both ends; pantographs which can be wired for actual operation; three-position E-unit; operating couplers. Part of Great Northern Fallen Flags No. 3 set, whose components were all sold separately. Similar to 8762 model of 1977, but includes Magnetraction and horn. Has the distinction of being the third (regular) issue of this engine with this road name, including the postwar 2358 (only one

A. Rudman Collection

8558 The Milwaukee Road "Little Joe" EP-5 electric.

A. Rudman, F. Stem, L. Caponi, and R. LaVoie Collections

The three ungainly but impressive E-33 electrics produced by Lionel to date.
Top shelf: **8659 Virginian.**
Middle shelf: **8754 N H.**
Bottom shelf: **8859 Conrail.**

	GD	VG	EXC	MT

of two engines issued three different times — the other is the Santa Fe F-3). It is not clear why Lionel did this, but may explain the sluggish sales of its Fallen Flags No. 3 set.

	—	—	—	250

E-33 ELECTRICS

In 1976 Fundimensions resurrected the ungainly and brutish 8659 Virginian rectifier of postwar fame. Despite its boxy look, this locomotive was welcomed by collectors because of its appealing glossy blue and yellow colors. It is modeled after GE's 3300-horsepower freight electric.

The Virginian was followed by a New Haven model (8754) in 1977, painted bright orange with white striping, a black roof and frame, and the famous McGinnis "NH" logo. And in 1978, Fundimensions produced a blue and white Conrail rectifier (8859). No other locomotives of this type have been made since.

These locomotives, still reasonably priced, are excellent runners worth attention.

Common Features

These engines, like their EP-5 and GG-1 cousins, have a single pantograph which can be wired for actual powered catenary operation. All engines have two operating couplers, lights at each end, three-position E-unit and a single Type I motor.

E-33 LISTINGS

	GD	VG	EXC	MT

8659 VIRGINIAN: 1976-77, GE E-33 electric; blue body with yellow stripe and lettering; yellow frame; single Type I motor; a single pantograph which can be wired for actual powered catenary operation; interior lights at both ends; three-position E-unit; operating couplers.
(A) Thin, light-colored nose decal. The decals can peel easily.
— 100 125 175
(B) Same as (A), but with thick, light-colored nose decal.
— 100 125 175

	GD	VG	EXC	MT

(C) Same as (A), but with regular dark yellow nose decal.
— 100 125 175

8754 N H: 1976-78, (New Haven) GE E-33 electric; black frame and roof; orange sides with white stripes and black lettering; large black serif "N" over "H" on rear of cab; single Type I motor; a single pantograph which can be wired for actual powered catenary operation; lights at both ends; three-position E-unit; operating couplers. Announced in a late 1976 brochure and catalogued the next two years.
— 100 150 200

8859 CONRAIL: 1978-80, 1982, GE E-33 electric; gray plastic body painted blue with white lettering and Conrail rail-wheel design; single Type I motor; a single pantograph which can be wired for actual powered catenary operation; lights at both ends; three-position E-unit; operating couplers. Although as many of this rectifier were produced as the Virginian and the New Haven models, the 8859 Conrail is found less often. Montgomery Ward offered it in 1982 with a display case for $149.00.
— 90 150 195

GG-1 ELECTRICS

Although the EP-5s and E-33s were fine electrics, collectors were really waiting for the "creme de la creme" of all the electrics — the famous Pennsylvania GG-1. The prototype, an amazing machine, had a service life of nearly 50 years. Even

B. Greenberg photograph

More of Lionel's fabulous GG1s.
Top shelf: 4935 (8150) Pennsylvania GG-1 with both pantographs extended.
Bottom shelf: 8303 Amtrak GG-1 with both pantographs extended.

A. Rudman, F. Stem, L. Caponi, and R. LaVoie Collections

Three of the modern era's magnificent twin-motored GG-1 electrics.
Top shelf: 18300 Pennsylvania from 1987 in bronze, made as a match for the mint car production.
Middle shelf: 8753 Pennsylvania in tuscan from 1977, the first of the modern GG-1s.
Bottom shelf: 8850 Penn Central model in black from 1978.

today, its Raymond Loewy-designed lines look fresh and contemporary. Two of these locomotives, including the original 4800, are preserved at the Railroad Museum of Pennsylvania in Strasburg, Pennsylvania. (For the full story of this electric, see Karl Zimmerman's book, *The Remarkable GG-1*.) Eleven others can be found carefully preserved at other railroad museums around the country.

Finally, in 1977, patience had its reward. Fundimensions put out a tuscan 8753 GG-1 which had the original die-cast body, two motors, and Magnetraction. The overall end-result was good, but a few minor flaws needed correcting. Collectors claimed that the nylon gearing did not hold up very well in this locomotive, and the body casting was rougher than it should have been. In 1978 Fundimensions issued an all-black GG-1 in Penn Central markings (8850). This locomotive

was an operational and cosmetic improvement over its predecessor, but collectors did not like its paint scheme. It was a slow seller.

In 1981, the 8150 Pennsylvania GG-1 was produced in gloss Brunswick green with gold striping, and this time the quality was right. The striping was the best ever applied to a GG-1 and the finish was very attractive. In addition, this model included a prototypical number (4935) on the cab. For 1987, Lionel produced another Pennsylvania GG-1 (18300) in a new bronze color with bluish-black striping and a matching N5C caboose to power the previously produced bullion cars. This combination formed a unique "money train." Like all the GG-1 locomotives except the Penn Central, the 1987 model was a hot seller, despite the fact that its unusual color scheme produced howls of dismay from some traditionalists. The 1989 model (18303) saw a prototypical Amtrak paint scheme applied to the GG-1.

The modern era GG-1 locomotives are highly prized and sought by collectors and operators alike. These massive (seven-pound!) engines will outpull any other locomotive (except perhaps the Fairbanks-Morse Trainmaster) because all twelve wheels are drivers. Even the Penn Central GG-1 is beginning to attract attention, though it is not as highly valued as the others. In fact, a case could be made that the Penn Central locomotive is a good bargain where GG-1s are concerned.

Common Features

All GG-1s are powered by two Type I "Pullmor" motors with Magnetraction, which explains their pulling capacity (and price!). In addition, each model features operating couplers, headlights at each end, pantographs capable of being wired for actual overhead catenary operation, and a three-position E-unit.

GG-1 LISTINGS

	GD	VG	EXC	MT

4935 PENNSYLVANIA: See 8150.

8150 PENNSYLVANIA: 1981, dual-motored GG-1 electric; dark Brunswick green die-cast body; five gold stripes; prototypical number "4935" on cab (the real 4935 was one of the last ones in service); two Type I motors with Magnetraction; headlights at both ends; pantographs which can be wired for actual overhead catenary operation; three-position E-unit; operating couplers. Railfans saved it from destruction and donated it to the Pennsylvania Railroad Museum in Strasburg, Pennsylvania. K. Wills comment. — 475 525 650

	GD	VG	EXC	MT

8300 PENNSYLVANIA: 1987, GG-1; see 18300.

8303 AMTRAK: 1989, GG-1; see 18303.

8753 PENNSYLVANIA: 1977, dual-motored GG-1 electric; uncatalogued; tuscan die-cast body; gold stripes; two Type I motors with Magnetraction; headlights at both ends; pantographs which can be wired for actual overhead catenary operation; three-position E-unit; operating couplers. 6000 produced. Announced in a late 1976 dealer brochure. — 375 500 600

8850 PENN CENTRAL: 1978-79, dual-motored GG-1 electric; black-painted die-cast body with white "PENN CENTRAL" and P C logo on side; two Type I motors with Magnetraction; head lamps at both ends; operating pantographs with black insulators and shiny metal shoes; three-position E-unit; operating couplers. Did not sell as well as the first GG-1 rerun. However, according to reliable sources, about the same number of the 8850s and 8753s were made. Service Stations report that due to their sluggish sales, many of these engines have been custom repainted. Announced in a late 1978 dealer brochure and catalogued in 1979. — 300 375 475

18300 PENNSYLVANIA: 1987, dual-motored GG-1 electric; bronze-painted die-cast body; black striping and lettering; red keystones on sides and ends; "8300" on cab; two Type I motors with Magnetraction; lights at both ends; headlights at both ends; pantographs which can be wired for actual overhead catenary operation; operating couplers. Offered with matching Pennsylvania N5C porthole caboose sold separately. Designed to pull train of various Lionel bullion cars issued in previous years. — — 450 525

18303 AMTRAK: 1989, dual-motored GG-1 electric; flat-silver-painted body; black lettering and numbers; "8303" on cab; blue stripes running the length of the body; red nose; casting and paint have rough edges; two Type I motors with Magnetraction; headlights at both ends; pantographs which can be wired for actual overhead catenary operation; three-position E-unit; operating couplers. Offered as part of Amtrak passenger set with six separate-sale, long aluminum cars. Though not Lionel's best paint effort, this engine sold reasonably well because of the Amtrak colors and the popular aluminum cars. — — — 425

M⬥ CHAPTER 3 ⬥S
OTORIZED UNIT

One of the most fascinating areas of production in the postwar era was that of the motorized unit, little specialty self-propelled cars which buzzed around layouts of the mid-1950s. These motorized units, delightful to watch in action, are eagerly sought by collectors. It was only natural that collectors would get curious about any possible reissue of them.

Perhaps because of the complicated gearing in some of these units, Fundimensions did not begin to revive them until 1982. At that time, the company issued an attractive 8264 snowplow locomotive in Canadian Pacific maroon and gray markings. Since then, each year has seen the emergence of more of these little novelties. In 1983, an 8368 Vulcan 2-4-2 engine was produced in blue and yellow Alaska markings as a light-duty switcher with two operating couplers. In 1984 the 8459 rotary snowplow came out in black and yellow Rio Grande markings. (This time, the "a" in "Rio Grande" was stamped correctly; most of the postwar Rio Grande snowplows had the "a" backwards!) In the same year a Pennsylvania fire car (8379) was produced, complete with hose reels and rotating fireman, just like the original. The 8578 New York Central ballast tamper unit in yellow and black was produced in 1985. This interesting piece is activated by track trips: when the locomotive encounters a track trip it slows down, and miniature pile drivers "tamp" stone ballast between the rails and ties.

Lionel has gotten great mileage out of the stocky little cab it used on many of the motorized units. It was created for the Army, Navy and Minuteman switchers in the postwar years. In the modern era it has served as the basic body for snowplows (straight and rotary), Vulcan (2-4-2) and gas turbine diesel (0-4-0) switchers. These units also provide good opportunities for the beginning collector to acquire powered engines inexpensively, but keep in mind that they are meant for light yard-switching or stand-alone duty. Typically, a motorized unit can only pull two to three cars. Recently, Lionel has placed them at the front of some of its low-cost

Traditional Line sets. The Vulcan (2-4-2) switchers have a large smokestack, decorative bell and at least one operating coupler; whereas the lower-cost gas turbine diesel switchers have none of these extra features. The turbine uses the same four-wheel truck/side frame design as the earlier NW-2 switchers, but with a DC-only can motor.

In 1987 came the modern reincarnation of Lionel's famous little Birney trolley of the mid-1950s in the form of a bright orange and blue Lionelville 8690. Delayed in production for almost two years, this little trolley represented significant advances in operation over its ancestor. It used a spur-gear drive instead of the old crosscut-gear system, so it ran much more quietly and efficiently. The new trolley's body casting was more detailed, with headlight lenses and open stepwork. Silhouette figures filled all the windows, including a conductor figure at the end windows. It ran so efficiently that sometimes the reversing slide rebounded too far and the trolley froze in neutral when it hit a bumper. When allowed to run slowly at low voltage, this problem did not occur. Lionel did a fine job of improving the original design of the trolley, and it has sold very well. In 1988, the two-tone green 18404 San Francisco version followed the Lionelville 8690 model.

The popular operating burro crane was revived in 1988, 1989 and 1990. This incredibly complex little device — complete with actual controls — allows the operator to use the crane and hook to pick up trackside structures or debris. With a work caboose or gondola in tow, this intricate crane provides hours of operating enjoyment.

Another exciting revival occurred in 1987 — the 18401 Lionel handcar. The original Lionel handcar of the mid-1960s burned out very easily, but Lionel redesigned its drive system this time around. Significantly, it was listed as part of the Traditional Series and had a very reasonable price. Santa Claus versions were produced in 1988 (18403) and 1989 (18408), followed by an 18407 Snoopy and Woodstock handcar in late 1990. Perhaps someday soon Lionel will put numbers on the handcars so we can keep track of them!

---

* Asterisk found in listings indicates that the information within that listing was derived from Lionel catalogue only.

A. Rudman, F. Stem, L. Caponi, and R. LaVoie Collections

Top shelf: 8264 Canadian Pacific snowplow; 8368 Alaska Railroad switcher.
Middle shelf: 8379 Pennsylvania fire car; 18400 Santa Fe rotary snowplow.
Bottom shelf: 8459 Rio Grande rotary snowplow (the *a* in "Grande" is printed correctly rather than backwards as in the 1950s' Lionel unit); 8578 N Y C ballast tamper.

The power for all these units varies across the board. The trolleys and smaller Vulcan diesels (snowplows, tampers, etc.) use a cut-down version of the Type II integral motor/truck, which is geared slower than a road diesel. One of the unsung achievements of modern Lionel is its rearrangement of the gearing in many of these pieces for smoother operation. The only significant operating problem has come when a softer nylon gear, which strips easily, was used for the main drive gear on the armature shaft. The lowest-end 0-4-0 gas turbines use an early form of the can motor without the rectifier circuit, meaning they operate only on DC. The handcars use a small version of the Type III can motor with rectifier.

The larger Budd RDC cars, which are discussed at the end of this chapter, use the premium Type I motor. These unusual powered passenger cars could not correctly be categorized as diesel engines or passenger cars, and so are listed here.

8350 U.S. Steel.

MOTORIZED UNIT LISTINGS

	GD	VG	EXC	MT

8161 L. A. S. E. R.: 1981-82, gas turbine; bright chrome; blue lettering; DC-powered; dummy couplers. Part of 1150 L. A. S. E. R. train set, a return to a late 1950s-type Lionel space set.
— — **60 100**

8264 CANADIAN PACIFIC: 1982, 2-4-2 Vulcan switcher snowplow; gray body; maroon snowplow, frame and trim; yellow lettering; non-operating headlight; gold ornamental bell; die-cast chassis; three-position E-unit; operating die-cast coupler on rear.

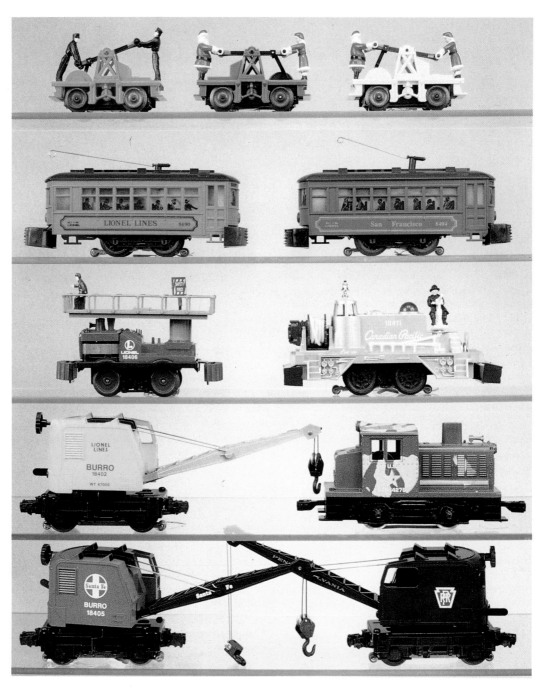

B. Greenberg photograph

Some of Lionel's more interesting motorized units.
Top shelf: 18401 Lionel handcar; 18403 Santa Claus handcar; 18408 Santa Claus handcar.
Second shelf: 8690 (18404) Lionel Lines trolley; 8404 San Francisco trolley.
Third shelf: 18406 Lionel track maintenance car; 18411 Canadian Pacific fire-fighting car, a great match for the
   12768 burning switch tower made in 1990.
Fourth shelf: 18402 Lionel Lines Burro crane; 8377 U.S. Marines gas turbine.
Bottom shelf: 18405 Santa Fe Burro crane; 18410 Pennsylvania burro crane.

	GD	VG	EXC	MT

This unit often requires servicing before use because grease coagulates in the gear sump. Remedy: flush out grease and lubricate sparingly. Gears are noisy, as were original mid-1950s Lionel units. Body should be handled carefully because window struts break easily. R. Sigurdson comment. — — **110** **150**

8350 U S S: 1974-75, (U. S. Steel) gas turbine; red plastic body; silver lettering; forward and reverse by polarity reverse on power pack; dummy couplers. The first DC-powered engine offered by Lionel; motor will burn out if run on AC. Part of 1380 U. S. Steel industrial switcher set. — — **20** **30**

GD   VG   EXC   MT

8368 ALASKA RAILROAD: 1983, 2-4-2 Vulcan switcher; yellow and blue; blue "ALASKA/RAILROAD/8368" and Eskimo logo on cab sides; silver-finished bell; operating headlight; die-cast frame; three-position E-unit; two operating couplers; came in Type V orange and blue box. This unit often requires servicing before operation because grease coagulates in the gear sump. Flush out grease and lubricate sparingly. Gears are noisy, as were those on the motorized units of the 1950s. This unit intended to pull only two or three cars. Body should be handled carefully because the window struts break easily. R. Sigurdson comment.

— — **100   140**

8377 U. S. MARINES: 1983, gas turbine; olive drab; engine does not have applied lettering as shown in the Traditional Series catalogue; DC-only Type III can motor. Lionel supplied a decal sheet for the operator. This locomotive is part of the Traditional Line 1355 Commando Assault Train set.

— — **60   100**

8379 PENNSYLVANIA: 1983-84, motorized fire-fighting car; uncatalogued; highly detailed tuscan body; black and white bumpers; black wheel; white fire hose with gold nozzle; gray hose, reel and pump; black-clad fireman with flesh-colored hands and face; yellow outriggers; gold plastic bell; illuminated red dome light atop cab, which blinks after warm-up; bump reverse; gold "PENNSYLVANIA" P R R keystone and "8379" on side of body; number is divided in center by keystone. Shown incorrectly with number "6521" on it in 1983 Fall Collector Center brochure. After some use, there is a tendency for the bumper frame to loosen and slide to the neutral position. This can be alleviated by increasing the reversing slide contact spring tension. The reversing slide adjustment can also be made by bending the two tabs on the slide outward to increase friction between the shoe assembly and the car frame. The operating instructions state that the unit should not be left in the neutral position for more than five minutes, because the contact spring may bridge the gap between the contact rivets, which can cause the two fields to buck each other and burn out. The earliest instruction sheet did not mention this potential problem. In some cases, this unit needed adjustment prior to initial operation. Announced in late 1983 Fall Collector Center brochure, but not released until 1984. R. Sigurdson, C. Rohlfing and D. Johns comments. — — **140   175**

8400 SANTA FE: 1987; see 18400.

8404 SAN FRANCISCO: 1988; see 18404.

8459 RIO GRANDE: 1984, 2-4-2 Vulcan rotary snowplow; black cab; yellow cab sides with black "Rio Grande" script and number (this time the "a" in "Grande" has been printed correctly, rather than backwards as in the Lionel unit of the 1950s); yellow handrails and plow housing; black plow fan with yellow markings; no headlight, but lens is present; gold ornamental bell; three-position E-unit; one operating die-cast coupler on rear. This unit runs well and its gears are quieter than the previous 8264, 8368 and 8379. The window struts are less likely to break because they are made with a double section. Designed to pull only two or three cars. Packed in Type V collector box; Mt. Clemens production. R. Sigurdson and R. LaVoie comments.   — — **100   135**

8490 LIONEL LINES: 1987; see 8690.

8578 N Y C: 1985, (New York Central) 0-4-0 ballast tamper; yellow body; black frame, railings, lettering and tamper frame; silver tampers, battery box, and ornamental headlight atop cab; brown central window; blue man inside cab; dummy rear coupler. Track trip activates tampers and reduces speed of unit.

— — **100   125**

8670 Chessie System.

GD   VG   EXC   MT

8670 CHESSIE SYSTEM: 1976, gas turbine; yellow body with blue trim; runs only on DC; polarity reverse; sliding shoe pickup; not lighted; fixed couplers. Part of 1660 Yard Boss set. Somewhat hard to find now.   — — **35   65**

8690 LIONEL LINES: 1986-87, four-wheel Birney-style trolley; bright orange-painted gray body; newer-style open steps and headlight openings; blue lettering, striping, number and roof; large, outsized blue plastic sheathing over bumpers; silhouettes in all windows, ends and sides; illuminated; "8490" in number slots and in packing box, possibly indicating delay in production; 8490 part number also shows up on the window inserts; bump reverse can rebound and stall trolley in neutral if unit is operated at too high a voltage (this model runs much better at lower voltage); spur-gear drive motor replaces crosscut gear of postwar unit. Much-improved reissue of postwar No. 60. Reportedly, this was a project largely encouraged by Lenny Dean, long-time Lionel Service Manager. The trolley has sold very well. Catalogued in 1986, but not released until 1987. R. Sigurdson, W. Berresford and R. LaVoie comments.   — — **100   125**

8769 REPUBLIC STEEL: 1977, gas turbine; blue with yellow trim; fixed couplers; sliding contact pickups; DC current. Part of 1760 Steel Hauler set.   — — **20   40**

8900 PENNSYLVANIA: 1989; see 18900.

18400 SANTA FE: 1987, 2-4-2 Vulcan rotary snowplow; red oxide body; yellow snowplow fan with brown spiral stripe; yellow and brown Santa Fe cross logo; yellow "8400" on cab; lack frame and railings; three-position E-unit; operating coupler on one end.

— — — **145**

8769 Republic Steel.

A selection of Baltimore and Ohio Budd Cars.
Top shelf: 8764 powered passenger coach; 8765 dummy baggage/mail car.
Second shelf: 8766 powered baggage/mail car; 8767 dummy passenger coach.
Bottom shelf: 8768 dummy passenger coach.

R. Kaptur Collection; B. Greenberg photogr

	GD	VG	EXC	MT

18401 LIONEL: 1987, handcar; bright orange body with no number; black push handles; two blue men with flesh-painted faces; no reverse; DC can motor with rectifier for AC operation; newer spur drive motor; partially exposed gearwork. Advertised in catalogue with remote-control reverse, but not made that way.
(A) First run: dark orange body. M. Sabatelle comment.

— — — **50**

(B) Second run: light orange body. M. Sabatelle comment.

— — — **50**

18402 LIONEL LINES BURRO: 1988, operating burro crane; black die-cast frame; yellow cab; red lettering; light gray boom; three control levers for switching from self- propulsion to rotating cab, raising or lowering the hook, and reversing functions of both levers. Essentially a revival of the 3360 unit of the mid-1950s. This has always been a cleverly designed and interesting operating unit, although its complexity makes it susceptible to breakdown. — — — **120**

18403 SANTA CLAUS: 1988, handcar; green body; figures of Mr. and Mrs. Claus dressed in traditional attire; black hand pump; no lettering on car; DC can motor with rectifier for AC operation.

— — — **40**

18404 SAN FRANCISCO: 1988, Birney-style trolley; four-wheel green body; dark olive green roof; yellow lettering; black plastic bumper covers; "8404" on cab window insert; illuminated; mechanically identical to 8690. — — — **120**

18405 SANTA FE BURRO: 1989, operating burro crane; black die-cast base; light gray cab (pictured as dark gray in catalogue); white lettering, number and logo on cab and black boom; "BUILT BY/LIONEL" embossed into cab body at lower rear. See 18402 for description of operating modes.

— — — **110**

	GD	VG	EXC	MT

18406 LIONEL: 1989, 1991, motorized track maintenance car; unpainted dark red plastic body; white lettering, number and Lionel circle logo; dark gray motor cover; black frame; medium gray superstructure (pictured as white in catalogue); bumper reverse mechanism; red- and white-striped sign reading "DANGER" on one side and "SAFETY/FIRST" on the other; olive-painted man on superstructure. Reissue of No. 69 postwar model.

— — — **90**

18407 SNOOPY AND WOODSTOCK: 1990-91, handcar; blue handcar body; no lettering on car; white and black Snoopy standing on a box; yellow Woodstock figure resting on the hand pump; DC can motor with rectifier for AC operation.

— — — **45**

18408 SANTA CLAUS: 1989, handcar; similar to 18403 released in 1988, except handcar body is light gray and pump handle is green; no lettering on car; DC can motor with rectifier for AC operation. It is not clear why Lionel produced a near-duplicate car rather than re-cataloguing the 18403.

— — — **40**

18410 P R R: 1990, operating burro crane; black die-cast frame with Brunswick green body; P R R keystone logo in red and white on cab; gold "Burro" and "18410" on cab door; black boom with gold "PENNSYLVANIA". See 18402 for description of operating modes. — — — **110**

18411 CANADIAN PACIFIC: 1990, motorized fire-fighting car; silver body; white number, script lettering and base unit; maroon generator and hose reel; dark blue bumpers with white safety stripes; blue fireman with white-painted face; gold decorative bell; flashing warning light; bump reverse mechanism; "BLT 1-90". Includes outriggers and two feet of hose that winds with a ratchet crank. — — — **90**

Modern era Budd diesel railcars. An 8764 Baltimore and Ohio powered passenger car, an 8765 Baltimore and Ohio dummy baggage car and an 8871 Amtrak dummy baggage car were also made to accompany these cars. The three pictured Baltimore and Ohio cars were part of an uncatalogued and hard to find 1977 Service Station set.

Top shelf: 8766 Baltimore and Ohio powered baggage car; 8767 Baltimore and Ohio dummy passenger car.

Middle shelf: 8768 Baltimore and Ohio dummy passenger car; 8868 Amtrak powered baggage car.

Bottom shelf: 8869 and 8870 Amtrak dummy passenger cars.

	GD	VG	EXC	MT

18412 UNION PACIFIC: 1991, motorized fire-fighting car. Announced in Lionel's 1991 Book 1 catalogue, but not manufactured. **Not Manufactured**

18413 CHARLIE BROWN AND LUCY*: 1991, handcar; light blue handcar body; no lettering or number on car; Charlie Brown in red and black; Lucy in yellow dress; DC can motor with rectifier for AC operation. — — — **52**

18900 PENNSYLVANIA: 1988-89, gas turbine; tuscan cab; gold lettering and number; gold stripe along lower flange of cab; "8900" on cab; black plastic truck frame with DC-only motor; white P R R logo on cab rear; front headlight; decorative bell; two-position forward/reverse switch; fixed couplers; "BLT 1-88". Part of 1989 Midnight Shift set 11708, but released first in an uncatalogued Toys 'R Us set (also 11708) in 1988. — — — **40**

THE BUDD CARS

In the early 1950s, railroads began to demand self-propelled passenger railcars for light rail service where their lines were not electrified. The Budd Company responded with an all-aluminum self-contained passenger car powered by two 275-horsepower diesel engines. These cars, formally named "Rail Diesel Cars" (RDCs) came to be known popularly as the "Budd Cars," and were very popular in short commuter service. They could still be seen in service on some Eastern lines into the late 1980s.

By 1956, postwar Lionel had released its own version of the Budd Car in Baltimore and Ohio markings. Though typically shorter than scale, these railcars were good sellers.

In 1977 Fundimensions introduced a Service Station Special set which was completely different from its predecessors: the firm finally revived the handsome Budd diesel railcars in their original Baltimore and Ohio markings. The set had a powered baggage car (8766) and two dummy passenger coaches (8767 and 8768). Soon afterward, Fundimensions issued an 8764 powered passenger coach and an 8765 dummy baggage car. In 1978, Fundimensions issued another set, this time in colorful Amtrak markings (8868, 8869, 8870 and 8871).

The Budd railcars were very attractive, and they ran well because of the premium Type I separate motor and power truck. The silver paint on the Fundimensions cars was brighter than that of the Lionel originals, and is expected to have better wear characteristics. The silver color on these and the Santa Fe F-3 looked more grainy than the postwar color.

Common Features

The principal operating difference between the modern era and postwar Budd cars is the lack of Magnetraction on the Fundimensions version. The Budd cars have translucent window strips with silhouetted passenger figures, as well as an unusual lighting scheme — a bulb at each end and a third in the middle.

BUDD CAR LISTINGS

	GD	VG	EXC	MT

8764 BALTIMORE AND OHIO: 1977, powered Budd RDC passenger car; uncatalogued; gray plastic body painted silver with blue lettering; metal frame; plastic battery box hangs from frame; rubber tires on the two wheels with gears; Type I power trucks with plastic two-step assembly (plastic assembly formerly appeared on the Lionel 44-ton dummy truck); three-position E-unit with lever on bottom; two operating couplers. This is a reissue of the Lionel 1950s version with the following differences: a plastic trim horn replaces a metal trim horn, rubber tire traction replaces Magnetraction, and glossy silver paint replaces the original flat silver-gray paint. — 80 125 175

8765 BALTIMORE AND OHIO: 1977, dummy Budd RDC baggage/mail car; uncatalogued; "US Mail Railway Post Office"; gray plastic body painted silver; blue "Budd RDC" lettering pierced by red line on small decal; two operating couplers. — — 100 125

8766 BALTIMORE AND OHIO: 1977, powered Budd RDC baggage/mail car; uncatalogued; gray plastic body painted shiny silver; blue lettering; two operating couplers. Part of uncatalogued 1977 Service Station Special set 1766. *Priced as a set with 8767 and 8768.* — 250 300 450

8767 BALTIMORE AND OHIO: 1977, dummy Budd RDC passenger coach; uncatalogued; two operating couplers; matches 8766. Part of Service Station Special set 1766. *Priced as a set with 8766 and 8768.* — 250 300 450

8768 BALTIMORE AND OHIO: 1977, dummy Budd RDC passenger coach; uncatalogued; two operating couplers; matches 8766. Part of Service Station Special set 1766. *Priced as a set with 8766 and 8767.* — 250 300 450

8868 AMTRAK: 1978, 1980, powered Budd RDC baggage/mail car; gray plastic body painted silver; blue lettering; white band with red and blue stripes through windows; Type I motor; three-position E-unit; two operating couplers. R. Pauli Collection. — 100 150 200

8869 AMTRAK: 1978, 1980, dummy Budd RDC passenger car; two operating couplers; matches 8868. — — 70 100

8870 AMTRAK: 1978, 1980, dummy Budd RDC passenger car; two operating couplers; matches 8868. — — 70 100

8871 AMTRAK: 1978, 1980, dummy Budd RDC baggage/mail car; two operating couplers; matches 8868. — — 70 100

MULTIPLE UNIT (M.U.) COMMUTER CARS

The predecessors to the diesel-powered Budd cars were the electrically-powered Multiple Unit commuter cars. Built in the 1920s and 1930s, these elegant long passenger cars serviced the electrified commuter routes of the northeast United States before World War II. They reduced the turnaround time and pollution associated with steam-powered trains in the crowded urban areas. After the war, diesel-powered units like the Budd cars took over commuter duties.

Lionel had never modeled these handsome motorized trains until 1991, when two MU commuter cars appeared in Lackawanna colors. The cars were roughly modeled on the heavyweight "Madison"-type passenger cars released the same year, but are distinguished by their overhead pantographs, which can be wired to actually operate the train. At 15 inches long, they are close to scale. The Lionel Multiple Unit cars have some fine detailing: chains on the doors at each end, cow-catcher pilot, red marker lights, die-cast trucks, interior illumination, and constant-voltage headlights.

These cars, along with the new long Madison cars, are obviously Lionel's response to increasing competitive pressure toward longer scale-detailed passenger cars. Preliminary reports are that this set has sold well, so we should expect more releases in the future.

MULTIPLE UNIT COMMUTER CAR LISTINGS

	GD	VG	EXC	MT

18304 LACKAWANNA*: 1991, powered/dummy Multiple Unit commuter car set; new Lionel model of electrically-powered passenger cars used on commuter lines in the 1920s, 30s, and 40s; body based on long Madison-style heavyweight cars also produced in 1991; dark gray/green car body; gold lettering; "2401" on powered unit; "2402" on dummy unit; twin Type III can motors; electronic three-position reverse unit; directional headlights with constant voltage; each car illuminated with window silhouettes; red marker lights; door chains; cow catcher on powered car; two operating couplers on each car; die-cast trucks. Powered/dummy unit sold together as a set, not individually. — — — 480

◆ CHAPTER 4 ◆
STEAM ENGINES

During its existence, Lionel has been very creative with its steam engines in one sense, and not so creative in another. This apparent contradiction is not easy to explain, but some knowledge of the manufacturing process might help in understanding the paradox.

The Manufacturing Process

The molds for steam engines tend to be more detailed and expensive than those for the diesel engines. In the first place, the boilers are rounded instead of square-sided, resulting in a more intricate mold-creating process. Additionally, the molds must be made strong enough to withstand die-casting with metal, even though the same mold can be (and has been) used with plastic. Tooling costs can be enormous. For example, when Fundimensions issued its American Flyer passenger cars, it found that key pieces of the observation car molds were missing. It cost Fundimensions well over $30,000 just to obtain those pieces and change the molds.

Imagine, if you will, the enormous cost of creating a steam engine mold from scratch, and you will understand why Lionel chose not to be creative, at least initially. Instead, Fundimensions almost always used the steam engine molds it inherited from the original Lionel Corporation and modified them as needed. Now, if you want to put out a product which at least seems to be new, what would you do? The most cost-effective strategy would be to modify currently existing molds and issue new paint schemes; and in that sense, Lionel has been extremely creative with its steam engines.

Of course, there is a price to be paid — dies and molds eventually wear out with use. Lionel has reached the time when it must invest in retooling with entirely new steam engine dies or updated versions of the old ones. Either way, this involves considerable expense. The changes since 1986 reflect this new approach.

For example, consider the two basic molds for the Hudson 4-6-4 steam engine — the smaller Baldwin boiler and the larger Alco boiler. The last time the Baldwin mold was used (until recently) was in 1979 for the 8900 A.T.S.F. Hudson. Since then, every Hudson made by Lionel used the larger Alco boiler. The probable reason is wear and tear on the Baldwin boiler mold. Compare an 8603 or 8900 Fundimensions locomotive with an original 665 or 2065 Lionel Hudson from the 1950s and 1960s, and you will see the advance of fuzziness of detail as the die has worn. The Wabash 4-6-2 Pacific issued in 1986 used the Baldwin mold once again. It is obvious the die had been cleaned and reworked, most likely by a new plating of chrome on the inside of the die surface. The foregoing explanation probably accounts for the slow variation in steam engines relative to the rapid expansion of the diesel engines.

In 1970 Fundimensions began its production of steamers with simple 2-4-2 Columbia locomotives in plastic. A die-cast Great Northern Hudson was pictured in the catalogue, but never made. In 1972, Fundimensions issued the 8206 Hudson steamer, the only large steamer made until 1976, when the 8600 and 8603 Hudsons appeared. After that, however, the story gets much more complicated, probably because Fundimensions had built its market to sufficient numbers to justify the issue of many new steamers.

Establishing why Lionel/Fundimensions produced so few variations of the medium and large steamers in its first decade or so helps us understand the magnitude of the revolution now occurring at Lionel Trains, Inc. Since 1987, the company has produced four entirely new die-cast steam bodies (the Northern, the T-1, the Mohawk, and the Steam Turbine) and reintroduced two other classics (the 700E scale Hudson and the B-6), which required heavy investment in new tools and dies. By making such risky moves, Lionel is stating that it trusts the train-collecting hobbyists for their support. The explosive growth of the hobby in recent years appears to be paying off for Lionel, so far.

In summary, Lionel Trains, Inc. has succeeded in carrying on the great tradition of tinplate steam engines with some

---

* *Asterisk found in listings indicates that the information within that listing was derived from Lionel catalogue only.*

of the most appealing and best made products imaginable — even though the cost of these locomotives has proven prohibitive for some collectors. The lower-priced Lionel steamers run reasonably well, are highly collectable, and, as a group, offer the chance for a fine collection. It took a while to achieve the variety, but it was worth the wait.

This chapter categorizes the steam engines into three sections: **large** (or Collector-level steam engines, including the larger six- and eight-drive-wheel locomotives), **small** (four drive wheels and some smaller six-wheelers — generally translated into the Traditional Line engines), and the unique **Generals**. But before we discuss these individual engine types, a few notes on wheel arrangements, motor types, and tender types are necessary.

Steam Engine Wheel Arrangements

Wheel arrangements on steam locomotives (based on number of pilot truck wheels/driving wheels/trailing truck wheels) have been assigned certain descriptive names by the prototype railroads and rail watchers over the years. For example, a 4-6-4 is called a *Hudson* because the New York Central made that arrangement famous with the Twentieth Century Limited, pulling it along the banks of the Hudson.

Other names, given by the railroads or the manufacturers to the most prominent engines which used the wheel types, are as follows (based on *Whyte's Classification*):

STEAM ENGINE WHEEL ARRANGEMENTS
0-4-0 Switcher
2-4-0 Porter
2-4-2 Columbia
4-4-0 General/American
4-4-2 Atlantic
0-6-0 Switcher
2-6-0 Mogul
2-6-2 Prairie
2-6-4 Lionel K-4 (arrangement used mostly in Europe)
4-6-2 Pacific
4-6-4 Hudson
2-8-0 Consolidation (not yet modeled by Lionel)
2-8-2 Mikado
2-8-4 Berkshire
4-8-2 Mohawk/Mountain
4-8-4 Northern/Niagara/Pocono and others
6-8-6 Steam Turbine

Figure 4.1

There are ten-wheel-drivered locomotives and articulated locomotives (e.g., the 4-6-6-4 compound Mallets) not yet made by Lionel and not included on this list. Some compound engines have been made by other manufacturers.

The unique "Generals," modeled after the classic wood-burning locomotives of America's nineteenth century, feature a 4-4-0 arrangement (sometimes called "American"). The different switcher bodies take some getting used to, but there is no mistaking the thin boiler and huge, bulbous smokestack of the famous General!

Unhappily, things are not so neat that we can identify one body type with one wheel arrangement, either on the prototype roads or in Lionel-land. There are many cases where Lionel placed a body style on a wheel arrangement on which it was not normally found in real life. For example, many different body styles were placed on the 4-6-4 wheel arrangement — the Alco small Hudson boiler, the Baldwin small Hudson boiler, and, of course, the semi-scale Hudsons themselves. Berkshire, "J"-class, Northern and T-1 bodies have been placed on 4-8-4 wheel sets.

It is relatively easy for Lionel to change pilot and trailing trucks, whether it produces a prototypically correct body/wheel combination or not. *Figure 4.1* merely identifies the way the bodies and wheel sets are *usually* related.

A Note About Reverse Units

One important terminology note on the reverse units: Prior to the development of the circuit board reverse unit in 1980, Lionel used a gravity-operated mechanical plunger-drum device known as the "E-unit" to reverse its locomotives. The E-unit can has become familiar to millions of Lionel operators, along with the unmistakable buzz of its internal solenoid. E-units came in two varieties: two-position (forward/reverse) and three-position (forward/neutral/reverse).

The micro circuit board reverse device that made its appearance in 1980 is absolutely silent and not mechanical in function at all. It is really not appropriate to call it an E-unit (although Lionel does), because the only thing it has in common with a mechanical E-unit is its ability to reverse the motor. The circuit is also used to rectify AC into DC for the can motor, so it can run on both types of power. The older mechanical E-unit does not do this.

To avoid confusion, this Guide refers to the older devices as the *E-unit* (or mechanical E-unit) and to the circuit board as the *electronic reverse unit*. The former is associated with AC brush motors and the latter with the DC can motors.

Steam Engine Motor Types

In terms of the motors, Lionel concerned itself principally with the drive wheels; so it had one motor frame for four-wheelers (the Columbias and Switchers), one for the six-wheelers, one for the scale Hudsons, and another for the eight-drivered monsters. A still larger eight-drivered motor was created in 1989 for the huge Reading T-1. Unique frame/motor assemblies have been made for the General and the B-6 scale switcher. Each of the four- and small six-wheel motor frames has a variation to accommodate an AC brush or DC can motor. The nine types of steam engine motors used by modern era Lionel are as follows:

TYPE I: The most common steam engine Lionel made is the *four-wheel AC brush motor* (see Figure 4.2), with the armature and field mounted transversely (horizontally) in a frame consisting of two parallel metal plates. The metal frame is fitted with spacers, which keep the plates a specified distance apart. To this structure literally everything else on the engine is attached — the wheels, pickup rollers, E- units (when present), smoke units and the boiler body itself. The motor is a standard carbon-brush type, although the brushplate is a lighter-weight plastic than the older postwar versions. A pinion gear, mounted to the end of the armature shaft, transmits torque through cluster gears and idler gears to the drive wheels. Reversing this motor requires the mechanical E-unit wired in series to the motor. Except for the very inexpensive DC-only engines, this motor was used on most of the Fundimensions small steam engines before approximately 1979. In the last decade, the Type II DC motor was phased in.

TYPE II: The *four-wheel DC can motor* (see Figure 4.3) has been used in the small steam locomotives since about 1979. It consists of the same type of frame as the Type I motor, except that a DC can motor replaces the brushes, armature, brushplate and field of the older AC design. The motor is completely self contained, with only the shaft and pinion gear protruding. The remaining gearing and wheel arrangement are very similar to Type I, since the structure was intended to fit inside the same boiler designs. The can motor represents a major technical innovation on the part of Lionel in the last twenty years, important to nearly every form of motive power it has made. The can itself operates on DC power. This feature means it is silent, smooth and able to move on very low voltages which would stall an AC motor. Direction can be reversed by simply changing the polarity at the transformer. The signature buzz of the mechanical E-unit is slowly becoming history.

Lionel has used this configuration on many lower-end steam engines. The 8350 U S S switcher was the first Lionel engine to use the DC can motor (though not in this frame). The first steam engine to use this frame and DC motor was the 8903 Rio Grande Columbia in 1979. One important operating problem is that AC current inadvertently applied to this motor burns it out. It is fun to read the stern, no-nonsense warnings to this effect directed at the purchaser of such trains. Sometime in the late-1970s, micro-circuit technology had advanced to the point where Lionel could create an electronic equivalent of the E-unit which rectified the power so that the can-motored engines could operate on AC-power. There is no difference in the motor itself; the difference between an AC/DC can motor and a DC-only can motor is the presence or absence of the reverse circuit board. The circuit board and its components still took up volume, which required some maneuvering to fit inside the smaller steamers. On the very smallest Lionel did not bother, and these remain DC-only powered. The board also functioned to create a standard three-position forward/ neutral/reverse sequencing to which Lionel hobbyists have become accustomed over the years. In terms of numbers, the quantity of engines which used this type (AC/DC or DC-only) is about the same as for the Type I motor.

TYPE III: The *six-wheel AC brush motor* (see Figure 4.4) appears today as the standard for the six-wheeled medium steam engines and the smaller Hudsons. It is mechanically similar in form to the Type I motor, except that the frame is

somewhat larger to support the six drive wheels and the larger boilers associated with these models.

TYPE IV: The *six-wheel can motor* (not illustrated) is a version of the Type III six-wheel engine. It bears the same relationship to Type III as the four-wheel can does to its AC Type I equivalent. An interesting note on this motor is that it was used in its DC-only form on only two engines, the 8001 and 8007, which were apparently issued just before the electronic reverse unit was perfected. Additionally, these two strange engines are the only K-4-type locomotives modern Lionel has made, the only plastic six-drivered engines, and among the few which have a light in the firebox! Slow sellers due to the DC-only restriction, the 8001 and 8007 were not repeated and are now somewhat hard to find. The Type IV motor reappeared recently (with the electronic reverse enabling AC/DC operation) on the 18606-18609 Atlantic steam engines.

TYPE V: The *scale Hudson* (see Figure 4.5) is a massive engine consisting of a die-cast chassis to which the six drive wheels (larger than on the Type III and IV motors) are fitted with all their attendant rods and cranks. The motor itself is similar to the Pullmor type (described in the diesel section). It rests horizontally near the cab and is connected via a complex set of flexible universal joint couplings and bearings to a worm shaft, which in turn drives the wheels. One attractive feature of this design is its lack of unsightly external gearing, thereby enhancing the scale model appearance. It has been used for the "Big Three" (the 783, 784 and 785 Hudsons) and the new 1-700E for 1990. The 785 and the 1-700E feature an upgrade of the armature bearings to reduce binding on the brushplate. Another feature worth noting is the center drive axle, which actually utilizes the rods and cranks to drive the rear and front wheels.

Type VI: The *eight-wheel Berkshire* (see Figure 4.6) is another massive model engine used on the earlier eight-drivered monsters of the Lionel Line — the Berkshires and bullet-nosed J-types and Northerns. In each case, the front and rear trucks vary. This motor is similar in concept to the scale Hudson with its Pullmor motor mounted to the rear of a long die-cast chassis, long enough here for eight main wheels. Again, the side rods actually assist the motor in driving all the wheels. This style engine, but with smaller wheels, was used for the Pennsylvania 6-8-6 steam turbine.

Type VII: In keeping with its unique body style, drive train and graphics, the *General*-type engine (see Figure 4.7) also features a unique motor arrangement. It consists of a Pullmor-type motor assembly mounted nearly vertically in the cab, and a worm shaft/wheel arrangement driving the back set of main wheels. This arrangement and the light weight of the engine itself produce an unusually powerful locomotive. Recent lower-end Traditional General engines employ a modified four-wheel chassis supporting the can motor and the reverse unit/rectifier circuit board. On some very low-end versions, the board is absent and the engine is DC-only. The *can motor version* is designated *Type VIIA* (see Figure 4.8).

Type VIII: In 1989, Lionel introduced the **Reading T-1** (not illustrated) with an eight-drivered chassis even bigger and more massive than the Hudsons and Berkshires. It uses the same concept as the scale Hudsons and Berkshires — a Pullmor motor driving the rear main axles, but applied on a new frame design. Like the scale Hudsons, the assembly uses a universal-joint coupling concept for smoother operation. Lionel introduced a new design of large, spoked wheels for this engine, with holes machined directly in the casting. The motor appeared again in 1990 for the 18009 4-8-2 Mohawk, for the 18011 Chessie T-1 in 1991, and for the large Pennsylvania Turbine that year, as well. Due to its recent issue, no illustration is available for this motor type.

Type IX: The **B-6** (not illustrated) is essentially a shortened version of the Hudson engine — die-cast frame with a Pullmor-type motor mounted horizontally in the cab. Because of its size, this engine is quite unique and in a category of its

own. Also because of its size, weight and low center-of-gravity, the B-6 is an excellent puller.

Steam Engine Tender Types

The descriptions of steam engine tenders can be somewhat confusing, even for experienced Lionel collectors. This section attempts to clarify the listings of the tenders, with a short introduction to help keep them straight.

Descriptive names (such as *slope-back*) are used for the listings, as well as a prewar or postwar number (such as 1130 or 243), which many readers will recognize as the original engine on which the tender type was introduced. A few recently introduced tender types, like the interesting Rock Island Northern from 1987, have modern era numbers. Lionel created three entirely new steam engine and tender body styles (the Northern, the T-1 and the Mohawk) in the last three years, and reintroduced the prewar long slope-back tender for the modern era B-6 switcher.

Tenders are unique pieces of rolling stock in model railroading because they are always associated with their engines, and therefore are not usually numbered themselves, although exceptions do exist. In addition, Lionel itself causes endless confusion by often assigning the tender a catalogue number identical to the engine number (without actually printing it on the tender itself). This practice gives no clue of the tender's basic body style. This book reorganizes the listings to reflect the basic styles. There are many minor variations in types of trucks, back-up lights, and interior electronics. Due to the ease with which tenders can be mixed and matched, accurate documentation of the factory-produced combinations is essential. Most engines only display their road names on the tenders. To make matters worse, some engines used the same number, but different road names (as evidenced by the tender): the 8304 4-4-2 steamer is a good example. A tender with another road name can easily be

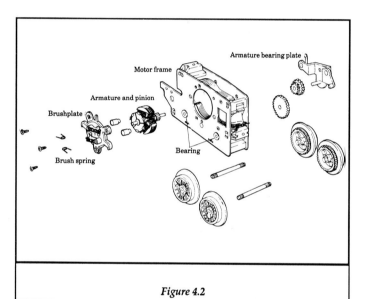

Figure 4.2

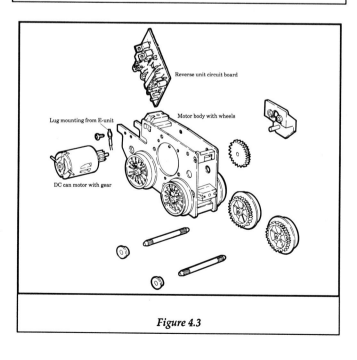

Figure 4.3

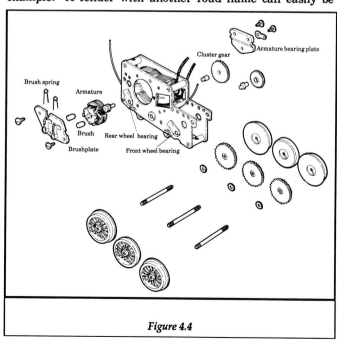

Figure 4.4

substituted and claimed as a variation, unless properly documented as original production.

There are more types of steam engine tenders than even the most expert hobbyists realize. See *Figure 4.9* for illustrations of these tenders.

SHORT STREAMLINED (1130 or 6066) is probably the most prevalent tender used on the low- to medium-end steam engines in the Lionel line. Do not confuse it with its longer 2046 cousin, which looks the same but is about an inch longer. The 1130 gains its "streamlined" moniker due to the smooth,

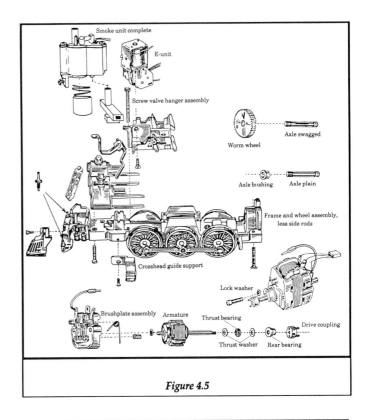

Figure 4.5

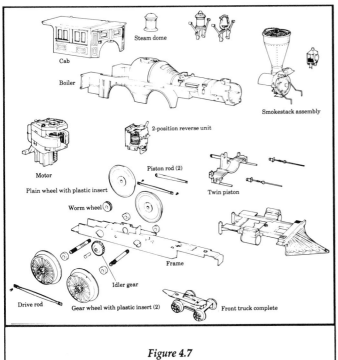

Figure 4.7

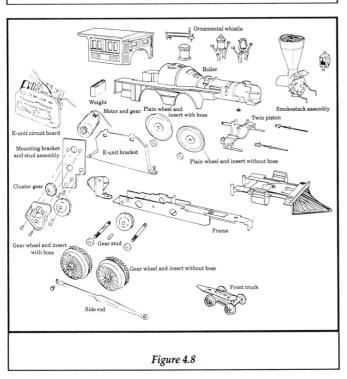

Figure 4.8

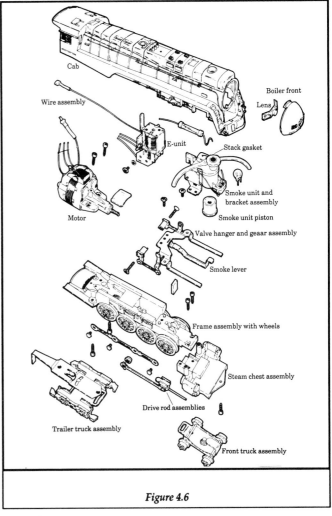

Figure 4.6

rounded side and rear top edges (contrasted with the 243 square-back type). It came in many subvariations. Some had a molded coal load and others had the top closed off with a simulated oil tank and hatch. This book's listings differentiate these variations with the terms "oil" and "coal." Others came with the strange "Mechanical Sound of Steam," recognizable in the pictures as a large cylinder protuding under the body. This unusual but oddly clever device incorporated a plastic cylinder filled with ball bearings which rolled along the center rail, rattling the bearings in a rather rackety simulation of a steam chug. Unfortunately, more often than not it sounded like radio static, and the rolling cylinder would sometimes lift the tender off the track on switches. The device was not popular with operators, but continues to appear even now in the Cannonball Express Traditional Line set.

The 1130, unlike the 2046, did not come with a water scoop, and it always had four-wheel trucks. Early versions featured postwar bar-end trucks or plastic AAR trucks, and later ones were fitted with Symington-Wayne wheel sets. The 1130 traces back to the 1130 engine in 1953, but did not appear in the prewar era. It was used on many postwar engines. Regular readers of the current *Lionel Service Manual* will recognize this one as the "Small Round Top."

LONG STREAMLINED (2046 or 2671) represents the longer version of the 1130 tender used on many of the higher-end and larger steam engines. It can be discerned from its smaller brother by the spacing between the wheel sets, and more easily by the prominent front platform on the smaller 1130. These long streamlined tenders came with plastic bodies. They were always coal-type tenders, except on the Southern Pacific Daylight 8307, for which collector pressure forced a change to the prototypical oil-type. All these tenders have a water scoop under the body, except the 8206 and 8600 (which were the earliest versions of the small Hudsons). The long 2046 is found with four-wheel Symington-Wayne trucks, or with six-wheel die-cast passenger-type trucks. As with other tender types, the 2046 can be found with and without the electronic Sound of Steam. This tender was first created for the postwar 2046 in 1950. This same tender is found with a "2671W" plate on the rear on a few recent modern era versions. It is also sometimes referred to as a "Pennsy"-style and as the "Large Round Top" (in the Lionel Service Manual). Like the 1130, the 2046 has no prewar counterpart.

SLOPE-BACK (1615 or 1050) defines a very recognizable small tender which first appeared for the prewar 201 switcher in 1940 and the postwar 1665. It is used on many small steam engines in the modern era, including such excellent pieces as the 8516 New York Central and 8635 Santa Fe switcher engines. The operating backup light on some recent versions appeals to many hobbyists. All of these tenders have at least a simulated backup light, but it only operates on the higher-end versions. Wire handrails have also been added on some of the higher-end tenders. The 1615 has always used four-wheel Symington-Wayne trucks during the modern era, except for the most recent 18615 Rock Island which was fitted with the new ASF strong-arm trucks. That will presumably be the case for all future tenders of this and other Traditional

styles. Its signature down-sloped coal load looks very realistic behind some of Lionel's small steam engines. A newer, scale-length die-cast model of this tender was produced for the long-awaited reissue of the B-6 scale 0-6-0 switcher (18000) in 1989.

SQUARE-BACK SANTA FE (243 or 6026) tender has embodied all these names since its initial appearance on the postwar 243. Approximately the same length as the 1130, the square-back tender consists of flat, angled top edges and a multitude of boxes attached to the top and front — it is decidedly un-streamlined! The "Santa Fe" designation does not mean it always came in that road name, only that it first appeared in the postwar era behind a small Hudson using the Santa Fe-style boiler. Once again, this type tender became known as the 243/6026 only because the 243 engine happened to have the number stamped visibly on the tender side.

There has been some confusion related to this tender in this and other postwar Guides: references to the tender style have sometimes used the number 234, not 243. This is because one postwar engine (the 239) had the tender with "234W" stamped on its side. Its initial appearance was on the 600-series Santa Fe Hudsons in the mid-1950s and the 243 in 1960, where the number also was printed on the side, this time as "243W". The 239 engine (which, oddly enough, came after the 243) had this same tender body except with different trucks, which apparently prompted Lionel to number it differently. It is also possible this was a stamping error. There never was a 234 engine produced. Either way, the author and editors of this book believe 243 is the correct designation and have revised the listings accordingly.

The square-back uses four-wheel trucks (Symington-Wayne mostly, with AAR or other trucks in the early modern era). This tender also received the strange mechanical Sound of Steam on some models, as did the 1130. Recently, Lionel produced an upgraded model of this tender lettered for Northern Pacific which included wire handrails and the new ASF strong-arm trucks. Readers of Lionel's Service Manual will find this tender also called "Large Square-Top."

SHORT BOX (8040) tender is an infrequently-used short, square-back piece which appeared first with the 8040 Nickel Plate Road 2-4-2 in 1972, and not again until the 18602 Pennsylvania 4-4-2 in 1987. The latter sported handrails on the deck. Both versions used Symington-Wayne trucks. This strange, stubby tender is an early Fundimensions product — it was never produced in either the prewar or postwar eras. The Service Manual refers to it as a "Small Square-Top."

NEW YORK CENTRAL-STYLE represents a series of handsome tenders which have graced the Hudsons and larger steam engines through the years since 1938. Four different versions of this tender exist, each slightly different in length and detail. This book designates them as *small*, *medium*, *large* and *scale*. The last is the granddaddy of them all, which came with the prewar 700E scale Hudson and did not appear again until 1990. Lionel derived the other smaller ones from this style, which features a long detailed coal load and a flat rear water tank deck which may or may not come with railings. Possibly the most recognizable feature of this tender style is the semi-circular plate which protrudes from the tender top at a 30-degree angle and separates the coal bin from the water tank. The body has somewhat streamlined shoulders like the Pennsy, but they are not as pronounced. The flat, rear deck is more evident on this tender. The four major variations are as follows:

A. *Small New York Central (2466, 6466 or 2666)* was recently resurrected after a long absence. This tender is a simplified plastic version of the 2224 (medium New York Central), without the die-cast six-wheel trucks. It actually comes with postwar bar-end trucks, an extremely unusual case of usage this late after the postwar period. The coal load is less detailed than its 2224 cousin and is missing the latter's rear steps and front wire handrails. Although popular in the early postwar period, it had not appeared again until it was included in the Desert King Service Station Special set in 1989. It has roots all the way back to the prewar-era 225 and 229 engines.

The 2466 is actually very difficult to differentiate from the 2224 because it is only approximately 1/2-inch shorter. The other major difference is that this tender is plastic. Most of the time, but not always, handrails are not included on the 2466.

B. *Medium Die-Cast New York Central (2224)* tender was a surprise resurrection on the 8101 Chicago & Alton in 1981, after not appearing since the prewar era. This wonderfully detailed tender features a die-cast body with grab-rails on the front and rear, a high molded coal pile which is prototypically higher than the engine cab, and a flat-topped water tank at the rear. This tender is somewhat less streamlined than the 2046 and 1130, but should not be considered square in the nature of the 243. It comes with die-cast six-wheel trucks and is used with some of the small Hudsons (including the T C A's special passenger engine) and several of the Berkshires. The 2224 tender is only slightly longer than its less detailed plastic 2466 brother and is often mistaken for it.

C. *Large Die-Cast New York Central Hudson (2426 or 2226)* is the top-of-the-line tender, designed to be close to scale length to match the magnificent scale Hudsons. It features all the detailing described above for the 2224, but is approximately three-quarters of an inch longer. This is often hard to tell unless two are placed together, but can be discerned by the difference in spacing of the trucks. Both the medium and large die-cast New York Central tenders come with many of Lionel's top features — Sound of Steam, RailSounds or whistles. It dates from the prewar 763 Hudson of 1940, a stepped-down version of the 700E, and was known in the prewar period as the 2226.

To date, this tender has only been used on the "Big Three" Hudsons issued by modern Lionel — the 783, 784 and 785. To be precise, just as the 763 was a slightly stripped version of the 700E original Hudson (but still magnificent!), so, too, this tender is a slightly stripped and shorter version of the actual scale Hudson tender, the 700.

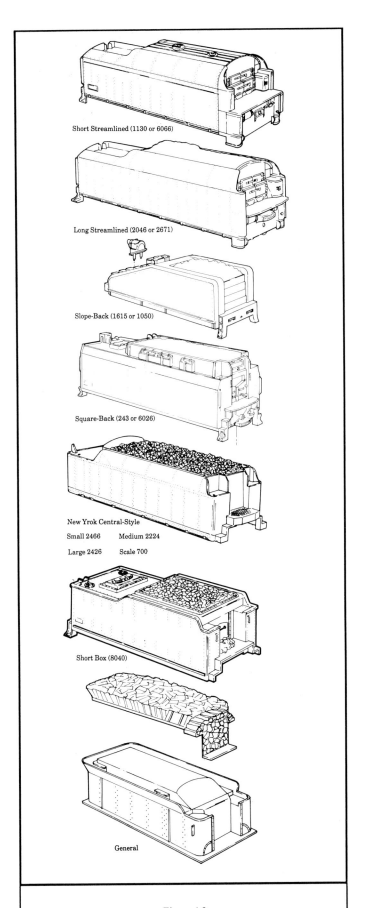

Figure 4.9

D. *Scale New York Central Hudson (700)* represents the big brother of all steam engine tenders. Until 1990 it had appeared only once in the history of Lionel, on the 700E Hudson of 1937. This tender sparked the famous "rivet debate" between Joshua Cowen and several hard-nosed scale model railroaders, which challenged whether or not the Lionel version had exactly the same number of rivets as did the real-life prototype. (For a more complete accounting of this story, see the 1991 book *All Aboard*, by Ron Hollander.) In 1990 Lionel revived this tender with the reissue of the 700E — the 18005 Hudson. Modern technology enabled new Lionel to add a refinement not possible in 1937 — the RailSounds system. Both the 1937 and 1990 versions are die-cast, with die-cast six-wheel trucks and complete piping and rivet detail. An interesting, unique feature is that they come with both NMRA scale couplers and Lionel standard couplers, which can be changed out. This holds true for the engine, as well. The only non-scale element of the 700E Hudsons are their oversized wheel flanges needed to operate on the tubular track. If scale wheel flanges were used, the engine would become airborne as soon as it hit a curve!

NORTHERN (18001) is a relatively new, long, square-back die-cast tender (much longer than its 243 predecessor) which features perfectly straight sides with excellent rivet detail. This entirely new tender style introduced in 1987 imitates its engine in being a faithful reproduction of the Class R67 locomotive described in the *Model Railroader Cyclopedia*. This piece bears a shorter coal load and longer water tank than most other tenders. It continues Lionel's recent trend toward scale and detail with six-wheel die-cast trucks and chromed handrails on front and rear. The coal load reaches above the cab roof as on prototypical engines. So far, the two versions of this tender (Rock Island and Lackawanna) also include the electronic Sound of Steam and the electronic whistle.

T-1 (18006) presents a brand-new tender body mold introduced for the much-hyped Reading T-1 in 1989. Incredibly, Lionel built a longer tender for this engine than the Northern or scale Hudsons! It not only features the same detailing and sounds as those pieces, but is one of the first recipients (along with the B-6 tender) of the RailSounds innovation. The tender is entirely smooth-sided. And in addition, Lionel developed an amazingly detailed new six-wheel die-cast truck for this tender, complete with molded-in brake pads. Together, this die-cast tender and its engine produce a model 25-inches long, far longer than anything else Lionel has ever produced in O Gauge! Needless to say, the engine runs only on wide-radius track.

MOHAWK (18009) is yet another huge tender released for the 18009 New York Central Mohawk in 1990. This phenomenal tender is a streamlined type resembling the 2046, but is almost 50 percent longer. It has the Type XI full-scale die-cast six-wheel trucks introduced on the T-1 tender. Other features include RailSounds, a small scale-size water scoop on the bottom, and an operating backup light. (It is interesting to note that while most Lionel tenders were under-scale in length, the water scoops under them were over-scale. Not this

time, though!) This tender has outstanding rivet detail rivaling that of the 700, but its most recognizable characteristic is the gray-tinted long coal load — made much longer than on other tenders.

B-6 SLOPE-BACK (18000) switcher tender was created in 1989 for the scale die-cast Pennsylvania B-6, recreating the classic B-6 of 1939-1942, also known as the 701. This die-cast tender is slightly longer (ie., closer to scale) than its 1615 predecessor, and came with four-wheel die-cast arch bar trucks. It came with metal handrails and an operating backup light. This tender received the important Lionel innovation, RailSounds. The three new tenders and two revivals introduced in the last three years give strong testament to a major shift at Lionel toward scale railroading and new style model trains.

GENERAL style tender is easy to recognize and categorize because it only appears with the unique 4-4-0 General engines, and is the only one to carry a simulated wood load. These tenders, normally plastic, come with arch bar trucks and are decorated in colorful schemes to match the old-time style of the engine. The General engines and their tenders first appeared in the 1800-series of the mid-1950s.

DOCKSIDE style tenders are, in essence, four-wheel gondolas that, depending on one's principles, may or may not be considered tenders at all. These unusual pieces only appeared with some of the tiny Dockside switcher engines. Completely plastic (including the wheels), they resemble nothing more than the very small and inexpensive Kickapoo rolling stock. This is an early Fundimensions product directed, of course, at the low-end Traditional Line market.

LARGE STEAM ENGINES

For most people, the name "Lionel" conjures images of huge puffing steam engines roaring down the track, rods and cranks a spinning blur. This is the essence of Lionel trains, the heart of the Lionel hobby. It does not require much imagination to picture these glorious engines, although motionless in the photographs, speeding down the straightaway on our own layouts. You will find the photographs here the most mouth-watering of the entire collection, representing the top-of-the-line engines Lionel has produced in the modern era (with price tags to match). These include the Hudsons, Berkshires, "J"-class, Turbines, Northerns, T-1s and Mohawks.

HUDSON

The name "Hudson" causes most railfans and train hobbyists to drool. Lionel continues to capitalize on this fact, going back to its celebrated release of the first scale Hudson, the 700E, in 1937. Since then, many small and scale Hudsons have appeared — all good sellers — and the production continues today.

Except for the scale Hudson with a 773 boiler, Fundimensions made small Hudsons with only two boiler styles. The smaller of the two is the Baldwin boiler, with horizontal shaded windows on its cab. The larger one, the Hudson with an Alco boiler, has square windows on the cab, cross-hatched into four smaller windows.

The 4-6-4 Hudson locomotives did not show much variation until 1977. Beginning in that year, Fundimensions issued many new ones, culminating in the reissue in 1984 (actually released in 1985) of the magnificent scale 8406 New York Central Hudson, and the reissue in 1990 of the granddaddy of them all — the 1-700E Hudson. By 1977, collectors began to ask for revivals of their favorite Lionel postwar steamers. Fundimensions responded well, but not quite as expected. The firm put out a beautiful 8702 Southern Crescent Hudson in Southern green and gold livery; it also made five matching passenger cars, each for separate-sale only. In reality, this usually meant there were many more sets of cars than locomotives.

So well received was this Hudson, that the next year Fundimensions revived one of the most revered names in Lionel history, the Blue Comet. This locomotive (8801), produced in two shades of glossy blue with gold trim, sported a feedwater heater on its boiler front. It, too, had its own set of matching passenger cars in a rich two-tone blue color scheme with gold lettering and a broad cream stripe. Collectors snapped up this locomotive and its cars even more eagerly than they had the Southern Crescent, even though the plain 2046W tender did not do the locomotive full justice. New diner cars were recently issued for both sets.

After issuing the 8900 Santa Fe Hudson, the first in the Famous American Railroad (FARR) Series, Fundimensions released another Hudson-powered passenger set, the Chicago & Alton, in 1981. This time the company surprised collectors. Instead of the plastic 2046W tender, the Chicago & Alton locomotive came with a revived 2224W tender not seen on a Lionel product since 1940! This magnificently detailed, die-cast tender had new six-wheel die-cast trucks, a whistle and the Sound of Steam. Many collectors liked the maroon, red and gold paint scheme of this set.

The last regularly issued small Hudson to date has been the 8210 Joshua Lionel Cowen Commemorative locomotive in bronze, black and gold of 1982. The same boiler has been used since then, but with different wheel arrangements. Mention must also be made of a very scarce Hudson, the 8006 Atlantic Coast Line, made for J. C. Penney as a special in 1980. This engine, almost impossible to acquire, has shown substantial appreciation in value.

Development of the semi-scale Hudsons continued since the original 8406 (actually numbered "783" on the boiler cab) became such a big collector favorite. Unfortunately, scale Hudsons are rather difficult and expensive to acquire.

In 1986, the 8606 Boston & Albany came out as part of a mail-order offer available only from Lionel itself, and not the usual dealer network. This arrangement, as one may guess, did not sit well with the dealers. So when Lionel Trains, Inc. management took control, it declared that this particular distribution scheme would not occur again. Due to its limited distribution, the Boston & Albany Hudson has been very hard to acquire. It is somewhat dressier than its New York Central predecessor with its white-painted smokebox front and white-edged driver wheels. A third scale Hudson, released in late 1988, was one collectors eagerly awaited. This is the 18002 New York Central (actually numbered "785" on the cab) in gun-metal gray — with, amazingly, spoked driver wheels which had not been seen since the prewar 763E of 1938-1942! This locomotive commemorated the 50th anniversary of the New York Central's proud thoroughbred steamer.

In 1990, Lionel finally committed the resources necessary to recreate the legendary king of all Lionel engines — the 700E scale Hudson of 1937. As the 1990 catalogue stated, it was "equipped with every extra feature we could load in." To be accurate, it should be pointed out that the 763-, 773-, 783-, 784- and 785-series Hudsons are really semi-scale. This means that although they are correct in size, their couplers and wheel flanges are somewhat larger than scale in order to run on the tubular three-rail track with standard Lionel rolling stock. Also, their 2426 tender is slightly smaller than scale length, and the boiler piping detail is not as complete as on the original 700E. These slight downgrades were made on the 763 and 773 in the 1940s and 50s to make the engine a bit more affordable. The 700E, and now its 1-700E modern reincarnation (actually catalogued 18005, and with a cab number "5340"), have taken those extra steps to scale.

This super-detailed engine has greater boiler piping and handrail detail than the 783-, 784- and 785-series semi-scale engines, along with many more details on the chassis, rods and cranks. It also features a National Model Railroad Association (NMRA) scale coupler on the front, which can be changed to a regular Lionel coupler if desired. The tender, a remake of the original scale 700W in all its riveted glory, also comes with both scale and Lionel couplers. Only the wheel flanges remain non-scale, so that it can be run on standard Lionel track.

Modern Lionel has taken this Hudson still further than the 1937 favorite: smoke emanates from the steam chest as well as from the smokestack, and the tender has been fitted with RailSounds. There is no question that this engine, even given its steep price, will achieve collector-classic status.

BERKSHIRE

In 1980 Lionel began a revival of the popular postwar 736 2-8-4 Berkshire locomotive with several models. These included the 8002 Union Pacific in a two-tone gray with smoke deflectors; the 8003 Chessie System Steam Special locomotive with a bright paint scheme of blue, gray, yellow and vermilion Chessie colors; and a pleasing 8215 Nickel Plate Road locomotive in traditional black. Only the Nickel Plate locomotive used the 2224W die-cast tender; the other two used the plastic 2046W tender.

Another beautiful Berkshire, the 8615 Louisville & Nashville model of the L & N's "Big Emma" series, emerged in 1986 as a special issue for J. C. Penney. The Berkshire boiler (the same Alco-style used on the small Hudsons) was used for two offshoots: the 2-8-2 8309 Southern Mikado in green, tuscan and gold Southern markings with the 2224W tender, and the 3100 Great Northern 4-8-4 locomotive in green and tuscan with the 2046W tender. These engines used Berkshire-type bodies, but not on the correct wheel arrangement.

Reader George Romich pointed out an interesting manufacturing quirk about the Hudsons and Berkshires. On some of these engines, an irregular-shaped metal fitting is present on the piston. The steam chest (on the engineer's cab side only) is recessed so that this fitting goes all the way in on each stroke. This strange fitting appears to do nothing, but, as Lionel aficionado I. D. Smith points out, it could be an artifact of an older smoke unit design, on which it was used to activate the smoke unit piston crank. If so, it would date back to the 1950s, and indicates how reluctant Lionel was to change proven, existing dies. It seems the part was used when available — some examples of the same engine have it, and some do not.

"J"-CLASS

In 1981 Fundimensions revived the beautiful Norfolk and Western "J"-class streamlined 4-8-4 locomotive. The original postwar engine was numbered 746. The modern one is numbered "611" after the prototype. This locomotive headed a matched set of maroon and black "Powhatan Arrow" aluminum passenger cars to form a train well over ten-feet long. It included all the deluxe Lionel characteristics, such as smoke from the cylinders, a feature introduced by Marx a long time ago. (The maintenance crew at the Norfolk and Western shops in Roanoke, Virginia, would have been greatly troubled by any sign of steam leaking from the cylinders because this would indicate a bad job of packing the seals!) The "J" boiler and frame were used again in 1983 for the 8307 Southern Pacific "Daylight" locomotive (a fine model of the original), which also pulled matching aluminum passenger cars. This colorful engine and set have become some of the most valuable and difficult to find pieces made by modern Lionel. In 1991, Lionel reissued the streamlined "Daylight" (as a Gs2, versus the Gs4 of the 1983 version) numbered 18007, this time with RailSounds.

TURBINE

In 1985 Lionel revived one of the great favorites of all its steamers — the Pennsylvania 6-8-6 S-2 steam Turbine. The original 671, 2020, 681 and 682 versions of this locomotive sold by the tens of thousands in the postwar era. Modern Lionel issued the locomotive in a handsome gray, Brunswick green and black color scheme with a streamlined tender, whistle, Sound of Steam, smoke, and even the delicate oiler linkage from the old 682. Despite its smaller-than-scale wheels, this

locomotive became a collector favorite very rapidly. It even has the legendary backup lights in the tender!

But that is not half the story. In 1991, Lionel did this engine true justice by making a full-scale model (30 inches long) that competed with the scale Hudson, Mohawk and T-1 in mass, size and quantity of detail. The new semi-scale Turbine (18010), unlike its earlier smaller brother, has Rail-Sounds, firebox glow, and a huge scale-length tender.

NORTHERN

Remember that Lionel placed many body (boiler) styles on the 4-8-4 (Northern) wheel arrangement. Until 1987, none were actual models of the real Northern steam engine prototype. An entirely new Rock Island 4-8-4 Northern steam locomotive, in gun-metal gray with a die-cast tender and all the deluxe features of the Hudson, surprised the collecting world in 1987. The 18001 (actually numbered "5100" on the cab) used an all-new boiler and tender design with the proper chunky look of the real Northerns. It rode on a tried and true chassis, that of the Norfolk and Western "J"-class model of 1981. Collectors lined up for this engine, which was delayed in production due either to delays in parts or trouble with the boiler castings. When the engine came out, some examples had defective armatures which caused serious running problems. However, Lionel Trains, Inc. corrected the problem quickly, and the engine is an excellent runner. A Lackawanna version followed in 1988.

T-1

Still another surprise stunned the collector world in mid-1989, when Lionel unveiled the gigantic scale 4-8-4 Reading T-1. This engine established a previously inconceivable milestone — it is considerably larger than the scale Hudson. It is literally new from front to back: a new pilot truck, new scale-size chassis with large wheels machined with lightening holes, a beautiful streamline boiler with smooth lines, and a brand-new long tender with newly designed Type XI die-cast six-wheel trucks. Needless to say, this engine, even though it runs only on wide-radius track, has been a sellout. It was followed by a Chessie model in 1991.

MOHAWK

The introduction of this engine in 1990 should lay to rest any doubts regarding Lionel's future direction in the hobby. Lionel is taking the scale-minded collector very seriously and seems to respond more rapidly to collector concerns and competitors' innovations. The release of five completely new major types of large steam engines in quick succession in three years (the Northern, T-1, scale Hudson, B-6 and Mohawk) would have been unimaginable as little as ten years ago. But apparently the direction of the company has been altered: it is aware of its growing competition, the clamour of the growing number of collectors for top-of-the-line new engines, and the ability of those pieces to sell. Still, the cost of new tools and dies for these major engines is enormous, and Lionel is taking risks by introducing so many new ones. Lionel must have concluded that the risk merits the cost.

The 4-8-2 Mohawk continues the new design trend. Another all-new boiler style, it rides on the chassis introduced on the T-1 with a two-wheel trailing truck. This engine also pulled a new-design extra-long tender. An interesting controversy ensued when Lionel introduced the Mohawk with New York, Ontario and Western markings, as shown in the 1990 Holiday brochure. It was an attempt to generate interest in railroads other than the usual N Y C, Pennsy and Santa Fe. But collectors complained that the engine was properly a New York Central in the prototype, so Lionel relented and lettered it N Y C for production.

Common Features

As one would expect, all the large steam engines in this section feature top-of-the-line details: die-cast bodies and boilers, headlights, three-position reverse units and smoke from the stack (and in some cases, from the steam chest). All engines feature one of several types of steam or whistle sounds. Oddly enough, one or two of the earlier ones have a dummy coupler on the tender, a somewhat dubious shortcut on such high-priced items.

LARGE STEAM ENGINE LISTINGS

	GD	VG	EXC	MT

611 NORFOLK AND WESTERN: 1981, "J"-class; see 8100.

659 C & A: 1981, (Chicago & Alton) small Hudson; see 8101.

672 WABASH: 1986-87, Pacific; see 8610.

779 NICKEL PLATE ROAD: 1982, 2-8-4 Berkshire; see 8215.

783 NEW YORK CENTRAL: 1984, 1/4- inch-scale Hudson; see 8406.

784 BOSTON & ALBANY: 1986, 1/4-inch-scale Hudson; see 8606.

785 NEW YORK CENTRAL: 1987-88, 1/4-inch-scale Hudson; see 18002.

1501 LACKAWANNA: 1988, 4-8-4 Northern; see 18003.

1970 LOUISVILLE & NASHVILLE: 1986, Berkshire; see 8615.

2100 READING: 1989, 4-8-4 T-1; see 18006.

3000 NEW YORK CENTRAL: 1990, 4-8-2 Mohawk; see 18009.

	GD	VG	EXC	MT

3100 GREAT NORTHERN RAILWAY: 1981, 4-8-4 Berkshire; dark green Alco-type die-cast boiler; tuscan cab roof; black sand and steam domes; white-edged running board; silver boiler front and smokebox; "elephant ears"; electronic whistle and Sound of Steam; Magnetraction; headlight; smoke; Type VI Berkshire motor; three-position E-unit. Dark green streamlined 2046-style tender with "GREAT NORTHERN RAILWAY" goat logo and FARR Series 3 diamond insignia on side. Superb runner. The catalogue number — 3100 — of this engine constitutes an unusual variation in Lionel's 8000-series locomotive numbering scheme. From Famous American Railroad Series No. 3.
       —   350   495   575

4410 SOUTHERN PACIFIC: 1991, 4-8-4 Gs4 "J"-class; see 18007.

4449 SOUTHERN PACIFIC: 1983, 4-8-4 Gs2 "J"-class; see 8307.

4501 SOUTHERN: 1983, 2-8-2 Mikado; see 8309.

5100 ROCK ISLAND: 1987, 4-8-4 Northern; see 18001.

5340 NEW YORK CENTRAL: 1990, 1/4- inch-scale Hudson; see 18005.

5484 T C A: 1985. See Volume II, first edition.

6200 PENNSYLVANIA: 1991, 6-8-6 S-2 Turbine; see 18010.

6200 PENNSYLVANIA: 1984-85, 6-8-6 S-2 Turbine; see 8404.

8002 UNION PACIFIC: 1980, 2-8-4 Berkshire; two-tone gray Alco-style die-cast boiler; yellow-edged running board; electronic whistle; electronic Sound of Steam; Magnetraction; headlight; smoke; Type VI Berkshire motor; three-position E-unit. Gray 2046-style streamlined tender with dark gray center band, yellow "UNION PACIFIC" letters, with FARR diamond insignia. The U P prototype is actually a 4-8-4 Northern, since the U P did not use a 2-8-4 Berkshire. The first Lionel locomotive with smoke deflectors astride the boiler. The gray paint on the boiler has a tendency to turn to an olive-gray shade when it is exposed to heat over a long period of time. Second in Lionel's Famous American Railroad Series. Approximately 6,000 made. L. Bohn, M. Sabatelle and R. LaVoie comments.   —   350   450   575

8003 CHESSIE SYSTEM: 1980, 2-8-4 Berkshire; the Chessie Steam Special; die-cast Alco-style boiler is light gray (forward of the bell) and dark gray (behind the bell); yellow-edged running board; yellow and red stripes beneath the cab window; "8003" under cab window; electronic whistle; electronic Sound of Steam; smoke; Magnetraction; headlight; Type VI Berkshire motor; three-position E-unit. Dark gray 2046 streamlined tender with six-wheel trucks and large yellow area topped by orange band, and "Chessie System" lettering on side. This locomotive marked an important development in Fundimensions' history, the rerun of the 2-8-4 Berkshire, Lionel's top-of-the-line postwar steam engine. Fundimensions also offered handsome matching passenger cars as separate-sale items. In 1986 Lionel Trains, Inc. added a diner car to the set. The Chessie Steam Special engine and cars were based on a prototype Chessie train which actually toured the United States in 1977 to celebrate the 150th Anniversary of American railroading. Hard to find without passenger cars. Approximately 4,500 made; about 5,000 sets of cars produced. C. Lang and M. Sabatelle comments.   —   400   500   600

8004 READING: 1989, 4-6-2 Pacific; see 18004.

8006 ATLANTIC COAST LINE: 1980, 4-6-4 small Hudson; uncatalogued; gun-metal-painted die-cast Alco-style boiler numbered "2065-15" on inside; known as The Silver Shadow; has white

The "Big 3." Lionel's magnificent Hudson fleet!
Top shelf: 783 New York Central.
Second shelf: **784 Boston & Albany, offered as part of a late 1986 direct-mail campaign from Lionel, is now very scarce.**
Bottom shelf: **785 gray New York Central, note the 50th Anniversary Edition plate.**

R. Kaptur Collection; B. Schwab photo

	GD	VG	EXC	MT

tires and high-gloss black paint beneath the white- painted running board edge; steam chest side is decorated in white with a rectangle; inside of the rectangle is another rectangle with rounded corners; smoke; Sound of Steam; electronic whistle; headlight; Type III AC brush motor; three-position E- unit. The tender has four-wheel Symington-Wayne trucks on a 2046 streamlined body. This model was made for J. C. Penney as part of its continuing special engines series and was not catalogued by Lionel. It came with a display track mounted on a wooden base in a clear plastic case. Only 2,200 reportedly were manufactured and these sold out very quickly. Degano, Lang and White observations.
— — **700 1000**
See Factory Errors and Prototypes chapter in Volume II, first edition.

8014 LIONEL LINES: 1991, 2-6-4 Atlantic; see 18014.

8062 GREAT NORTHERN: 1970, 4-6-4 Hudson; catalogued, but not manufactured. **Not Manufactured**

8100 NORFOLK AND WESTERN: 1981, 4-8-4 "J"- class; engine and tender paint match extruded aluminum "Powhatan Arrow" passenger cars; black, die-cast, streamlined "J"-class boiler with black plastic "bullet" boiler front; broad maroon trim stripe edged in yellow; whistle; electronic Sound of Steam; headlight; Type VI Berkshire motor and chassis; three-position E-unit. The N & W was the first Lionel engine to simulate steam smoke

	GD	VG	EXC	MT

actually issuing from its steam cylinders. (Marx introduced this feature many years before on its little 1666, and the Marx version works better!) Matching long-striped 2046-type streamlined tender with die-cast six-wheel trucks. "611" appears on the side of the engine; "8100" appears on box only. Reissue of classic postwar 746. These cars were available only as separate-sale items. — **750 1000 1400**

8101 C & A: 1981, (Chicago & Alton) 4-6-4 small Hudson; Alco-style maroon-painted die-cast boiler which rests on a Type III AC motor (color scheme based on "The Red Train," which actually was pulled by a 4-6-2 Pacific, not a 4-6-4 Hudson); gold striping with gold "C & A" inside rectangle under cab window; silver smokebox and boiler front; whistle; electronic Sound of Steam; Magnetraction; headlight; smoke; three-position E-unit. Maroon die-cast 2224W tender with red frame; fully detailed riveting, steps and handrails; black coal pile; gold striping; six-wheel die-cast trucks and gold- numbered "659" on side; "8101" appears only on box. Matching passenger cars available for separate-sale. Hard to find without passenger cars. Tender is a remake of Lionel 2224 tender not produced since it came with the 224 2-6-2 engine beginning in 1938. R. LaVoie comment. — **300 500 600**

8206 NEW YORK CENTRAL: 1972-74, 4-6-4 small Hudson; die-cast Baldwin-type body; white lettering; Sound of Steam; smoke; whistle; headlight; rubber tire on one driver; Type III AC

A. Rudman, F. Stem, L. Caponi, and R. LaVoie Collections

ree big, desirable eight-drivered Lionel locomotives.
 shelf: 3100 Great Northern Railway 4-8-4 from Famous American Railroad set No. 3 of 1981.
ldle shelf: 8002 Union Pacific Berkshire 2-8-4 from Famous American Railroad Set No. 2 of 1980.
om shelf: 8003 Chessie System Steam Special Berkshire of 1980.

	GD	VG	EXC	MT

six-wheel motor; three-position E-unit. Many of these locomotives were assembled with off-center drive wheels which cause the locomotives to wobble from side to side as they run. The 2046 streamlined tender has Symington-Wayne trucks. Typically, the die casting is very fuzzy on the shiny black engine bodies, and the whistles and Sound of Steam do not sound clear. Used examples should be tested before purchase. R. LaVoie comments.

(A) Flat charcoal black body.   —   175   225   275
(B) Shiny black body.   —   175   225   275

8210 JOSHUA LIONEL COWEN: 1982, 4-6-4 small Hudson; gold- and burgundy-painted die-cast Alco-style boiler; headlight; smoke; Magnetraction; electronic whistle and Sound of Steam; Type III AC six-wheel motor; three-position E-unit; simulated gold "Joshua Lionel Cowen" nameplate. Die-cast 2224-style tender with six-wheel die-cast trucks. Note: when boxes are opened many units are reported to have broken rear trucks. This engine was offered by American Express in 1983 as a special edition with a display case. Regular and American Express versions are scarce today.   —   325   425   500

8215 NICKEL PLATE ROAD: 1982, 2-8-4 Berkshire; uncatalogued; die-cast Alco-type black-painted boiler with white stripe on side; white-painted wheel rims; gold "779" on cab; Magnetraction; smoke; optical headlight lens on swing-out boiler front; Type VI Berkshire motor; three-position E-unit. Die-cast 2224W

tender in black with gold script lettering; six- wheel die-cast trucks; operating coupler; electronic whistle and Sound of Steam. Reader Bill Meyer reports this is a prototypical number: No. 779 was the last steam locomotive built by Lima — rolled off the line in May 1949. Offered only in 1982 Fall Collector Center brochure. Excellent runner; hard to find.   —   475   600   650

8307 SOUTHERN PACIFIC: 1983, 4-8-4 Gs4 "J"- class; "Daylight" orange, white and black paint scheme; "4449" below cab window and on silver boiler front; die- cast boiler; vertical dual headlight; Magnetraction; smoke from stack and "simulated" steam (actually smoke from generator) from cylinders; electronic Sound of Steam and whistle; Type VI Berkshire motor; three-position E-unit. Catalogue portrays a 2046 coal tender, but production version has prototypical oil-burning tender and "99" unlighted number boards halfway down the top of the boiler sides. Reports indicate that this locomotive is an outstanding runner. However, in early production there was a problem with chipping paint on the boiler. Lionel corrected this problem quickly. Since its issuance, this locomotive has become one of the scarce and most desirable of the modern era's steam engines. It now has the distinction of being the most valuable single piece produced since 1970. A near-matching engine was issued in 1991 (the 18007) with a different headlight configuration. Matching passenger cars were available for separate-sale.   —   1300   1800   2200

Two recent small Hudsons and the first modern era model. Note the differences between the Alco-type boiler shells of the first two and the Baldwin-boiler shell of the 8206.

Top shelf: 5484 TCA special production model (see listing in Special Production chapter in Volume II.

Middle shelf: 8101 C & A, which reintroduced the 2224W tender after an absence of over 40 years.

Bottom shelf: 8206 New York Central, the first Hudson from 1972.

	GD	VG	EXC	MT

8309 SOUTHERN: 1983-84, 2-8-2 Mikado; die-cast locomotive uses a Berkshire (Alco) body, except with a two-wheel rear truck; gold "4501" beneath locomotive cab window; green with silver boiler front and tuscan cab roof; smoke; electronic Sound of Steam and whistle; headlight; Type VI Berkshire motor; three-position E-unit. "SOUTHERN" and FARR Series 4 diamond insignia on die-cast 2224W-type tender side. Headed Famous American Railroad Series No. 4 with five cars sold separately. Scheduled for release in 1983, but not made until mid-1984 due to Lionel's problems with its Mexico move. — **350 425 550**

8404 PENNSYLVANIA: 1984-85, 6-8-6 S-2 turbine; Brunswick green-painted die-cast boiler with graphite gray smokebox and boiler front; white striping, trim, and "6200" on boiler cab; red and gold "6200" keystone on boiler front; oiler linkage; white-edged drive wheels; Magnetraction; electronic Sound of Steam and whistle; smoke; headlight; Type VI Berkshire motor with small wheels. Streamlined 2046-type tender with operating red backup lights; painted Brunswick green with white "PENNSYLVANIA" lettering high on sides; die-cast six-wheel passenger trucks; water scoop. The boiler style of this engine is unique in the modern Lionel line, although some collectors were not pleased with the out-of-scale small wheels. There have been a few complaints about poorly operating reversing units and

Sound of Steam units which do not work well in reverse, but direct observation has shown that this locomotive (essentially a dressed-up postwar 682) is an excellent runner and a strong puller which operates efficiently on as little as eight volts. Engine headed the last Famous American Railroad Series No. 5 — the Pennsylvania. Getting hard to find. — **375 500 575**

8406 NEW YORK CENTRAL: 1984, 4-6-4, 1/4-inch scale die-cast Hudson; 23 inches long; locomotive has detailed Baker valve gear and die-cast smoke unit with simulated steam from the smoke chests (something the proud New York Central would have not allowed, since this would indicate leaky valve packing); Magnetraction; optical headlight; electronic Sound of Steam and whistle; Type V scale Hudson motor; three-position E-unit. Die-cast 2426-type tender has six-wheel die-cast passenger trucks and "NEW YORK CENTRAL" in small white serif lettering ("783" is the number on the boiler cab). This engine's Magnetraction has been improved over its predecessor 773 because there are more magnets. The steps on the boiler front are missing in catalogue photographs, but are included in the production run. At the time of its issue, such was the demand for this locomotive that it was easily the most expensive single item ever produced by either the original Lionel Corporation or Fundimensions. Although the boiler detail was generally sharp, collectors had some complaints

Spectacular steamers, all three! All are stamped with prototype numbers.
Top shelf: 8404 Pennsylvania Steam Turbine (numbered 6200), part of Famous American Railroad Set No. 5.
Middle shelf: 8307 Southern Pacific "Daylight" 4-8-4, (numbered 4449). This engine has become very hard to find.
Bottom shelf: 8100 Norfolk and Western (numbered 611) "J" Class 4-8-4, for which matching passenger cars were made for a "Powhatan Arrow" set.

	GD	VG	EXC	MT

about a poor parting line on the boiler top and about the plastic tender coupler. Reissue of the 1964 version of the 773 without the cylinder slide valve casting, but with the die-cast 2426W tender. There were persistent reports of hoarding of this locomotive; its initial purchase price for those who pre-ordered it was about $575, but the price nearly doubled in just a few months. Purchasers of the current model should beware of sharp fluctuations in supply and demand, especially at the time any new Hudson is produced. In fact, the price of this model has softened somewhat since the introduction of the 8606 Boston & Albany and the 18002 gun-metal New York Central Hudson. R. LaVoie comments.

— — **950 1100**

8600 NEW YORK CENTRAL: 1976, 4-6-4 small Hudson; black die-cast Alco-style body with white lettering; silver boiler front, shown as somewhat blurry "646" in 1976 catalogue, but produced with white "8600" on cab (this is probably because this engine used a modified version of the postwar 646 die-cast Alco body); electronic Sound of Steam; headlight; smoke; Magnetraction; Type III AC six-wheel motor; three-position E-unit. Long streamlined 2046-type tender, lettered "NEW YORK CENTRAL"; with Symington-Wayne trucks. Part of 1665 Empire State Express set. This engine marked modern Lionel's second foray into Hudsons since 1964, its first to use the Alco body, and the first modern engine fitted with Magnetraction. Its success opened the way for a flood of small Hudsons during the next few years.

— **200 250 300**

8603 CHESAPEAKE & OHIO: 1976-77, 4-6-4 small Hudson; black die-cast Baldwin-type body; white lettering and running board; silver boiler front; electronic Sound of Steam; headlight; smoke; rubber tires; Type III AC six-wheel motor; three-position E-unit. Streamlined 2046-type tender lettered "CHESAPEAKE & OHIO" with a dummy coupler (which is strange for a top-of-the-line engine); over 19½ inches long; Symington-Wayne trucks. The earlier Baldwin disc drivers had polished steel rims, but when reports of corrosion arose, Fundimensions changed production to white-painted driver rims. The painted rims are probably more scarce. Typically, the details on the Baldwin disc drivers on these locomotives are not very sharp. As with the earlier 8206 New York Central Hudson, many examples were assembled with off-center drive wheels, causing the locomotive to wobble when it moves down the track. Used examples should be test-run before purchase. R. LaVoie comment.
(A) Polished-steel driver rims. R. LaVoie Collection.

— **150 175 275**

(B) White-painted driver rims. Boehmer Collection.

— **150 200 300**

8606 BOSTON & ALBANY: 1986, 773-type 1/4-inch scale Hudson; uncatalogued; die-cast black boiler; white-painted boiler front; white striping on running board and driver edges; white "784" on cab; smoke with emissions from cylinders; headlight; Magnetraction; solid drivers; electronic Sound of Steam and whistle; Type V scale Hudson motor; three-position E-unit. The 2426-type die-cast tender has six-wheel die-cast passenger trucks

Lionel's march toward scale and realism is evident with these massive steam engines.
Top shelf: 8603 Chesapeake & Ohio 4-6-4 small Hudson with 2046 tender.
Second shelf: 8004 Reading 4-6-2 Pacific with 2046 tender.
Third shelf: 1501 (18003) Lackawanna 4-8-4 Northern. This is a brand new steam engine model from 1987.
Bottom shelf: 2100 (18006) Reading 4-8-4 T-1. This huge semi-scale model is the biggest engine Lionel has made in O scale to date. Notice the beautiful spo
wheels on this locomotive.

R. Kaptur Collection; B. Schwab photo

	GD	VG	EXC	MT

and white lettering. The engine was offered as part of a late 1986 direct-mail campaign from Lionel; the firm's bypassing of its usual dealer network caused considerable friction between the company and its distributors. Some reports state that only a little more than 2,000 of these engines were made. The few train dealers who have these locomotives are asking double or triple Lionel's original asking price. The Boston & Albany has become very scarce and highly desirable. It remains Lionel's only scale Hudson not lettered for New York Central.   —   —   **1500 2150**

8610 WABASH: 1986-87, 4-6-2 Pacific; Santa Fe-type Baldwin Hudson boiler casting painted dark blue with graphite silver smokebox; gold "WABASH" on cab; smoke deflectors; white stripe along cab; smoke; headlight; Magnetraction; electronic Sound of Steam and whistle; Type III AC six-wheel motor; three-position E-unit. Streamlined 2046-type tender with gold stripes and gold "672"; six-wheel die-cast passenger trucks. The locomotive, as produced, is much more attractive than it appears in the 1986 Collector Catalogue. The 1987 catalogue accurately depicts it. First of the new Fallen Flags- series locomotives.
              —   **350   500   650**

	GD	VG	EXC	MT

8615 L & N: 1986, (Louisville & Nashville) 2-8-4 Berkshire; uncatalogued; gloss black-painted Alco-type die-cast boiler; yellow stripe on running boards; yellow "1970" on cab; white-painted driver edges; Magnetraction; headlight; smoke; Type VI Berkshire motor; three-position E-unit. Plastic 2046-type tender with electronic Sound of Steam and whistle; large yellow "1970" on tender between two yellow lengthwise stripes; six-wheel die-cast passenger trucks. Made as a special Christmas 1986 offering from J. C. Penney. Came with display case, wood base with track, and plastic bumpers. Patterned after the L & N steamer nicknamed "Big Emma." According to 1986 J. C. Penney catalogue, this was a limited edition of 3,000. Very scarce now.
              —   —   **950   1200**

8702 SOUTHERN CRESCENT LIMITED: 1977, 4-6-4 small Hudson; the "Southern Crescent"; green-painted die-cast Alco-style boiler with silver-painted boiler front; gold crescent and border on steam chest; crescent emblem and "8702" in gold on cab; white-outlined drivers; Magnetraction; smoke; headlight; Type III AC six-wheel motor; three-position E-unit. Originally, the 8702 came in flat green; the second run was in shiny green. It appears that equal quantities were produced. The 2046 streamlined

A. Rudman, F. Stem, L. Caponi, and R. LaVoie Collections

Two more Hudsons and an adapted Pacific.
Top shelf: 8210 Joshua Lionel Cowen Commemorative.
Middle shelf: 8600 New York Central, available only with the 1976 Empire State Express Set.
Bottom shelf: 8610 Wabash, first in the Fallen Flags Series sets. **The two wheel rear truck makes it a Pacific style, though it uses a Baldwin boiler, the same as several of the Hudsons.**

	GD	VG	EXC	MT

tender is painted green with a black coal pile, lettered "CRESCENT LIMITED" in gold with gold border with Symington-Wayne trucks, Sound of Steam and dummy coupler.

— 225 375 475

8801 NEW JERSEY CENTRAL: 1978-79, 4-6-4 small Hudson; die-cast Alco boiler similar to 8600; dark blue upper boiler section; lighter blue lower boiler section; gold-outlined steam chest; "8801" in gold on cab; decal on locomotive feedwater tank reads "THE BLUE COMET"; "LIONEL" on small plate beneath headlight; drivers outlined in white; blind center drivers; plastic trailing truck frames; Magnetraction; smoke; electronic Sound of Steam; Type III AC six-wheel motor; three-position E-unit. A major deviation of The Blue Comet from the usual Hudson Alco design is the added feedwater tank and the 665 boiler front with marker lights on the boiler front door and a small nameplate beneath the headlight. The tender's paint design is similar to that of the locomotive, with a dark blue upper section, black coal pile, light blue lower section with gold circle, and gold-lettered "New/Jersey/Central". Tender is a 2046-style with Symington-Wayne trucks. The Blue Comet brings back memories of the top-of-the-line, classic Standard and O Gauge locomotives of the 1930s. The Blue Comet has met with great popularity, recalling the prominence of the real Blue Comet, which ran from Jersey City to Atlantic City in the 1930s. As with many of the limited sets, the

passenger cars made to match this locomotive are still readily available, but the locomotive itself is very hard to find. This lends support to the belief that many more sets of cars were produced than were the locomotives needed to pull them as part of a matched set. **— 300 400 500**

8900 A. T. S. F.: 1979, 4-6-4 small Hudson; black-painted die-cast boiler with silver-painted boiler front; green marker lights; tuscan-painted cab roof; same boiler as 2065 (Baldwin style) without the feedwater tank; rear trailing truck has same side frames as 2065; side configuration same as 2065 but brighter, shinier plating; nylon gears substitute for metal gears; Magnetraction; smoke; headlight; Type III AC six-wheel motor; three-position E-unit. Tender has "8900" in very large white numerals; FARR Series diamond insignia outlined in gold with gold-lettered "Famous American Railroad Series" with a spike (indicates it is first in a series); water scoop pickup; Sound of Steam inside tender (power pickup for Sound of Steam comes in part from tender trucks and in part from wire from locomotive); tender has dummy coupler on rear with rear number plate "2671W-6" and gray wheels. Our search indicates that most, if not all, pre-Fundimensions 2671W tenders did not carry a plate with such a number. This tender is the same as the Pennsy 2046 long-streamlined type. The number has been carried on the tender plate since MPC began using this tender. **— 300 350 425**

Three more eight-drivered steamers from Lionel's recent production.

A. Rudman, F. Stem, L. Caponi, and R. LaVoie Collection

Top shelf: 8215 Nickel Plate Road 2-8-4 Berkshire, numbered 779 after its prototype.
Middle shelf: 8309 Southern 2-8-2, numbered 4501 after its prototype and part of Famous American Railroad Set No. 4 of 1983.
Bottom shelf: 8615 L & N (numbered 1970) "Big Emma" Berkshire of 1986, sold through J. C. Penney. This is a very difficult engine to find.

	GD	VG	EXC	MT

18001 ROCK ISLAND: 1987, 4-8-4 Northern; completely new die-cast scale design using new boiler on Berkshire (Type VI) motor and chassis; dark gun-metal gray die-cast boiler, faithfully reproducing the class R67 Northern owned by the Rock Island; graphite-gray smokebox; headlight with number boards centered in boiler front (actually numbered 5100 after prototype); top-mounted metal bell on boiler front; eight-paneled cab windows; white "5100" on cab; electronic Sound of Steam and whistle; Magnetraction; smoke with cylinder emissions; headlight; three-position E-unit. New long die-cast square-back Northern tender painted gun-metal gray with white Rock Island logo, detailed side riveting and coal load (molded rubber!); six-wheel die-cast passenger trucks. Collectors objected again (as they did on the 783 Hudson) to the plastic tender coupler, which was finally fixed on the next Northern, the 18003. The prototype casting for this locomotive was too rough for production, but it illustrated the proper chunky look of the real locomotive. This engine is unlike any steam locomotive ever produced by Lionel; despite initial castings and parts supply problems, the locomotive received considerable collector praise when it was finally issued. Early examples surfaced with defective armatures, but Lionel Trains, Inc. was very attentive to the problem. It is an excellent runner. See entry for 18003 for an interesting story about the boiler casting. Its price stabilized when the Lackawanna version was announced. G. Romich comments. — — **500 650**

	GD	VG	EXC	MT

18002 NEW YORK CENTRAL: 1988, 1/4-inch-scale 773-type Hudson; uncatalogued; gun-metal gray die-cast boiler; black pilot and lower frame; spoked drivers with chromed metal rims (the first appearance of these drivers since the 763E of 1938); locomotive lacks Magnetraction because of these wheels; white "785" on cab; smoke with cylinder emissions; headlight; Type V scale Hudson motor; three-position E-unit. 2426-type die-cast gun-metal tender with six-wheel die-cast passenger trucks and electronic Sound of Steam and whistle. This locomotive was offered in a 1987 year-end package to commemorate the 50th anniversary of the introduction of the Lionel New York Central Hudson in 1937, but was not released until 1988. It comes with a 5⁄8" x 3⁄8" commemorative metal plaque with an adhesive backing (though why one would adhere a plate to such an expensive engine defies reason!). The engine has climbed in price because it is modeled after the highly desirable 763E of prewar years. At one time, rumors were afoot that this locomotive would even be issued with the round Vanderbilt tender, but this proved untrue. This locomotive featured an improved motor design over its two predecessors. To prevent binding of the armature against the brushplate, a specially-slotted armature and an additional retaining clip (671M-22) were used. This design uses four thrust washers (671M-23), two thrust bearings (681-12), and two retaining clips (671M-22) instead of the old design, which had a single-slotted armature shaft, two thrust washers (671M-23), and one

	GD	VG	EXC	MT

thrust bearing (681-121). All armatures are interchangeable, but if an earlier type is used in a revised motor, it must be properly spaced. M. Sabatelle comments. — — **950 1100**

18003 LACKAWANNA: 1988, 4-8-4 Northern; semi-gloss black-painted die-cast boiler with graphite gray-painted smokebox; white prototype "1501" below cab window and on sand dome; white stripe along boiler and white-striped drivers; number in white alongside and below headlight; silver-plated ornamental bell on boiler front; green marker light; smoke from stack and steam chests; headlight; Magnetraction; Type VI Berkshire motor; three-position E-unit. Large die-cast Northern tender with coal load, white "Lackawanna" lettering, die-cast six-wheel passenger trucks and electronic Sound of Steam and steam whistle. The tender has a stronger die-cast coupler than its 18001 predecessor. Note: When the Rock Island predecessor to this engine came out in 1987 after delays in production, collectors noted that its boiler casting was made in Taiwan. This bears explanation, in view of Lionel Trains, Inc.'s determination to make its products domestically. Our sources tell us that the original domestically-produced castings for the Rock Island engine were extremely rough and unacceptable to Lionel. These were rejected, and a hurried call to the Orient found a source for properly made castings. The Lackawanna casting is significantly improved over the Rock Island casting; however, we do not know if the casting on this version was made domestically or abroad (reader comments invited). In addition to the casting problem, early versions of the Rock Island came through with defective armatures which quickly burned out motors. These have been repaired by Lionel, and when properly outfitted the Northern runs extremely well.
— — — **650**

18004 READING: 1989, 4-6-2 Pacific; die-cast Baldwin-type black boiler, using a reworked die to add piping detail; decorative steam whistle and bell; gold "8004" on cab; gold stripes on running board; white-wall drive wheels; electronic Sound of Steam and whistle; Magnetraction; smoke; headlight; Type III AC six-wheel motor; three-position E-unit. Die-cast 2046-type tender with six-wheel die-cast trucks. Gold rectangle with "READING" in gold on tender sides. This engine was a slow seller due to the simultaneous release of the Reading T-1. — — — **350** See Factory Errors and Prototypes chapter in Volume II, first edition.

18005 NEW YORK CENTRAL: 1990, 1/4-inch-scale 4-6-4 Hudson; black Hudson die-cast boiler with "5340" on cab, prototypically correct for the J-series Hudsons; the catalogue shows "5390" on the cab, but this was changed for production; headlight; smoke from stack and steam chests; without Magnetraction due to its spoked wheels; improved Type V scale Hudson motor; three-position E-unit. The casting of this engine body is reportedly better and smoother than any previous Hudson, similar in quality to the T-1 casting. Revival of full-scale 700W tender — die-cast body and trucks. Unlike the original, this tender includes RailSounds. Tender is lettered in white for "NEW YORK CENTRAL". Molded coal load was modified to add extra detailing. The number sequence indicates it may have been planned before the T-1 came out the year before. This engine quickly sold out when announced and is hard to obtain even though brand new. Reissue of the most famous Lionel engine of all time — the 700E Hudson of 1937. This new version is referred to by modern Lionel as "1-700E." Unlike the 783-, 784- and 785-series, this engine is a complete scale model including full boiler piping and riveting detail, and both engine and tender have NMRA-standard couplers. Includes Lionel standard couplers

which can be changed in if desired (the instructions for doing so are complicated, however). — — — **1395**

18006 READING: 1989, 4-8-4 T-1; black body; yellow "2100" on cab, after the prototype; yellow stripe on running board; Reading Line diamond logo on front; "2100" number plate under headlight; wire handrails and white-wall drive wheels are a new casting with round lightening holes molded in; smoke from stack and steam chests, three-position E-unit and RailSounds — first appearance of this system on a large steam engine. Tender is a new, very long, squared-off model using die-cast body, wire handrails and newly designed Type XI six-wheel die-cast trucks. It even has snap-in water tank covers under the coal load. Base of tender is a sheet metal frame stamped "LTI"; large yellow rectangle on tender sides with "READING" inside; "2100" on tender rear, along with operating backup lights. Perhaps a measure of Lionel's health and willingness to take risks, the T-1 represents new designs from front to back and has been a brisk seller. Engine is an all-new die-cast boiler casting using a Northern wheel arrangement. Chassis is larger with larger-diameter wheels and Pullmor motor attached to universal joint drive train in the style of the Hudson (Type VIII T-1 motor). This huge (27-inch) engine is larger than anything Lionel has made in O Gauge. Offered in 1989 year-end Holiday Collection flyer. — — — **1000**

18007 SOUTHERN PACIFIC*: 1991, 4-8-4 Gs2 "J"-class; the "Daylight"; die-cast "J"-series boiler first seen on the 8100 Norfolk and Western; "Daylight" orange, red, white and black paint scheme; "4410" below cab window in white; "Daylight" in white script on orange stripe near front; "98" on boiler top number boards; silver boiler front with "4410" number board; single front headlight; Magnetraction; smoke from stack and cylinder chest; white sidewall drivers; Type VI Berkshire motor; three-position E-unit. 2046-type long streamlined oil tender has RailSounds, six-wheel die-cast trucks and operating coupler. This engine may do relatively well due to the scarcity of the 8307. However, since there are now three engines to pull one set (the 8307 and 18007 steam engines and the 8260-8262 F-3 ABA diesels), demand will certainly increase for the already- scarce Southern Pacific passenger cars. Essentially a reissue of 8307 from 1983, but with a modified boiler front with single headlight
— — — **595**

18009 NEW YORK CENTRAL: 1990-91, 4-8-2 L-3a-class Mohawk; black die-cast body with white lettering, derived from the T-1 but with many differences; new boiler style represents the third major steam engine style brought out by Lionel in four years; scale model of L-3/L-4-class Mountain engine produced at Lima; engine rides on a Type VIII motor and chassis like the T-1; two-wheel rear trucks; three-position E-unit. "3000" and "L3A" in white on cab sides; "3000" on number board under front headlight with red NYC emblem below that; Lionel builder's plate under stack; engine has smoke through stack and steam chests; headlight; firebox light; retractable front coupler (a first on a regular-issue engine); wire handrails; spoked drive wheels. Yet another new extra-long tender with RailSounds, die-cast six-wheel trucks, operating coupler, and small water scoop on undersides. This tender has a detailed gray-tinted coal load longer than loads on other tenders, and is lettered on the rear with a large "3000" and capacity data. Tender also has a backup light. A good seller, despite its price tag. (Collectors in 1990 were probably reeling from the prices of the 700E!) Initial reports say this engine is an excellent puller. Shown in 1990 Holiday flyer as New York, Ontario & Western, but collector pressure forced a change to the more prototypical New York Central. The change also deleted the

Three attractive Hudsons, Lionel's steamers at their best.
Top shelf: 8702 Southern Crescent Limited of 1977.
Middle shelf: 8801 New Jersey Central "Blue Comet" of 1978.
Bottom shelf: 8900 A.T.S.F from Famous American Railroads set No. 1 of 1979.

A. Rudman, F. Stem, L. Caponi, and R. LaVoie Collection

	GD	VG	EXC	MT

silver boiler front shown in the flyer. This engine is pictured correctly in the 1991 Book 2 catalogue. — — — **960**

18010 PENNSYLVANIA*: 1991, 6-8-6 S-2 steam turbine; semi- scale big brother to the 8404 turbine from 1984; die-cast black metal body with silver boiler front; "6200" (a prototypical number) in gold on the cab and on the tuscan keystone on the boiler front; smoke unit with two stacks; Type VIII T-1 motor with eight polished-steel spoked wheels; three- position E-unit; finely detailed six-wheel pilot and trailing trucks; Baldwin builder's plate; operating headlight and backup light on tender, wired to constant-voltage circuit; firebox light; wire handrails; extra long tender lettered "PENNSYLVANIA" with die-cast six-wheel trucks and Railsounds. Together, engine and tender are 30 inches long (120 scale feet!), and are intended to run only on wide-radius track. This engine is the latest example of modern Lionel's strong move toward scale railroading since 1987. It is also now the single most expensive item sold by Lionel to date. — — — **1500**

18011 CHESSIE SYSTEM*: 1991, 4-8-4 T-1; long die- cast T-1 boiler in black with silver smokebox; yellow and vermilion running board and tender sides; large diameter drive wheels with lightening holes and traction tires; yellow "2101" under cab window; 2101 number boards on front around operating headlight; smoke from stack and steam chests; firebox light; RailSounds; Type VIII T-1 motor and chassis; three-position E-unit. Long T-1-style die-cast tender with six- wheel die-cast trucks, backup

light and operating coupler; large blue "Chessie System" lettering on tender. Follow-up to the successful Reading T-1 released in 1984. This engine is a more accurate model of the actual Chessie Steam Special than the earlier 8003 Chessie Berkshire.
— — — **875**

18014 LIONEL LINES*: 1991, 2-6-4 Atlantic steam locomotive; die-cast boiler; all-pink body and tender; blue lettering and "8014" on cab; headlight; smoke unit; Magnetraction; Type IV six-wheel can motor; three-position electronic reverse; short streamlined 1130 tender with plastic arch bar trucks. This engine is a revival of the famous 2037-500 Girls' Set engine from 1957. The original engine and set are scarce today. Lionel reissued both in 1991 with identical pastel colors but new numbers. Although the Atlantic engine type is normally used in the Traditional Line, this one is considered a Collector engine because it headed the Collector Line 11722 Girls' Train set. — — — **220**

SMALL STEAM ENGINES

The small steam engines issued by modern Lionel range from very inexpensive 0-4-0 switchers made almost entirely of plastic, to die-cast 4-4-2 and 2-6-4 main line locomotives.

This chapter categorizes the body and motor types for easier reference, including side view drawings to assist readers in understanding the comparisons between the body styles (see Figure 4.10).

Note that the larger die-cast 2-6-4 engines (for which Lionel uses Atlantic-type bodies on a 2-6-4 drive train) are really medium-sized "bridges" between the small and large (or Collector) steam engines. We include them here because Lionel still refers to them as "Traditional" pieces. Similarly, though small in size and included in this chapter as a small engine, the Pennsylvania B-6 switcher can certainly be considered a Collector engine, especially in terms of price! Ten different body styles have appeared in Lionel's extensive small steamer line.

Small Steam Engine Body Styles

COLUMBIA represents by far the most prevalent body style Lionel has used. It can be discerned most easily by its thick running board, often painted; by a two-paned window (window types are good indicators of the body styles); and by an inverted "V" pattern of piping under a relatively flat sand dome. The engine rides on a 2-4-2 wheel arrangement. The photos of the 8041 and 8141 show classic examples. A total of fifteen engines used this style from the early 1970s to the early 1980s, in both plastic and die-cast versions. After that an Elongated Columbia boiler was used on fourteen more engines, including several current models. Before 1979, the motor was a standard AC brush motor on a four-wheel chassis. After that it changed to a transverse- mounted can motor. In the postwar era these engines were made by the tens of thousands in the 200-series and were considered near the bottom-of-the-line. Modern Lionel has raised them in status a bit with desirable extra features and by creating smaller steam styles for the very low-priced sets.

As Roland LaVoie stated in his excellent treatise on Columbias in the second edition of this Guide, this little engine bore the "corporate risk" of Lionel in the early days of its recovery, much more than the high-priced Collector engines. No other locomotive, diesel or steamer, has been so versatile or served Lionel so well for so long. Yet because of its mundane and unimpressive appearance, it never raised much collector attention. One Columbia, the 8142 Pennsylvania, received a significant technical innovation — the electronic Sound of Steam. An intermittent contact was attached to the smoke unit, activated by the rotation of the drive wheels. Power was thus pulsed to a circuit board and speaker in the tender, which translated it into a realistic chug of a steam engine. With a few refinements, this system is still in use, now being slowly replaced by the digital RailSounds system.

ELONGATED COLUMBIA uses the same basic boiler style as the regular Columbia, except the front is extended about 3/4-inches, which can be discerned by the greater distance of the smokestack from the front. The die change was made around 1983 to allow a change to a four-wheel pilot truck. This design is still in use now. Therefore, this Columbia derivative rides on a 4-4-2 (normally Atlantic) wheel arrangement. It

first appeared on the 8402 Reading, and uses the AC/DC transverse can motor type and electronic reverse unit. So far, all have been die-cast bodies.

K-4 is a medium-sized steam boiler style that appeared only on the 8001 and 8007 engines in 1980. Revivals of the popular postwar 675/2025 Pennsylvania K-4s, these modern ones were plastic shell, DC-only locomotives which apparently did not sell well. They have not been seen since. Distinguishing features of this engine, which rode on a 2-6-4 chassis with DC can motor and no reverse unit, are a headlight mounted on top of the boiler front (not in the center as on other engines) and a prominent step-up/step-down running board. The real Pennsylvania K-4 steam engine rode on a 4-6-2 (Pacific) wheel arrangement, so both the postwar and modern era engines were riding on prototypically incorrect 2-6-4 chassis. This points up the difficulty in associating a given wheel arrangement with a given body style, and demonstrates why this book lists both a body style (e.g., Atlantic) and a wheel arrangement (e.g., 2-6-4). They may not always match in the usual way. Figures 4.1 and 4.10 show the *usual* arrangements, but Lionel reserves the right to mix and match!

ATLANTIC, the second most-frequently used body style for Lionel, appeared in fourteen engines from the early 1970s to the present. It started on the 8142 in 1971 with an AC brush motor on the usual 4-4-2 wheel arrangement. Collectors would have favored the early engines more had they been given a three-position reverse unit. This complaint was resolved in recent years when the Atlantic was converted to a 2-6-4, using the can motor with electronic reverse unit. The 2-6-4 drive train matched the way it first appeared in the postwar era — as the 2026/2036. Note that a 2-6-4 is not correct for an Atlantic. The 2-6-4 wheel arrangement is used on the real railroads mostly in Europe, not in America. But postwar and modern Lionel have used it rather frequently on their model engines. Lionel has also used the Atlantic boiler on a 2-6-2 Prairie wheel arrangement.

The Atlantic boiler is slightly larger and more massive than the Columbia, distinguished by its quartered window, condenser box on the pilot, larger sand dome and large feedwater heaters on the left side. So far these engines are all die-cast with smoke and headlight. One Atlantic, the 8204 C & O, received a technical innovation which was not so successful — an electronic steam whistle. It made the Sound of Steam muddy and the controller diode tended to stick in the closed position. This problem was resolved on two Berkshires issued in 1980. This time, Lionel wisely let operators use the old Lionel transformers with DC rectifiers to work the whistle.

PORTER, a smaller boiler than the Columbia or Atlantic, features higher rounded domes on top and a distinctive shade over the windows. This is the same as the Scout (or 1060) locomotive of postwar fame, but has been produced only in plastic by modern era Lionel. It has appeared on nine engines in the modern era, usually on a 2-4-0 chassis, but sometimes on a 0-4-0. One durable version, the Atlantic Coast Line 8902, has headed a myriad of catalogued and special sets since it first appeared over a decade ago.

CAB-DOOR is an unusual little plastic steamer that has no postwar counterpart. It is distinguished by the permanent door molded into the cab (the only such of all the steamers) and by the closely-spaced domes and flared smokestack on top. Used briefly in 1973 and 1975, it has not appeared since. These engines appeared on a 2-4-0 drive train with an AC brush motor. The three existing examples are the 8300 Santa Fe, 8500 Pennsylvania and the 8502 Santa Fe.

1665 SWITCHER is another short steamer derived from the 1665 steamer of 1948. The modern one retains the die-cast boiler of the original. It is recognized by the unsupported length of boiler in front of the steam chest, and by the operating front coupler on later modern era versions. The style appeared first on the 8310 without the coupler but with a front axle (i.e., a 2-4-0) for some reason. It came back recently in its original 0-4-0 switcher form with the coupler, heading an excellent N Y C Yard Chief set and the A T S F Service Station Special in 1985-1986. This time Lionel outfitted it with the can motor, three-position reverse and a smoke unit (the first for any switcher) which emitted a substantial amount of smoke.

PLAIN SWITCHER, for lack of a better term, describes an infrequently-used 0-4-0 switcher derived from the Cab-Door type except with the door removed, ladder detail eliminated and the domes spread apart. These little engines are all plastic and feature none of the extras of their larger brothers, not even a headlight. Like the Cab-Door type, this engine has no postwar predecessor. It used the DC can motor with no reverse unit. The style first appeared in 1976 with Rock Island markings. Along with the Dockside, the Plain Switcher represents the bottom of the inexpensive line. It is remarkable for how few pieces of metal are used in its construction. Still, if one is not concerned with glamour it is possible to get this engine for less than the price of a collector boxcar. A few of them even boast oddball "collectable" trim such as the glow-in-the-dark deco of the Black Cave Flyer (8212).

DOCKSIDE, first introduced in 1972, is a strange but whimsical locomotive heading a set with a four-wheel tender; it was marketed later for separate-sale without it. It is hard to imagine an engine body getting any smaller. It barely covers the frame on which it sits, which is otherwise a fairly standard 0-4-0 steam chassis. It used a Type I brush motor initially, and switched to a Type II DC can in 1979. Needless to say, it features none of the higher-end goodies such as smoke, reverse units or headlights. Still, like the Plain Switcher, it can be purchased for next to nothing. Lionel has even managed some rather standout color schemes for it, such as on the 1990 Badlands set, which also featured several other interesting cars. The Dockside's profile is unmistakable, with its General-type bulbous smokestack and prominent side number plate.

B-6, revived in 1989, represents one of the most revered engines in Lionel history — the scale 0-6-0 B-6 switcher last seen in 1939. An extended-version big brother of the 1665, the B-6 is a near-true scale model of the Pennsylvania workhorse; and Lionel's version (18000) even comes with an extended slope-back tender to enhance the scale appearance. This

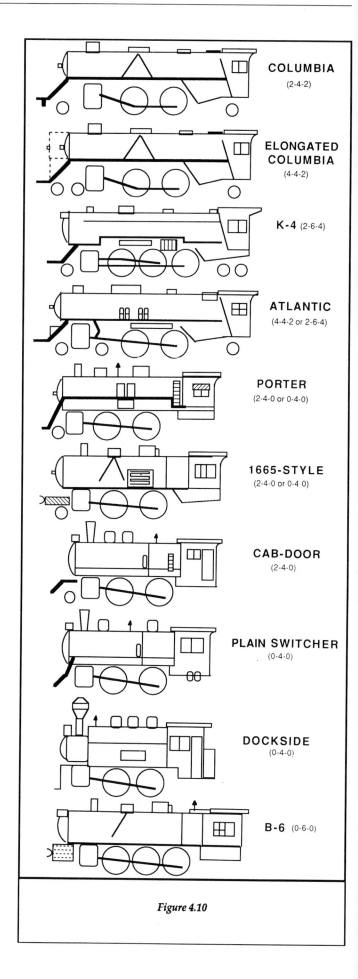

Figure 4.10

tender featured the first appearance of the new RailSounds system. The engine rode on a remake of the original six-driver chassis, complete with spoked wheels and a top-of-the-line Pullmor AC brush motor mounted horizontally under the cab. This eagerly awaited engine had a steep price, so should not rightfully be considered a "small" steam engine at all!

SMALL STEAM ENGINES LISTINGS

	GD	VG	EXC	MT

1987 MOPAR EXPRESS: 1987-88; see 18605.

1989 SEARS CIRCUS: 1989; see 18614.

8001 NICKEL PLATE: 1980, 2-6-4 K-4; uncatalogued; plastic body; smoke; red firebox light (feature not seen since the 226E steamer was made in 1938); headlight; Type IV six-wheel DC-only can motor (running on AC current will burn out the motor). 243-type square-back tender with mechanical Sound of Steam. Reader comments are requested as to the literature in which this engine may have appeared. Remake of 2025/675 steamer from late 1940s which was die-cast. This (with 8007) is the first Lionel six-wheel driver plastic locomotive. — — **50 60**

8007 NEW YORK, NEW HAVEN & HARTFORD: 1980, 2-6-4 K-4; plastic body; silver boiler front; smoke; red firebox light; headlight; gold-striped running board edge; Type IV six-wheel DC-only can motor (running on AC will burn out the motor). Square-back 243-type tender with gold "NEW YORK, NEW HAVEN & HARTFORD", gold stripe and mechanical Sound of Steam. The K-4 prototype appeared only on the Pennsylvania Railroad, but Fundimensions' management reportedly liked the New Haven logo. The real K-4 also had a 4-6-2 wheel arrangement, not a 2-6-4. Came as part of 1050 New Englander set. A remake of 2025/675 steamer from later 1940s. This (with 8001) is the first Lionel six-driver plastic locomotive.
— — **40 50**

8008 CHESSIE SYSTEM: 1980, 4-4-2 Atlantic; dark blue-painted die-cast locomotive; yellow-painted running board edge; smoke; headlight; red firebox light; Type II DC-only can motor (running on AC will burn out the motor). Dark blue 243-type tender with large yellow area topped with orange stripe, Chessie System logo and mechanical Sound of Steam. Came as part of 1052 Chesapeake Flyer set. One example has been found mounted on an 8800 Lionel Lines AC-drive chassis. 10,000 units made. M. Sabatelle Collection. — — **50 75**

> **Note:** *The 8040 has been made in two different railroad markings.*

8040 NICKEL PLATE ROAD: 1970-72, 2-4-2 Columbia; black plastic body; no light; manual reverse switch atop boiler; Type I brush motor.
(A) 1970; black motor sides; plastic cylinder slide valves; white flat "NICKEL PLATE/ROAD" lettering on slope-back tender; came with set 1081 (the Wabash Cannonball), lowest-priced set in the 1970 line. The tender carries Symington-Wayne trucks and a dummy coupler. R. LaVoie and G. Halverson comments.
— **15 20 30**

	GD	VG	EXC	MT

(B) Same as (A), but 1971-72 production: shiny metal motor sides; metal cylinder slide valves. R. LaVoie Collection.
— **15 20 30**
(C) 1972, same as (B), but white raised lettering, "NICKEL PLATE / ROAD" on 8040 short box tender; replaced version (A) in 1972 version of set 1081, the Wabash Cannonball. This tender was not used again until 1987. G. Halverson comment.
— **15 20 30**
(D) Same as (B), but locomotive has raised numbers. R. LaVoie comment and C. Rohlfing Collection. — **15 20 30**

8040 CANADIAN NATIONAL: 1971, 2-4-2 Columbia; black plastic body; smoke; headlight; flat numbering on locomotive; rubber tire on rear driver; Type I brush motor; two-position E-unit. Slope-back tender with white "CANADIAN NATIONAL" on side in rectangular box; AAR trucks; dummy coupler. Came as part of Canadian set T-1171. Listed in both the small and the large versions of the 1971 Canadian catalogue. K. Wills and D. Anderson Collections. — **30 50 100**

8041 NEW YORK CENTRAL: 1970-71, 2-4-2 Columbia; silver-gray plastic body; red stripe on locomotive; Type I brush motor; smoke; headlight. 1130T-style tender with white lettering, AAR trucks, dummy coupler and plastic base.
(A) 1970; number on cab in white. — **20 30 40**
(B) 1971; same as (A), but shows changes made to locomotive for 1971; has "PENNSYLVANIA" tender, Electronic Sound of Steam and red "8041" on cab. This is actually a locomotive which should have been numbered 8141, but in production some examples were made before the number was changed. The sample examined came as part of an original Silver Star set in 1971. Very hard to find. R. LaVoie Collection. — **40 60 75**

> **Note:** *The 8042 has been made in two different railroad markings.*

8042 GRAND TRUNK WESTERN: 1970, 2-4-2 Columbia; black die-cast metal body; headlight; smoke; white lettering; Type I brush motor. Pictured in 1970 catalogue with 1130T tender, but came with 243-type square-back tender with AAR trucks and dummy coupler. Part of set 1084, Grand Trunk Western.
(A) 1970; thin cab floor. — **15 30 40**
(B) 1970; thick cab floor. — **15 30 40**

8042 PENNSYLVANIA: 1972, 2-4-2 Columbia; uncatalogued; black die-cast body; off-white lettering on cab; headlight; smoke; Type I brush motor. Came as part of uncatalogued Sears set 1291 with 1130T Pennsylvania tender painted flat black with white lettering, Symington-Wayne trucks and dummy coupler. R. LaVoie Collection. — **25 30 40**

8043 NICKEL PLATE ROAD: 1970, 2-4-2 Columbia; uncatalogued; black plastic body with white lettering; smoke; headlight; Type I brush motor. Slope-back tender. Manufactured for Sears as part of set 1091. Very hard to find.
— **35 50 75**

8102 UNION PACIFIC: 1981-82, 4-4-2 Atlantic; dark gray-painted die-cast boiler; yellow-edged running board; yellow numbers and letters; electronic Sound of Steam; smoke; headlight; traction tires; Type I brush motor; two-position E-unit. 243-style square-back tender. Part of 1151 Union Pacific Thunder Freight and the 1153 Union Pacific Thunder Freight Deluxe sets made for J. C. Penney. — **50 60 75**

R. LaVoie and R. Kaptur Collections; B. Greenberg photograph

Some unusual features on these small steam engines.

Top shelf: 8200 Kickapoo Dockside switcher, with bell missing. It did not come with a tender. It is one of the most inexpensive locomotives made by Lionel.

Second shelf: 8040 Nickel Plate Road 2-4-2 Columbia with slope-back tender from 1970.

Third shelf: 8040 Nickel Plate Road 2-4-2 Columbia with short box tender, one of the very few times this tender appeared.

Bottom shelf: 8702 V. & T.R.R. General locomotive and tender from an uncatalogued 1988 Service Station set.

	GD	VG	EXC	MT
8140 SOUTHERN: 1971, 2-4-0 or 0-4-0 Porter; uncatalogued; green and black plastic body with gold lettering on tender and cab; Type I brush motor. Tender is 1130-type short streamlined with mechanical Sound of Steam. Reportedly available as part of Sears set 1190 with all-black body.				
(A) 2-4-0.	—	15	25	35
(B) 0-4-0.	—	15	25	35

8141 PENNSYLVANIA: 1971, 2-4-2 Columbia; gray plastic body with red stripe; electronic Sound of Steam (the first locomotive to carry this feature); smoke; headlight; Type I brush motor.

8140 Southern 0-4-0.

8140 Southern 2-4-0.

	GD	VG	EXC	MT

1130T tender lettered in white for "PENNSYLVANIA" with Symington-Wayne trucks and a dummy coupler. See 8041 entry for a misnumbered version of this engine.

(A) White number on cab; from set 1183, the Silver Star; confirmation requested. — 25 30 40

(B) Same as (A), except heat-stamped red number on cab. This was the version sold separately, but it is also found with sets. Riley Collection. — 25 30 40

(C) Same as (B), but number raised in relief as part of locomotive's boiler casting and then painted red. This was a very unusual practice for Lionel. J. Bratspis Collection. — 30 40 55

(D) Same as (A), except no smoke or headlight; manual reverse. This locomotive was probably part of an uncatalogued Sears set. Reader confirmation requested. **NRS**

8142 CHESAPEAKE & OHIO: 1971, 4-4-2 Atlantic; black die-cast metal body; white lettering; headlight; smoke; Type I brush motor. 243-type square-back tender. Part of set 1184, the Allegheny.

(A) Electronic Sound of Steam. — 40 55 65

(B) Same as (A), but also has electronic whistle. — 50 60 70

(C) Special model for Ford Motor Parts Division promotion, about 100 made: no center-rail pickup assembly; hole drilled and tapped into underside of pilot to mount engine just above a section of two-rail modified O27 track on maple display board. The board also had a transformer so that the engine could be used as a static display. For a more detailed story of this piece, see the second edition of *Greenberg's Guide to Lionel Trains (1970-1988)* by Roland LaVoie. R. Steffani Collection. **NRS**

(D) Same as (A), but gold lettering on engine and tender. Part of 1199 Allegheny Special set for Ford with two Ford billboards and the 9042 Autolite boxcar. See the 9042 entry in the Boxcar chapter for more details. — 50 70 90

2 Chesapeake & Ohio.

8200 KICKAPOO DOCKSIDE: 1972, 0-4-0 Switcher; black plastic body; gold lettering and trim; Type I brush motor; manual reverse switch. Did not come with tender. Part of 1280 Kickapoo Valley and Northern set. Remarkable for its simplicity, this tiny engine, with no trim such as headlights or smoke, is one of the most inexpensive locomotives ever made by Lionel. It is somewhat hard to find now, however, so it no longer holds that distinction. — 20 40 50

8203 PENNSYLVANIA: 1972, 2-4-2 Columbia; charcoal black plastic body with red stripe and lettering; electronic Sound of Steam; smoke; headlight; Type I brush motor. Came in set 1183, the Silver Star.

(A) With 1130T oil-type tender. G. Salamone Collection. — 20 30 40

(B) With 1130T coal-type tender. G. Salamone Collection. — 20 30 40

8204 CHESAPEAKE & OHIO: 1972, 4-4-2 Atlantic; black die-cast metal body; whistle; smoke; headlight; Type I brush motor; two-position E-unit. Electronic Sound of Steam in 243-type square-back tender. Came in set 1284, the Allegheny. — 45 60 70

8209 Pioneer Dockside Switcher.

8209 PIONEER DOCKSIDE SWITCHER: 1972, 0-4-0; same as 8200, except for number and four-wheel tender. This locomotive with its tender bears a very close resemblance to a logging engine once used by the Northern Pacific. Sold in 1972 as part of 1287 Pioneer Dockside Switcher set with tender, but became separate-sale item without tender in 1973. I. D. Smith comments.

(A) With tender. — 30 40 60

(B) Without tender. — 20 40 50

8212 BLACK CAVE: 1982, 0-4-0 Plain Switcher; black plastic body; luminous side rods, stack, ornamental bell and boiler front; glow-in-the-dark decals; Type II DC-only can motor (running on AC power will burn out motor). 1615T slope-back tender. Part of 1254 Black Cave Flyer set. Based on earlier Santa Fe Working-on-the-Railroad engine. — 15 30 50

8213 RIO GRANDE: 1982-83, 2-4-2 Columbia; die-cast metal body; smoke; headlight; Type II AC-DC can motor; electronic reversing unit. 1130-type tender with mechanical Sound of Steam. Part of 1252 Heavy Iron set. — — 60 70

8214 PENNSYLVANIA: 1982-83, 2-4-2 Columbia; die-cast metal body; headlight; smoke; electronic reverse unit; Type II AC-DC can motor. 1130-type tender with mechanical Sound of Steam. — — 60 75

8300 A T S F: 1973-75, 2-4-0 Cab-Door; black plastic body; Type I brush motor; manual reverse. Slope-back tender with gold "ATSF" lettering, Symington-Wayne trucks and dummy coupler. Headed the 1381 Cannonball set. — 15 20 25

8302 SOUTHERN: 1973-76, 2-4-0 Porter; black plastic body painted green; plastic ornamental silver bell on top; headlight; MPC logo on both sides; mechanical Sound of Steam; Type I brush motor. 1130 oil-type tender. From set 1384, the Southern Express. — 20 25 30

8303 JERSEY CENTRAL LINES: 1973-74, 2-4-2 Columbia; blue die-cast body; light blue and gold lettering; dark blue

GD   VG   EXC   MT

lower frame and trim; electronic Sound of Steam; smoke; head-light; Type I brush motor. 1130T oil tender with Symington-Wayne trucks and a dummy coupler. Part of the 1385 Blue Streak freight set.   —   30   40   50

> **Note:** *There are four different 8304 locomotives, all with smoke, headlight, two-position E-units, Type I brush motor and electronic Sound of Steam.*

8304 Rock Island.

8304 ROCK ISLAND: 1973-74, 4-4-2 Atlantic; black die- cast body; white lettering on cab; smoke; headlight; electronic Sound of Steam; Type I brush motor; two-position E-unit. 243- style square-back tender. Part of 1386 Rock Island Express set.
(A) Die-cast (675-type) trailing truck. C. Rohlfing Collection.
                           —   50   100   150
(B) Sheet metal trailing truck.   —   40   90   125

8304 BALTIMORE AND OHIO: 1975, 4-4-2; same engine as 8304 Rock Island, except with long streamlined 2046 tender with scoop and Symington-Wayne trucks; smoke; headlight; electronic Sound of Steam; Type I brush motor; two-position E- unit. Came as part of 1587 Capitol Limited passenger set.
                           —   50   90   125

8304 CHESAPEAKE & OHIO: 1974-77, 4-4-2; same as 8304 Rock Island, except gold lettering and square-back 243-type tender with Symington-Wayne trucks and a dummy coupler; smoke; headlight; electronic Sound of Steam; Type I brush motor; two- position E-unit. Part of 1586 Chesapeake Flyer set.
                           —   40   90   125

8304 Pennsylvania.

8304 PENNSYLVANIA: 1974, 4-4-2; same as 8304 Rock Is-land, except with gold lettering and 2046 long streamlined tender; smoke; headlight; electronic Sound of Steam; Type I brush motor; two-position E-unit. Came as part of 1487 Broadway Limited passenger set.   —   50   90   125

8203 Pennsylvania.

GD   VG   EXC   MT

8305 THE MILWAUKEE ROAD: 1973, 4-4-2 Atlantic; black die-cast body; same type engine as the 8304; electronic Sound of Steam and whistle; smoke; headlight; Type I brush motor; two- position E-unit. Red and gold stripes with gold lettering on long streamlined 2046-type tender; dummy coupler, water scoop and Symington-Wayne trucks on tender. Came as part of 1387 Milwaukee Special passenger set.
                           —   50   90   125

8308 JERSEY CENTRAL LINES: 1973-74, 2-4-2 Colum-bia; uncatalogued; black plastic body; gold lettering; smoke; head-light; Type I brush motor. 1130-type tender. Two types of 1130T tender shells exist. One is a black plastic unpainted shell with gold lettering. The other is a blue plastic shell painted black with gold lettering, probably an 8303 leftover shell. Made for Sears set 1392. M. Sabatelle Collection.   —   30   40   50

> **Note:** *The following three locomotives are similar except for their road names and paint schemes. They are die-cast modifications of postwar 1665 switcher boiler pieces with new long plastic pilot pieces to accommodate the front trucks and coupler. Each has a headlight and two-position reverse, operating on a Type I brush motor.*

8310 Nickel Plate Road.

8310 NICKEL PLATE ROAD: 1973-75, 2-4-0 1665 Switcher; uncatalogued; black die-cast body; gold lettering; headlight; Type I brush motor; two-position E-unit. Slope-back tender lettered "NICKEL PLATE/ROAD". Part of uncatalogued Sears set 1390 in 1973. Offered for separate-sale by Sears in 1974-75.
                           —   20   30   60

8310 JERSEY CENTRAL LINES: 1974, 2-4-0 1665 Switcher; uncatalogued; black die-cast body; gold lettering; headlight; Type I brush motor; two-position E-unit. Mechanical Sound of Steam in 1130-type tender. Part of Sears set 1492.
                           —   20   30   60

8310 A T S F: 1974-75, 2-4-0 1665 Switcher; uncatalogued; black die-cast body; gold lettering; headlight; Type I brush motor; two-position E-unit. Slope-back tender lettered "A T S F". Made

10 Jersey Central. for Sears; pictured in 1974 Sears catalogue with 1130 oil tender as part of set 79N96185C. Also available for separate-sale through Sears as 79N 96462. W. Haffen and K. Wills Collections.
(A) With 1615 slope-back tender. — 20 30 40
(B) With 1130 oil-type tender. — 20 30 40

8311 SOUTHERN: 1973, 0-4-0 Porter; uncatalogued; black plastic body; headlight; Type I brush motor; manual reverse. 1130 oil tender. Made for J. C. Penney set 1395.
— 20 30 40

8313 A. T. & S. F.: 1983, 0-4-0 Plain Switcher; black plastic body with gold boiler front, stack and bell; gold "8313" under cab window; no headlight; Type II DC-only can motor (running on AC will burn out motor); no reverse switch; fixed coupler on tender. Gold Santa Fe logo and "A. T. & S. F." on slope-back tender. This is the same locomotive model that appeared in the Black Cave set and is noteworthy for how few pieces of metal are used in its construction. Part of set 1352, Rocky Mountain Freight, shown in Traditional Series catalogue. — — 15 20

8314 SOUTHERN STREAK: 1983, 2-4-0 Porter; dark green plastic locomotive body; headlight; white "8314" under cab window; Type II DC-only can motor (running on AC will burn out motor); no reverse switch. White "SOUTHERN STREAK" on tender sides; 1130T oil-type tender with hatch and mechanical Sound of Steam; fixed coupler on tender. Part of 1353 Southern Streak set shown in Traditional Series catalogue.
— — 20 25

8402 READING: 1984-85, 4-4-2 Elongated Columbia; black die-cast body, an extended version of previous Columbia models; silver number on cab; headlight; smoke; Type II AC-DC can motor; electronic reverse unit. 1130T oil-type tender with mechanical Sound of Steam, silver lettering, and black and silver Reading logo. — — 60 75

8403 CHESSIE SYSTEM: 1984-85, 4-4-2 Elongated Columbia; die-cast blue-painted boiler; headlight; smoke; Type II AC-DC can motor; electronic reverse unit; same type of engine as 8402. 1130T oil-type tender with mechanical Sound of Steam, Symington-Wayne trucks and dummy coupler; yellow stripe on running board, yellow number and Chessie Cat logo on tender. Part of Chessie System set 1402. — — 60 75

8500 PENNSYLVANIA: 1975, 2-4-0 Cab-Door; black plastic body; gold lettering; mechanical Sound of Steam; Type I brush

0 Pennsylvania.

motor; manual reverse. 1130T oil-type tender. Part of Traditional Line Thunderball freight set 1581. — 15 20 25

8502 A.T.S.F.

8502 A. T. S. F: 1975, 2-4-0 Cab-door; black plastic body; gold lettering; Type I brush motor; manual reverse. Slope-back tender. Part of Cannonball Traditional Line set 1381.
— 15 20 25

8506 PENNSYLVANIA: 1975-77, 0-4-0 1665 Switcher; black die-cast body; headlight; gold lettering; Type I brush motor; three-position E-unit. Slope-back tender with diode-controlled red light which lights only when locomotive is in reverse; Symington-Wayne trucks; operating couplers on front and rear.
— 80 100 150

8507 A. T. S. F.

8507 A. T. S. F.: 1975, 2-4-0 Porter; uncatalogued; black plastic cab with gold heat-stamped number; detailed cab interior; "LIONEL" on firebox door (as on postwar 1060); molded window shades; plated main rods only; shiny ornamental bell; headlight; Type I brush motor; manual reverse with curved reversing lever slot in boiler top behind Phillips screw. Slope-back tender with simulated backup light; "A. T. S. F." in gold on tender sides; Symington-Wayne trucks; dummy coupler. Part of a set sold by K-Mart in 1975; reader comments needed concerning set details. Triezenberg Collection. — 20 25 30

8512 SANTA FE: 1985-86, 0-4-0 Dockside; dark blue plastic body; yellow lettering and number; silver smokebox, stack and steam chests; yellow Santa Fe cross logo; short coal box behind cab instead of tender; Type II DC-only can motor (running on AC will burn out motor); one dummy coupler on rear. Part of 1501 Midland freight set in 1985 Traditional catalogue, and a J. C. Penney version of the set the next year.
— — 25 35

8516 NEW YORK CENTRAL: 1985-86, 0-4-0 1665 Switcher; headlight; smoke (a first for any 0-4-0 Lionel switcher); three-position electronic reversing switch; operating coupler on front and rear. Slope-back tender with Symington-Wayne trucks; white "NEW YORK CENTRAL"; operating backup light with white lens; four-prong connector plug from locomotive to tender. Despite its light tender, the engine is a superb runner on low voltage, thanks to its Type II AC-DC can motor connected to spur-drive gearing. It may very well be the best smoking engine Lionel has ever

R. Kaptur and R. LaVoie Collections; B. Greenberg photograph

Some early MPC/Lionel production. All the locomotives in this photograph are die-cast.
Top shelf: 8042 Grand Trunk Western 2-4-2 Columbia with 243 square-back tender from 1972.
Second shelf: 8042 Pennsylvania 2-4-2 Columbia with 1130T tender. Sometimes Lionel would simply switch tenders on these early
small locomotives.
Third shelf: 8303 Jersey Central Lines 2-4-2 Columbia with 1130T tender in striking two-tone blue coloring.
Bottom shelf: 8304 Baltimore and Ohio 4-4-2 Atlantic with 2046 tender, one of four different versions of these engine.

	GD	VG	EXC	MT

produced! This is an improved model of the 8310 and 8506. (For operating details, see John Kouba's article on the Santa Fe Service Station Special in the second edition of *Greenberg's Guide to Lionel Trains (1970-1988)* by Roland LaVoie.) Part of 1502 Yard Chief set in Traditional catalogue. Die-cast modern version of the popular postwar 1665 switcher. — — **125 150**

8601 GREAT NORTHERN: 1988; see 18601.

8601 ROCK ISLAND: 1976-77, 0-4-0 Plain Switcher; black plastic body; large white numbers on cab; Type I brush motor; manual reverse. Slope-back tender with red "Rock/Island" logo. Part of set 1661, the Rock Island Line — lowest priced set in Traditional Line in 1976. Body is a modified 8500 Cab-Door switcher without the door and ladder details, and with top domes spread further. — **15 20 25**

8602 RIO GRANDE: 1976-78, 2-4-0 Porter; black plastic body; white lettering; headlight; Type I brush motor; two-position

E-unit. 1130 oil tender with mechanical Sound of Steam. Part of set 1662, the Black River Freight. — **20 25 30**

8602 PENNSYLVANIA: 1987; see 18602.

8604 JERSEY CENTRAL LINES: 1976, 2-4-2 Columbia; uncatalogued; black plastic body; gold number on cab; smoke; headlight; Type I brush motor; two-position or manual reversing unit.

8601 Rock Island.

A tale told by three early Columbia steamers.

Top shelf: The 8041 New York Central version of 1970. Note the white number, the visible armature shaft end, and the plastic slide valve guides.

Middle shelf: The mis-numbered 8041 Pennsylvania model of early 1971 with Sound of Steam. This example came from a Silver Star set and is very hard to find.

Bottom shelf: The regular-issue 8141 Pennsylvania model of later 1971. Does anyone have a white-numbered 8141 out there?

	GD	VG	EXC	MT

(A) Part of Sears set 1696; 1130 oil-type tender; gold "JERSEY CENTRAL LINES" lettering and logo; mechanical Sound of Steam; Symington-Wayne trucks; dummy coupler. G. Halverson and L. Kositsky Collections. — 30 40 45

(B) Same locomotive as (A), but slope-back tender with no lettering. G. Halverson Collection. — 30 40 45

(C) Same as (A), but locomotive has manual reverse and no headlight; no smoke unit; green plastic 1130T oil-type tender painted gloss black. R. LaVoie Collection. — 30 40 45

8604 WABASH: 1988; see 18604.

8606 NEW YORK CENTRAL: 1989; see 18606.

8607 UNION PACIFIC: 1989; see 18607.

8608 RIO GRANDE: 1989; see 18608.

8609 NORTHERN PACIFIC: 1990; see 18609.

8610 ROCK ISLAND: 1990; see 18610.

8611 LIONEL LINES: 1990; see 18611.

8612 CHICAGO & NORTH WESTERN: 1990; see 18612.

8615 GRAND TRUNK WESTERN: 1990; see 18615.

8616 A. T. & S. F.: 1986, 4-4-2 Elongated Columbia; flat-nosed boiler front; white lettering on cab; die-cast boiler; headlight; smoke; Type II AC-DC can motor; electronic three-position reverse. 1130 oil-type tender with mechanical Sound of Steam, Symington-Wayne trucks and large white number on tender sides. — — 65 75

8616 NORTHERN PACIFIC: 1990; see 18616.

8617 NICKEL PLATE ROAD: 1986-91, 4-4-2 Elongated Columbia; die-cast boiler with yellow running board stripe; N K P logo on steam chest; headlight; smoke; Type II AC-DC can motor; electronic three-position reverse. 243 Santa Fe-type square-back tender with mechanical Sound of Steam, Symington-Wayne trucks and yellow lettering and logo. Part of set 1602, the Nickel Plate Special. This particular set has been used for many special promotions; for example, it was one of the prizes offered in McDonald's Monopoly game promotion. — — 65 75

8618 BALTIMORE AND OHIO: 1991; see 18618.

8620 ILLINOIS CENTRAL: 1991; see 18620.

8625 PENNSYLVANIA: 1986-90, 2-4-0 Porter; black plastic boiler; white stripe and number on cab; headlight; Type II DC-only can motor (running on AC will burn out motor). 1130 oil-type tender with mechanical Sound of Steam and Symington-Wayne trucks. Part of the Cannonball Express set 1615. — — 25 35

Lionel Atlantics and Columbias with some famous railroad names. *B. Greenberg photograph*
Top shelf: **8304 Chesapeake & Ohio 4-4-2 Atlantic with 243 square-back tender.**
Second shelf: **8305 The Milwaukee Road 4-4-2 Atlantic with 2046 tender.**
Third shelf: **8403 Chessie System 4-4-2 Elongated Columbia with 1130T oil tender.**
Bottom shelf: **8604 Jersey Central Lines 2-4-2 Columbia with 1130T oil tender.**

	GD	VG	EXC	MT

8635 A. T. S. F.: 1986, 0-4-0 1665 Switcher; uncatalogued; black die-cast boiler with white number on cab; headlight; smoke unit; Type II AC-DC can motor; electronic three-position reverse; operating couplers on front and rear. Slope-back tender with white lettering and cross logo, backup light and Symington-Wayne trucks. Identical in construction to 8516 New York Central produced the year before. This engine was part of the Santa Fe Work Train, the 1986 Service Station Special set. (For additional information see John Kouba's article in the second edition of *Greenberg's Guide to Lionel Trains (1970- 1988)* by Roland LaVoie.) — — **120 145**

8700 ROCK ISLAND: 1987-88; see 18700.

8703 WABASH: 1977, 2-4-2 Columbia; black plastic body; smoke and headlight; white stripe on locomotive and tender; Type I brush motor. Tender is 1130 oil-type with Symington-Wayne trucks and electronic Sound of Steam. As catalogued, the tender had compressed "WABASH" lettering and a coal load. As produced, it had spaced-out lettering and an oil tank lid. Part of set 1762, the Wabash Cannonball. — **20 25 35**

8704 LIONEL LINES: 1989; see 18704.

8705 NEPTUNE: 1990; see 18705.

	GD	VG	EXC	MT

8706 A. T. & S. F.: 1991; see 18706.

8707 MICKEY'S WORLD TOUR '92: 1991; see 18707.

8800 LIONEL LINES: 1978-81, 4-4-2 Atlantic; die-cast boiler; red marker lights; battery box on pilot. Similar to postwar 2037 with the following modifications: the marker lights, which protrude above the boiler on a 2037, were moved to a more protected location inside the boiler front; the "Made by Lionel" builder's plate was replaced with a Lionel / MPC logo; and the valve gear was given a moving control rod reminiscent of the 1666. The main rod is heavily sculptured with ridges; there is a side rod; smoke; headlight; Type I brush motor; two-position E-unit. Electronic Sound of Steam in the 243-type square-back tender, and a fixed rear tender coupler; tender base is marked "8141T-10" and has a large black "L" in white and black box and "LIONEL LINES" in sans-serif rounded letters across its side. Same engine as 8304 Chesapeake Flyer with one rubber tire on locomotive. — **60 100 125**

8803 SANTA FE: 1978, 0-4-0 Plain Switcher; black plastic body with silver boiler front and red plastic drivers; Type II DC-only can motor (running on AC will burn out motor); two-position reverse switch on boiler top. Slope-back tender with

R. *Kaptur and F. Stem Collections; B. Schwab photograph*

Some of Lionel's best steam switchers. All the tenders have operating backup lights.
Top shelf: **8506 Pennsylvania 0-4-0 1665 switcher with slope-back tender. Note the upgraded side rods.**
Second shelf: **8516 New York Central 0-4-0 1665 switcher with slope-back tender.**
Third shelf: **8635 A.T.S.F. 0-4-0 1665 switcher with slope-back tender from the 1986 Service Station set.**
Bottom shelf: **8977 Pennsylvania 0-6-0 B-6 semi-scale switcher with extended (18000) slope-back tender. This was an 1989 re-issue of the famous 227 semi-scale B-6 switcher of 1939.**

	GD	VG	EXC	MT

Santa Fe cross logo. Part of 1860 Timberline set, 1862 Logging Empire set, 1892 Penney Logging Empire, and 1893 Toys 'R Us Logging Empire. Also known as the "Working on the Railroad" engine. — — **10 20**

8902 ATLANTIC COAST LINE: 1979-82, 1985-90, 2-4-0 Porter; black plastic engine; headlight; Type II DC-only can motor (running on AC will burn out motor). Slope-back tender with "ATLANTIC/COAST/LINE" logo and Symington-Wayne trucks. Available as part of 1960 and 1993 Midnight Flyer sets, 1990 Mystery Glow Midnight Flyer, 1155 Cannonball freight set, and 91687 Freight Flyer. Also resurrected many times since first issuance for low-priced department store special sets.
— — **15 20**

8903 RIO GRANDE: 1979, 2-4-2 Columbia; black plastic engine; headlight; Type II DC-only can motor (running on AC will burn out motor). 1130 oil tender with mechanical Sound of Steam; white script "Rio Grande". Available as part of 1963 Black River freight set. — **15 20 25**

8904 WABASH: 1979, 1981, 2-4-2 Columbia; die-cast; white stripe along running board; smoke; headlight; Type I brush motor; two-position E-unit. 1130 oil-type tender with or without mechanical Sound of Steam; dark-lettered "WABASH" on white stripe across tender side. From 1962 Wabash Cannonball set or 1991 Wabash Deluxe Express.
(A) With mechanical Sound of Steam; 8906T.
— **30 35 40**
(B) Without mechanical Sound of Steam; 8904T.
— **25 30 35**

8905 SMOKEY MOUNTAIN: 1979, 0-4-0 Dockside; plastic engine; dummy headlight; diamond-shaped stack; Type II DC-only can motor (running on AC will burn out motor); fixed coupler. No tender. Part of set 1965, the Smokey Mountain Line.
— — **10 20**

8977 PENNSYLVANIA: 1989, B-6; see 18000.

18000 PENNSYLVANIA: 1989, 1991, 0-6-0 scale B-6 Switcher; black die-cast body; gold "8977" on cab and "PENNSYLVANIA"

R. LaVoie Collection; B. Greenberg photograph

8902 Atlantic Coast Line 2-4-0 Porter with slope-back tender.

GD   VG   EXC   MT

on new scale-length die-cast slope-back tender (catalogue incorrectly shows lettering in white); smoke; headlight; metal handrails on engine and tender. Spoked whitewall drivers; three-position E-unit. The tender is a die-cast stretched version of the 1615 slope-back. This one features die-cast four-wheel leaf-spring (or arch bar) trucks. This B-6 was the first Lionel engine with RailSounds. This locomotive further dramatizes Lionel's' move toward scale and greater detail. Reportedly a good puller. Selling well. Although listed in this chapter as a "small" engine, the B-6 is in truth a Collector-level piece. Reissue of classic postwar 227/701 from 1939. Although the 8506, 8516 and 8635 engines are a similar style, this engine is a scale version placed on the correct 0-6-0 wheel arrangement, using a shorter variation of the Hudson motor. — — — **675**

18600 ATLANTIC COAST LINE: 1987, 4-4-2 Elongated Columbia; uncatalogued; die-cast boiler; smoke; headlight; Type II AC-DC can motor; three-position electronic reverse. Slope-back tender with Symington-Wayne trucks. Part of 11752 Timberline Freight set sold through J. C. Penney. — — — **95**

18601 GREAT NORTHERN RAILWAY: 1988, 4-4-2 Elongated Columbia; die-cast boiler painted dark green with silver-painted smokebox and front; white "8601" on cab; headlight; smoke unit; Type II AC-DC can motor; three-position electronic reverse. Santa Fe 243-type square-back tender painted dark green with black coal load; red, white and green circular "goat" logo; Symington-Wayne trucks; operating coupler. Does not have mechanical Sound of Steam feature as on previous locomotives of its type; wire handrails on boiler — an unusual feature for a Columbia. — — — **95**

18602 PENNSYLVANIA: 1987, 4-4-2 Elongated Columbia; flat-front die-cast boiler; white "8602" on cab; smoke; headlight; Type II AC-DC can motor; three-position electronic reverse. Short box tender not issued since an 8040 model of 1972 carried it. This engine's tender differs from the earlier model in that it has a railing added to the tender's back deck; also has small, compressed "PENNSYLVANIA" lettering in white (very true to prototype), and Symington-Wayne trucks. Advertised in catalogue as match for 16000-series Pennsylvania passenger cars, but sold separately in Type II box. — — — **90**

18604 WABASH: 1988-91, 4-4-2 Elongated Columbia; die-cast boiler; headlight; smoke; wide white stripe along boiler; "8604" on cab; Type II AC-DC can motor; electronic three-position reverse. 243 Santa Fe-style square-back tender with Symington-Wayne trucks, "WABASH" lettering on white stripe and operating coupler. Essentially an updated version of the 8904 Wabash steamer produced in 1979, but with the extended Columbia boiler and new tender. Part of 11703 Iron Horse freight set. — — — **80**

GD   VG   EXC   MT

18605 MOPAR EXPRESS: 1987-88, 4-4-2 Elongated Columbia; uncatalogued; black die-cast boiler; white "1987" on cab and black "ME" inside white rectangle on steam chest; white stripe on running board; headlight; smoke; green jewels on front marker lights; rubber tires on rear drivers; AC-DC Type II can motor; three-position electronic reverse. Black plastic square-back 243-type tender with mechanical Sound of Steam, three white stripes and "MOPAR EXPRESS" on sides; Symington-Wayne trucks. This engine headed an uncatalogued Chrysler set in 1987 and 1988 (11757). The 1988 set came with an additional tank car. This engine is based on the 8617 Nickel Plate Special, but was offered only through a special Chrysler dealer promotion for its "Chrysler Motors Genuine Parts" — MOPAR. Reportedly 1,500 made. L. Bohn Collection. — — — **60**

18606 NEW YORK CENTRAL: 1989, 2-6-4 with Atlantic boiler; black die-cast boiler; white "8606" on cab and "NEW YORK CENTRAL" on tender; smoke; headlight; Type IV AC-DC can motor with six wheels; three-position electronic reverse unit. First re-use of this motor since 8001/8007 in 1980. 6466-type tender with wire handrails and bar-end trucks. (See comments on tender under 18608.) Engine is similar to 18607, 18608, 18609 and 18611. Frequent reports of off-center axle mounting causing engine to wobble down track. Purchasers should test before buying. Six companion passenger cars (16016- 16021) issued separately. — — — **165**

18607 UNION PACIFIC: 1989, 2-6-4 with Atlantic boiler; light gray die-cast boiler; yellow-striped running board; yellow "8607" on cab and "UNION PACIFIC" on matching gray tender; smoke; headlight; Type IV AC-DC can motor on six-wheel chassis; three-position electronic reverse. Tender is 6466-type with die-cast postwar bar-end trucks and w e handrails. Engine is similar to 18606 and 18608. See comment under 18608. See 18606 for operating cautions. — — — **165**

18608 RIO GRANDE: 1989, 2-6-4 with Atlantic boiler; uncatalogued; black die-cast boiler; white "8608" and "Rio Grande" on tender; smoke; headlight; ornamental bell; Type IV AC-DC can motor on six-wheel chassis; three-position electronic reverse unit. 6466-type tender with wire railings and postwar die-cast bar-end trucks; no whistle. This is the first appearance of this style tender since the postwar era. Engine is similar to the old postwar 2037 and headed the 1989 Service Station Special set 11758, the Desert King. See comments on 18606 for operating cautions. — — — **150**

18609 NORTHERN PACIFIC: 1990, 2-6-4 with Atlantic boiler; black die-cast body similar to 18606-18608; white "8609" on cab; smoke; headlight; Type IV AC-DC can motor on six-wheel chassis; three-position electronic reverse. "NORTHERN PACIFIC" in white on the 243-type square-back tender, which features new ASF strong-arm trucks and wire railings — an un-

	GD	VG	EXC	MT

usual addition for this tender; no sound effects. Six companion passenger cars (16034-16039) were issued separately.

— — — **180**

18610 ROCK ISLAND: 1990, 0-4-0, 1665 Switcher; black die-cast boiler with white "8610" on cab. Same construction details as for the 8516 and 8635 switchers: smoke, headlight, three-position electronic reverse, Type II AC-DC can motor. Operating front and rear couplers. Slope-back tender has wire railings, "ROCK ISLAND" lettering, ASF strong-arm trucks, and a diode-controlled operating backup light. — — — **190**

18611 LIONEL LINES: 1990, 2-6-4 with Atlantic boiler; uncatalogued; die-cast boiler in smoke-gray; white "8611" on cab; white stripe on running board; white "LL" in stylized rectangle on steam chest; headlight; smoke; Type IV AC- DC six-wheel can motor; three-position electronic reverse; body is same as 18606-18609 engines. Tender is a plastic 1130-type small streamlined oil version with first-class trim, such as die-cast leaf spring trucks and wire railings, yet without sound system. Apparently, Lionel has a variety of tender types planned for this engine style. Came with 1990 Service Station Special set 11712, the Great lakes Express. Four O27 passenger cars came with set.

— — — **175**

18612 CHICAGO & NORTH WESTERN: 1989, 4-4-2 Elongated Columbia; black die-cast body with silver-painted boiler front; white "8612" on cab; steel driver rims; wire handrails on boiler; headlight; smoke; Type II AC-DC can motor; three-position electronic reverse unit. 243-type square- back tender with red, white and black C N W logo and Symington-Wayne trucks. Engine is the same as 18601. — — — **100**

18613 ATLANTIC COAST LINE: 1989, 4-4-2 Elongated Columbia; uncatalogued; same engine as 18602 Pennsylvania, but came with Atlantic Coast Line slope-back tender as found on 8902 and 18600; white lettering; smoke; headlight; Type II AC-DC can motor; three-position electronic reverse unit. This engine was issued for an uncatalogued Sears set 11773 which came with three of the regular production N Y C O27 passenger cars (the Pullman, baggage and observation cars). The Sears catalogue shows a photo of the 18602, but the engine was made as the 18613.

— — — **90**

18614 SEARS CIRCUS TRAIN: 1989, 4-4-2 Elongated Columbia; uncatalogued; die-cast boiler painted light blue; "1989" on cab; headlight; smoke; Type II AC-DC can motor; three-position electronic reverse. Plastic 243-type square-back tender in matching blue with white "CIRCUS TRAIN" lettering, and clown and tent electrocal. This engine was part of an uncatalogued 11770 Sears Circus Train set in 1989. — — — **75**

18615 GRAND TRUNK WESTERN: 1990, 4-4-2 Elongated Columbia; black die-cast boiler; new boiler style with feedwater heater added to the front; wire handrails; white stripe on running board; white "8615" under cab; headlight; smoke unit; Type II AC-DC can motor; three-position electronic reverse; bright steel rims on drive wheels. Engine is similar to 18612 from 1989, except for added feedwater tank. 243-type square-back tender with G T W white and blue logo, and ASF strong-arm trucks.

— — — **100**

18616 NORTHERN PACIFIC: 1990, 4-4-2 Elongated Columbia; uncatalogued; black die-cast boiler; white "8616" on cab; white "NORTHERN PACIFIC" lettering on slope-back tender; headlight; smoke; Type II AC-DC can motor; three-position electronic reverse. Tender has ASF strong-arm trucks. Engine was made

for an uncatalogued 1990 Sears set (49N95266) pulling three regular-issue Northern Pacific O27 streamlined passenger cars (the combo, vista dome and observation). The regularly catalogued engine for the passenger set was 18609.

— — — **90**

18617 ADOLPHUS III: 1989, 4-4-2 Elongated Columbia; uncatalogued; black die-cast boiler with no number; same type of engine as Pennsylvania 18602, except with 1615-type slope-back tender; smoke; headlight; only lettering on cab is white "ADOLPHUS/III"; wire handrails on engine and tender (unusual for Columbia); AC-DC can motor; three-position electronic reverse. Black plastic tender with white "ANHEUSER-BUSCH" and red and gold "A"-eagle logo; Symington-Wayne trucks. 18617 is its catalogue number, but this is not mentioned in any Lionel literature. Part of uncatalogued Anheuser Busch Budweiser set 11775. Reportedly only 2,500 made. Available only through an Anheuser-Busch gift catalogue. — — — **190**

18618 BALTIMORE AND OHIO: 1991, 4-4-2 Elongated Columbia. Announced in Lionel's 1991 Book 1 catalogue, but not manufactured. **Not Manufactured**

18620 ILLINOIS CENTRAL*: 1991, 2-6-2 Atlantic steam locomotive; Atlantic boiler body on a Prairie-style wheel arrangement; black die-cast boiler; yellow lettering on tender and yellow running board on engine; "8620" on cab; headlight; smoke unit; Type IV six-wheel can motor; three- position electronic reverse unit; small New York Central-style tender (2466 type) with plastic arch bar trucks. Intended as a match for the Illinois Central O27 streamlined passenger cars (16042-16047) released the same year. Strangely enough this is the first steam engine lettered for the Illinois Central Lionel has ever made. — — — **195**

18700 ROCK ISLAND: 1987-88, 0-4-0 Dockside; bright red plastic body; silver-painted smokebox, stack and steam chests; white "8700" and Rock Island logo; Type II DC-only can motor (running on AC will burn out motor). No tender. Part of the 11701 Rail Blazer set. — — — **25**

18704 LIONEL LINES: 1989, (Microracers) 2-4-0 Porter; uncatalogued; black plastic body; headlight; white "8704" on cab; Type II DC-only can motor (running on AC will burn out motor). White "LIONEL LINES" on Santa Fe slope-back tender; Symington-Wayne trucks. Part of unusual uncatalogued Microracers set 11771 made for K-Mart. R. LaVoie Collection.

— — — **60**

18705 NEPTUNE: 1990-91, (Badlands Express) 0-4-0 Dockside; black plastic body; gold trim and drive rods; red boiler front; gold "8705" and "NEPTUNE" on cab; Type II DC-only can motor (running on AC will burn out motor). No tender. Part of 11714 Badlands Express set. — — — **30**

18706 A.T.&S.F*: 1991, 2-4-0 Porter steam locomotive; black plastic body; white lettering; "8706" in large numbers on the tender; headlight; Type II DC-only can motor (running on AC will burn out motor); polarity reverse at transformer; 243-type square-back tender with ASF strong-arm trucks. Part of 11720 Santa Fe Special set. — — — **35**

18707 MICKEY'S WORLD TOUR '92*: 1991, 2-4-0 Porter steam locomotive; black plastic body; red lettering and running board stripe; "MICKEY'S WORLD TOUR '92" printed on cab roof (an unusual feature) and on the Santa Fe type slope-back tender; "8707" in red on cab; multicolor Mickey tour logo on tender side; headlight; smoke unit; Type II DC-only can motor (running on AC will burn out motor); ASF strong-arm trucks on tender. Part of

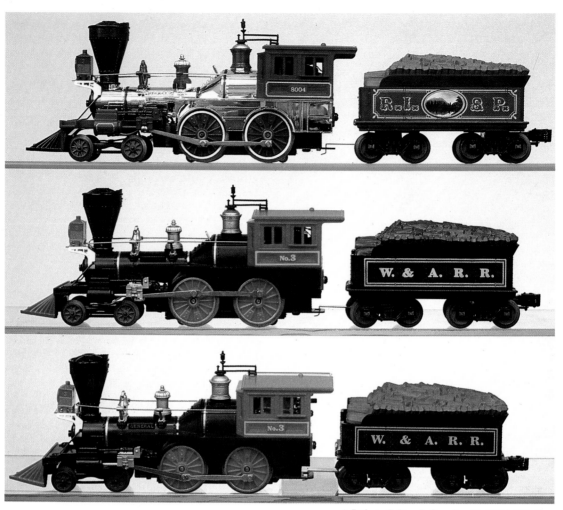

Some General-style steamers and a tricky comparison.   *A. Rudman, F. Stem, L. Caponi, and R. LaVoie Collections*
Top shelf: **8004 R. I. & P.**
Middle shelf: **8701 W. & A. R. R.,** the first modern General engine from 1977.
Bottom shelf: **8630 W. A. & R. R.,** which appears identical to 8701 but has an entirely different drive system. **Note small reversing switch projecting from back of cab. This model came as part of uncatalogued American Express General set in 1986.**

	GD	VG	EXC	MT

11721 Mickey's World Tour train set. Since a smoke unit has never before been included on a DC-only train (it normally requires AC to operate), it will be interesting to see if this engine is actually made with a smoke unit as advertised.

— — — 45

GENERAL STEAM ENGINES

Lionel resurrected another old favorite, the General old-time 4-4-0 locomotive first made by Lionel in the late 1950s. In 1977 the Western & Atlantic No. 3 (8701) met with great success, especially after the old-time cars were issued for it. Since then, the General locomotive has been used in chromed Rock Island, blue and black B & O, and other color schemes. One version of this locomotive became a special issue for J. C. Penney, another was part of a special American Express offer,

and yet another was part of the 1988 Service Station set. The most recent one has achieved a new status in the Collector Line — a Disneyland 35th anniversary commemorative for 1990.

Lionel used the General steam engines to lead some handsome 19th century passenger sets, and has applied several attractive color schemes to it. All of them pull a wood-toting tender (the only such tender Lionel makes in O Gauge).

Common Features

Two types of frames and motors are used with the General steam engines. First is the Type VII motor with an AC brush type armature and plate, as described in the motor section earlier in this chapter. These are used on the Collector models. A second type is the Type VIIA DC can motor mounted in a frame similar to the small Columbias. These Generals were intended for the Traditional Line and came with and without the electronic reverse unit, enabling AC operation.

Two General steam locomotives. Note stack and headlight differences between the two.
Top shelf: 8315 B & O from B & O passenger set of 1983.
Bottom shelf: 8410 Redwood Valley Express, part of one of the most inexpensive sets made by Modern Lionel.

GENERAL STEAM ENGINES LISTING

	GD	VG	EXC	MT

3 UNION PACIFIC: 1981; see 8104.

3 W. & A. R. R.: 1977, see 8701; 1986, see 8630.

4 DISNEYLAND: 1990; see 18008.

8004 R. I. & P.: 1980, 1982, (Rock Island & Peoria) 4-4-0 General chassis; chrome boiler; tuscan cab; steam chest; black stack and boiler bands; smoke; Type VII General-style motor; two-position reverse unit. Tender has tuscan sides with mountain mural. Modeled after an engine built by the Rock Island and Peoria Railroad in the late 1800s for the World's Fair. About 4,000 made. M. Sabatelle comment.　　　—　　—　　**150**　　**170**

8005 A T S F: 1980, 1982, 4-4-0 General chassis; very lightweight locomotive; red and maroon engine with gold trim; Type VIIA can motor with and without reverse. 8005T tender with gold rectangle trim with "ATSF". Came as part of 1053 The James Gang set with three cars, figures and building. Observed with two frame types. Type I uses leftover AC frames from previous production with worm wheel on axle. Type II frames lack this worm wheel on axle. (M. Sabatelle comment.) About 50,000 made. Price for engine and tender only.
(A) With electronic reverse (AC/DC operation).
　　　　　　—　　—　　**30**　　**40**
(B) Without reverse (DC-only operation).
　　　　　　—　　—　　**25**　　**35**

8104 UNION PACIFIC: 1981, 4-4-0 General; uncatalogued; green cab, pilot, lamp, wheel spokes and ornamental bell; black stack; yellow chrome-finished boiler; "3" appears on side of head

GD	VG	EXC	MT

lamp and under cab window; Type VII General-style AC motor. Green plastic "General"-style tender with arch bar trucks and simulated woodpile. This locomotive was sold by J. C. Penney as a special called "The Golden Arrow". Display case for locomotive with wooden base and plastic cover.　　—　　—　　**300**　　**395**
See also Factory Errors and Prototypes chapter in Volume II, first edition.

8315 B & O: 1983, 4-4-0 General; plastic locomotive with blue boiler and stack; black pilot, steam cylinders, cab and tender; white "8315" beneath cab windows and "B & O" on tender sides; illustrated with non- illuminating headlight, but made with operating headlight which takes a small screw-based bulb; Type VIIA DC can motor; electronic three-position reverse unit; fixed coupler on tender. Part of 1351 Baltimore & Ohio set, shown in Traditional Series catalogue.　　　　—　　**70**　　**85**　　**120**

8410 REDWOOD VALLEY EXPRESS: 1984-85, 4-4-0 General; tuscan boiler; yellow cab, pilot and drive wheels; cylindrical headlight; tall thin stack instead of usual balloon stack; gold trim; Type VIIA DC-only can motor (running on AC will burn out motor); no reverse. Tender with simulated woodpile, plastic arch bar trucks with dummy coupler, and brown "REDWOOD VALLEY/EXPRESS" and logo on tender sides. Came as part of Redwood Valley Express set 1403.　　　—　　—　　**40**　　**60**

8630 W. & A. R. R.: 1986, (Western & Atlantic) 4-4-0 General; uncatalogued; no number on engine except "No. 3"; headlight; smoke; identical to 8701 in color and lettering, but powered by Type VIIA DC can motor-drive system instead of Type VII AC crosscut-geared motor of earlier version; three-position electronic reverse. Offered as part of uncatalogued set 1608 through American Express Travel-Related Services.

　　　　　　　　—　　—　　—　　**135**

	GD	VG	EXC	MT

8701 W. & A. R. R: 1977-79, (Western & Atlantic) 4-4-0 General; cab numbered "No. 3"; black plastic boiler and frame; red cab; gold boiler bands, dome and bell; yellow lettering; headlight; smoke; Type VII General-type AC motor; two-position E-unit. Black plastic tender with yellow "W. & A. R. R." Rerun of Lionel 1862-1872-1882 Generals of 1959-1962. Initially offered alone in 1977, this engine was pictured in a set with two General-sstyle passenger cars and a flatcar in the 1978 and 1979 catalogues.
— 100 150 200

8702 V. & T. R. R.: 1888; see 18702.

8716 LIONELVILLE CIRCUS: 1990; see 18716.

18008 DISNEYLAND RAILROAD: 1990, 4-4-0 General; dark gray boiler with light gray front section and black boiler front; red cab, wheels and pilot; gold and brass trim; wire handrails on boiler; intricate decals in several locations; white "4" on cab; polished-steel wheels; smoke; headlight; Type VIIA General-style can motor; three-position electronic reverse. Tender bears Disney 35th anniversary herald and "DISNEYLAND RAILROAD" inside gold accents; die-cast leaf-spring trucks on tender. Engine came with oak display base, Gargraves track, acrylic cover and silver nameplate. Issued to mark the 35th anniversary of Disneyland.
— — — 335

18702 V. & T. R. R.: 1988 (Virginia and Truckee Railroad), 4-4-0 General; uncatalogued; dark maroon boiler and cab; gold trim; gold "8702" and "RENO"; smoke; headlight; Type VIIA can motor; three-position electronic reverse. Tender with maroon body, gold outlining and "V. & T R. R.", plastic arch bar trucks, brown simulated woodpile and operating coupler. Part of "Dry Gulch Line" Service Station set 11706 for 1988.
— — — 140

18716 LIONELVILLE CIRCUS: 1990-91, 4-4-0 General; red boiler; green cab; black frame and smokestack; yellow "8716" on cab; gold "LCS" on boiler number board; gold trim and drive rods; wire handrails; operating headlight; Type VIIA AC-DC can motor; three-position electronic reverse. Woodpile tender painted green with yellow "Lionelville Circus" and plastic ASF strong-arm trucks; operating coupler. Part of the popular Lionelville Circus Special Traditional Line set 11716.
— — — 175

CHAPTER 5

AUTOMOBILE CARRIERS

Introduction by Dick Johnson

One of the least produced, and perhaps least popular, freight cars manufactured by Lionel during 1973-1989 was the 60-foot open automobile carrier. Nevertheless it is an interesting car because it is not a remake of an old Lionel item, and also because it is a reasonably accurate representation of a piece of contemporary rolling stock. In 1989, Lionel announced a new enclosed automobile carrier for release in 1990. Since the enclosed auto carrier differs greatly from the open auto carrier, each will be discussed separately.

OPEN AUTOMOBILE CARRIERS

The open automobile carrier is essentially an extra long, 14-inch flatcar to which one or two racks (called "carriers") have been added, thereby making either a two-tier car 2¾-inches high or a three-tier car 4⅛-inches high. Because of their unusual length, these cars require a special offset truck to allow them to negotiate the tight O27 and O31 curves. On the early models, the trucks were fastened to the bodies with plastic rivets, which allowed a great deal of play between the trucks and the bodies. This, coupled with their high center of gravity and light weight, caused them to tip over as they rounded curves. Adding metal weights or metal automobiles 1:55-scale or smaller does not reduce the unsteadiness. The rocking problem was reduced on later models when Lionel switched to a metal truck rivet, and it was essentially eliminated on the recent P R R 16208. This car has a molded semi-circular ridge on the underside on which the top rear of the wheel set rides, preventing rocking.

Despite its operational problems, the automobile carrier offers the collector an opportunity to pursue a neglected area

of production, since only eleven different car numbers were made between 1973 and 1989. The history of Lionel Trains is replete with poor sellers which later became very valuable, and the auto carrier may some day fall into this category.

Except for the 9216 Great Northern, every auto carrier produced through 1989 had Type IIC or IID Symington-Wayne plastic trucks equipped with metal disc-operating couplers with tabs. This type of Symington-Wayne truck was specially developed for the auto carrier. The trucks on the later models were fastened with metal rivets. The ends of each tier on the car body are closed off by black plastic latches, which are also referred to as gates or car stops. Safety tread is molded into the deck of the car and the decks of the carriers on all of the auto carriers, except for most of the black versions of the 9123 C & O. This is because the majority of the black versions were produced before the safety tread design was added to the molds. Lionel cannot state when this occurred, but does know that the design was not added to the drawings until October 25, 1972. The molds were not changed again until 1989, when twelve raised wheel stops were added to the flatcar and the decks of the carriers of the 16208 P R R. Their purpose was to hold in place the die-cast metal automobiles that were packaged with that car. This is the only modern era auto carrier issued to date that came with automobiles. Unfortunately, they are HO-scale — the only size that fits into the car!

The bodies of the auto carriers are all unpainted, so the body color of each car is the color of the plastic used in the mold. The graphics on all of these cars were applied by heat stamp, except for the road logos on the 9145 Illinois Central Gulf, 9281 Santa Fe and 9351 Pennsylvania, which were applied by electrocal.

Variations for any given car are possible, and the auto carrier is no exception. Variations occurred only in the first three model numbers produced — the 9123 C and O, 9125 N & W, and 9126 C and O.

Of all the auto carriers produced, the 9123 has caused the most confusion for collectors. Most people associate the 9123 with the blue, single-stamped C and O three-tier with yellow markings, which was catalogued only in 1974 (variation (A) in the listings). However, there are six other variations bearing the number 9123, none of which were catalogued. Four are regular production cars and two are special production cars. Far more blue-bodied cars (variations (A) and (B)) were produced than black-bodied cars (variations (C), (D) and (E)). Six medium blue- and ten yellow-bodied cars were produced for the T C A (see Volume II, first edition). The medium blue T C A 9123 was created by changing from a gondola mold to an auto carrier mold. This happened before the injection-molding machine had been purged of the blue plastic being used to produce the 9136 Republic Steel gondola. The yellow 9123 was created by applying blue 9123 graphics to yellow 9126 bodies.

All 9123s were three-tiered, except the medium blue T C A version and variation (E). This latter variation cannot be faked by removing the upper carrier from variations (C) or (D). When a three-tiered car is assembled, the tabs on the bottom of the upper carrier are pressed into the slots on the top of the lower carrier. The pressure of the tabs passing through the slots creates grayish-white stress marks in the plastic around the slots. If an upper carrier has been removed, the stress marks would be visible.

The term "single-stamped" is used to describe a three-tier auto carrier which has the road logo stamped only on the boards of the upper carrier. The term "double-stamped" is used when a three-tier car has the road logo stamped on the boards of both the upper and lower carriers. Double-stamped cars (variations (B) and (D)) are legitimate variations and cannot be faked: installing a lower tier (with lettering) on another car to create a double-stamped version would mean the "TRAILER TRAIN" lettering would incorrectly appear on both tiers. The only decoration on the upper carrier should be the road logo stamped on both of the boards. The lower carrier should display the road logo stamped on both of the boards, and the remaining graphics stamped along the bottom of the carrier. Any car that does not have the graphics so positioned is not a legitimate double-stamped variation. The collector is advised to double-check the true variations listed here before purchasing one that is not documented.

The only two-tiered regular production auto carrier made, the 9125 N & W, came in two variations — one blue and one black. Because these cars were sold primarily in sets, both versions are hard to find. Very few black ones were produced, adding to its scarcity.

Four variations of the 9126 C and O exist, attributable to differences in the body color (yellow versus light yellow) and stamping (single versus double). These cars were produced between 1973 and 1975, when Lionel used colored plastic pellets in its injection-molding machine. While using this coloration process, Lionel experienced difficulty maintaining color consistency between production runs. Differences in color are much more noticeable in lighter colors, especially yellow.

ENCLOSED AUTOMOBILE CARRIERS

Although the open automobile carrier may not have met Lionel's expectations, perhaps the new enclosed auto carrier will. In the fall of 1989, Lionel announced a totally new-style two-tier carrier for production in 1990. The new design features a cover for the top tier, screened sides, and sliding double doors at both ends of the car. Apparently, Lionel wanted to keep pace with the real railroads, which switched to 89-foot cars with covers and screened sides and doors. These changes were made to prevent damage to the cargo of automobiles by vandalism, flying debris and overgrown foliage along the right of way. The new enclosed auto carrier is not longer or higher than the old open auto carrier, but is nearly ½-inch wider and much heavier. Excluding the trucks and truck rivets, it is composed of 35 separate pieces (instead of the three pieces used for the open three-tier auto carrier). Also in contrast to the open auto carriers, the roof pieces of the new enclosed models are painted, although the main body remains unpainted plastic. The first two cars in this series are the 16214 Denver & Rio Grande and the 16215 Conrail. You can be sure that we will see more of these modern "covered wagons" in the future, since entirely new molds were needed to produce this car.

AUTOMOBILE CARRIER LISTINGS

	GD	VG	EXC	MT

1973 T C A: See Volume II, first edition.

9123 C & O: 1973-74, two- or three-tier open-style auto carrier; dark blue or black body; yellow lettering; C and O logo on either upper boards only or on upper and lower boards; "TRAILER TRAIN" across bottom of lower carrier; Type IIC or IID Symington-Wayne trucks fastened with plastic rivets; "BLT 1-73"; Type II box.

(A) 1974; three-tier; blue body; C and O logo on upper boards only. This is the catalogue version. — — — 30

(B) 1974; uncatalogued; three-tier; blue body; C and O logo on upper and lower boards. — — — 100

(C) 1973 and 1974; uncatalogued; three-tier; black body; C and O logo on upper boards only. — — — 45

(D) 1973 and 1974; uncatalogued; three-tier; black body; C and O logo on upper and lower boards. — — — 100

(E) 1973; uncatalogued; two-tier; black body; C and O logo on boards; came in a factory-sealed 1386 Rock Island Express set in lieu of the blue 9125 N & W two-tier auto carrier shown on the set box and in the 1973-74 catalogues; no box; very rare. R. Johnson Collection. **NRS**
See Volume II, first edition.

9125 N & W: 1973-77, two-tier open-style auto carrier; dark blue or black body; white lettering; N & W logo on boards; "TRAILER TRAIN" across bottom of carrier; Type IIC or IID Symington-Wayne trucks fastened with metal rivets; "BLT 1-73". Sold separately and in 1386 Rock Island Express set and 1586 Chesapeake Flyer set. R. Johnson comment.

(A) Dark blue body; catalogued. **15 20 30 40**

R. Johnson Collection; B. Schwab photograph

here are seven of the 9123 automobile carriers counting two T C A Specials. Five are shown here, four of which are very scarce.

op shelf: 9123 C&O (Volume II, first edition), exceptionally scarce.

econd shelf: 9123(E) black C&O two-tier car, very rare; 9125 black N&W two-tier car.

hird shelf: 9123 yellow C&O three-tier car (see Volume II, first edition), very rare; 9123(D) black C&O three-tier car, quite rare.

ottom shelf: 9123(A) blue C&O three-tier car, regular production; 9126 yellow C&O three-tier car.

	GD	VG	EXC	MT

(B) Black body; uncatalogued; scarce. G. Wilson Collection.

| | 20 | 30 | 40 | 60 |

9126 C & O: 1973-75, three-tier open-style auto carrier; catalogued; yellow or light yellow body; blue lettering; C and O logo on either upper boards only or on upper and lower boards; "TRAILER TRAIN" across bottom of lower carrier; Type IIC or IID Symington-Wayne trucks fastened with plastic rivets; "BLT 2-73"; Type II box. Sold separately and in 1388 Golden State Arrow and 1460 Grand National sets.

(A) Yellow body; C and O logo on upper boards only.

| | 10 | 12 | 15 | 25 |

(B) Yellow body; C and O logo on upper and lower boards.

| | 30 | 50 | 75 | 100 |

(C) Light yellow body; C and O logo on upper boards only.

| | 10 | 12 | 15 | 25 |

(D) Light yellow body; C and O logo on upper and lower boards.

| | 30 | 50 | 75 | 100 |

9129 N & W: 1975-76, three-tier open-style auto carrier; brown body; white lettering; N & W logo on upper boards only; "TRAILER TRAIN" across bottom of lower carrier; Type IIC or IID Symington-Wayne trucks fastened with plastic rivets; "BLT 2-75";

	GD	VG	EXC	MT

Type II box. Sold separately and in 1560 North American Express and 1584 N & W Spirit of America sets (1975).

| | — | — | 30 | 45 |

9139 PENN CENTRAL: 1976-77, three-tier open-style auto carrier; jade green body; white lettering; P C logo on upper boards only; "PENN CENTRAL" across bottom of lower carrier; Type IIC or IID Symington-Wayne trucks fastened with metal rivets; "BLT 1-76"; Type II box. Sold separately and in 1664 Illinois Central freight set.

| | — | — | 20 | 30 |

9145 ILLINOIS CENTRAL GULF: 1977-80, three-tier open-style auto carrier; orange body; black lettering; electrocal ICG "I-beam" logo in black and white on upper boards only; "ILLINOIS CENTRAL GULF" across bottom of lower carrier; Type IIC or IID Symington-Wayne trucks fastened with metal rivets; "BLT 1-76"; Type III box.

| | — | — | 20 | 35 |

9216 GREAT NORTHERN: 1978, three-tier open-style auto carrier; sky blue body; white lettering; G N goat logo on upper boards only; "GREAT NORTHERN" across bottom of lower carrier; Type III Standard O sprung trucks (the only auto carrier so equipped); "BLT 1-78"; Type III box. Available only in 1867 Milwaukee Limited set.

| | — | — | 25 | 40 |

Three-tier automobile carriers.

R. Johnson Collection; B. Schwab photograph

Top shelf: **9129 N&W; 9139 Penn Central.**
Second shelf: **9145 Illinois Central Gulf; 9216 Great Northern.**
Third shelf: **9281 Santa Fe; 9351 Pennsylvania.**
Bottom shelf: **16208 PRR Trailer Train.** This is the only automobile carrier that came with cars to date.

	GD	VG	EXC	MT

9281 SANTA FE: 1978-80, three-tier open-style auto carrier; red body; white lettering; electrocal Santa Fe cross logo in red and white on upper boards only; "SANTA FE" across bottom of lower carrier; Type IIC or IID Symington-Wayne trucks fastened with metal rivets; "BLT 1-78"; Type III box.   —   —   **20   30**

9351 PENNSYLVANIA: 1980, three-tier open-style auto carrier; tuscan body; gold lettering; electrocal gold and scarlet P R R keystone logo on upper boards only; "PENNSYLVANIA" across bottom of lower carrier; Type IIC or IID Symington-Wayne trucks fastened with metal rivets; "BLT 1-80"; Type III box.   —   —   **20   40**

16208 P R R: 1989, three-tier open-style auto carrier; tuscan body; white lettering; white P R R keystone logo on upper boards only; yellow "TRAILER TRAIN" across bottom of lower carrier; Type IIC or IID Symington-Wayne trucks fastened with metal rivets; "BLT 1-89"; new-style box; packaged with six HO die-cast autos, the only modern era auto carrier issued with autos.   —   —   —   **35**

16214 RIO GRANDE: 1990, two-tier enclosed-style auto carrier with screened sides and sliding double doors at both ends; painted white cover; orange plastic side supports, ends, ladders and doors; unpainted gray screened sides; yellow "TRAILER TRAIN" flat; black and white lettering on flatcar; black "RIO GRANDE" logo on boards; new-style ASF ride control trucks with strong-arm couplers fastened with metal rivets; "BLT 1-90".   —   —   —   **31**

16215 CONRAIL: 1990, two-tier enclosed-style auto carrier with screened sides and sliding double doors at both ends; painted white cover; tuscan plastic side supports, ends, ladders and doors; unpainted gray screened sides; yellow "TRAILER TRAIN" flat with black and white lettering; white "CONRAIL" logo on boards; black lettering; new-style ASF ride control trucks with strong-arm couplers fastened with metal rivets; "BLT 1-90". Not released until early 1991.   —   —   —   **31**

17890 C S X: 1991, two-tier enclosed-style auto carrier; LOTS; see Volume II, first edition.

CHAPTER 6

BOXCARS AND STOCK CARS

Ask a Lionel collector about his specialty, and chances are that person will tell you about some form or class of boxcar. That really is no surprise, for box, refrigerator and stock cars are by far the most numerous and variable pieces of rolling stock issued by Lionel in its modern era. This was also true of postwar production, and it is easy to see why.

In the first place, boxcars are fixed in the public mind as the "typical" rolling stock, aside from passenger cars, which tell their own stories. Just look at any movie dealing with railroads, and most likely you will see an abundance of boxcars. Or read some of the great railroad fiction by such luminaries of the genre as Gilbert Lathrop and E. S. Dellinger, which often portray some desperate struggle against the elements by courageous brakemen trying to control a runaway train by turning brakewheels — atop the boxcars. Another reason for the popularity of collecting boxcars is more specific to tinplate production. As we have seen many times, color and graphics sell toy trains, and what better place to put your most colorful graphics than on the flat sides of a box or refrigerator car? The many types of box, refrigerator and stock cars outsell all other types of tinplate rolling stock combined. These cars have been truly crucial to the success of Lionel as a producer of toy trains.

The only real trouble in collecting these cars lies in their utterly astonishing variety and vast quantity. Type collectors experience a difficult time collecting all of a particular series because of the sheer mass of numbers. Consider the 80 boxcars in the 9700-series, the 70 or so 9800-series refrigerator cars, the 9200-and 9400-series boxcars, the woodsided reefers, the bullion cars, the bunk cars, the Bicentennial Series, the Tobacco Road and Favorite Spirits series, and the smaller box and stock cars. The total is staggering!

Variation collectors have even more problems than the type collectors, because many of these cars have seemingly endless variations in body styles and molds, frames, doors, colors and so on. It is not unusual for some cars, like the 9748 C P Rail, to exist in 15 or more variations.

Therein lies considerable controversy. Why should collectors bother with variations of the same car at all, if it is nearly impossible to get them all? Some collectors believe that these variations should be neither stressed nor even mentioned in pricing guides. The answer to this question revolves primarily around interest: a collector should have the opportunity to observe what interests him. Simply put, this Guide tries to list as many pertinent details of a car as possible, because they may interest various groups of Lionel collectors. Many collectors are particularly curious about boxcar variations because of the heritage of research on the venerated postwar 6464-series. Dr. Charles Weber, a noted expert on the 6464 cars, states it succinctly: "Whether one collects these minor variations or not, it is still interesting for many of us to learn about them. If a given collector isn't interested, that's his business, but lots of us are interested. That's why they make chocolate and vanilla!"

The reader is referred to the authoritative discussion on the 6464 cars by Dr. Weber in *Greenberg's Guide to Lionel Trains, 1945-1969, Volume I,* and to Bob Swanson's exhaustive study of the 6454 boxcars in the Tenth Anniversary (1987) edition of that volume. Their pioneering efforts have indeed carried over into Lionel's modern era production, which also has its interesting variations.

What is the best advice for the beginning collector? The best place to start collecting boxcars is probably the 9800-series refrigerator cars, more familiarly known as "reefers." Only a few cars in this series are really hard to find, and the number of variations is not particularly large. These cars are rather handsome, in addition to being attractively priced; some of the more common cars have recently been sold at "clearance" sales for as little as $15, brand-new in the box! Collectors have not shown as much interest in these cars as they have in the "classic" (or "Famous Name") 9200, 9400 and 9700 boxcar series, so the field is wide open for the beginner. After gaining experience with the toy train marketplace, the collector can then turn to other box and refrigerator car series

---

* *Asterisk found in listings indicates that the information within that listing was derived from Lionel catalogue only.*

R. Kaptur and M. Solly Collections; B. Greenberg photograph

The bullion car is one of Lionel's most unusual boxcars. This is the complete regular production except for the T C A Special car from 1979.
Top shelf: **7515 Denver Mint; 7517 Philadelphia Mint.**
Second shelf: **7518 Carson City Mint; 7522 New Orleans Mint.**
Third shelf: **7530 Dahlonega Mint; 9320 Fort Knox Gold Reserve, the first modern mint car and the hardest one to find.**
Bottom shelf: **9349 San Francisco Mint.**

where the prices are more volatile and the variations more complex.

This Guide divides the boxcar listings into eight major types of cars, and, in the case of the "classic" boxcars, into the important series contained therein:

CATEGORY	PAGE
Bullion Cars	106
Bunk and Tool Cars	107
"Classic" Boxcars	111
Hi-Cube Boxcars	158
O27 Short Boxcars	161
Standard O Boxcars	170
Stock Cars	172
Woodside Boxcars	176

BULLION CARS

In 1979 Fundimensions included a revival of the postwar Fort Knox bullion car in its Southern Pacific Limited Collector set. This fanciful car, rather silly in terms of any real railroad, always had a whimsical charm to it, and its inclusion was one of the reasons why this set sold out so quickly. The car uses the body first developed in the postwar years for the operating aquarium car. The sides of this modified boxcar each have two large clear plastic panels. These are "revealed" by imitation fold-up curtains molded into the car body atop the clear panels. The clear panels are separated in the center of the car by a door resembling a safe with a combination lock. Inside the car, a gold or silver plastic insert simulates stacks of bullion. The roof has a coin slot and the ends of the car have circular ventilation grates. Since the gold or silver inserts can be exchanged, each can be considered a variation with equal value. The Fort Knox and San Francisco cars normally came with gold ingots, and the others with silver; but variations have been reported both ways.

All of the Lionel bullion cars produced in the modern era are equipped with Standard O trucks, except one special Train Collectors Association version, which had Symington-Wayne trucks. All the cars have two operating couplers. Eight have been issued since 1979. Aside from the Fort Knox car and the special T C A car, one car has been issued for each of the real mints of the United States, past and present: San Francisco, Denver, Philadelphia, Carson City, New Orleans and Dahlonega (a Georgia mint used during the Civil War). In the late 1800s, the Carson City mint processed the silver from Nevada's massive Comstock Lode. The issue of the Dahlonega car should mark the end of this series, unless Lionel Trains, Inc. decides to issue cars named after famous banking houses. (The mind boggles a bit at the thought of a Chase-Manhattan bullion car or a Crocker National Bank bullion car!)

Many collectors consider these cars a little silly, but they are so impossibly whimsical that they have an appeal of their own. The Carson City and New Orleans cars seem to be the easiest to find. The Philadelphia, San Francisco, Denver and Dahlonega cars are a notch above these in scarcity, while the Fort Knox and the T C A Special are the hardest to find.

As it turns out, Lionel did have a special train in mind for these cars all along. In 1987 the firm issued a special bronze-painted GG-1 electric locomotive with a matching Pennsylvania N5C caboose. According to the catalogue description, this engine and caboose were meant to accompany the bullion cars. If you really have dreamed of running a "money train," now's your chance.

BULLION CAR LISTINGS

	GD	VG	EXC	MT

7515 DENVER MINT: 1981, bullion car; light gold paint on clear plastic; maroon lettering; stack of silver or gold ingots inside car; coin slot; circular grates in each end; safe molded into car sides; Standard O trucks; "BLT 1-81". — — 75 85 See Factory Error and Prototypes chapter in Volume II, first edition.

7517 PHILADELPHIA MINT: 1982, bullion car; clear plastic body painted burnished bronze; silver lettering; silver or gold bullion inside; coin slot; circular grates at each end; safe molded in car sides; Standard O trucks; "BLT 1-82". From Spring '82 Collector Center. — — 45 55

7518 CARSON CITY MINT: 1983, bullion car; clear plastic body painted black; gold lettering; silver or gold bullion inside car; plastic appears to be thinner and less crisply cast than other bullion cars; coin slot; circular grates in each end; safe molded into car sides; Standard O trucks; "BLT 1-83". — — 35 50

7522 NEW ORLEANS MINT: 1984-85, bullion car; uncatalogued; dark gloss blue body; silver lettering; silver or gold ingots stacked inside car; coin slot; circular grates on each end; safe molded into car sides; Standard O trucks; "BLT 1-84". Offered in 1984 Spring Collector Center brochure, but not made until 1985. — — 35 45

	GD	VG	EXC	MT

7530 DAHLONEGA MINT: 1986, bullion car; uncatalogued; dark pink-orange-painted body; silver lettering; silver or gold bullion load; clear sides; Standard O trucks; "BLT 1-86". Part of 1986 year-end "Stocking Stuffer" package. — — 65 75

9319 TRAIN COLLECTORS ASSOCIATION TWENTY FIFTH ANNIVERSARY: 1979, bullion car; see Volume II, first edition.

9320 FORT KNOX GOLD RESERVE: 1979, bullion car; uncatalogued; clear plastic body painted silver; black lettering; "gold reserve" gold or silver bullion stacks inside; coin slot; circular grates at each end; safe molded into car sides; Standard O trucks; "BLT 1-79". First of the modern era bullion cars. Reissue of postwar 6445; from 1970 Southern Pacific Limited set. This car and set appeared in the 1979 advance catalogue, but not in the regular catalogue because the set was a sell-out. Very hard to find. — 100 175 250

9349 SAN FRANCISCO MINT: 1980, bullion car; dark maroon body; gold lettering; gold or silver ingots stacked inside car; coin slot; circular grates on each end; safe molded into car sides; Standard O trucks; "BLT 1-80"; Type III box with ends marked "9349 Gold Bullion Car". — 7 110 150

BUNK AND TOOL CARS

In 1983 Lionel produced a surprise for collectors in the form of a totally new piece of rolling stock — the bunk car. In the real world of railroading, these cars provided overnight housing to the track gangs working on long-term repair jobs out on the road. Usually, the bunk car was converted from a boxcar, and Lionel has followed the prototype extremely well.

The Lionel bunk car uses the ends, roof and trucks of the woodsided reefer series, but the sides and bottom show Lionel's ingenuity in combining parts from existing series. The side and bottom pieces are unmistakably 9800-series refrigerator car parts which have been heavily modified. The bottom retains the air tanks of the 9800-series, and the wooden scribing on the sides is vertical instead of horizontal, as on the woodsided reefers. Four windows per side, each divided into four panes, have been added. A new insert has been added to the door openings so that the sides are one piece with a much smaller entrance door instead of the plug door of the 9800s. Small square holes cut out of the sides accommodate clear marker lamps next to the doors, while another hole in the roof is provided for a short smokestack. The result of these modifications is a car which is remarkably faithful to its prototype.

So far, quite a few bunk cars have been produced, some as part of limited end-of-year packages or special sets. The first five produced were the gray 5717 Santa Fe, the yellow 5724 Pennsylvania, the dark green 5726 Southern, the olive drab 5727 U. S. Marines and the gray 5735 New York Central. All but the U. S. Marines and New York Central cars came with interior illumination; the Marines car partially compensated for its unlighted status by including a sheet of decals for the owner to customize the car. Each of the lighted cars has a small plastic envelope in its box which contains the detach-

B. Greenberg photo

A selection of the earliest bunk and tool cars.
Top shelf: 5717 A.T.S.F., the first bunk car; 5724 P.R.R.
Second shelf: 5726 Southern.; 5727 U.S. Marines
Third shelf: 5728 Canadian Pacific; 5733 Lionel Lines, a hard-to-find car.
Bottom shelf: 5735 NYC; 5739 Baltimore & Ohio, the first tool car.

able smokestack and two clear marker lights for the car sides. In lighted cars, there is a plastic window insert to diffuse the light. Before 1987 it was rather clear. After that it was a thick white plastic.

Most bunk and tool cars are equipped with the Type V plastic arch bar trucks and two operating couplers. A few have Symington-Wayne trucks, and a few more recent ones have Standard O or ASF strong-arm trucks.

Because these cars are relatively recent, it is somewhat difficult to predict their order of scarcity. However, most collectors feel that the 5726 Southern will become a relatively scarce car, while the 5724 Pennsylvania will be fairly common. At this point, the 5727 U. S. Marines Car is probably the easiest to obtain. The 5735 New York Central Car is also desirable because it was part of a special freight set, the Yard Chief, which was popular with collectors. The recent Railroader Club cars are hard to come by, because they are uncatalogued. And the current Milwaukee Road and Wabash

are certain to be very popular, because they have operating smoke units.

For 1986 Lionel had another surprise in mind. In that year, a B & O freight set was portrayed in the Traditional Catalogue. This set had a new and attractive variation of the bunk car, Lionel's new tool car. Lionel modified the sides of the bunk car by replacing the four square windows with two large rectangular ones. In addition, doors were molded into the car ends, the marker lights and smokestack of the bunk car were eliminated, and the molded ladder was relocated next to the door. In recent years, Lionel has taken to releasing the bunk and tool cars in attractive matching pairs. These have come in handsome A T S F maroon and silver colors for the Work Train Service Station Special set, a pair of Lionel Railroader Club cars, a bright red Jersey Central set, and bright orange Amtrak cars. No doubt many more will follow, because the tool car is an excellent variant of the bunk car and has met with an enthusiastic reception.

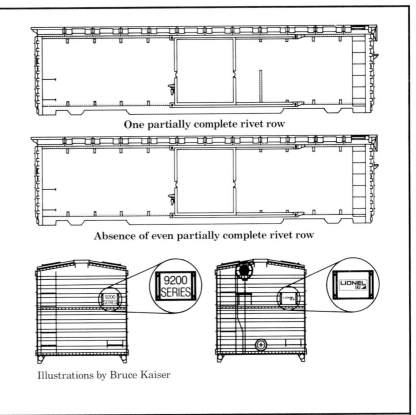

CLASSIC BOXCAR VARIATIONS

Type V Body

One partially complete rivet row
Blank end plates
Metal or plastic door guides at top and bottom

Type VI Body (previously '70 Body)

Absence of even partially complete rivet row
Blank end plates

One partially complete rivet row

Absence of even partially complete rivet row

Illustrations by Bruce Kaiser

Figure 6.1

Classic Boxcar Variations. Illustrations by Bruce Kaiser.

The bunk and tool cars are good additions to a beginner's set, if only because they represent a very creative approach to rolling stock on the part of Lionel. These unusual cars will probably show good appreciation in value.

BUNK AND TOOL CAR LISTINGS

	GD	VG	EXC	MT

5717 A. T. S. F.: 1983, bunk car; gray body; black lettering and number. This was the first in a series of cars original to the Fundimensions line. Basically, it featured heavily modified 9800-series reefer sides and bottom combined with a 5700-series reefer roof and ends; original door opening is made narrower and a smaller, non-opening door is made as part of the car side; four square windows per side are present, each cross-hatched into four smaller sections; holes in the sides for clear plastic marker lights and a hole in the roof for a short black chimney stack (these pieces come in a plastic packet included with the car); translucent plastic window pieces are fitted into the windows from the inside in lighted versions of the car; plastic arch bar trucks. The first production pieces of this car were found with parts missing, broken or haphazardly assembled, but the problem was soon corrected. Fewer of the Santa Fe cars were produced than expected, making this model somewhat scarce. R. LaVoie comment and Collection. — — **40 55**

	GD	VG	EXC	MT

5724 P. R. R.: 1984, (Pennsylvania) bunk car; light yellow-painted gray body; black "P.R.R. / 5724"; black and yellow keystone logo; illuminated with translucent window inserts; plastic arch bar trucks. See 5717 for construction details. R. LaVoie Collection. — — **20 25**

5726 S. R.: 1985, (Southern) bunk car; uncatalogued; dark green-painted gray body; white "S.R. / 5726" below left pair of windows; illuminated with translucent window inserts; plastic arch bar trucks. Advertised in an early 1984 brochure, but not made until 1985. See 5717 for construction details. (R. LaVoie Collection.) — — **30 40**

5727 U. S.: 1984-85, (Marines) bunk car; camouflage-painted olive and yellow-gray plastic body; white lettering; no window inserts; unlighted; plastic arch bar trucks. Came with sheet of decals with U. S. Army and U. S. Marines markings for application to car by purchaser. — — **15 20**

5728 CANADIAN PACIFIC: 1986, bunk car; maroon-painted body; white lettering and script logo; illuminated with translucent window inserts; plastic arch bar trucks. Has a "BLT 1-85" date, but not catalogued or available until 1986. — — **15 20**

5733 LIONEL LINES: 1986, bunk car; uncatalogued; bright orange sides; bright blue roof and ends; new Lionel, Inc. logo applied by decal on side; blue and black lettering; illuminated with translucent window inserts; plastic arch bar trucks. Part of 1986 year-end "Stocking Stuffer" package and somewhat hard to find. — — **40 50**

B. Greenberg photogr

More of Lionel's later bunk and tool cars, now in matching pairs.
Top shelf: 5745 ATSF bunk car and matching 5760 tool car from an uncatalogued Santa Fe Service Station set.
Second shelf: 19652 Jersey Central Lines bunk car with matching 19653 tool car.
Third shelf: 19651 ATSF tool car; 19654 Amtrak bunk car.
Bottom shelf: 19655 Amtrak tool car does not quite match the 19654; 19656 The Milwaukee Road bunk car, the first bunk car with smoke.

	GD	VG	EXC	MT

5735 NEW YORK CENTRAL SYSTEM: 1985-86, bunk car; light gray body; black lettering and NYC oval logo; number over-scored; unlighted; Symington Wayne trucks; one dummy coupler. Part of 1501 Yard Chief Steam Switcher set. Catalogued as illuminated with arch bar trucks and number 6127, but not produced that way. — — **35 45**

5739 BALTIMORE & OHIO: 1986, tool car; modified gray bunk car body; black lettering and logo; centered small doors on sides and ends; two tall eight-pane windows flanking doors on each side; 9800-series reefer bottom piece; not illuminated; Symington-Wayne trucks; one dummy coupler. This was the first tool car produced. Part of set 1652, the B & O Freight. — — **40 50**

5745 A T S F: 1986, bunk car; uncatalogued; red oxide sides; silver-painted roof and ends; yellow lettering and cross logo; number under- and over-scored; not illuminated; Standard O sprung trucks. Part of 1632 Santa Fe Work Train Service Station Special set; matches 5760. — — **40 50**

5760 A. T. S. F.: 1986, tool car; uncatalogued; red oxide sides; silver-painted roof and ends; red oxide doors in ends; yellow lettering and cross logo; not illuminated; Standard O sprung trucks. Part of 1632 Santa Fe Work Train Service Station Special set; matches 5745. — — **40 50**

6127 NEW YORK CENTRAL: See 5735.

16701 SOUTHERN: 1987, tool car; uncatalogued; green sides; black roof and ends; gold Southern lettering and circular logo; unlighted, but has translucent window inserts; Standard O sprung trucks. Part of 11704 Southern Freight Runner Service Station Special set. — — — **45**

16702 AMTRAK*: 1991, bunk car; orange body; light gray roof and ends; black lettering; illuminated; ASF strong-arm trucks. "BLT 1-91". A near duplicate of the 19654 car from 1989. Part of the 11723 Amtrak Maintenance Train set.

— — — **35**

16801 LIONEL RAILROADER CLUB: 1988, bunk car; see Volume II, first edition.

16802 LIONEL RAILROADER CLUB: 1986, tool car; see Volume II, first edition.

GD VG EXC MT

19651 A T & S F: 1987, tool car; medium gray body; black lettering; translucent window and door inserts; illuminated; plastic arch bar trucks. — — — 25

19652 JERSEY CENTRAL LINES: 1988, bunk car; red body; white lettering; number; and Jersey Central logo; illuminated with translucent window inserts; plastic arch bar trucks; matches 19653. — — — 25

19653 JERSEY CENTRAL LINES: 1988, tool car; red body; white lettering, number and Jersey Central logo; illuminated with translucent window inserts; plastic arch bar trucks; matches 19652. — — — 25

19654 AMTRAK: 1989, bunk car; orange body; black lettering; illuminated; translucent window inserts; plastic arch bar trucks; "BLT 1-89 0; matches 19655. — — — 30

19655 AMTRAK: 1990-91, tool car; orange body; gray roof and ends; black lettering; illuminated with translucent window inserts; plastic arch bar trucks; "BLT 1-90". Intended as a match for 19654, but this car is a brighter orange than 19654. — — — 30

19656 THE MILWAUKEE ROAD: 1990, bunk car; orange body; brown roof and ends; black lettering and square Milwaukee Road herald between two right-hand windows; illuminated with translucent window inserts; Standard O sprung trucks (the underside of the car was modified slightly to accept these trucks); "BLT 1-90". First bunk/tool car equipped with smoke. Sprung trucks adapted for power with a snap-on roller pickup and copper ground strip. — — — 60

19657 WABASH: 1991, bunk car. Announced in Lionel's 1991 Book 1 catalogue, but not manufactured. **Not Manufactured**

19658 NORFOLK & WESTERN: 1991, tool car; green sides; white roof, ends and lettering; N & W circle logo on left side; illuminated with translucent window inserts; ASF strong-arm trucks; "BLT 1-91".* — — — 31

THE "CLASSIC" BOXCARS

The term "classic," as used here, refers to the regular-production boxcars from modern era Lionel which trace their heritage to the revered 6464-series boxcars of the postwar era. This category includes the series and groups shown in the accompanying chart.

There are a few "classic"-type boxcars which do not fall into the group number sequences listed above. These cars are listed in correct numerical order within the above-mentioned series. Also, some boxcars listed in this section have operating mechanisms, such as an underbody plunger that opens a side door which causes a man to appear, or the rather complicated mechanisms in the operating milk and ice cars. Many classic boxcars produced for the train clubs are described in the Volume II, first edition.

The body, door and frame variations described below apply to all the classic boxcar series cars listed previously. Some listings will include the reference "9700-style" or "9400-style" boxcar, since these are the predominant groups of classic-style boxcars. As the higher end of Lionel's freight line, nearly every one of the classic boxcars has two operating

6464-series	Carry-overs
7500-series	Anniversary Boxcars
7800-series	Soda Pop Boxcars
9200-series*	Boxcars (1970-1972)
9400-series*	Boxcars (1978-1986)
9620-series	Sports Boxcars
9700-series*	Boxcars (1972-1978)
16600-series	Operating Boxcars (1989-present)
19200-series*	Boxcars (1987-present)
19800-series	Operating Boxcars (1987-present)
19900-series	Special Series (1987-present)
	Toy Fair Boxcars (several number groups)
	Seasons Greetings Boxcars (several number groups)

* Lionel refers to these as its "Famous Name Collector Series."

couplers at each end. There are a very few isolated exceptions, as described in the individual listings.

Body Styles

Six basic body styles — Types V through X — comprise the classic-series of modern era boxcars. Type V features one partially complete, vertical rivet row to the right of the door. The end plates are blank, and it is found with Type I or II door guides (see Figure 6.1). Type VI is identical except for the absence of the partially complete rivet row. The Type VII body has Type I or II door guides, and the end plates are stamped "9200 / SERIES" at one end and "LIONEL" at the other end with the early MPC logo. The Type VIII body is the same as Type VII, but has Type III door guides. The Type IX body, by far the most common and in use since late in 1972, has Type III door guides and a "9700 / SERIES" end plate. A new boxcar body sstyle at last appeared in 1991. Full rivet detail has been restored on the boxcar sides on body style designated as Type X. The first new boxcars to receive this style were the 19228 Cotton Belt and the 19233 Southern Pacific. (Body Types I, II, III and IV refer to postwar production and therefore require no discussion here. However, *Greenberg's Guide to Lionel Trains, 1945-1969, Volume I*, provides a complete rundown on these types.)

Curiously, when Fundimensions changed from the 9700-series to the 9400-series, the firm never changed the end plate. It still reads "9700 / SERIES". Even the five-digit boxcars made by Lionel Trains, Inc. today still carry this end plate — a curious carry-over!

Door Guides

Lionel used three basic types of door guides in its classic boxcars. Type I, a repetition of postwar usage, features metal upper and lower door guides fastened by rivets. The Type II door guide is somewhat less common, representing a brief transition period. This arrangement uses two plastic door guides which simply snap into the rivet holes. The common

Type III door guide has a plastic top guide, and the lower end of the car door has two plastic hook extensions which slide back and forth on a sill molded into the car body.

Frame Types

Since these frames are easily switched, the frame type is not a major factor in determining the car's value. The Type I stamped-metal frame has a concave "bubble" on the bottom center and two holes, no doubt once intended for an operating car's wiring. In the Type II frame, the "bubble" is no longer present, but the two holes are still there. The Type III frame retains the holes, but this time stamped lettering is present: "LIONEL 00-6464-009". This is the original 6464 part number; the body and doors also carry 6464 part numbers, reflecting the ancestry of these cars.

Body Mold Colors

The phrase "body mold" refers to the color of plastic used for the body, whether it is painted or not. In the first five years of its existence, Fundimensions used plastic which came in the form of solid pellets. Since it was hard to control the color of the plastic, some odd combinations sometimes resulted. For example, a car painted brown might have been molded in orange plastic one time, and brown plastic another. To compound matters further, the door might have been molded of an entirely different color than the body. Some time in late 1975 or early 1976, Fundimensions switched to a liquid plastic compound which was much easier to color-control. As a result, boxcars made after 1975 show far fewer variations in body mold and paint. To determine the body mold color, open the car door and look inside the car; the inside surfaces are unpainted. Be mindful that in some cases, the body itself is unpainted plastic. Sometimes the body is found both ways! A typical entry might read: "Tuscan-painted orange body, tuscan-painted gray doors."

A Note on "Automobile" Boxcars

Technically, the two-door automobile boxcars should not be considered "classic" boxcars at all. Although the basic car body and frame are the same, other major differences occur — a wider door opening, metal door guides, and completely different split doors. When Lionel made these cars in the postwar era (2458 and 6468 from 1947-1958), it did not classify them in the regular 6464 series. Modern Lionel, however, numbered them in the 9200-, 9400- and 9700-series. Therefore, they are reluctantly included in this chapter.

These handsome double-door cars are modeled after a prototype used in the 1950s and 1960s to actually transport automobiles — four of them could be loaded on ramps in a standard boxcar with sides modified for a large opening. The Lionel model doors, considerably smaller than scale, enable their use on the 9700 standard body. (Marx made a model closer to the prototype.) Still, the Lionel cars have enjoyed great popularity.

Two surprise newcomers appeared in 1991. These were the 17203 and 17204 scale 50-foot automobile boxcars which

are magnificent, full-length and fully ribbed models of the real thing.

Detail-oriented collectors will be happy to know that the boxcar body used on the earliest Fundimensions production of these cars (the 9701, 9210, 9712, 9719 and 9747) returns some of the vertical rivet detail present on the postwar 6468 versions. In fact, portions of a few rivet rows are missing, meaning the body style used for these five cars is unique from both postwar and modern styles. Starting with the 9764 G T W and since, all the vertical rivet detail has been wiped clean for maximum stamping area.

For the type collectors, here is a list of automobile double-door boxcars created by modern Lionel. They represent an eminently collectable group:

9210	B & O (several versions)
9425	British Columbia Railway
9456	P R R
9460	Detroit, Toledo, Shore Line (L C C A — See Volume II, first edition)
9468	Union Pacific
9701	B & O (several versions) (T C A & L C C A — See Volume II, first edition)
9712	B & O
9719	New Haven
9747	C & O Chessie System
9764	Grand Trunk Western
16623	M K T (Katy) with ETD
17203	Cotton Belt (Standard O)
17204	Missouri Pacific (Standard O)
17882	B & O (L O T S — See Volume II, first edition)
19205	Great Northern
19207	CP Rail
19208	Southern
19213	Spokane, Portland & Seattle
19215	Union Pacific
19230	Frisco
19231	Tennessee, Alabama & Georgia
19232	Rock Island

The B & O Railroad dominates this group (as it did with the postwar pieces). The distinct "AUTOMOBILE" lettering on them lent its name to the car type. Of these, the special 9701 made for T C A and L C C A, and the 17882 L O T S car, are the hardest to find.

Top shelf: 7800 Pepsi; 7801 A&W Root Beer. Both boxcars are from the Soda Pop series.
Bottom shelf: 7802 Canada Dry from the Soda Pop series; 7803 Trains n' Truckin', which was a special dealer bonus.

B. Greenberg photograph

"CLASSIC" BOXCAR LISTINGS

	GD	VG	EXC	MT

0780 LIONEL RAILROADER CLUB: 1982; see Volume II, first edition.

6464-SERIES CARRY-OVERS

6464-1 WESTERN PACIFIC: See Factory Errors and Prototypes chapter in Volume II, first edition.

6464-50 MINNEAPOLIS & ST. LOUIS: See Factory Errors and Prototypes chapter in Volume II, first edition.

6464-500 TIMKEN: 1970, boxcar; uncatalogued; Fundimensions product with postwar number; identifiable by "BLT. 1970/BY LIONEL MPC" to right of doors; "ROLLER FREIGHT"; Roller Freight logo; metal door guides. Made specially for Lionel dealer Glen Uhl of Ohio.
(A) Type V body; yellow body and doors; black lettering; orange, black and white Timken decal logo; postwar die-cast bar-end trucks. Rare — approximately 500 made. G. Halverson comment.
— — — **250**
(B) Same as (A), but light yellow body and door paint.
— — — **200**
(C) Type VI orange-painted body and doors; AAR trucks; approximately 1,300 made. G. Halverson comment.
— — **100** **150**
(D) Same as (C), but postwar die-cast bar-end trucks.
— — **100** **150**
(E) Same as (C), but Type VII body with 9200 number board; extremely rare — about 50 produced. G. Halverson comment.
— — — **450**

6464-1970: 1970, boxcar; T C A Convention; see Volume II, first edition.

6464-1971: 1971, boxcar; T C A Convention; see Volume II, first edition.

6700 PACIFIC FRUIT EXPRESS: 1982-83, operating ice car; modified 9700-style body; orange body with black doors; Type III door guides; black and white UP and SP logos; Standard O

	GD	VG	EXC	MT

trucks; operating hatch and bin cut into roof; "BLT 1-82". Made for 2306 icing station. Price for car only.
— — **50** **65**

7403 L N A C: 1984, L C C A Convention boxcar; see Volume II, first edition.

7404 JERSEY CENTRAL LINES: 1986, boxcar; dark green classic-style body; cream lettering and logo; "PASSENGER EQUIPPED/ON LINE SERVICE"; "CRP"; number under- and over-scored; Standard O trucks; same design as 9787 except for trucks and cream lettering instead of gold. Made to accompany Jersey Central "Miss Liberty" Fairbanks-Morse locomotive and extended vision caboose, but sold separately. Unusual number of this car is attributable to its production late in the Fundimensions/Kenner-Parker period. — — **40** **50**

7500-SERIES ANNIVERSARY BOXCARS

Lionel celebrated its 75th anniversary in 1975 with a set of three reefers, a hopper, three boxcars and an N5C caboose — all given 7500 numbers — headed by a 7500 U36 diesel. The 7502, 7503 and 7507 can be found in the Refrigerator Cars chapter; the 7508 in the Caboose chapter; and the 7504 in the Hopper chapter. Each boxcar, despite its unusual number, is a classic-style with Type IX 9700-type body, and is equipped with Symington-Wayne trucks with two operating couplers.

7501 LIONEL 75TH ANNIVERSARY: 1975-76, 9700-series boxcar; blue body; silver roof and ends; white lettering; full-color logos picturing J. L. Cowen and early Lionel equipment; 75th anniversary circle logo to left of door; Symington-Wayne trucks.
— **10** **15** **20**

7505 LIONEL 75TH ANNIVERSARY: 1975-76, 9700-series boxcar; famous Lionel cars and accessories pictured on sides; black lettering; silver body; red roof and ends; 75th anniversary logo to left of doors; Symington-Wayne trucks.
— **10** **15** **20**

7506 LIONEL 75TH ANNIVERSARY: 1975-76, 9700-series boxcar; famous catalogues pictured on sides in full color; green body; white lettering; gold roof and ends; 75th anniversary circle logo to left; Symington-Wayne trucks. — **10** **15** **20**

Top shelf: 6464-500 Timken, a rare early boxcar made in 1970 especially for Ohio dealer Glenn Uhl.
Middle shelf: 7808 Northern Pacific Pig Palace stock car; 7809 Vernors boxcar from the Soda Pop series.
Bottom shelf: 7810 Orange Crush; 7811 Dr Pepper.

B. Greenberg photos

GD VG EXC MT

7520 NIBCO: 1982, 9700-type boxcar; uncatalogued; special promotion for Nibco Plumbing Products offered as a premium to plumbers, reportedly only 500 made; Type IX body; Type III frame; white body; green doors; green and blue ribbon running across car on both sides of door; blue lettering; gold NIBCO emblem on upper left side; blue "NIBCO/EXPRESS" and "QUALITY PIPING PRODUCTS" to right of door; "BLT 8-82". This car was offered independently of the NIBCO 1264 train set; see 8182 diesel engine entry for further details. Very hard to find.

— — — 545

7525 TOY FAIR: 1986, 9700-series boxcar; uncatalogued; white sides; glossy dark blue roof, ends and door; Lionel circle-L logo; red "A/NEW/TRADITION" and number to right of door; "Welcome to/TOY FAIR/1986" in red to left of door; Symington-Wayne trucks; "BLT 1-86". "Triple T" Collection.

— — 150 175

THE SODA POP SERIES

The 7800 Soda Pop series could have been a very popular set when it was first introduced in 1977, but only six cars were ever produced. Of these cars, which use 9700-style bodies with colorful corporate logos, the Pepsi car is slightly more in demand than the other five. Cars with Sprite, Tab and Fanta logos were included as part of a Coca-Cola set, but they are part of the 9700 series. Each of this six cars in the 7800 Soda Pop series has Symington-Wayne trucks with two operating couplers.

7800 PEPSI: 1976-77, boxcar; from Soda Pop series; white body painted white; red roof and ends; blue doors painted blue; red and blue lettering; "JOIN THE/PEPSI/GENERATION"; Pepsi logo; Type IX body; Type III door guides; Type III frame; Symington-

GD VG EXC MT

Wayne trucks; "BLT 1-76". Announced in a 1976 dealer brochure and catalogued in 1977. — 15 25 45

7801 A & W: 1976-77, boxcar; from Soda Pop Series; white body painted straw-yellow; orange roof and ends; brown and orange lettering; "That frosty mug taste."; white doors painted brown; root beer glass to right of "BLT 1-76"; Type IX body; Type III door guides; Type III frame; Symington-Wayne trucks. Announced in a 1976 dealer brochure and catalogued in 1977.

— 10 15 30

7802 CANADA DRY: 1976-77, boxcar; from Soda Pop Series; green body painted green; gold roof and ends; cream doors painted gold; white and gold lettering; "Ginger Ale"; Canada Dry logo; Type IX body; Type III door guides; Type III frame; Symington-Wayne trucks; "BLT 1-76". Announced in a 1976 dealer brochure and catalogued in 1977. — 10 20 30

7803 TRAINS N' TRUCKIN': 1977, boxcar; white body; gold-painted doors and roof; green and gold lettering; Symington-Wayne trucks. Not part of Soda Pop Series, but numbered within that sequence. This car, created to trumpet Lionel Trains n' Truckin' sets, appeared only in a 1977 accessory brochure as a dealer bonus. C. Rohlfing and R. LaVoie Collections.

10 15 20 35

7806 SEASONS GREETINGS: 1976, 9700-style boxcar; uncatalogued; Type IX body; train and poinsettia in red to right of door; Symington-Wayne trucks; no "BLT" date.

(A) Silver-painted body; green door; red and green lettering. R. P. Bryan Collection. — 60 80 100

(B) Same as (A), but white-painted body; black doors; red lettering. Other variations may exist; reader comments and confirmation requested. R. P. Bryan comment. **NRS**

GD   VG   EXC   MT

7807 TOY FAIR: 1977, 9700-style boxcar; uncatalogued; green body; gold-painted doors, roof and ends; white lettering, "TRAINS 'N TRUCKIN'" on right side of door with white locomotive and truck logos; Type IX body; Symington-Wayne trucks; "BLT 1-77". C. Lang comment.   —   —   150   175

7809 VERNORS: 1977-78, boxcar; from Soda Pop Series; gloss dark green roof, ends and doors; yellow-painted sides; dark green lettering and logos; Symington-Wayne trucks; "BLT 1-77". Announced in a 1977 accessory brochure and catalogued in 1978. C. Rohlfing Collection.   —   10   15   25

7810 CRUSH: 1977-78, boxcar; from Soda Pop Series; orange sides; light green roof and ends; white doors and lettering; green, orange and silver logos; Symington-Wayne trucks; "BLT 1-77". Announced in a 1977 accessory brochure and catalogued in 1978. C. Rohlfing Collection.   —   15   15   25

7811 DR PEPPER: 1977-78, boxcar; from Soda Pop Series; dark maroon body; dark orange-painted roof and ends; white doors and lettering; Dr. Pepper oval logo to right of doors; Symington-Wayne trucks; "BLT 1-77". Announced in a 1977 accessory brochure and catalogued in 1978. C. Rohlfing Collection.   —   10   15   25

THE SEASONS GREETINGS SERIES

Lionel and trains have been associated with the holidays for generations. During the modern era many special cars have been decorated for holiday themes by train clubs and special car manufacturers. The Club Car chapter has more details on most of these pieces.

Lionel began making its own holiday cars in 1973 and 1974 with two regular issue 9700-series boxcars which were overstamped with holiday messages. Only a few hundred of these were made. Lionel may have subcontracted out the overstamping of these cars — it is a bit rough and not up to the company's usual standards. From 1975 through 1978, Lionel itself made dedicated Seasons Greetings boxcars (i.e., decorated, and not overstamped regular issue cars), again in very limited quantities. The cars from these years are very hard to find.

There was no production of Seasons Greetings cars from 1979 to 1984. Lionel made a few hundred special 9490 holiday cars which they handed out to its employees in 1985. This is an exceptionally scarce and expensive car today. Starting in 1986, Lionel made cars for general sale, and these are relatively easy to obtain. The cars, unlike the various styles of cars in the Toy Fair series, have all been classic (9700-series) boxcars. They do not appear in the regular catalogue, but are announced in yearly holiday or "stocking stuffer" packages. Since the Seasons Greetings cars have a wide variety of numbers, we list them all below for the benefit of series collectors:

1973: 9742	Minneapolis & St. Louis boxcar, over-stamped.	
1974: 9713	C P Rail boxcar, overstamped.	
1975: 9778	boxcar	
1976: 7806	boxcar	
1977: 7813	boxcar	
1978: 7814	boxcar	
1979 through 1984: no production		
1985: 9490	boxcar	
1986: 9491	boxcar	
1987: 19903	boxcar	
1988: 19904	boxcar	
1989: 19908	boxcar	
1990: 19910	boxcar	

GD   VG   EXC   MT

7813 SEASONS GREETNGS FROM LIONEL: 1977, 9700-type boxcar; uncatalogued; white body; gold roof and ends; unpainted red doors; red and dark green lettering to left of door; red and dark green toy logos to right of door; Symington-Wayne trucks; no "BLT" date.   —   —   150   175

7814 SEASONS GREETINGS: 1978, 9700-style boxcar; uncatalogued; white body; royal blue doors; red "1978 SEASONS GREETINGS" to left of door; Fundimensions "F" logo in red and blue to right of door; Symington-Wayne trucks; "BLT 1-78".
(A) Dark blue roof and ends.   —   —   175   200
(B) Glossy royal blue roof and ends (same as door).   —   —   175   200

7815 TOY FAIR: 1978, 9700-style boxcar; uncatalogued; silver body; silver doors; red roof and ends; gloss black lettering; "Big Trains/for Small/Hands" and boy with locomotive electrocals to right of door in black; Symington-Wayne trucks; no "BLT" date.   —   —   125   150

7816 TOY FAIR: 1979, 9700-style boxcar; uncatalogued; white body; gold roof and ends; dull gold doors; red and blue lettering; train electrocal to right of door; blue and red Fundimensions "F" to left of door; Symington-Wayne trucks; no "BLT" date.   —   —   125   150

7817 TOY FAIR: 1980, 9700-style boxcar; uncatalogued; white body; red roof and ends; red and blue lettering; red door; blue and red Fundimensions "F" to the left of door; picture of J. L. Cowen to right of door; Symington-Wayne trucks; no "BLT" date. When this car was produced, Lionel stated it was the "last boxcar" in the series, implying the series would end. But Lionel simply switched to reefers in 1981 and back again to boxcars in 1986.   —   —   125   150

THE 9200-SERIES BOXCARS

The 9200-series boxcars were first out of the block when Fundimensions began its production of Lionel trains in 1970. They featured the same construction characteristics as their illustrious 6464 predecessors, along with Fundimensions improvements such as Delrin plastic trucks with fast angle wheels. They were advertised as part of a "Famous Name Collector Series," evidence that Fundimensions had an adult audience in mind for these cars, at least in part. These cars were produced until 1972, when they were superseded by the 9700-series. The "Famous Name" designation for collector boxcars continues for production today.

The type collector will have a comparatively easy time acquiring a representative sample of the 9200 cars, because strictly speaking, there are only 15 cars in the series: numbers 9200 through 9211, 9214, 9215 and 9230. But oh, the variations in these cars! The 9200 Illinois Central, probably the most common, has at least a dozen variations, with more yet to be catalogued. The series makes use of all five body types (yes, there are 9200 boxcars with 9700 end boards!), all three door attachment types, and all three frame types. Sometimes all the body types and all the door types can be found on different samples of the same car number. To

R. Kaptur, R. LaVoie, A. Rudman, and F. Stem Collections; B. Greenberg photograph

The earliest 9200-series boxcars, the first descendants of the great postwar 6464 boxcars.
Top shelf: 9200 Illinois Central, one of at least twelve variations of this car; 9201 Penn Central.
Second shelf: 9202 Santa Fe; 9203 Union Pacific.
Third shelf: 9204 Northern Pacific Railway; 9205 Norfolk and Western.
Bottom shelf: 9206 Great Northern, 9207 Soo Line.

make matters worse, some cars, such as the 9210 B & O automobile double-door boxcar, have had different colors of doors added outside the factory. These are not regarded as legitimate factory pieces, but some collectors are still interested in them.

Most of the 9200-series boxcars come in Type I boxes, but a few of the later ones come in the earliest of the Type II red and white boxes. These are worth looking for, since they represent late production and often indicate a 9200 boxcar with 9700 features. The 9200, 9206, 9209, 9214 and 9230 are known to come in Type II boxes, and no doubt many others do as well.

Unlike the later 9400- and 9700-series, which involve only boxcars, the 9200 numbers do include other types of rolling stock. Some of the listings here include a reference to the "MPC" logo — the black and white diagonal rectangle used as a trademark for the Model Products Corporation. MPC, a division of General Mills, owned Fundimensions (and Lionel) during the 1970-1972 period, so the appearance of its logo on a car dates it precisely to that period. As the 9700-series boxcars took over in 1972-1973, the MPC logo began to disappear. This coincided in time with the Fundimensions/Lionel break as its own division, separate from MPC. All

the early (i.e., non-operating) 9200-series boxcars feature this logo.

Only a few of the 9200 boxcars are truly rare; specific examples are the 9202 Santa Fe in orange with black lettering, and the pre-production 9207 Soo Line in 9700 white and black colors. The orange and black 9202 has a particularly fascinating story. The assembly line workers had to clear a small quantity of orange plastic from the molds before they began production of the red 9202. Enough plastic remained to make about 65 "shots," as trial moldings are called. Normally, these "shots" are discarded, but this time some of the workers added detail to them. Eventually, these cars made their way into the collector mainstream, becoming the single most rare Fundimensions boxcar to date. (A letter from Lee Jones to Frank Hare tells the story of this car a little differently. According to Jones, the orange 9202 was deliberately made in its small quantity to supply gifts to executives and friends of the management at the time.) The same thing happened to the two dozen or so pre-production samples of the 9207 Soo Line cars. In recent years, Lionel's management has been very careful not to

Later 9200-series production.

Top shelf: **9208** C P Rail; **9209** Burlington Northern.

Second shelf: **9210** Baltimore & Ohio double-door automobile car; **9211** Penn Central.

Third shelf: **9214** Northern Pacific Railway; **9215** Norfolk and Western.

Bottom shelf: **9217** Soo Line operating boxcar with worker that moves forward as door opens; **9218** Monon operating boxcar with worker that tosses magnetic mail sack out of door.

let odd production slip past the assembly line, but now and then peculiar lots still emerge.

Only a few 9200-series cars came in sets, because in the early 1970s Lionel was not as serious about "Collector" line sets as it was later. So for the most part, these cars were offered only for separate-sale. One notable exception is the rare 1971 Service Station Special set 1187, which included no less than five of the 9200-series cars.

Some of the 9200 boxcars are harder to find than others, of course, but good stocks of new cars with their boxes can be found rather easily. As the first of the new Fundimensions line, the 9200-series cars are eminently collectable.

9200 ILLINOIS CENTRAL: 1970-72, boxcar; several body types; black and white lettering; "MAIN LINE OF MID-AMERICA" and "HYDRAULIC UNDERFRAME"; "BLT 1-70". This is the only boxcar produced since 1970 with body Types V through IV, all three door guide types, and all three frames! It also is found with several truck and uncoupler armature varieties. We expect several more variations of this car to surface eventually.

	GD	VG	EXC	MT

(A) Orange-painted Type V orange body and doors; "IC" spread out; deep heat-stamped lettering; metal door guides; plastic AAR trucks with bar set in uncoupler discs; MPC logo to left of fourth bottom rivet. G. Halverson Collection. **10 15 25 35**

(B) Same as (A), but Type VI body; "IC" tightly spaced. G. Halverson Collection. **8 10 20 30**

(C) Type VI body; metal door guides; flat orange-painted orange body and doors; plastic AAR trucks; Type I frame; "IC" spread out. **8 10 20 30**

(D) Dull orange-painted Type VI body; orange-painted orange doors (brighter than body paint); "IC" spread out; metal door guides; Symington-Wayne trucks; wheel axles blackened. G. Halverson Collection. **8 10 20 30**

(E) Orange-painted orange plastic Type VI body and doors; "IC" spread out; two plastic door guides; MPC logo atop fourth bottom rivet; Symington-Wayne trucks with black uncoupler discs. G. Halverson and R. LaVoie Collections. **10 15 25 35**

	GD	VG	EXC	MT

(F) Type VII body; metal door guides; glossy orange-painted orange body and doors; plastic AAR trucks; Type I frame; "IC" tightly spaced. — 8 10 20 30

(G) Same as (F), but plastic door guides. — 8 10 20 30

(H) Same as (F), but plastic door guides; Symington-Wayne trucks; "IC" spread out. — 8 10 20 30

(I) Same as (F), but dull dark orange-painted orange body; "IC" spread out. — 8 10 20 30

(J) Type VIII body; flat orange-painted gray body and doors; Symington-Wayne trucks; Type II frame; "IC" spread out. — 8 10 15 20

(K) Same as (I), but Type IX body. — 10 15 25 35

(L) Type IX body; glossy orange-painted orange body; flat orange-painted gray doors; Symington-Wayne trucks; Type II frame; "IC" spread out; came in Type II box; also found with Type III frame. R. LaVoie Collection. — 10 15 25 35

(M) Unpainted orange Type VII body; Type II door guides; postwar bar-end trucks with plastic knuckles; Type I box. Reader comments requested. J. Porter Collection. — **NRS**

See also *Factory Errors and Prototypes* chapter in Volume II, first edition.

9201 PENN CENTRAL: 1970-71, boxcar; Type VI body; metal door guides; white lettering; Type I frame; plastic AAR trucks; "1-70"; MPC logo.

(A) Jade green-painted jade green plastic body and doors. — 12 15 20 30

(B) Dark green-painted dark green plastic body and doors. — 12 15 30 35

9202 SANTA FE: 1970-71, boxcar; Type VI body; metal door guides; Type I frame; all have red-painted red bodies and white lettering; "DF...with...SHOCK/CONTROL" and "FLOATING UNDERFRAME GIVES FREIGHT A SMOOTHER ROLL"; plastic AAR trucks; no "BLT" date; MPC logo. Reissue of postwar 6464-700, except for door color. Variations exist as to the number of white dots to the left of the door.

(A) Silver-painted gray doors. — 12 20 30 40

(B) Same as (A), but only two white dots to left of doors. — 20 30 40 75

(C) Gray-painted gray doors. — 20 30 40 55

(D) Same as (A), but plastic Type II door guides; one side of car has two white dots to left of door, the other side has three. C. Letterese Collection. — **NRS**

See *Factory Errors and Prototypes* chapter in Volume II, first edition.

9203 UNION PACIFIC: 1970-71, boxcar; Type V body; metal door guides; yellow-painted yellow doors; blue lettering; red-, blue-and white-striped U P shield to right of doors; Type I frame; MPC logo; plastic AAR trucks; "BLT 1-70". Factory prototypes of this car exist without the U P shield decal; in other cases it has peeled.

(A) Yellow-painted yellow body. — 15 20 35 45

(B) Light yellow-painted light yellow body. — 15 20 35 40

See *Factory Errors and Prototypes* chapter in Volume II, first edition.

9204 NORTHERN PACIFIC RAILWAY: 1970-71, boxcar; white and black-outlined letters; Type I frame; plastic AAR trucks except as noted; "BLT 1-70", except for (D); MPC logo.

(A) Type VI body; dark green-painted dark green body and shiny green doors; metal door guides; dark red Monad logo insert. — 10 22 30 35

(B) Green-painted Type VI green body; bright lime green unpainted doors; metal door guides; plastic AAR trucks with bar in uncoupler discs. G. Halverson Collection. — 10 22 30 35

(C) Same as (A), but light red logo insert. — 10 22 30 35

(D) Type VII body; apple green-painted apple green body and doors; no "BLT" date; metal door guides. — 10 17 28 35

(E) Same as (D), but plastic door guides and Symington-Wayne trucks. — 10 17 28 35

(F) Same as (C), but body is painted same green color as 9209 Burlington Northern boxcar. C. Lang Collection. — 10 22 30 35

9205 NORFOLK AND WESTERN: 1970-71, boxcar; Type VI body; metal door guides; white lettering; Type I frame; plastic AAR trucks except as noted; "BLT 1-70"; MPC logo.

(A) Dark blue-painted dark blue body; navy blue doors. — 10 15 20 25

(B) Same as (A), but Symington-Wayne trucks. — 10 15 20 25

(C) Medium blue-painted medium blue body; navy blue doors. — 10 15 20 25

(D) Royal (reddish) blue-painted royal blue body and doors. G. Halverson and R. LaVoie Collections. — 12 20 25 35

(E) Same as (A), but postwar bar-end trucks with plastic knuckles. Reader comments requested. J. Porter Collection. — 10 15 20 25

9206 GREAT NORTHERN: 1970-71, boxcar; white lettering; metal door guides; Type I frame; plastic AAR trucks except as noted; "BLT 1-70"; MPC logo.

(A) Type VI body; light blue-painted body and doors. — 10 15 20 25

(B) Type VII body; paler blue-painted paler blue body; light blue doors. — 10 15 20 25

(C) Type VII body; palest blue-painted palest blue body; light blue doors; Symington-Wayne trucks; Type II box. — 10 15 20 25

9207 SOO LINE: 1971, boxcar; Type VII body; Type I frame; white lettering; number under- and over-scored; "BLT 1-71"; MPC logo.

(A) Red-painted red body and red doors; plastic AAR trucks; metal door guides. — 10 15 20 25

(B) Flat red-painted red body and doors; Symington-Wayne trucks; metal door guides. — 10 15 20 25

(C) Shiny red-painted red body and doors; white lettering; Symington-Wayne trucks; plastic door guides. — 10 15 20 25

See also *Factory Errors and Prototypes* chapter in Volume II, first edition.

9208 C P RAIL: 1971-72, boxcar; Type VII body; black lettering; black and white Pac-man logo; Type I frame; "BLT 1-71"; MPC logo. One sample observed came in Type I box dated 2/71. T. Rollo comment.

(A) Medium yellow-painted medium yellow body and doors; metal door guides; Symington-Wayne trucks. — 10 15 20 25

(B) Light yellow-painted light yellow body and doors; metal door guides; Symington-Wayne trucks. — 10 15 20 25

(C) Light yellow-painted light yellow body; light yellow-painted medium yellow doors; plastic door guides; AAR trucks. — 10 15 20 25

	GD	VG	EXC	MT

(D) Dark yellow-painted dark yellow body; dark yellow-painted medium yellow doors; plastic AAR trucks; plastic door guide.

| | 10 | 15 | 20 | 25 |

(E) Same as (D), but Symington-Wayne trucks; Type II frame. C. Rohlfing Collection.

| | 10 | 15 | 20 | 25 |

9209 BURLINGTON NORTHERN: 1971-72, boxcar; Type I frame; white lettering; large "BN" logo to right; "BLT 1-71"; MPC logo.

(A) Type VII body; apple green-painted apple green body; dark green-painted dark green doors; plastic AAR trucks; metal door guides.

| | 10 | 15 | 20 | 25 |

(B) Type VII body; dark green-painted dark green body and doors; metal door guides; Symington-Wayne trucks.

| | 10 | 15 | 20 | 25 |

(C) Same as (B), but Type VIII body. 10 15 20 25

(D) Same as (B), but Type IX body and Type III door guides; Type II box.

| | 15 | 20 | 25 | 40 |

(E) Same as (B), but plastic door guides.

| | 10 | 15 | 20 | 25 |

(F) Same as (A), but Type VII body and plastic door guides. Knopf Collection.

| | 10 | 15 | 20 | 25 |

9210 BALTIMORE AND OHIO: 1971-72, double-door automobile boxcar; 6468-type body; metal door guides; Type I frame; number under- and over-scored; white lettering; "AUTOMOBILE"; all doors with different colors added outside the factory (only the black door is authentic factory production, but the other varieties are listed here because there is considerable collector interest in them); all Symington-Wayne trucks except version (A); MPC logo. The first of the modern era double-door automobile boxcars.

(A) Black-painted black body and doors; plastic AAR trucks.

| | 10 | 12 | 20 | 30 |

(B) Same body as (A), but navy blue-painted blue doors (as on the 9771 N & W). C. Lang Collection. 8 10 15 20

(C) Same body as (A), but jade green-painted green doors (as on the 9749 P C). C. Lang Collection. 8 10 15 20

(D) Same body as (A), but orange-painted orange doors (as on the 9200 I C). C. Lang Collection. 8 10 15 20

(E) Same body as (A), but burnt-orange-painted orange doors (as on the 9703 C P Rail). C. Lang Collection. 8 10 15 20

(F) Same body as (A), but turquoise-painted turquoise doors. 8 10 15 20

(G) Unpainted black body and doors; Symington-Wayne Type IIA trucks; plastic wheels; Type I box. J. Porter Collection. 10 12 20 25

9211 PENN CENTRAL: 1971-72, boxcar; Type VII body, except for (A); silver-painted gray doors; white lettering (pattern similar to 9201); MPC logo; Type I frame; "2-11".

(A) Jade green-painted Type VI jade green body; plastic AAR trucks; metal door guides; 1000 made. 15 20 30 35

(B) Jade green-painted jade green body; Symington-Wayne trucks; metal door guides. 12 15 20 25

(C) Pale green-painted pale green body; plastic AAR trucks; metal door guides. 12 15 20 25

(D) Medium green-painted medium green body; plastic AAR trucks; metal door guides. 12 15 20 25

(E) Same as (D), but plastic door guides. 12 15 20 25

(F) Same as (D), but Symington-Wayne trucks. 12 15 20 25

(G) Dark green-painted dark green body; Symington-Wayne trucks; plastic door guides. 12 15 20 25

(H) Same as (A), but postwar die-cast bar-end trucks with plastic knuckles; Type I box. Reader comments requested. J. Porter Collection. 12 15 20 25

9214 NORTHERN PACIFIC RAILWAY: 1971-72, boxcar; Type VII maroon plastic body except for (D); white- and black-outlined lettering (pattern similar to 9204); Type I frame; metal door guides; red oxide-painted maroon doors; "BLT 2- 71"; MPC logo.

(A) Flat red oxide-painted body; Symington-Wayne trucks. 10 12 20 25

(B) Red oxide-painted body; plastic AAR trucks. 10 12 20 25

(C) Red oxide-painted Type VII body and doors; two plastic door guides; Symington-Wayne trucks; black uncoupler discs. G. Halverson Collection. 10 20 30 40

(D) Red oxide-painted Type IX tuscan body; tuscan-painted tuscan doors; Symington-Wayne trucks; Type II frame; Type II box. R. LaVoie Collection. 10 20 30 40

9215 NORFOLK AND WESTERN: 1971-72, boxcar; Type VII body; silver-painted gray doors; white lettering (pattern similar to 9207); Type I frame; "BLT 2-71"; MPC logo.

(A) Royal blue-painted royal blue Type VI plastic body; plastic door guides; plastic AAR trucks; 1000 manufactured; very hard to find. 15 20 30 35

(B) Dark blue-painted dark blue body; metal door guides; Symington-Wayne trucks. 10 15 20 25

(C) Same as (B), except plastic door guides. 10 15 20 25

(D) Same as (B), except plastic door guides and AAR trucks. 10 15 20 25

(E) Same as (A), but postwar bar-end trucks with plastic knuckles; Type I box. Reader comments requested. J. Porter Collection. 10 15 20 25

Operating Boxcars

In 1972, amid much fanfare, Fundimensions began the production of a car which has defied obsolescence; it did not vanish from the catalogues until 1985. This was the 9301 operating Post Office car, in which the press of a button opens the car door and activates a little man who tosses a mail sack out the door. This car had no company until as late as 1982, when the 9218 Monon mail delivery car joined it in the Fundimensions line-up. Since that year, other operating boxcars modeled after the old postwar 3484-94 cars have been revived.

Most appeared in the higher 9200-series, since they were made with classic boxcar bodies. The operating man comes either plain (as on the 9217, 9219, 9223 and 9228) or with a mail sack attached to him via a magnet (on the 9218, 9229 and 9301). Depending on the magnet's strength, it sometimes takes a good voltage to dislodge the mail sack from the man!

New versions of the operating ice and milk cars were issued in the late 1980s in the 19800-series. The operating boxcars have become welcome additions to the Lionel train consist because they add animation to an operator's layout. Many of these cars are still priced very reasonably, and no collection is really complete without a few of them.

Some wonderful operating cars.

Top shelf: 9219 Missouri Pacific Lines; 9223 Reading Lines. Both are operating boxcars with a gray man.
Second shelf: 9228 Canadian Pacific; 9229 Express Mail. Both are operating boxcars with a gray man.
Third shelf: 9230 Monon; 9280 A.T.S.F. short-body horse transport stock car.
Bottom shelf: 9301 United States Mail Railway, perhaps the longest running Lionel boxcar; 9308 Traveling Aquarium, a very unusual operating car.
  Compare the body to the bullion cars.

R. Kaptur, R. LaVoie, A. Rudman, and F. Stem Collections; B. Greenberg photograph

GD VG EXC MT

9217 SOO LINE: 1982-84, operating boxcar; brownish-maroon-painted body; white lettering; number under- and over-scored; Standard O trucks. When activated, plunger opens door, worker moves towards door. Reissue of postwar 3494-625 from 1957. — — **15 25**

9218 MONON: 1981-82, operating mail delivery boxcar; tuscan body; white stripe across top of car and door with maroon lettering, "THE HOOSIER LINE"; white lettering elsewhere; number under- and over-scored; Standard O trucks. When activated, plunger opens door, worker tosses mail sack out of door. This car was also sold at a lesser price by removing the plunger mechanism and figure, and replacing the trucks with plastic Symington-Waynes. Reissue of postwar 3494-550. C. Lang comment. C. Lang Collection. — — **15 25**

9219 MISSOURI PACIFIC LINES: 1983, operating boxcar; blue sides with gray stripe; gray ends and roof; black and white lettering; "Eagle" in script; "MERCHANDISE/SERVICE"; Standard O trucks; "BLT 1-83". When activated, plunger opens door, worker moves toward door; figure can be blue or gray. Reissue of

3494-150 MP from 1956, except 9219 does not have "XME" lettering found on the 3494-150 at the lower right. (J. Kroll comment.) This car was also sold at a lesser price by removing the plunger mechanism and figure, and replacing the trucks with plastic Symington-Waynes. C. Lang comment and Collection. — — **25 35**

9223 READING LINES: 1984-85, operating boxcar; tuscan-painted body and doors; white "READING" lettering; number under- and over-scored; black and white diamond-shaped Reading Lines logo; gray man appears when plunger is actuated to open car door; Standard O trucks. — — **25 30**

9228 CANADIAN PACIFIC: 1986, operating boxcar; silver-painted sides; black-painted roof and ends; red lettering and Canadian Pacific "beaver" logo; number under- and over-scored; Standard O trucks. When actuated, plunger opens door, gray man appears. This has been a poor-selling car in the U.S. with stock still available at a number of dealers. C. Lang comment. — — **20 30**

	GD	VG	EXC	MT

9229 EXPRESS MAIL: 1985-86, operating boxcar; dark blue sides and doors; orange ends and roof; white lettering and US Mail logo; "NEXT DAY SERVICE"; white and yellow-orange Express Mail logo; Symington-Wayne trucks; one dummy coupler; "BLT 1-85". Gray man tosses out mail sack when door opens by plunger action. **— — 25 35**

9230 MONON: 1971-72, boxcar; uncatalogued; Type VII body (A)-(D); Type IX body (E)-(F); white lettering; number under- and over-scored; Symington-Wayne trucks; "BLT 1-72"; MPC logo. One sample had box dated 2/70. (T. Rollo comment.) This car was available in one of many versions of set 1187, the 1971 Illinois Central Service Station Special set. It was also listed on dealer order forms for 1972, but was never catalogued. Note: this is not an operating boxcar, but is listed here in the numerical sequence of the 9200-series.
(A) Tuscan-painted maroon body; red oxide-painted maroon doors; Type I frame; metal door guides. **8 10 12 15**
(B) Same as (A), but red oxide-painted red oxide body. **10 12 15 20**
(C) Same as (A), but Type VII postwar bar-end metal trucks which appear to be original with car. Probable early production. J. Aleshire Collection. **NRS**
(D) Flat red oxide-painted flat red oxide body; red oxide-painted maroon doors; Type I frame; plastic door guides. **10 12 15 20**
(E) Tuscan-painted tuscan body; tuscan-painted tuscan doors; Type I frame. **10 12 15 20**
(F) Same as (E), but Type II frame; came in Type II box. **10 12 15 20**

9237 UNITED PARCEL SERVICE: 1984, operating boxcar; dark brown body; white U P S logo and lettering; plunger opens door and gray man advances to door opening. Pictured in 1984 Traditional catalogue, but never produced because at the last moment, after the prototypes had been made, United Parcel Service withdrew its permission to make the car. Two prototypes with decals, both painted flat medium brown, are in the collection of Richard Kughn, owner of Lionel Trains, Inc., since 1986. **Not Manufactured**

9301 UNITED STATES MAIL RAILWAY: 1973-84, operating boxcar; red-, white- and blue-painted red plastic body and doors; white and black lettering; "POST OFFICE"; Type IX body mold; Type I frame; single door guides; "LIONEL" on left; Symington-Wayne trucks. Gray man tosses mail sack when door is opened by plunger. Reissue of postwar 3428 from 1959.
(A) Dark blue paint; MPC plate. **10 15 20 30**
(B) Light blue paint with darker blue doors; MPC plate. **10 15 20 30**
(C) Medium blue paint; no MPC plate. **10 15 20 30**
(D) Light blue paint; no MPC plate. **10 15 20 30**
See Volume II, first edition.

9308 TRAVELING AQUARIUM: 1981-84, green-painted clear plastic body; gold lettering; windows with fish tanks; two bayonet-based bulbs inside car for illumination; vibrator motor turns two spools with film attached which is painted with fish; turning action makes fish appear to swim through car; Symington-Wayne trucks. Although not a "classic" boxcar, this one-of-a-kind car resembles nothing else in the Lionel line. Reissue of 3435 from 1959-62. T. Ladny Collection. **— — 75 85**

See also Factory Errors and Prototypes chapter in Volume II, first edition.

THE 9400-SERIES BOXCARS

Though lower numerically, the 9400-series boxcars were produced later than the 9700-series. Fundimensions began the 9400-series in 1978 with a tuscan 9400 Conrail boxcar. The 9400-series cars are identical in construction techniques (all have Type IX bodies) to their 9700 predecessors, even to the extent that all the 9400-series cars still have 9700-series end plates! Not one is labeled 9400 on the endplate. However, there are two very important differences between the 9400-series and the 9700-series, one of which makes it very difficult to collect the whole series.

One major difference between the 9400s and the 9700s is the presence of many color schemes of short-line railroads, in contrast to the almost exclusive modeling of Class I railroads within the 9700-series, including many "old standard" reissues of postwar favorites from the 6464-series. In the 9400-series, the collector will find cars modeled after the Minneapolis, Northfield and Southern, the New Hope and Ivyland, the Chattahoochee Industrial Railroad and the Napierville Junction Railroad — all of which are short-line, local railroads. This represents the real world rather well because of the increased number of these railroads in recent years. Many of the paint schemes are very colorful and attractive to operators as well.

The other difference is much more significant to collectors. A large number of the 9400-series boxcars are special issues which can only be found in collector sets or as special package issues produced in extremely limited quantities. For this reason, many of the 9400-series cars command high prices, and this makes the series less feasible for a beginning collector than the 9700-series would be. It is also significant that far fewer variations of these cars have turned up; essentially, this means that Lionel had standardized its plastics and paints much more than for the early 9700 boxcars. It also means that many of the 9400-series boxcars have had only one production run. A look at the catalogues tends to confirm this supposition. In the earlier Fundimensions years, a 9700 boxcar might run through three years in the catalogues. The 9400 boxcars, on the other hand, were only catalogued for one year — if they were catalogued at all. Therefore, we are seeing more variety with less production — almost a guarantee of future scarcity. With some of the cars, the future is now!

It is not unusual for a 9400-series boxcar out of a collector set to double or even triple in value before it even hits the toy train marketplace. That makes collecting the 9400-series a difficult proposition. Some marketing ploys between series have annoyed collectors quite a bit. For example, in 1978 Fundimensions produced its Great Plains Express with a 9729 C P Rail boxcar available only in that set. Since it was not sold separately, the collector of 9700 boxcars had to purchase the set to get the boxcar. In the next year, Fundimensions marketed the set again, but this time it had a 9417 C P Rail boxcar identical to its 9729 predecessor except for the number and gold lettering. The collector who wanted complete numbers for both series had to buy the Great Plains Express set all over again to get the 9417 boxcar! Neither Fundimensions nor its successors have made this mistake since, but the severe restriction of some cars in the 9400-series to limited sets has angered some collectors.

One interesting graphics characteristic of the 9400-series is that it witnessed the first large-scale applications of the new "electrocal" decorating process by Lionel. The scheme uses an electrothermal procedure to impress intricately detailed decals onto the car bodies. It enables more complicated decorating than the usual heat-stamp or Tampo techniques, and avoids the peel-off problems of normal decals. The heating affects the surface of the car,

The first of Lionel's excellent 9400-series boxcars.
Top shelf: **9400** Conrail; **9401** Great Northern.
Second shelf: **9402** Susquehanna; **9403** Seaboard Coast Line.
Third shelf: **9404** Nickel Plate Road; **9405** Chattahoochee Industrial Railroad.
Bottom shelf: **9406** Rio Grande; **9407** Union Pacific Livestock Dispatch stock car.

R. Kaptur, R. LaVoie, A. Rudman, and F. Stem Collections; B. Greenberg photogra

	GD	VG	EXC	MT

however, especially on dark-colored paint. It leaves an outline of flat paint around the decal where the glossy sheen of the paint was removed. This will even be found on brand-new cars.

The 9400-series concluded in 1986 with the production of the 9492 Lionel Lines boxcar, the highest number in the series. The new 19200-series was introduced in 1987. It is somewhat early to predict the relative scarcity of the whole 9400-series, but the extensive use of special issues would indicate that these will get collector attention at the expense of the regular issues.

9400 CONRAIL: 1978, boxcar; white lettering; Type IX body mold; Type III door guides; Type III frame; Symington-Wayne trucks; "BLT 1-78".
(A) Tuscan-painted tuscan plastic body and doors.

8   10   15   20

(B) Same as (A), but brown-painted brown body and doors.

8   10   15   20

See Volume II, first edition.

9401 GREAT NORTHERN: 1978, boxcar; pale green- (or aqua) painted pale green plastic body and doors; black and white lettering (the white lettering can be difficult to see); red, white and

black goat logo at left; Type IX body mold; Type III door guides; Type III frame; Symington-Wayne trucks; "BLT 1-78".

6   8   15   20

9402 SUSQUEHANNA: 1978, boxcar; forest green-painted green plastic body and doors; gold lettering; red, gold and gray "SHIP/WITH/SUSIE-Q" logo to right of door; "LIONEL" and "BLT 1-78" to left of door; Type IX body mold; Type III door guides; Type III frame; Symington-Wayne trucks. 10 15 30 35

9403 SEABOARD COAST LINE: 1978, boxcar; black-painted black plastic body and doors; pale yellow lettering; "SMOOTH/CUSHIONED/LOAD"; Type IX body mold; Type III door guides; Type III frame; Symington-Wayne trucks; "BLT 1-78".
(A) Yellow lettering. 8 10 15 20
(B) Extremely bold yellow lettering. 10 15 20 25
(C) Shiny white lettering; scarce. At least one observed sample has had its lettering chemically altered from yellow to white. We do not know if this caution applies to all such pieces. C. Weber comment. **NRS**

More from the 9400-series. All were catalogued in only one year.
Top shelf: 9408 Lionel Lines Circus Car stock car; 9411 Lackawanna.
Second shelf: 9412 Richmond Fredericksburg Potomac; 9413 Napierville Junction Railway.
Third shelf: 9414 Cottom Belt; 9415 Providence & Worcester Railroad.
Bottom shelf: 9416 M D & W; 9417 C P Rail.

R. Kaptur Collection; B. Greenberg photograph

	GD	VG	EXC	MT

9404 NICKEL PLATE ROAD: 1978, boxcar; maroon-painted maroon sides and doors; silver roof, ends and stripe which runs through doors; black and white lettering; "Nickel Plate High Speed Service" in script; Type IX body mold; Type III door guides; Type III frame; Symington-Wayne trucks; "BLT 1-78".
10   12   30   40

9405 CHATTAHOOCHEE INDUSTRIAL RAILROAD: 1978-79, boxcar; silver-painted gray plastic body and doors; orange and black lettering; "BETTER BY A DAM SITE"; Type IX body mold; Type III door guides; Type III frame; Symington-Wayne trucks; "BLT 1-78". Pictured in 1979 advanced catalogue, but not in regular catalogue.
4   6   15   20

9406 RIO GRANDE: 1978-79, boxcar; white-painted white plastic sides; brown roof and ends; brown-painted brown plastic doors; black "INSULATED", BAKERY GOODS" and "D & R G W" lettering; "Cookie Box" in red script; Type IX body mold; Type III door guides; Type III frame; Symington-Wayne trucks; "BLT 1-78". Pictured in 1979 advance catalogue, but not in regular catalogue.
3   5   15   20

9411 LACKAWANNA: 1978, boxcar; tuscan-painted tuscan plastic body and doors; white lettering; number under- and over-scored; "The Route/of/PHOEBE SNOW" script to right of doors; Type IX body mold; Type III doors guides; Type III frame; Standard O trucks; "BLT 1-78". Available only in 1867 Milwaukee Limited set.
20   30   50   60

9412 RICHMOND FREDERICKSBURG POTOMAC: 1979, boxcar; blue-painted body; silver-painted doors; white lettering and Virginia map logo; "Llinking/NORTH/and/SOUTH"; Symington-Wayne trucks; "BLT 1-79". C. Rohlfing and G. Rogers Collections.
7   9   12   18

9413 NAPIERVILLE JUNCTION RAILWAY: 1979, boxcar; yellow-painted sides; red-painted roof and ends; black lettering; red and yellow N J maple leaf logo at right; Symington-Wayne trucks; "BLT 1-79".
(A) Red leaf logo, same red as roof and ends. R. Vagner Collection.
6   8   10   15
(B) Light red leaf logo, different red from roof and ends. C. Rohlfing and R. Vagner Collections. 8   10   15   20

Top shelf: **9418** Famous American Railroad; 9419 Union Pacific.
Second shelf: **9420** Baltimore & Ohio; 9421 Maine Central Modern Efficient Cushioning.
Third shelf: **9422** Elgin Joliet & Eastern; 9423 The New York, New Haven and Hartford Railroad Co.
Bottom shelf: **9425** British Columbia Railway; 9426 Chesapeake & Ohio.

R. Kaptur Collection; B. Greenberg photograp[h]

	GD	VG	EXC	MT

9414 COTTON BELT: 1979, boxcar; tuscan body; white lettering; blue and white lightning streak logo; Symington-Wayne trucks; "BLT 1-79". This car has been repainted and overstamped by the thousands for special train club cars.

	4	6	15	20

See Volume II, first edition.

9415 PROVIDENCE & WORCESTER RAILROAD: 1979, boxcar; red-painted body; white and black lettering; "WORCESTER" spelled incorrectly on many boxes; large red, white and black P W logo to left; Symington-Wayne trucks; "BLT 1-79".

	4	6	10	15

See Volume II, first edition.

9416 M D & W: 1979, 1981, (Minnesota, Dakota & Western) boxcar; white sides; green-painted roof and ends; green doors; green and black lettering; large green pine tree logo; Symington-Wayne trucks; "BLT 1-79". Catalogued in 1979 and 1981, but not in 1980, although it was certainly available that year.

	4	6	10	15

9417 C P RAIL: 1979, boxcar; black body; white and red Pacman logo; gold lettering; Symington-Wayne trucks; "BLT 1-79".

From the second version of the 1860 Great Plains Express set. This car was shown in the 1979 catalogue, but it did not become part of the set until 1980, when it replaced the 9729 car identical except for number and white lettering. This car is considered somewhat more scarce and valuable than the 9729. C. Lang comment.

	—	25	35	45

9418 LIONEL SALUTES AMERICA'S FAMOUS HISTORIC RAILROADS: 1979, boxcar; uncatalogued: Famous American Railroad Series railroad emblem car with markings of Southern, Santa Fe, Great Northern, Union Pacific and Pennsylvania Railroads — the five railroads Lionel commemorated in its Famous American Railroad Series sets; FARR Series 1 diamond insignia; gold-painted body; red roof and ends; orange, white and black lettering; Symington-Wayne trucks. Came as a separate-sale item in year-end package. C. Rohlfing Collection.

	—	60	75	90

9419 UNION PACIFIC: 1980, boxcar; tuscan sides; black roof and ends; black doors; white "SHIP & TRAVEL/THE/AUTOMATED/RAILWAY" lettering; red, white and blue U P shield; gold FARR Series 2 diamond insignia; Symington-Wayne trucks; "BLT 1-80". Part of Famous American

R. Kaptur, A. Rudman, and F. Stem Collections; B. Greenberg photograph

The Cowen Commemorative Set is shown on the bottom three shelves, issued to celebrate Joshua Cowen's 100th birthday. The last three cars in the sequence are very hard to find.
Top shelf: 9427 The Bay Line.
Second shelf: 9429 The Early Years; 9430 Standard Gauge Years.
Third shelf: 9431 Pre War Years; 9432 Post War Years.
Bottom shelf: 9433 Golden Years; 9434 Joshua Lionel Cowen — The Man.

	GD	VG	EXC	MT

Railroad Series No. 2, but like all components of the FARR Series sets, sold separately. — — 25 35

9420 BALTIMORE & OHIO: 1980, boxcar; silver body with dark blue stripe at bottom; blue lettering "Sentinel/FAST FREIGHT SERVICE"; same color scheme as 9801 Standard O-series boxcar, except decals on that car are done with electrocals on this car. Similar to postwar 6464-325, one of the more popular and scarce 6464 cars. For some reason, it was not made during the 9200-series run. — 20 25 35
See Volume II, first edition.

9421 MAINE CENTRAL: 1980, boxcar; yellow body; dark green doors; dark green "MAINE/CENTRAL" logo and lettering; "MODERN/EFFICIENT/CUSHIONING"; Symington-Wayne trucks; "BLT 1-80". C. Rohlfing and G. Rogers Collections. — — 12 20

9422 ELGIN, JOLIET & EASTERN: 1980, boxcar; light green body with orange upper stripe; light green and orange contrasting lettering and "E J & E" logo; Symington-Wayne trucks; "BLT 1-80". This and the 9470 E J & E car are often confused. C. Lang comment. C. Rohlfing and G. Rogers Collections. — — 15 25

9423 THE NEW YORK, NEW HAVEN AND HARTFORD RAILROAD: 1980, boxcar; tuscan-painted tuscan sides and doors; black roof and ends; white New Haven script logo; Symington-Wayne trucks; "BLT 1-80". G. Rogers Collection. — — 20 35
See Volume II, first edition.

9424 T P W: 1980, (Toledo, Peoria & Western) boxcar; orange sides; silver roof and ends; white lettering "DUAL air/pak/CUSHION-PAK"; Symington-Wayne trucks; "BLT 1-80". — 10 15 20

9425 BRITISH COLUMBIA RAILWAY: 1980, double-door automobile boxcar; dark green sides and roof; one light green and one dark green door per side; white lettering; yellow and white logo; Symington-Wayne trucks; no "BLT" date. — 15 20 25

These 9400-series cars all date from 1981.

R. Kaptur, R. LaVoie, A. Rudman, and F. Stem Collections; B. Greenberg photogra

Top shelf: **9435 Central of Georgia, a special for LCCA (see Volume II); 9436 Burlington.**
Second shelf: **9438 Ontario Northland; 9439 Ashley Drew & Northern.**
Third shelf: **9440 Reading; 9441 Pennsylvania.**
Bottom shelf: **9443 Florida East Coast Railway; 9444 Louisiana Midland.**

	GD	VG	EXC	MT

9426 CHESAPEAKE & OHIO: 1980, boxcar; horizontally divided blue and yellow sides; silver roof and ends; yellow and blue contrasting lettering; Symington-Wayne trucks; "BLT 1-80".

(A) Yellow-painted blue plastic body. — **15 20 35**

(B) Blue- and yellow-painted white plastic body. C. Diaz Collection. **NRS**

9427 THE BAY LINE: 1980-81, boxcar; Symington-Wayne trucks.

(A) Green body with yellow logo; green lettering; "THE BAY LINE" inside of broad yellow stripe; white number and technical data; "BLT 1-80". — — **10 20**

(B) Similar to (A), but logo and stripe are white. May be a chemically altered version. See comments under 9403 by Charles Weber. **NRS**

9428 T. P. & W.: 1980-81, (Toledo, Peoria & Western) boxcar; distinctive forest green and cream body; same colors used in lettering to contrast with sides; "The Progressive Way"; very different from 9424; Symington-Wayne trucks; "BLT 1-80". Came only with 1072 Cross Country Express set. This set was the

top-of-the-line Traditional set in 1981, but its outstanding rolling stock qualifies it as a Collector set. — **25 35 50**

The Cowen Commemorative Set

In 1980, Fundimensions issued a set of six 9400-series boxcars (9429 through 9434), celebrating founder Joshua Lionel Cowen's 100th birthday — even though he never actually admitted to his birth date. All the cars had the top-of-the-line Standard O trucks and came in limited edition boxes. Each featured a logo depicting the progressive Lionel trademark changes through the years. Two of the last three cars were sold only in sets, and the last in a year-end dealer bonus package. Consequently, they are much more expensive and hard to find than the first three. Prototypes of these cars exist without any text in the scrolls to the right of the doors.

9429 THE EARLY YEARS: 1980, boxcar; light yellow sides; red roof and ends; red and black lettering; "COMMEMORATING / the 100th BIRTHDAY of / JOSHUA L. COWEN" in yellow scroll

Top shelf: **9445 Vermont Northern; 9446 Sabine River & Northern.**
Middle shelf: **9447 Pullman Standard; 9449 Great Northern, from Famous American Railroad Series No. 3.**
Bottom shelf: **9451 Southern, from Famous American Railroad Series No. 4; 9452 Western Pacific.**

	GD	VG	EXC	MT

to left; Standard O trucks; "BLT 1-80". Part of separate-sale Cowen Commemorative set. — — 25 30

9430 STANDARD GAUGE YEARS: 1980, boxcar; black and maroon lettering; matches 9429; silver sides; wine-colored roof and ends; Standard O trucks; "BLT 1-80". Part of separate-sale Cowen Commemorative set. — — 25 30

9431 PRE WAR YEARS: 1980, boxcar; matches 9429; gray sides; black roof, ends and lettering; Standard O trucks; "BLT 1-80". — — 25 30

9432 POST WAR YEARS: 1980, boxcar; matches 9429; tan sides; green roof and ends; green lettering; Standard O trucks; "BLT 1-80". Part of Cowen Commemorative set, but available only in 1070 Royal Limited set. — — 85 125

9433 GOLDEN YEARS: 1980, boxcar; matches 9429; gold sides; dark blue roof and ends; black and blue lettering; Standard O trucks; "BLT 1-80". Part of Cowen Commemorative set, but available only in 1071 Mid-Atlantic Limited set. — — 85 125

9434 JOSHUA LIONEL COWEN — THE MAN: 1980, boxcar; uncatalogued; yellow sides; brown roof and ends; brown lettering; Standard O trucks; "BLT 1-80". The last car in the Cowen Commemorative series, which began with 9429. Available only in the 1980 Fall Collector Center brochure. — — 70 100

9435 CENTRAL OF GEORGIA: 1981, boxcar; L C C A; see Volume II, first edition.

9436 BURLINGTON: 1981, boxcar; red body with white lettering; "WAY OF/THE ZEPHYRS"; Burlington Route logo; number

under- and over-scored; Standard O trucks; "BLT 1-81". Copy of postwar prototype which was never produced. Came only with 1160 Great Lakes Limited set. — — 40 50

9438 ONTARIO NORTHLAND: 1981, boxcar; dark blue body; yellow ends; yellow lettering; "triple lightning" logo in yellow on side; white "Rail/Services"; Symington-Wayne trucks; no "BLT" date. Harding Collection. — — 20 25

9439 ASHLEY DREW & NORTHERN: 1981, boxcar; green with white doors and lettering; "CUSHION/SERVICE"; yellow, green and white logo; Symington-Wayne trucks; "BLT 1-81".
— — 10 20

9440 READING: 1981, boxcar; yellow sides; green roof and ends; green doors; green "READING" serif lettering; number under- and over-scored; Reading Lines diamond logo; Standard O trucks; "BLT 1-81". Available only in 1158 Maple Leaf Limited set. — — 40 70

9441 PENNSYLVANIA: 1981, boxcar; tuscan with white stripe which runs through door; white and red lettering; "MERCHANDISE SERVICE"; number under-scored; P R R keystone in red and white; Standard O trucks; "BLT 1-81". Available only in 1158 Maple Leaf Limited set. — — 40 70

9442 CANADIAN PACIFIC: 1981, boxcar; silver-painted gray body; dark red lettering; number under- and over-scored; black roof and ends; Symington-Wayne trucks; "BLT 1-81". C. Lang and C. Rohlfing comments; G. Rogers Collection.
— — 15 20

9443 F. E. C. FLORIDA EAST COAST RAILWAY: 1981, boxcar; tuscan sides; silver roof and ends; white lettering; white striping on sides; number under- and over-scored; multicolor

Top shelf: 9453 M P A; 9454 New Hope & Ivyland RR.

R. Kaptur and R. LaVoie Collections; B. Greenberg photograph

Second shelf: 9455 Milwaukee Road; 9456 Pennsylvania double-door automobile car, from Famous American Railroad Series No. 5.

Third shelf: 9460 Detroit & Toledo Shore Line, a special LCCA car (see Volume II); 9461 Norfolk Southern.

Bottom shelf: 9462 Southern Pacific.

	GD	VG	EXC	MT

"FLORIDA EAST COAST RAILWAY" logo to right; Symington-Wayne trucks; "BLT 1-81". — — **15 20**

9444 LOUISIANA MIDLAND: 1981, boxcar; white sides and roof; blue ends and doors; red and blue lettering; Symington-Wayne trucks. — — **15 20**

9445 VERMONT NORTHERN: 1981, boxcar; yellow sides; silver roof and ends; black lettering; VN logo; "CUSION/SER-VICE"; Symington-Wayne trucks; "BLT 1-81".
 — — **15 20**

9446 SABINE RIVER & NORTHERN: 1981, boxcar; red body and doors; silver roof and ends; white logo and lettering; Symington-Wayne trucks; "BLT 1-81". R. DuBeau and J. Vega Collections. — — **15 20**

9447 PULLMAN STANDARD: 1981, boxcar; black lettering "This is the/1,000,000th/freight car built by/Pullman Standard."; Symington-Wayne trucks; "BLT 1-81".
(A) Silver body. R. LaVoie Collection. — — **15 20**
(B) Gold body. This and a similar silver-bodied car with gold lettering may have been faked by a chemical change. It is generally agreed that this is a chemical, not factory, alteration. **NRS**

9449 GREAT NORTHERN: 1981, boxcar; dark green and orange body; FARR Series 3 diamond herald in gold; black and white lettering; number under- and over-scored; Great Northern goat logo to right; Symington-Wayne trucks; "BLT 1-81". From Famous American Railroad Series No. 3; car and other set components sold separately. — — **35 50**
See Factory Errors and Prototypes chapter in Volume II, first edition.

9451 SOUTHERN: 1983, boxcar; tuscan body; white lettering; white S R circular logo to right; FARR Series 4 diamond insignia in gold; Standard O trucks. From Famous American Railroad Series No. 4; car and other set components sold separately.
 — — **40 55**

9452 WESTERN PACIFIC: 1982-83, boxcar; tuscan-painted body; white lettering; rectangular feather logo to right; Symington-Wayne trucks; "BLT 1-82". — — **15 20**

9453 M P A: 1982-83, boxcar (Maryland and Pennsylvania); dark blue-painted body; yellow lettering and star logo at upper right; Symington-Wayne trucks; "BLT 1-82"; somewhat plain appearance. — — **10 15**

R. Kaptur, R. LaVoie, and A. Rudman Collections; B. Greenberg photograph

Top shelf: **9466** Wanamaker Railway Lines. The John Wanamaker gift box was a source of controversy.
Second shelf: **9464** N C & St L; **9465** Santa Fe.
Third shelf: **9467** The 1982 World's Fair; **9468** Union Pacific.
Bottom shelf: **9469** New York Central Lines Standard O boxcar; **9470** E.J. & E.

	GD	VG	EXC	MT

9454 NEW HOPE & IVYLAND R R: 1982-83, boxcar; dark green-painted body; white lettering; shown in catalogue with circular arrow logo, but not made that way; instead, "McHUGH / BROS. / LINES" is present in white at upper right; Symington-Wayne trucks; "BLT 1-82". R. LaVoie comment.
— — **10** **15**

9455 MILWAUKEE ROAD: 1982-83, boxcar; yellow-painted body; black lettering; black "America's/Resourceful/Railroad/MILW" to left of doors; Symington-Wayne trucks; "BLT 1-82".
— — **15** **20**

9456 PENNSYLVANIA: 1984-85, double-door automobile boxcar; tuscan-painted tuscan body and doors; metal door guides; white lettering; white and black PRR keystone logo on black circle; gold FARR Series 5 diamond insignia; Standard O trucks; "BLT 1-84". From P R R Famous American Railroad Series No. 5; car and other components sold separately.
— **25** **35** **50**

9460 DETROIT, TOLEDO & SHORE LINE: 1982, double-door automobile boxcar; L C C A; see Volume II, first edition.

9461 NORFOLK SOUTHERN: 1982, boxcar; brown body; yellow doors; yellow lettering; number under- and over-scored; Standard O trucks; "BLT 1-82". Available only in 1260 Continental Limited set.
— — **35** **55**

9462 SOUTHERN PACIFIC: 1983-84, boxcar; silver-painted gray body; black-painted roof and ends; unpainted black doors; black lettering; circular black and white S P logo to right of doors; Symington-Wayne trucks. G. Rogers and R. LaVoie Collections.
— **15** **20** **25**

9463 TEXAS & PACIFIC: 1983-84, boxcar; yellow sides and roof; black lettering; yellow doors; black T & P logo; Symington-Wayne trucks.
— — **12** **15**

9464 N C & ST L: 1983-84, (Nashville, Chattanooga & St. Louis) boxcar; orange body; yellow-orange stripe on side does not go through doors; white lettering; "TO AND FROM/Dixieland" in white script to right; number under- and over-scored; Symington-Wayne trucks; Type III box ends are erroneously labeled "North Carolina & St. Louis". C. Lang and C. Rohlfing comments.
— — **12** **15**

Top shelf: **9471** Atlantic Coast Line; **9472** Detroit & Mackinac.
Second shelf: **9473** Lehigh Valley; **9474** Erie Lackawanna.
Third shelf: **9475** Delaware & Hudson, the first of the "I Love" state cars; **9476** Pennsylvania, from Famous American Railroad Series No. 5.
Bottom shelf: **9480** MNS; **9481** Seaboard System.

R. Kaptur, R. LaVoie, and A. Rudman Collections; B. Greenberg photograph

GD   VG   EXC   MT

9465 A T S F: 1983-84, boxcar; dark green body; yellow letter-ing and cross logo; "The/Super Chief/to/California" to right of doors; dark green doors; Symington-Wayne trucks; "BLT 1-83". Pictured as blue in catalogue, but not produced that way. Hard to find recently. C. Lang and C. Rohlfing comments.

— — **12   25**

9466 WANAMAKER RAILWAY LINES: 1982, boxcar; un-catalogued; wine-painted plastic body with gold-painted doors and gold lettering; "W.R.L."; number under- and over-scored; Symington-Wayne trucks. This car commemorated the Ives spe-cial Wanamaker cars of the early 1920s. At that time, Ives produced specially lettered cars for John Wanamaker, then and now the pre-eminent department store of Philadelphia. The moving force behind this commemorative car was Nicholas Ladd, a long-time train enthusiast and senior Wanamaker store manager. The Eagle logo is original Wanamaker art adapted by Arthur Bink. The Wanamaker Railway Lines logo was copied from the original lettering on an authentic Ives Wanamaker car. Note that the Lionel artist intentionally made the "M" look like an "N" in the script. It is not a factory error. Lionel produced 2,500 of these cars. Interested Wanamaker employees bought 1,400 of them, and another 1,000 were sold over the counter at a

special train fair held at Wanamaker's Philadelphia store in conjunction with the car's release. The remaining 100 cars were retained by the store. Earlier editions of this Guide erroneously reported that some cars were sold in a special red box which demanded a premium. Mr. Ladd advises us that this is not true — the box is a standard Wanamaker gift box available at no cost from the store. It happens to fit the Lionel box, but should in no way command any extra premium. This car was not announced in any published Lionel paper.

— — **90   120**

9467 THE 1982 WORLD'S FAIR: 1982, boxcar; un-catalogued; white-painted white body; tuscan-painted roof and ends; black lettering; "follow mme to Tennessee"; white doors; red, black and white World's Fair logo to left of door; Symington-Wayne trucks; "BLT 1-82". Reportedly only 2,500 made for Ak-Sar-Ben Hobby Company of Nashville. C. Darasko and J. Vega Collections.

— — **35   45**

9468 UNION PACIFIC: 1983, double-door automobile box-car; tuscan body; yellow lettering; "Be Specific-/Ship/Union Pacific" in script to left of doors; Standard O trucks. Came only in 1361 Gold Coast Limited set.

— — **40   50**

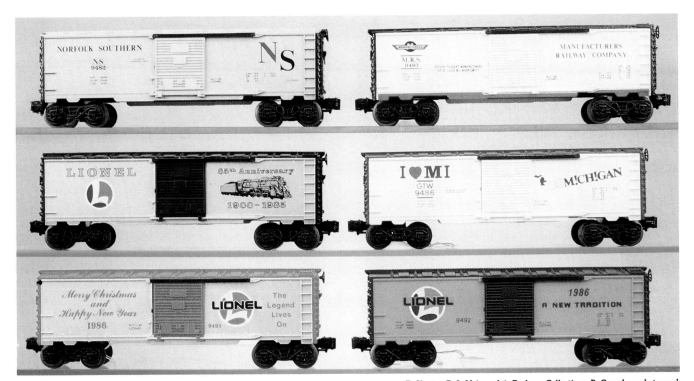

R. Kaptur, R. LaVoie, and A. Rudman Collections; B. Greenberg photograph

The last of the 9400-series boxcars from 1985-1986.
Top shelf: **9482** Norfolk Southern; **9483** Manufacturers Railway Company.
Middle shelf: **9484** Lionel 85th Anniversary; **9486** I Love Michigan, a rare variation of this car exists.
Bottom shelf: **9491** Lionel Seasons Greetings boxcar; **9492** Lionel, one of the few cars made during Kenner-Parker's stewartship of Lionel in 1986.

	GD	VG	EXC	MT

9470 E. J. & E.: 1984-85, (Elgin, Joliet & Eastern) boxcar; dark green body; yellow lettering and Great Lakes logo; number under- and over-scored; Symington-Wayne trucks. C. Rohlfing and G. Rogers Collections. — — **15 20**

9471 ATLANTIC COAST LINE: 1984-85, boxcar; tuscan body; white lettering; "Thanks/For/Using/Coast Line"; number under- and over-scored; circular white Atlantic Coast Line logo; Symington-Wayne trucks. — — **15 20**

9472 DETROIT & MACKINAC: 1984-85, boxcar; white roof and ends; white and red half-and-half sides and doors; white and red contrasting lettering; number under- and over-scored; Symington-Wayne trucks. — — **20 25**

9473 LEHIGH VALLEY: 1984-85, boxcar; light green body and doors; silver-painted roof; white lettering; Symington-Wayne trucks.
(A) Red and blue L V flag press-on sticker attached to doors. D. Anderson Collection. — — **15 20**
(B) Same as (A), but flag on doors is missing. P. Costa Collection. — — **15 20**

9474 ERIE LACKAWANNA: 1984-85, boxcar; tuscan-painted body and doors; white lettering and logo; Standard O trucks. Available only in 1451 Erie-Lackawanna Limited set. — — **45 55**

9475 D H N Y: 1984, (Delaware & Hudson) boxcar; uncatalogued; unusual blue and white paint scheme with colors on sides and doors separated diagonally from upper left to lower right; large black serif "I"; red heart and "N Y"; white D & H shield logo and lettering; Standard O trucks. Offered in 1984 Spring Collector Center brochure. Has been in demand by operators for

unit trains. First of an apparently annual "I Love"-State series planned by Lionel. This is the only one so far with Standard O trucks. C. Lang comment. — — **25 40**

9476 PENNSYLVANIA: 1984-85, boxcar; tuscan-painted body and doors; white lettering; white and black P R R keystone logo; gold FARR Series 5 diamond insignia; Standard O trucks. Part of P R R Famous American Railroad Series No. 5 set; car and other set components sold separately. — — **40 50**

9480 M N S: 1985-86, (Minneapolis, Northfield and Southern) boxcar; dark gloss blue body and doors; white lettering; dark red M N S logo (sometimes difficult to see); tuscan and white diamond-shaped logo; Symington-Wayne trucks.
— — **15 20**

9481 SEABOARD SYSTEM: 1985-86, boxcar; tuscan body and doors; white lettering; white interlocked "SS" logo; Symington-Wayne trucks.
(A) "BLT 1-85 Lionel". — — **15 20**
(B) Bar code in place of "BLT" date. Further confirmation requested. P. Crowell Collection. **NRS**

9482 NORFOLK SOUTHERN: 1985-86, boxcar; gray body, roof and doors; black ends; black lettering; black and red "NS" logo; orange rectangle; Symington-Wayne trucks.
— — **15 20**

9483 MANUFACTURERS RAILWAY COMPANY: 1985-86, boxcar; white sides and doors; red lower side sills; black roof and ends; black lettering; number under- and over-scored; black and yellow "MANUFACTURERS" logo; Symington-Wayne trucks. — — **12 15**

Top shelf: **9228 Canadian Pacific; 9486 I Love Michigan.**
Bottom shelf: **9491 Seasons Greetings; 9492 Lionel "A New Tradition".**

	GD	VG	EXC	MT

9484 LIONEL 85TH ANNIVERSARY: 1985, boxcar; silver-gray body; black doors; black roof and ends; gold lettering; "1900-1985"; red, white and blue circular Lionel logo; gold and black steam engine electrocal; Symington-Wayne trucks; the number 9484 is not on the car. C. Rohlfing, G. Rogers and R. LaVoie Collections. — — **20** **30**

9486 I LOVE MICHIGAN: 1986, boxcar; white sides; violet-painted roof and ends; red, white and violet lettering; "YES M!CH!GAN"; number under- and over-scored; Symington-Wayne trucks; "BLT 1-86". Part of continuing "I Love"-state annual series.
(A) As described. — — **15** **20**
(B) Same as (A), except overstamped with large red and black "150" beside "1837/1987" to mark the 150th anniversary of Michigan's statehood. This car was made specially as a fundraiser for Artrain, a Michigan-based non-profit organization which transports and exhibits art aboard train cars around the country. See the 17885 Artrain tank car entry for the second installment (1990) in the Artrain series. Reportedly less than 500 of these boxcars were made, and they are exceptionally hard to find.
— — — **400**

9490 SEASONS GREETINGS: 1985, boxcar; uncatalogued; silver sides; green roof, ends and doors; red lettering "Merry Christmas/and/Happy New Year/1985"; circle-L Lionel logo in red, blue, black and white to right of doors; "A/NEW/TRADITON" at far right; Symington-Wayne trucks; "BLT 1-85". Decoration pattern is very similar to that on the 9491, except red and green are reversed. Only 252 of these cars were made, reserved for Lionel employees in 1985, according to a letter enclosed with the car by Lionel's D. Kailing. Because of this and the popularity of the Seasons Greetings series, this car is nearly impossible to find. R. Artelli Collection. — — — **1500**

9491 SEASONS GREETINGS: 1986, Christmas boxcar; uncatalogued; silver sides; red roof, ends and doors; red, white, blue and black new Lionel circle-L logo; green lettering; "Merry Christmas/and/Happy New Year/1986" in script and "The/Legend/Lives/On"; Symington-Wayne trucks; "BLT 1-86". Part of 1986 year-end Stocking Stuffer package. Lettering pattern is similar to that on scarce 9490 car, with red and green colors reversed. R. Artelli comment. — — **35** **40**

	GD	VG	EXC	MT

9492 LIONEL LINES: 1986, boxcar; bright orange sides; blue roof and ends; blue doors; new red, white, black and blue Lionel logo to left of doors; "1986 / A NEW TRADITION" in blue lettering to right; Symington-Wayne trucks. — — **30** **50**

9620- SERIES SPORTS BOXCARS

Lionel apparently chose 1980 as the year in which to honor big-league sports in the United States. That year, it catalogued six 9700-type classic boxcars for each of the two divisions in baseball, basketball and hockey. Each car was covered with multicolor team logos from each division. However, as with the short O27 cars (9359, 9360 and 9362) issued a little earlier in a 1979 year-end package, the National Football League declined to participate. So Lionel "punted" those cars out of the line. Each sports boxcar has Symington-Wayne trucks with two operating couplers.

9620 N H L WALES CONFERENCE: 1980, Type IX 9700-style boxcar; white body with different Wales Conference hockey team symbols on each side; black roof and ends; Symington-Wayne trucks; "BLT 1-80". — — **15** **20**

9621 N H L CAMPBELL CONFERENCE: 1980, Type IX 9700-style boxcar; white body with different Campbell Conference hockey team symbols on each side; orange roof and ends; Symington-Wayne trucks; "BLT 1-80". — — **15** **20**

9622 N B A WESTERN CONFERENCE: 1980, Type IX 9700-style boxcar; white body with different Western Conference basketball team symbols on each side; silver roof and ends; Symington-Wayne trucks; "BLT 1-80". — — **15** **20**

9623 N B A EASTERN CONFERENCE: 1980, Type IX 9700-style boxcar; white body with different Eastern Conference basketball team symbols on each side; dark blue roof and ends; Symington-Wayne trucks; "BLT 1-80". — — **15** **20**

9624 NATIONAL LEAGUE: 1980, Type IX 9700-style boxcar; white body with different National League baseball team symbols on each side; red roof and ends; Symington-Wayne trucks; "BLT 1-80". — — **15** **20**

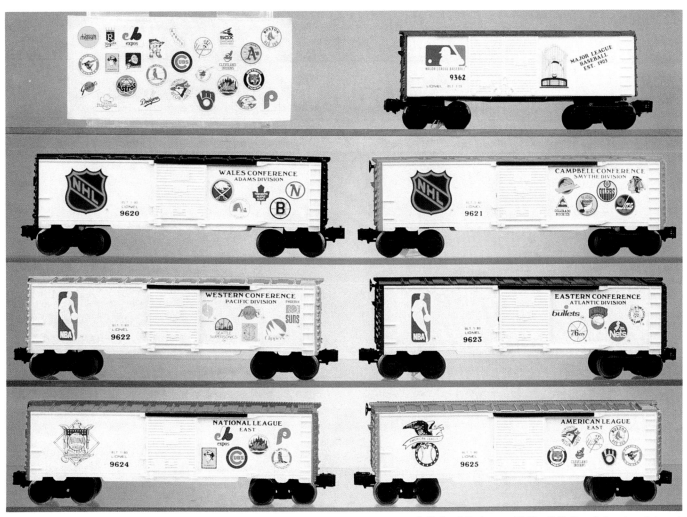

R. Kaptur, A. Rudman, and F. Stem Collections; B. Greenberg photograph

Major league sports cars. The NFL declined to participate.
Top shelf: Sheet of decals that were provided with the 9362 League Baseball short boxcar, shown on the right.
Second shelf: 9260 Wales Conference; 9621 Campbell Conference.
Third shelf: 9622 Western Conference; 9623 Eastern Conference.
Bottom shelf: 9624 National League; 9625 American League.

	GD	VG	EXC	MT

9625 AMERICAN LEAGUE: 1980, Type IX 9700-style boxcar; white body with different American League baseball team symbols on each side; gold-painted roof and ends; Symington-Wayne trucks; "BLT 1-80". — — **15 20**

THE 9700-SERIES BOXCARS

The 9700-series boxcars began with the production of the 9700 Southern boxcar in 1972 and ended in 1978; two additional "stragglers" were made in 1979 and 1982. By the time this series yielded to the 9400-series, 80 different numbers had been issued; every number from 9700 to 9789 was used except 9720-22, 9736, 9741, 9746, 9756 and 9765-66. The challenge for the collector, therefore, is one of types and varieties. It is possible to build up a very good type collection because only a few examples of the 9700-series are really hard to find. For the most part, these consist of special issues for Toy Fairs, Seasons Greetings, and various collectors clubs. (The reader will find some 9700-series stock cars in the stock car subheading of this chapter. Only classic boxcars are included in this section. The train club 9700-series cars can be found in the Volume II, first edition.)

Beginning with the cars first produced in 1976, the number of variations dropped off sharply. This occurred because Fundimensions redesigned its injection molders for liquid plastic instead of pelletized plastic. The color of the liquid plastic can be made to match the paint on the cars much more closely with liquid plastic. Between 1972 and 1975, or from numbers 9700 to about 9758, large numbers of variations abound. For instance, we have identified 19 variations of the 9748 C P Rail and 14 variations of the 9739 Rio Grande alone! A complete collection of variations would entail the acquisition of hundreds of boxcars, and more varieties turn up all the time.

Another interesting trademark of the early 9700 cars (as on the 9200 cars) is the presence of the MPC logo, indicating production before Lionel/Fundimensions was split from the Model Products

The first cars of a terrific boxcar series.

A. Rudman, L. Caponi, F. Stem, and R. LaVoie Collectio

Top shelf: 9700 Southern (note green dot added by dealer in the "O" of "Southern"); 9701 Baltimore & Ohio automobile boxcar, regular version.
Middle shelf: Special all-black 9701 Baltimore & Ohio issued for 1972 TCA Convention; 9702 Soo Line.
Bottom shelf: 9704 Norfolk and Western; 9703 C P Rail.

Division of General Mills in 1973. The reader will notice this logo begins to disappear after the 9710 Rutland car.

Still another interesting variation is the presence of under- and over-scoring lines around the number or road name initials on some cars. The presence or absence of these lines leads to some fun variations. Under- and over-scored numbers are very prevalent on hoppers and gondola cars, but can be found on the occasional boxcar, too.

It was with the 9700-series that Fundimensions began to resurrect old favorites from the 6464-series and other cars produced in postwar years. The first postwar revival was the 9707 M K T stock car in its original red color with white lettering and yellow doors; its predecessor (6556) with white lettering and doors is the scarcest of all the postwar stock cars. The next car in the series was a duplication of the red, white and blue Post Office car. The postwar 3428 was a very popular car from 1959. The modern era 9708 (non-operating) and 9301 Post Office operating cars proved equally popular. Many others followed. Unfortunately for collectors, some of the cars were considerably more difficult to acquire than others, thanks to Fundimensions' practice of including some cars with year-end special dealer promotions. In these packages dealers were required to purchase specified amounts of merchandise as a package, and a number of the special 9700 boxcars were included free. The dealer could then charge whatever he wanted for the special car. This made some collector favorites like the 9757 Central of Georgia quite difficult to obtain, while regular-issue favorites like the 9754 New York Central Pacemaker were readily available.

Another marketing ploy by Fundimensions was rather novel and fairly successful in building interest in new lines. Special coupons were included in some of the first runs of the 9800-series refrigerator cars and some of the 9100-series covered hopper cars. Two of these coupons, along with five dollars, enabled the customer to acquire a special 9700-series boxcar available direct from Lionel and nowhere else. The 9719 New Haven automobile double-door boxcar and the 9742 Minneapolis and St. Louis boxcar were marketed in this way. Both of these cars had been favorites in the postwar 6464-series, so the demand for the limited supply was brisk. Strangely enough, both of these cars can be found at a reasonable cost on the open market today. Fundimensions also marketed a 9511 Minneapolis passenger car in this manner.

One of the 9700 boxcars produced for the Lionel Collectors' Club of America was an anomaly which has not been repeated. The 9733 Airco boxcar was really two cars in one. When the collector took the boxcar body off the frame, he found a single-dome tank car included within the boxcar body. Many collectors have put the tank car body on its own frame and added trim pieces to form a second Airco car, which is numbered 97330. If you find this highly desirable car, make sure that both car bodies are included if the car's full price is demanded.

There are, more or less, three tiers of scarcity for the 9700-series boxcars. The most common cars are those which were catalogued as regular issues, although a few of the catalogued cars are somewhat harder to find than others. These cars, such as the 9781 Delaware & Hudson, the 9737 Central Vermont, and the 9768 Boston and Maine, are still readily available at this writing. The

A. Rudman, L. Caponi, F. Stem, and R. LaVoie Collections

These 9700 boxcars date from 1972-1973.
Top shelf: 9705 Rio Grande; 9706 Chesapeake & Ohio. Contrast these with the later 9714 and 9715 models in different colors.
Middle shelf: 9707 M-K-T stock car (note longer body); 9708 United States Mail Railway.
Bottom shelf: 9709 State of Maine (Bangor & Aroostook); 9710 Rutland. The 9708, 9709, and 9710 models have many variations.

	GD	VG	EXC	MT

second tier includes some scarcer regularly catalogued cars such as the 9710 Rutland, some cars included only in sets such as the 9772 Great Northern, and some of the more common collector organization cars such as the 9728 L C C A stock car. The third and scarcest tier includes cars which are catalogued but very scarce, such as the 9703 C P Rail; cars which were not catalogued but part of the series, such as the 9778 Seasons Greetings and the 9762 Toy Fair cars; and the scarcer collector organization cars such as the 9727 T. A. & G. You can expect the value of these cars to rise disproportionately as time passes.

The 9700-series boxcars are colorful, well made, and astonishingly diverse, thanks to Lionel's excellent use of both nostalgia and modern graphics. Most are still widely available at good prices, and collectors are only now beginning to appreciate their collectability. Therefore, these cars offer excellent collecting opportunities for the beginner who is willing to research and look in odd corners of dealers' stocks.

9700 SOUTHERN: 1972-73, boxcar; three shades of red as described below; Type IX body except for (A); red-painted red doors; white lettering; Type I frame; Symington-Wayne trucks; "BLT 1-72"; MPC logo.
(A) "SOO" red-painted (as in the 9207 Soo Line car); Type VI red plastic body; metal door guides. **NRS**
(B) Shiny red-painted shiny red body. 6 8 20 25
(C) Dark red-painted dark red body; green circular sticker inside "O" of "SOUTHERN". The prototype had green paint within the "O" to symbolize the railroad's motto; "SOUTHERN/GIVES A

GREEN LIGHT TO INNOVATIONS". To make the car more realistic, dealers received sheets of stick-on green dots to place inside the "O" of "SOUTHERN". C. Lang comment; R. LaVoie Collection. 6 8 20 25
(D) Same as (C), but no green dot sticker. 6 8 15 20
See Factory Errors and Prototypes chapter in Volume II, first edition.

9700: 1976, T C A boxcar; see Volume II, first edition under entry 9779.

9701 BALTIMORE & OHIO: 1971-73, double-door automobile boxcar; number under- and over-scored; metal door guides; Symington-Wayne trucks; "BLT 2-72"; MPC logo at right. Appeared in 1186 Cross-Country Express set and also sold separately. Different-colored doors were added outside the factory; only the black doors are authentic factory production. However, since there is substantial collector interest in the door variations, we include them in this listing. A black-bodied version of this car with white lettering was used for both the T C A and L C C A conventions in 1971 and 1972. See Volume II, first edition.
(A) Silver-painted gray plastic body; black-painted black doors; black lettering; Type II frame. 6 8 20 25
(B) Same as (A), but Type I frame. 6 8 20 25
(C) The following varieties have had doors installed outside the factory; all have silver sides and black lettering as in version (A). Values remain the same for all versions: 6 8 20 25

Patterns begin to repeat with these 9700s.

A. Rudman, L. Caponi, F. Stem, and R. LaVoie Collections

Top shelf: **9711** Southern (compare with 9700); **9712** Baltimore & Ohio double-door (compare with 9701).
Middle shelf: **9713** C P Rail (compare with 9703); **9714** Rio Grande (compare with 9705).
Bottom shelf: **9715** Chesapeake & Ohio (compare with 9706); **9716** Penn Central, first version (compare with later 9749).

	GD	VG	EXC	MT

1. Dark blue-painted dark blue doors; Type II frame.
2. Medium blue-painted medium blue doors; Type II frame.
3. Light blue-painted light blue doors; Type I frame.
4. 9209 (Burlington) green-painted green doors; Type I frame.
5. 9200 (I C) orange-painted orange doors; Type II frame.
6. Burnt orange-painted burnt orange doors; Type II frame.
7. Silver-painted gray doors; Type I frame.
8. Silver-painted gray doors; Type II frame.
9. 9205 (N W) dark navy blue-painted doors; Type II frame.
10. 9207 (Soo) red-painted doors; Type II frame.

See also Factory Errors and Prototypes chapter in Volume II, first edition.

9702 SOO LINE: 1972-73, boxcar; white sides; black roof painted on white body; red-painted red doors; black lettering; number under- and over-scored; Symington-Wayne trucks; "BLT 2-72"; MPC logo.

	GD	VG	EXC	MT
(A) Type VIII body; Type I frame.	6	10	20	25
(B) Type IX body; Type II frame.	8	10	20	30

9703 C P RAIL: 1972, boxcar; Type IX body; black lettering; black and white Pac-man logo at left end; Symington-Wayne trucks; "BLT 2-72"; MPC logo. Catalogued for separate-sale in 1972, but also came as part of T-1174 Canadian National set

distributed by Parker Brothers only in Canada. Also sold separately in Canadian Parker Brothers box. C. Rohlfing comment.

	GD	VG	EXC	MT
(A) Burnt-orange-painted burnt-orange body; burnt orange-painted red doors; Type II frame.	30	40	55	65
(B) Light burnt-orange-painted medium red body; medium red-painted red doors; Type I frame.	30	40	55	65

See Factory Errors and Prototypes chapter in Volume II, first edition.

9704 NORFOLK AND WESTERN: 1972, boxcar; Type IX body except (A); white lettering except (C); Symington-Wayne trucks; "BLT 3-72"; MPC logo.

	GD	VG	EXC	MT
(A) Tuscan-painted Type VII maroon body; metal door guides; tuscan-painted maroon doors; Type I frame.	—	100	125	150
(B) Tuscan-painted tuscan body; tuscan-painted tuscan doors; Type II frame.	—	6	10	25
(C) Same as (B), but gray lettering.	—	6	10	25
(D) Same as (B), but Type I frame.	—	10	15	25
(E) Tuscan-painted gray body; tuscan-painted tuscan doors; Type I frame.	—	10	15	30

9705 D & R G W: 1972-73, (Denver & Rio Grande) boxcar; silver-painted gray plastic doors; black "Rio Grande" lettering; Type IX body except versions (A) and (E); Symington-Wayne trucks; "BLT 1-72"; MPC logo. Though not shown in the 1973 United States catalogue, this car appeared in the 1972-73 Canadian Lionel catalogue.

A. Rudman, L. Caponi, F. Stem, and R. LaVoie Collections

...ne new patterns and great resurrections in this batch of 9700s.

shelf: 9717 Union Pacific (compare with later 9755); 9718 Canadian National.

ddle shelf: 9719 New Haven "coupon" car which retains the 1956 built date of its 6464 predecessor; 9723 Western Pacific.

tom shelf: 9724 Missouri Pacific Lines (compare with later 9219 operating version); 9725 M-K-T stock car (compare with earlier 9707).

	GD	VG	EXC	MT

(A) Dark orange-painted Type VIII orange plastic body; Type I frame. — 50 75 100

(B) Light orange-painted orange plastic body; Type I frame. — 10 12 25

(C) Dark orange-painted orange plastic body; Type I frame. — 10 12 25

(D) Dark orange unpainted orange body; very deeply stamped gloss black lettering; Type II frame; probably late production. R. LaVoie Collection. — 10 12 25

(E) Same as (D), but Type VII body and Type I frame. F. Barkschat Collection. — 10 12 25

(F) Same as (C), but Type II frame. C. Rohlfing Collection. — 10 12 15

9706 CHESAPEAKE & OHIO: 1972, boxcar; yellow lettering; Symington-Wayne trucks; "BLT 1-72"; MPC logo.

(A) Blue-painted blue plastic body; yellow-painted yellow doors; Type II frame; Type VIII body. — 8 15 20

(B) Same as (A), but Type I frame and Type IX body. 6 8 15 20

(C) Same as (A), but blue-painted gray plastic body. 6 8 15 20

See Factory Errors and Prototypes chapter in Volume II, first edition.

9708 UNITED STATES MAIL RAILWAY: 1972-75, boxcar; "POST OFFICE"; Type IX red plastic body except version (B); color variations exist in the body paint colors: red (dark, medium, light), blue (dark, medium, light), and the blue paint on the red plastic doors (medium and dark); red, white and blue horizontal stripes; white and black lettering; Type II frame; Symington-Wayne trucks; "BLT 1-72"; car comes with or without the MPC logo. At least eight common variations have been identified. This car appeared in the 1388 Golden State Arrow set in 1973 and the 1584 Spirit of America set of 1975, as well as for separate-sale.

(A) As described above, with the following variations: 5 10 15 25

1. Dark red-, white- and light blue-painted body; red-painted doors.
2. Dark red-, white- and light blue-painted body; red- and light blue-painted doors.
3. Dark red-, white- and medium blue-painted body; red- and medium blue-painted doors.
4. Dark red-, white- and medium blue-painted body; red- and dark blue-painted doors.
5. Light red-, white- and dark blue-painted body; red- and dark blue-painted doors; no MPC logo.
6. Dark red- and light blue-painted body; red- and medium blue-painted doors.
7. Dark red- and medium blue-painted body; red- and medium blue-painted doors.
8. Dark red- and medium blue-painted body; red- and dark blue-painted doors.

(B) Gray plastic body painted medium blue and dark red; red-painted doors. Rare. Reader comments requested. **NRS**
See also Factory Errors and Prototypes chapter in Volume II, first edition.

Some interesting history is behind these 9700 boxcars.

A. Rudman, L. Caponi, F. Stem, and R. LaVoie Collec

Top shelf: 9726 Erie Lackawanna from the Minneapolis & St. Louis Service Station set; 9727 Tennessee Alabama & Georgia for 1973 LCCA Conventio
rare car.

Middle shelf: 9728 Union Pacific stock car for 1978 LCCA Convention; 9729 C P Rail from Great Plains Express set of 1978, later replaced with 9417 mo
in the same set in 1980.

Bottom shelf: Two versions of the 9730 C P Rail boxcar. On the left is the later black-lettered version; on the right is the earlier white-lettered version. ₁
black-lettered version is scarcer.

	GD	VG	EXC	MT

9709 BANGOR AROOSTOOK: 1972-74, boxcar; "STATE OF MAINE PRODUCTS"; Type VIII bodies (A)-(C); Type IX bodies (D)-(F); white and black lettering; number under- and over-scored; Type II frame; Symington-Wayne trucks; "BLT 1-72". Reissue of postwar 6464-275, the most abundant of the 6464 series. This car was not catalogued until 1973, but came in the 1250 N Y C Hudson Service Station Special set in 1972. C Lang comment.

(A) Blue- and dark red-painted gray body. One observed example came in an original Type I box dated 1971 with a black-painted sticker on one end. R. LaVoie Collection.

	15	20	30	40

(B) Blue- and dark red-painted gray body; red-painted red doors. Red doors added outside factory. R. Vagner comment.

	15	20	30	40

(C) Dark blue- and medium red-painted blue body; blue- and red-painted blue doors.

	15	20	30	40

(D) Medium blue- and light red-painted medium blue body; dark blue- and red-painted red doors.

	15	20	30	40

(E) Blue- and light red-painted gray body; blue- and red-painted gray doors.

	20	35	40	50

(F) Blue- and red-painted blue body; dark blue- and dark red-painted dark blue doors. C. Rohlfing Collection.

	20	35	40	50

See Factory Errors and Prototypes chapter in Volume II, first edition.

	GD	VG	EXC	MT

9710 RUTLAND: 1972-74, boxcar; Type VIII bodies (A), (B), (C), (F) and (H); Type IX bodies (D), (E) and (G); yellow-painted yellow doors; green and yellow lettering; number under-scored; shield reading "GREEN MT./RAILWAY" surrounding "RUTLAND" at upper right; some versions have the word "RUTLAND" off-center in the shield; Type II frame; Symington-Wayne trucks; "NEW 1-72". Reissue of postwar 6464-300. Not catalogued until 1973, this car came in the 1250 N Y C Hudson Service Station Special set in 1972.

(A) Medium yellow- and green-painted gray body; shifted shield.

	12	20	30	40

(B) Light yellow- and green-painted gray body; shifted shield.

	12	20	30	40

(C) Same as (B), but shield centered; "9710" not underscored.

	25	30	40	50

(D) Dark yellow- and green-painted gray body; shifted shield.

	25	30	40	50

(E) Medium yellow- and light green-painted green body; shifted shield; no "CAPY 100000" lettering.

	20	25	40	50

(F) Light yellow- and light green-painted green body; shifted shield.

	20	25	30	40

(G) Dark yellow- and green-painted gray body; shifted shield.

	12	20	30	40

Top shelf: 9731 Milwaukee Road, beware of faked silver-painted roofs; all were plain red except the first 500 produced; 9732 Southern Pacific, available only in Southern Pacific set of 1979.

Middle shelf: 9733 Airco, an unusual car with a tank car body inside the boxcar produced for the 1979 LCCA Convention; 9734 Bangor and Aroostook from Quaker City set of 1978.

Bottom shelf: 9735 Grand Trunk Western, 9737 Central Vermont.

	GD	VG	EXC	MT

(H) Same as (A), but with die-cast bar-end trucks. C. Lang Collection. **NRS**

9711 SOUTHERN: 1974-75, boxcar; Type IX body; white lettering; Symington-Wayne trucks; Type II frame; "BLT 2-73" to the right of doors except (C). Compare to red 9700 Southern.

(A) Tuscan-painted tuscan body; tuscan-painted white doors.

	10	12	20	25

(B) Same as (A), but tuscan-painted tuscan doors.

	10	12	20	25

(C) Same as (A), but tuscan-painted tuscan doors; "LIONEL" and "BLT" date to the left of door. 10 12 20 25

(D) Tuscan-painted translucent body, reported but not verified. Reader comments invited. **NRS**

9712 BALTIMORE & OHIO: 1973-74, double-door automobile boxcar; metal door guides; blue-painted blue body; yellow-painted yellow doors; yellow lettering; number under- and over-scored; Type II frame; Symington-Wayne trucks; "BLT 3-73".

	9	12	30	40

9713 C P RAIL: 1973-74, boxcar; Type IX body; green-painted green doors; black lettering; black and white Pac-man logo at one end; Type II frame; Symington-Wayne trucks; "BLT 3-73".

(A) Green-painted green body. 8 10 20 30

(B) Light green-painted green body. 8 10 20 30

(C) Green-painted clear body; reported but not verified. **NRS**

	GD	VG	EXC	MT

(D) Same as (A), but overstamped with "SEASONS/GREET-INGS/1974" in gold lettering between the door and the Pac-man logo. This was the second of Lionel's annual Christmas cars, and the last overstamped one. Beginning in 1975, the cars were dedicated special issues with their own numbers.

	—	—	125	150

9714 RIO GRANDE: 1973-74, boxcar; Type IX body; silver-painted; red or orange lettering; orange-lettered versions could have been chemically altered; Type II frame; Symington-Wayne trucks.

(A) Silver-painted gray body; red-painted red doors; red lettering.

	10	15	20	25

(B) Same as (A), but silver-painted translucent white body.

	10	15	20	25

(C) Same as (A), but orange-painted orange doors; orange lettering. **NRS**

(D) Same as (A), but silver-painted translucent doors; dark orange lettering. **NRS**

(E) Same as (A), but unpainted red plastic doors. I. D. Smith observation. **NRS**

9715 CHESAPEAKE & OHIO: 1973-74, boxcar; Type IX body; Type II frame; yellow "C AND O/FOR/PROGRESS" at right; many examples have washed-out yellow lettering; slight premium for bold, well-contrasted lettering; Symington-Wayne trucks.

9738 Illinois Terminal; 9776 Southern Pacific Lines.

R. *Kaptur and A. Rudman Collections; B. Greenberg photograph*

	GD	VG	EXC	MT
(A) Black-painted black body; yellow-painted yellow doors.	10	15	20	25
(B) Same as (A), but yellow-painted white doors.	10	15	20	25
(C) Black-painted white body; light yellow-painted white doors.	10	15	20	25
(D) Same as (C), but dark yellow-painted white doors.	10	15	20	25

9716 PENN CENTRAL: 1973-74, boxcar; Type IX body; green-painted green body and green doors; white lettering; "PC" interlocked logo at right; Type II frame; Symington-Wayne trucks; "3-73".

	GD	VG	EXC	MT
	10	15	20	30

9717 UNION PACIFIC: 1973-74, boxcar; Type IX body; black roof; yellow-painted yellow doors; black lettering; "Be Specific-ship 'UNION PACIFIC'"; Type II frame; Symington-Wayne trucks; "BLT 2-73".

	GD	VG	EXC	MT
(A) Light yellow-painted yellow body.	10	15	20	30
(B) Medium yellow-painted yellow body.	10	12	15	20

9718 CANADIAN NATIONAL: 1973-74, boxcar; Type IX body; white lettering and large C N logo to right; number under- and over-scored; Type II frame; Symington-Wayne trucks; "BLT 1-73".

	GD	VG	EXC	MT
(A) Tuscan-painted tuscan body; yellow-painted yellow doors.	10	15	20	25
(B) Tuscan-painted orange body; yellow-painted translucent doors.	12	15	25	35
(C) Same as (B), but yellow-painted yellow doors.	12	15	25	35
(D) Tuscan red-painted tuscan red body; yellow-painted yellow doors.				NRS
(E) Tuscan red-painted gray body; yellow-painted yellow doors. J. Breslin and P. Catalano comments.	—	—	—	100

9719 NEW HAVEN: 1974, double-door automobile boxcar; uncatalogued; orange-painted orange body; black-painted black doors; number under- and over-scored; Type II frame; Symington-Wayne trucks; "BLT 3-56", the same built date as its 6468 postwar predecessor. Coupon car available only through special mail offer; see 9742 for more details; some dealers still have stock available. G. Rogers comment.

	GD	VG	EXC	MT
(A) Black and white lettering.	12	15	25	35
(B) Black overprinted on white lettering.	—	—	—	75
(C) White overprinted on black lettering.	—	—	—	75

9723 WESTERN PACIFIC: 1973-74, boxcar; Type IX plastic body; black lettering; number under- and over-scored; Type II frame; Symington-Wayne trucks; "BLT 2-73". Similar to, but not the same as, the postwar 6464-100 and -250 boxcars. The 9723, though not catalogued until 1974, also came as part of the 1350 Canadian Pacific Service Station Special set in 1973.

	GD	VG	EXC	MT
(A) Unpainted orange plastic body and doors.	15	20	30	40
(B) Fanta orange-painted (same darker orange color as 9745 Fanta car) orange body and doors.	30	35	40	45
(C) Fanta orange-painted orange body and white doors. Doors added outside factory. R. Vagner comment.	30	35	40	45
(D) Fanta orange-painted orange body and translucent doors. C. Rohlfing Collection.	30	35	40	45
(E) Light orange-painted orange body and translucent doors. J. Nowaczyk Collection.	30	35	40	45
(F) Same as (A), but with "Welcome/New York Toy Fair/1974" hot-stamped in gold and black to right of door. This is the second car in Lionel's annual Toy Fair series started by a special overstamped 9708 boxcar in 1973. After 1974, Lionel created dedicated cars, not overstamped regular issues, for the Toy Fair. This car is very hard to find.	—	—	175	225

9724 MISSOURI PACIFIC LINES: 1973-74, boxcar; Type IX body; black and white lettering; "Eagle MERCHANDISE/SERVICE"; silver-painted roof and side band; number under- and over-scored; Type II frame; Symington-Wayne trucks; "BLT 1-73". Reissue of postwar 6464-150. Though not catalogued until 1974, it came as part of the 1350 Canadian Pacific Service Station Special set in 1973.

	GD	VG	EXC	MT
(A) Medium blue-painted opaque-white body; yellow- and silver-painted yellow doors.	25	30	35	40
(B) Same as (A), but medium blue-painted gray body.	25	30	35	40
(C) Dark blue-painted gray body; yellow- and silver-painted yellow doors.	25	35	40	45
(D) Dark blue-painted navy body; yellow-painted yellow doors.	25	35	40	45

9726 ERIE LACKAWANNA: 1978, boxcar; glossy blue-painted Type IX body; blue-painted blue doors; white lettering and E-diamond logo; Type III frame; Standard O trucks; "BLT 1-78". Part of 1868 Minneapolis & St. Louis Service Station Special set.

	GD	VG	EXC	MT
(A) Shiny blue-painted blue body.	15	20	25	30
(B) Lighter shiny blue-painted blue body.	15	20	25	30
(C) Glossy Brunswick green-painted body and doors instead of blue. Reader comments requested concerning possibility of chemically altered change in color. R. Vagner Collection.				NRS

9727 TENNESSEE ALABAMA & GEORGIA: 1973, L C C A boxcar; see Volume II, first edition.

9729 C P RAIL: 1978, boxcar; Type IX body; black-, white- and red-painted black body; black-painted black doors; white lettering; red and white Pac-man logo at one end; Type III frame; Symington-Wayne trucks; "BLT 1-78". Came only in 1860 Great Plains set in 1978. When the set was reissued in 1979, this car was replaced by the nearly-identical 9417. C. Lang comment.

	GD	VG	EXC	MT
	10	20	30	40

A. Rudman, L. Caponi, F. Stem, and R. LaVoie Collections

ne standard production and special 9700s.

shelf: **9739** Rio Grande (compare with 9705 and 9714 models), which has a rare variation missing the black stripe; **9740** Chessie System.

dle shelf: **9742** Minneapolis & St. Louis, available only as part of a coupon mail promotion; **9743** Sprite.

om shelf: **9744** Tab; **9745** Fanta. The 9743, 9744, and 9745 cars came as part of an uncatalogued Coca-Cola set in 1974. The set was also catalogued in 1975.

	GD	VG	EXC	MT

9730 C P RAIL: 1974-75, boxcar; Type IX body; white-lettered and black-lettered versions exist; black and white Pac-man logo at one end; Type II frame; Symington-Wayne trucks; "BLT 4-74".

	GD	VG	EXC	MT
A) Silver-painted gray body; silver-painted gray doors; white lettering.	10	20	25	30
B) Same as (A), but silver-painted white body; white lettering.	10	20	25	30
C) Same as (A), but flat silver-painted white body; black lettering.	10	20	30	35
D) Same as (A), but silver-painted opaque doors; black lettering.	10	20	30	35
E) Same as (A), but silver-painted white doors; black lettering.	10	20	30	35
F) Same as (A), but silver-painted yellow doors; black lettering.	10	20	30	35

9731 MILWAUKEE ROAD: 1974-75, boxcar; Type IX body; white lettering; red doors; Type II frame; Symington-Wayne trucks; "BLT 1-74".

	GD	VG	EXC	MT
A) Light red-painted red body.	8	10	15	20
B) Medium red-painted red body.	8	10	15	20

C) Red-painted red body; silver-painted roof, as shown in 1974 catalogue. Reportedly, 100 examples were made this way. However, since the car can be easily faked by painting the roof, it is difficult to place a value on this variation. C. O'Dell, R. LaVoie and C. Lang comments. **NRS**

9732 SOUTHERN PACIFIC: 1979, boxcar; uncatalogued; black roof and ends; silver sides on gray plastic Type IX body; black-painted black doors; black and orange lettering; black-lettered "OVERNIGHTS" erroneously pluralized on all examples; orange and black circle logo on left; Type III frame; Standard O trucks; "BLT 1-79". From the Southern Pacific Limited set 1970.

	GD	VG	EXC	MT
	—	—	30	40

9733 AIRCO INDUSTRIAL GASES: 1979, combination boxcar/tank car; L C C A; see Volume II, first edition.

9734 BANGOR AND AROOSTOOK: 1979, boxcar; Type IX red body; red doors; white lettering; blue and white triangle logo; Standard O trucks; "BLT 1-79". From the Quaker City Limited set 1971.

	GD	VG	EXC	MT
	10	15	25	35

9735 GRAND TRUNK WESTERN: 1974-75, boxcar; Type IX body; white lettering and large G T logo to right; number under- and over-scored; Type II frame; Symington-Wayne trucks.

	GD	VG	EXC	MT
(A) Blue-painted blue body; blue-painted dark blue doors.	8	10	15	20
(B) Same as (A), but blue-painted opaque body.	8	10	15	20
(C) Blue-painted opaque body; blue-painted white doors.	8	10	15	20

9737 CENTRAL VERMONT: 1974-76, boxcar; Type IX body; white lettering, pattern similar to 9735; number under- and over-scored; large C V logo in white at right; Type II frame; Symington-Wayne trucks.

Standard production 9700s.

A. Rudman, L. Caponi, F. Stem, and R. LaVoie Colle...

Top shelf: 9747 Chessie System double-door automobile boxcar; 9748 C P Rail, which has more variations than any other 9700 boxcar.

Middle shelf: 9749 Penn Central (compare with previous 9716); 9750 D T & I.

Bottom shelf: 9751 Frisco; 9752 Louisville & Nashville.

	GD	VG	EXC	MT
(A) Tuscan-painted tuscan body and tuscan doors.	10	15	20	25

(B) Tuscan-painted orange body and tuscan-painted white doors. Hard-to-find variation.　　**30　35　45　60**

(C) Same as (B), but tuscan-painted tuscan body. R. LaVoie Collection.　　**10　15　20　25**

9738 ILLINOIS TERMINAL: 1982, boxcar; Type IX body; yellow-painted sides; light green roof and ends; light green- and red-outlined lettering; Standard O trucks. Part of 1260 Continental Limited set. A late addition to the 9700-series, three years after it supposedly ended. It is not clear why this car wasn't given a 9400-series number. C. Rohlfing Collection.

　　　　　　　　　　—　　—　　50　　60

9739 RIO GRANDE: 1974-76, boxcar; silver and yellow Type IX body; black lettering; silver roof; silver doors; Type II frame; Symington-Wayne trucks. Reissue of postwar 6464-650 except for door color. Common versions came with a black stripe separating the yellow and silver areas on the sides. Rare versions without the stripe exist. Though not catalogued until 1975, this car (with stripe) came with the 1450 Rio Grande Service Station Special set in 1974. At least 14 different variations of this car have been identified. Changes were made in: body mold color (opaque, yellow and white), body paint color (dark, medium or light yellow with silver), door mold color (yellow, gray or opaque), and stripe length (short, long or none). Variations are described below:

(A) Variations with stripe listed below: **10　12　15　20**

	GD	VG	EXC	MT

1. Yellow plastic body painted medium dark yellow and silver; gray plastic doors painted silver; long stripe.

2. Yellow plastic body painted dark yellow and silver; gray plastic doors painted silver; long stripe.

3. Yellow plastic body painted medium yellow and silver; gray plastic doors painted silver; long stripe.

4. Yellow plastic body painted light yellow and light silver; gray plastic doors painted yellow; long stripe.

5. Yellow plastic body painted light yellow and light silver; yellow plastic doors painted silver.

6. Yellow plastic body painted dark yellow and silver; gray plastic doors painted silver; short stripe.

7. Opaque plastic body painted light yellow and silver; opaque plastic doors painted silver; short stripe.

8. Opaque plastic body painted medium yellow and silver; opaque plastic doors painted silver; long stripe.

9. Opaque plastic body painted medium yellow and silver; gray plastic doors painted silver.

10. Opaque plastic body painted light yellow and light silver; opaque plastic doors painted silver; long stripe.

11. Yellow plastic body painted medium yellow and silver; translucent plastic doors painted silver; long stripe. R. LaVoie Collection.

(B) No black stripe. Rare.　　**100　140　160　200**

Standard production and special-interest 9700s.

Top shelf: 9753 Maine Central; 9754 New York Central System "Pacemaker", which suddenly became popular for unit trains when a matching extended vision caboose was issued.

Middle shelf: 9755 Union Pacific (compare with earlier 9717); 9757 Central of Georgia, part of dealer's end-of-year package.

Bottom shelf: 9758 The Alaska Railroad; 9759 Paul Revere, part of uncatalogued Liberty Special set in 1975.

	GD	VG	EXC	MT

1. Yellow plastic body painted dark yellow and silver; yellow plastic doors painted silver.

2. Transparent white plastic body painted light yellow and silver; gray plastic doors painted silver.

See Volume II, first edition.

9740 CHESSIE SYSTEM: 1974-75, boxcar; Type IX body; yellow-painted yellow doors, except (D) and (E); blue lettering; Type II frame; Symington-Wayne trucks. Came as part of 1460 Grand National set.

	GD	VG	EXC	MT
(A) Dark yellow-painted yellow body.	10	12	15	20
(B) Medium yellow-painted yellow body.	10	12	15	20
(C) Light yellow-painted yellow body.	10	12	15	20
(D) Light yellow-painted yellow body; yellow-painted white doors.	10	12	15	20
(E) Light yellow-painted opaque body; same doors as (D).	10	12	15	20

9742 MINNEAPOLIS & ST LOUIS: 1974, boxcar; uncatalogued; Type IX body; metallic gold lettering; number under- and over-scored; Type II frame; Symington-Wayne trucks. This was a coupon car offered to purchasers of specially marked boxes of 9800-series refrigerator or 9100-series covered hopper cars. Car could be obtained if two coupons (packaged with the above cars) and $5 were sent directly to Lionel at Mt. Clemens. Other cars which could be obtained using this marketing approach were the 9719 New Haven double-door boxcar and the 9511 Milwaukee "Minneapolis" passenger car. The cars originally could not be purchased from dealers. Although the body color is different, this car has the same M & St. L lettering design as the postwar 6464-50. R. LaVoie comment.

	GD	VG	EXC	MT
(A) Green-painted green body and doors.	10	15	25	35
(B) Green-painted white body; green-painted gray doors.	10	15	25	35
(C) Same as (B), but green-painted white doors.	10	15	25	35
(D) Same as (A), but green-painted gray doors. C. Rohlfing Collection.	10	15	25	35

(E) Same as (D), but with silver overstamping "Season's/Greetings/1973" to the right of the door. This was the first in Lionel's Seasons Greetings series, and is exceptionally hard to find.

	GD	VG	EXC	MT
	—	—	100	125

9743 SPRITE: 1974-75, boxcar; Type IX body; dark green lettering; red star above "i" in "Sprite"; number under- and over-scored; Type II frame; Symington-Wayne trucks; "BLT 1-74". This car and the next two entries listed were part of an uncatalogued 1463 Coca-Cola Switcher set in 1974. The set was catalogued, but not illustrated, in 1975. Not individually boxed.

	GD	VG	EXC	MT
(A) Light green-painted light green body; green-painted green doors.	7	9	15	25
(B) Medium green-painted dark green body; doors same as (A).	7	9	15	25
(C) Light green-painted white body; green-painted white doors.	7	9	15	25

More 9700s, including a surprise entry in the series.

A. Rudman, L. Caponi, F. Stem, and R. LaVoie Collecti

Top shelf: 9760 Liberty Bell; 9761 George Washington, both part of the Liberty Special uncatalogued set.
Middle shelf: 9762 Toy Fair car of 1975, the surprise (since the number is not on the car, many collectors are not aware that this car is part of the 9700-serie
9763 Rio Grande Stock Car.
Bottom shelf: 9764 Grand Trunk Western double-door automobile boxcar; 9767 Rail Box.

	GD	VG	EXC	MT
(D) Same as (C), but green-painted green doors.	7	9	15	25
(E) Medium green-painted medium green body; medium green-painted dark green doors.	7	9	15	25

9744 TAB: 1974-75, boxcar; Type IX body; white lettering; number under- and over-scored; Type II frame; Symington-Wayne trucks; "BLT 1-74". Part of 1463 Coca-Cola set. Not individually boxed.

	GD	VG	EXC	MT
(A) Medium magenta-painted light red body; magenta-painted red doors.	7	9	15	25
(B) Dark magenta-painted dark red body; magenta-painted red doors.	7	9	15	25
(C) Medium magenta-painted white body; magenta-painted white doors.	7	9	15	25
(D) Light magenta-painted white body; magenta-painted red doors.	7	9	15	25
(E) Same as (D), but pink body painted light magenta; magenta-painted red doors.	7	9	15	25

9745 FANTA: 1974-75, boxcar; Type IX body; black lettering; number under- and over-scored; Type II frame; Symington-Wayne trucks; "BLT 1-74". Part of 1463 Coca-Cola set. Not individually boxed.

	GD	VG	EXC	MT
(A) Light orange-painted orange body; orange-painted orange doors.	7	9	15	25
(B) Flat medium orange-painted orange body; same doors as (A).	7	9	15	25

	GD	VG	EXC	MT
(C) Shiny medium orange-painted orange body; same doors as (A).	7	9	15	25
(D) Same body as (C); orange-painted white doors.	7	9	15	25
(E) Dark orange-painted orange body; same doors as (A).	7	9	15	25
(F) Light orange-painted white body; same doors as (A).	7	9	15	25
(G) Medium orange-painted white body; orange-painted white doors.	7	9	15	25

9747 CHESSIE SYSTEM: 1975-76, double-door automobile boxcar; blue-painted blue doors; yellow lettering and Chessie Cat logo; Type II frame; Symington-Wayne trucks. This was the last automobile boxcar to use a partially-riveted body. The breaks in "Che-ssie" and "Sys-tem" attest to the presence of rivets.

	GD	VG	EXC	MT
(A) Flat blue-painted blue body.	10	15	20	25
(B) Slightly darker; shiny blue-painted blue body.	10	15	20	25

9748 C P RAIL: 1975-76, boxcar; Type IX body; medium blue plastic doors painted medium-blue on versions 1-7, white plastic doors painted medium blue on versions 8-14 (door colors for versions 15-19 listed below); white lettering; white and black Pac-man logo at one end; Type II frame; Symington-Wayne trucks; "BLT 5-75". There are more variations (19 and counting) of this car than any other 9700-series car. Variations exist in the door mold color (white, blue and royal blue), body mold color (dark blue,

...er production of the 9700-series.
 shelf: 9768 Boston and Maine Railroad; 9769 Bessemer & Lake Erie Railroad.
...*ddle shelf:* 9770 Northern Pacific Railway; 9771 Norfolk and Western.
...*tom shelf:* 9772 Great Northern; 9773 New York Central System stock car. Both of these came in the Empire State Express set of 1976.

	GD	VG	EXC	MT

medium blue, royal blue and white), and the exterior paint color (at least seven shades of blue, and one shade of purple). There is even one version with the roof a different shade of blue from the body. Dark blue-painted version on a medium blue body is the most common. None of these color combinations cause a difference in value: **10 15 20 30**

1. Dark blue plastic body painted dark blue.
2. Dark blue plastic body painted medium blue.
3. Dark blue plastic body painted medium light blue.
4. Medium blue plastic body painted medium light blue.
5. Medium blue plastic body painted darker light blue.
6. Medium blue plastic body painted medium dark blue.
7. Medium blue plastic body painted medium blue.
8. Medium blue plastic body painted flat medium dark blue.
9. Medium blue plastic body painted medium dark blue.
10. Medium blue plastic body painted medium light blue.
11. White plastic body painted medium light blue.
12. White plastic body painted medium dark blue.
13. White plastic body painted light blue.
14. Royal blue plastic body painted with royal blue sides and lighter royal blue top.
15. Royal blue plastic body painted royal blue; royal blue plastic doors painted royal blue.
16. Medium blue plastic body painted royal blue; white plastic doors painted royal blue.

17. Medium blue plastic body painted royal blue on sides and medium blue top; white plastic doors painted light blue.
18. Medium blue plastic body painted purple; white plastic doors painted purple.
19. Light blue plastic body painted royal blue; royal blue plastic doors painted royal blue.

9749 PENN CENTRAL: 1975-76, boxcar; Type IX body; white and red lettering; interlocked red and green PC logo at right; Type II frame; Symington-Wayne trucks; "4-75".
(A) Green-painted green body; green-painted gray doors.
  8 10 15 25
(B) Same as (A), but green-painted jade doors.
  8 10 15 25
(C) Same as (A), but green-painted lime green doors.
  8 10 15 25
(D) Slightly darker green-painted green body; green-painted gray doors. **8 10 15 25**
(E) Lightest green-painted white body; green-painted white doors. **8 10 15 25**
(F) Same as (A), but green-painted green doors.
  8 10 15 25

9750 D T & I: 1975-76, boxcar (Detroit, Toledo & Ironton); Type IX body; glossy green body except (E); yellow lettering; large "DT & I" letters at right; number under- and over-scored; Type II frame; Symington-Wayne trucks.
(A) Medium green-painted dark green body; medium green-painted dark green doors. **5 6 10 20**

More 9700s, including some specials.

A. Rudman, L. Caponi, F. Stem, and R. LaVoie Collec

Top shelf: 9774 TCA "The Southern Belle" made for 1975 TCA Convention; 9775 Minneapolis & St. Louis from Northern Pacific Service Station set of 19
Middle shelf: 9777 Virginian; the scarce 9778 Seasons Greetings car of 1975.
Bottom shelf: 9779 TCA U.S. Bicentennial Convention car of 1976, "Philadelphia" on all the cars is missing the second "L"; 9780 Johnny Cash from de
year-end special.

	GD	VG	EXC	MT
(B) Same as (A), but medium green-painted clear doors.	5	6	10	20
(C) Medium green-painted light green body; medium green-painted dark green doors.	5	6	10	20
(D) Medium green-painted white body; medium green-painted dark green doors.	5	6	10	20
(E) Flat green-painted light green body; flat green-painted light green doors.	5	6	10	20
(F) Light green-painted white body; medium green-painted dark green doors.	5	6	10	20

(G) Same as (A), but large yellow square "RIDIN' THE RAILS" logo with picture of Johnny Cash to left of doors. The authenticity of this car has been questioned. F. Cordone Collection. **NRS**

9751 FRISCO: 1975-76, boxcar; Type IX body; white lettering; black and white Frisco shield to left; red-painted red doors; Type II frame; Symington-Wayne trucks; "BLT 1-75".

	GD	VG	EXC	MT
(A) Flat red-painted red body.	8	10	15	20
(B) Shiny red-painted red body.	8	10	15	20

9752 LOUISVILLE & NASHVILLE: 1975-76, boxcar; Type IX body; yellow lettering; Type II frame; Symington-Wayne trucks.

	GD	VG	EXC	MT
(A) Light blue-painted royal blue body; medium blue-painted royal blue doors.	8	10	15	20
(B) Medium blue-painted navy blue body; same doors as (A).	8	10	15	20
(C) Light blue-painted royal blue body; medium blue-painted white doors.	8	10	15	20
(D) Medium blue-painted navy blue body; same doors as (C).	8	10	15	20

9753 MAINE CENTRAL: 1975-76, boxcar; Type IX body; green lettering; pine tree logo to left; Type II frame; Symington-Wayne trucks; "BLT 1-75".

	GD	VG	EXC	MT
(A) Medium yellow-painted yellow body; dark yellow-painted yellow doors.	8	10	15	25
(B) Light yellow-painted yellow body; light yellow-painted white doors.	8	10	15	25
(C) Medium yellow-painted yellow body; same doors as (B).	8	10	15	25
(D) Darker yellow-painted yellow body; medium yellow-painted white doors.	8	10	15	25
(E) Light yellow-painted white body; same doors as (D).	8	10	15	25

See Volume II, first edition.

9754 NEW YORK CENTRAL SYSTEM: 1975-77, boxcar; Type IX red body; gray stripe on lower half of sides; white lettering; red-painted red doors; "Pacemaker/FREIGHT SERVICE"; number under- and over-scored; Type II frame; Symington-Wayne trucks "BLT 1-75". Car was not catalogued until 1976, but appeared in the 1579 Milwaukee Service Station Special set in 1975. This car has been used extensively for overstamped commemora-

A. Rudman, L. Caponi, F. Stem, and R. LaVoie Collections

ne late 9700-series boxcars from 1977.
shelf: **9781** Delaware & Hudson; **9782** The Rock.
ddle shelf: **9783** Baltimore & Ohio "Time-Saver Service"; **9784** Santa Fe.
tom shelf: **9785** Conrail (dark blue; a lighter blue is very scarce), **9786** Chicago and North Western.

	GD	VG	EXC	MT
tives by various train clubs. Similar to postwar 6464-125. C. Lang comment.				
(A) Light flat red-painted red body.	10	15	30	40
(B) Medium red-painted red body.	10	15	30	40
(C) Dark red-painted red body.	10	15	30	40
(D) Same as (B), but Type III frame. R. LaVoie Collection.	10	15	30	40
(E) Same as (C), but Type III frame. C. Rohlfing Collection.	10	15	30	40

See Volume II, first edition.

9755 UNION PACIFIC: 1975-76, boxcar; Type IX body; white lettering; red, white and blue U P shield to left; Type II frame; Symington-Wayne trucks; "BLT 1-75". Part of 1560 North American Express set in 1975.

	GD	VG	EXC	MT
(A) Tuscan-painted brown body; tuscan-painted brown doors.	10	15	20	30
(B) Tuscan-painted white body; tuscan-painted white doors.	10	15	20	30
(C) Tuscan-painted brown body; tuscan-painted white doors.	10	15	20	30

9757 CENTRAL OF GEORGIA: 1974, boxcar; uncatalogued; Type IX body; tuscan car with large silver oval on side; red lettering; yellow and red Central of Georgia rectangle at right; number under- and over-scored; Type II frame; Symington-Wayne trucks; "BLT 1-75". Came as part of 1974 dealers' year-end special "profit bonus" package. Similar to postwar 6464-375. See introduction for details.

	GD	VG	EXC	MT
(A) Tuscan-painted brown body; silver-painted gray doors; lightly speckled oval.	10	15	20	30
(B) Same as (A), but medium speckled oval.	10	15	20	30
(C) Same as (A), but shiny silver oval.	10	15	20	30
(D) Same as (A), but silver-painted clear doors; shiny silver oval.	10	15	20	30
(E) Same as (A), but silver-painted yellow doors; shiny silver oval.	10	15	20	30
(F) Tuscan-painted clear body; silver-painted yellow doors; shiny silver oval.	10	15	20	30

See Factory Errors and Prototypes chapter in Volume II, first edition.

9758 THE ALASKA RAILROAD: 1975-77, Type IX body; blue car with yellow stripe; lettering usually yellow; number under- and over-scored; Type II frame; Symington-Wayne trucks. Similar to postwar 6464-825. Reader comments requested on possibility of chemical alteration on versions with white lettering. Though not catalogued until 1976, this car appeared in the 1570 Milwaukee Service Station Special set in 1975.

	GD	VG	EXC	MT
(A) Blue-painted dark blue body; blue-painted white doors.	10	20	30	40
(B) Same as (A), but blue-painted blue doors.	10	20	30	40
(C) Blue-painted medium blue body; blue-painted white doors.	10	20	30	40

The last of the 9700-series boxcars. The series was superseded in 1978 by the 9400-series boxcars.
Top shelf: 9787 Central Railroad Company of New Jersey; 9788 Lehigh Valley.
Bottom shelf: 9789 Pickens Railroad, available only in the Rocky Mountain Special Set of 1978.

A. Rudman, L. Caponi, F. Stem, and R. LaVoie Collection

	GD	VG	EXC	MT

(D) Blue-painted white body; blue-painted white doors.
10 20 30 40

(E) Same as (D), but white lettering; yellow stripe above lettering and logo. Possibly a chemically altered piece. R. M. Caplan Collection. **NRS**

(F) Blue-painted blue body; blue-painted blue doors; white lettering. Possibly a chemically altered piece. **NRS**
See Factory Errors and Prototypes chapter in Volume II, first edition.

9759 PAUL REVERE: 1975-76, boxcar; uncatalogued; Type IX white body; red roof and ends; blue- or dark blue-painted white plastic door; blue lettering; multicolor logos of Revere's ride and a Minuteman; Type II frame; Symington-Wayne trucks; "BLT 1-75". This and the next two entries were part of the Liberty Special uncatalogued set announced in a late 1975 special flyer.
10 12 40 55

9760 LIBERTY BELL: 1975-76, boxcar; uncatalogued; white Type IX body; dark blue roof and ends; red-painted red plastic doors; blue lettering; red stars; "SPIRIT of '76"; Liberty Bell logo to right; Type II frame; Symington-Wayne trucks; "BLT 1-75".
10 12 40 55

9761 GEORGE WASHINGTON: 1975-76, boxcar; uncatalogued; white Type IX body; red roof and ends; dark blue-painted white plastic doors; blue lettering; electrocals of Presidential Seal to right, and Washington and the Declaration to left; Type II frame; Symington-Wayne trucks; "BLT 1-75". C. Rohlfing comment. **10 12 40 55**

9762 WELCOME TOY FAIR: 1975, boxcar; uncatalogued; Type IX body; red painted white plastic body; silver roof; red-painted red plastic door; metallic silver lettering; 75th anniversary logo; "BLT 1-75"; "9762" does not appear on car. There is a distinctive orange tint to the red on the body. Quite hard to find.
— 125 150 200

9764 GRAND TRUNK WESTERN: 1976-77, double-door automobile boxcar; blue-painted blue plastic body; blue-painted dark blue doors; white lettering; number under- and over-scored;

Type II or III frame; all rivet detail removed; Symington-Wayne trucks. **10 15 20 25**

9767 RAIL BOX: 1976-77, boxcar; Type IX body; yellow-painted yellow plastic body; black-painted black plastic doors; black lettering; Symington-Wayne trucks. Came with the 1664 Illinois Central freight set in 1976-77, and also for separate-sale.
(A) Light yellow paint; Type III frame.
10 15 20 25
(B) Medium yellow paint; Type II frame.
10 15 20 25
(C) Dark yellow paint; Type II frame. **10 15 20 25**

9768 BOSTON AND MAINE: 1976-77, boxcar; Type IX body; black-painted black doors; black and white lettering; number under- and over-scored; Symington-Wayne trucks. Similar to postwar 6464-475.
(A) Glossy blue-painted gray body; Type II frame.
8 10 15 20
(B) Flat blue-painted gray body; Type III frame.
8 10 15 20
(C) Same as (B), but Type II frame. R. LaVoie Collection.
8 10 15 20

9769 BESSEMER & LAKE ERIE RAILROAD: 1976-77, boxcar; Type IX body; black and white lettering; red, white and blue savings bond logo to left; round Bessemer "I"-beam logo to right; Symington-Wayne trucks; "BLT 1-76".
(A) Flat orange-painted orange body; orange-painted white doors; Type II frame. **8 10 15 20**
(B) Shiny orange-painted orange body; orange-painted orange doors; Type III frame. **8 10 15 20**
(C) Shiny orange-painted orange body; orange-painted white doors; Type III frame. **8 10 15 20**
(D) Same as (C), but Type II frame. **8 10 15 20**

9770 NORTHERN PACIFIC RAILWAY: 1976-77, boxcar; Type IX body; orange-painted orange doors; white and black lettering; NP Monad logo to right; Symington-Wayne trucks; "BLT 1-76".

16617 Chicago and North Western boxcar showing the End-of-Train device intended to replace the caboose; 16801 Lionel Railroader Club (see Volume II).

	GD	VG	EXC	MT
(A) Glossy orange-painted orange body; Type II frame.	8	10	15	20
(B) Flat orange-painted orange body; Type III frame.	8	10	15	20
(C) Flat orange-painted opaque-white body; Type III frame.	8	10	15	20

9771 NORFOLK AND WESTERN: 1976-77, boxcar; Type IX body; white lettering; large "NW" to left of doors; Symington-Wayne trucks. This car was included as part of 1762 Wabash Cannonball steam engine freight set in 1977, and was also a separate-sale item.

(A) Dark blue-painted blue body; dark blue-painted blue doors; Type III frame. **8 10 20 30**

(B) Same as (A), but dark blue-painted gray body. **8 10 20 30**

(C) Same as (A), but dark blue-painted white doors; Type II frame. **8 10 20 30**

See Volume II, first edition.

9772 GREAT NORTHERN: 1976, boxcar; Type IX body; green- and orange-painted green body; yellow stripes; green- and orange-painted green doors; red; number under-scored; white and black G N goat decal; yellow and black lettering; Type III frame; Symington-Wayne trucks; "BLT 1-76". Came only in the 1665 N Y C Hudson Empire State Express set. Similar to postwar 6464-450. Hard to find now. **20 30 65 90**

See Factory Errors and Prototypes chapter in Volume II, first edition.

9774 THE SOUTHERN BELLE: 1975, T C A boxcar; see Volume II, first edition.

9775 MINNEAPOLIS & ST. LOUIS: 1976, boxcar; uncatalogued; Type IX body; red-painted red doors; white lettering; number under-scored; Type II frame; Standard O trucks; "BLT 1-76". From the 1672 Northern Pacific Service Station set of 1976.

(A) Light red-painted red body. **12 15 25 35**

(B) Dark red-painted red body. **12 15 25 35**

9776 SOUTHERN PACIFIC LINES: 1976, boxcar; uncatalogued; Type IX body; black-painted body; black-painted black doors; white and gold lettering; red and gold arrow logo to right; Type II frame; Standard O trucks. From the 1672 Northern Pacific Service Station set of 1976.

(A) Black-painted black body. **15 20 30 50**

(B) Black-painted opaque white body. **NRS**

See Factory Errors and Prototypes chapter in Volume II, first edition.

9777 VIRGINIAN: 1976-77, boxcar; Type IX body; yellow lettering and round "VGN" logo to right of doors; Symington-Wayne trucks; "BLT 1-76".

	GD	VG	EXC	MT
(A) Blue-painted light blue body; dark blue-painted dark blue doors; Type II frame.	8	10	15	20
(B) Blue-painted light blue body; light blue-painted light blue doors; Type III frame.	8	10	15	20
(C) Blue-painted medium blue body; light blue-painted light blue doors; Type III frame.	8	10	15	20
(D) Blue-painted light blue body; blue-painted white doors; Type II frame.	8	10	15	20

9778 SEASONS GREETINGS 1975: 1975, boxcar; uncatalogued; Type IX blue-painted blue body; silver-painted gray doors; silver "Seasons/Greetings/1975" to left of door; silver and red 75th anniversary logo to right; Symington-Wayne trucks; Type II frame; "BLT 1-75". This is the third car in Lionel's Seasons Greetings series, and the first one made specially for it (i.e., not an overstamped regular-issue car). **— 100 150 200**

9779 U. S. BICENTENNIAL 1976 T C A: 1979, boxcar; see Volume II, first edition.

9780 JOHNNY CASH: 1976, boxcar; uncatalogued; Type IX body; black roof and ends; silver sides painted on gray body; black-painted black doors; black lettering; picture of General-style engine at right; Type III frame; Symington-Wayne trucks; "BLT 1-76". Offered only to dealers in a 1976 year-end bonus special for group purchases. The 9757 Central of Georgia was also offered this way in 1974. **— 25 35 45**

9781 DELAWARE & HUDSON: 1977-78, boxcar; Type IX body; yellow-painted yellow doors; blue lettering; large blue D & H shield to right; Symington-Wayne trucks; Type III frame; "BLT 1-77".

(A) Light yellow-painted yellow body; blue lettering. **6 8 20 25**

(B) Medium yellow-painted yellow body; dark blue lettering. **6 8 20 25**

9782 THE ROCK: 1977-78, boxcar; Type IX body; white and black lettering; black and white "R" logo to right; Type III frame; Symington-Wayne trucks.

(A) Blue-painted gray body; blue-painted gray doors. **10 15 20 25**

(B) Blue-painted light blue body; blue-painted blue doors. **10 15 20 25**

(C) Same as (B), but white doors. Reader confirmation requested. T. Taylor Collection. **NRS**

9783 BALTIMORE & OHIO: 1977-78; boxcar; Type IX body; blue sides and ends; silver roof; blue-painted blue doors; white and blue lettering; large tapered orange arrowhead across sides; round "TIME-SAVER SERVICE" logo to right; Type III frame; Symington-Wayne trucks; "BLT 1-77". Similar to postwar 6464-400. Several dozen "test" shells of this car exist, without lettering

	GD	VG	EXC	MT

or decals. They are shells only, not complete cars. G. Salamone and G. Halverson comments. **6 12 30 40**

9784 A T S F: 1977-78, boxcar; Type IX body; red-painted red body and red doors; white lettering and Santa Fe cross logo; flat black-painted roof and ends; number under- and over-scored; Type III frame; Symington-Wayne trucks; "BLT 1-77".

10 15 25 35

See Factory Errors and Prototypes chapter in Volume II, first edition.

9785 CONRAIL: 1977-79, boxcar; Type IX body; white lettering and Conrail logo to right; Type III frame; Symington-Wayne trucks; "BLT 1-77".
(A) Medium blue-painted blue body and doors.

10 15 20 25

(B) Light blue-painted blue body and doors. This was not a normal paint variation, but an attempt by Fundimensions to correct the car's color. The sample paint chip sent by Conrail to Fundimensions was too dark to match the Conrail prototypes. This variety is more scarce than the medium blue version. R. LaVoie comment. **— — 40 50**
See Volume II, first edition.

9786 CHICAGO AND NORTH WESTERN: 1977-79, boxcar; Type IX tuscan-painted gray body; tuscan-painted tuscan doors; white lettering; "C & N W"; number under- and over-scored; Type III frame; Symington-Wayne trucks; "BLT 1-77".

10 12 20 25

See Volume II, first edition.

9787 CENTRAL RAILROAD COMPANY OF NEW JERSEY: 1977-79, boxcar; Type IX body; Brunswick green-painted green body and doors; gold lettering; number under- and over-scored; Type III frame; Symington-Wayne trucks; "BLT 1-77". 7404 boxcar is similar except for cream lettering and logo replacing the gold stamping on this version.

10 15 20 30

9788 LEHIGH VALLEY: 1977-79, boxcar; Type IX body; cream-painted cream body and doors; black lettering; Type III frame; Symington-Wayne trucks; "BLT 1-77".
(A) Decal flag on doors. **10 12 15 20**
(B) No decal flag on doors. **10 12 15 20**

9789 PICKENS RAILROAD: 1977, boxcar; Type IX body; blue-painted blue body and doors; white lettering; "THE ROUTE OF/NATIONAL RAILWAY UTILIZATION"; circular red, white and blue arrow logo; Type III frame; Symington-Wayne trucks; "BLT 1-77". From 1765 Rocky Mountain Special set.

10 15 25 40

16000-Series Boxcars

16206 DENVER & RIO GRANDE: 1989, boxcar; uncatalogued; orange body; silver-painted doors; black roof; black lettering, number and logo; Standard O trucks; "BLT 1-89". Came only in 11758 Desert King Service Station Special set in 1989. This car's number incorrectly implies it is a short "Traditional"-line boxcar. In fact, it is a "classic" boxcar of the 9700- and 19200-mold. But since the set was considered a Traditional set, the boxcar was numbered in the traditional boxcar category. M. Solly comment. **— — — 60**

16617 CHICAGO AND NORTH WESTERN: 1989, boxcar with End-of-Train Device (ETD), which is a blinking light box intended (on prototype railroads) to replace cabooses. This car is

the first Lionel car to include this device. Tuscan sides and roof; black ends; yellow ETD; white lettering "ROUTE OF/The/Challengers" to right of doors; number under- and over-scored; Symington-Wayne trucks; "BLT 1-89". Despite its number, this is a classic-body boxcar of the 9700- and 19200-mold, as are the following 16600-series boxcars. **— — — 25**

16622 C S X: 1990-91, boxcar with End-of-Train Device; dark blue body; yellow lettering and large "CSX" logo at upper right; ASF strong-arm trucks; "BLT 1-90". Despite its number, this is a classic-body boxcar of the 9700- and 19200-mold.

— — — 27

16623 M-K-T THE KATY*: 1991, double-door automobile boxcar with End-of-Train Device; yellow body; brown roof; black lettering; "M-K-T" and Katy script logo to left of doors; yellow ETD; ASF strong-arm trucks; "BLT 1-91". **— — — 29**

16631 ROCK ISLAND: 1990-91, boxcar with steam RailSounds; green body; gold lettering; red and yellow Rock Island shield logo to right of doors; ASF strong-arm trucks; "BLT 1-90". Apparently the popularity of RailSounds has prompted Lionel to begin putting it in boxcars as well as engines. It is, however, an expensive addition. Announced in 1990, but not released until early 1991. **— — — 140**

16632 BURLINGTON NORTHERN: 1990, boxcar with diesel RailSounds; yellow body; silver roof; black lettering; large B N logo to upper right; RailSounds circuit board mounted inside car body; ASF strong-arm trucks; "BLT 1-90".

— — — 140

16639 BALTIMORE & OHIO*: 1991, boxcar with steam RailSounds; silver body and door; black lettering; capitol logo to right of door; number under-scored; RailSounds circuit board mounted inside; ASF strong-arm trucks; "BLT 1-91".

— — — 150

16640 RUTLAND*: 1991, boxcar with diesel railsounds; bright green and yellow Rutland paint scheme; green roof, ends and lower portion of sides, yellow upper section; yellow door; yellow and green lettering; green Rutland shield logo to right of door; number under-scored; RailSounds circuit board mounted inside; ASF strong-arm trucks; "BLT 1-91". This car is a brighter yellow and green than the earlier Rutland boxcars (the popular postwar 6464-300 and the modern reissue, the 9710 from 1972).

— — — 150

17875 PORT HURON & DETROIT: 1989, boxcar; LOTS; see Volume II, first edition.

17882 BALTIMORE AND OHIO: 1990, double-door automobile boxcar; with ETD; L O T S; see Volume II, first edition.

19200-Series Boxcars

With the change in ownership of Lionel in 1986 came a complete changeover of the numbering system used on the trains. The classic boxcars, still bearing the "Famous Name" title (and still, strangely enough, bearing endplates with a "9700-series" stamping) were christened into the new 19200-series with the Tidewater Southern in 1987. The long line of "Famous Name" classic boxcars continues to the present day. To complete the circle, Lionel has announced that the 1991 issues of these boxcars will see the return of their riveting detail to its full glory — so that the newest boxcars will sport bodies as detailed as the Type I bodies not seen since

R. Kaptur, R. LaVoie, and A. Rudman Collections; B. Greenberg photograph

Some of Lionels new 1900 series boxcars. The latest sequence of Classic boxcar production.
Top shelf: 19204 Milwaukee Road; 19205 Great Northern.
Second shelf: 19206 Seaboard System; 19207 C P Rail.
Third shelf: 19208 Southern; 19209 Florida East Coast.
Bottom shelf: 19210 Soo; 19211 Vermont Railway.

the early 1950s. If carried out, this change will at last reverse the trend of eliminating rivet detail on the classic boxcars in favor of decorating schemes. Apparently Lionel has finally overcome the problem of imprinting colors and lettering over the riveting bumps on the body.

The 19200 boxcars were also among the first recipients of the new ASF Strong-Arm trucks in 1990, the first new rolling stock trucks to appear in nearly 20 years. They were described in the 1989 catalogue, but did not show up until 1990.

It is too early to discern the scarcity of the 19200-series boxcars, which, like the 9400- and 9700-series, also include double-door automobile boxcars. And like those earlier series, Lionel continues to offer some boxcars only in sets (not for separate-sale), which should lead to greater scarcity for some of them. The 19204 Milwaukee, the 19205 Great Northern, and the 19214 Western Maryland are showing signs of this.

Another marketing scheme which will certainly affect scarcity in the long term is Lionel's policy of cataloguing its recent production boxcars for one year only. This has been the case for virtually every five-digit boxcar so far.

The reader is again advised that Lionel continues to produce classic boxcars for special train club events, for the Toy Fair and Seasons Greetings series, and for operating boxcars and a new "I Love"-State series. The firm has reserved special numbering sequences for each of these series: 17800s for the train club cars, 19800s for the operating boxcars, and 19900s for the "I Love"-State, Toy Fair and Seasons Greetings cars.

A warning to the classic boxcar collector: as if this was not difficult enough to keep straight, Lionel throws ringers in other number series. A 16206 Denver Rio Grande boxcar was included in the handsome Desert King Service Station Special set in 1989. The 16200-series is normally reserved for "Traditional" (i.e., short) boxcars, but the 16206 is definitely a "classic" boxcar of the 9700-series mold. It even has Standard O trucks. It is not clear why Lionel numbered it that way, except that lately it has considered Service Station Special sets as Traditional sets. Now that a numbering system exists which distinguishes Traditional from Collector pieces, Lionel installed this boxcar in the former series. But its number is not consistent with its status as a true "Collector" boxcar. This was not the only unusual thing about the Desert

Boxcars and reefers, a good mix. From Lionel's most recent classic boxcar series.   *A. Rudman, L. Caponi, F. Stem, and R. LaVoie Collection.*

Top shelf: 19200 Tidewater Southern; 19201 Lancaster and Chester. The first two of the new 19200-series boxcars.

Second shelf: 19202 Pennsylvania (in considerable demand); 19203 Detroit & Toledo Shore Line.

Third shelf: 19802 Union Refrigerator Transit Co. "Carnation" operating milk car is considered a reefer car though it has riveted boxcar sides, note differences in door and body length; 19803 Reading Lines Icing Station car meant to accompany the Icing Station accessories.

Bottom shelf: 19805 Santa Fe operating boxcar; 19504 Northern Pacific wood-sided reefer (watch for peeling red Monad decals). This is technically a refrigerator car (note longer body). See Refrigerator Cars chapter for listing.

	GD	VG	EXC	MT

King set — see the 18608 entry in the Steam Engine chapter for another interesting story.

Finally, the collector should be aware that "classic"-style boxcars also show up in the 16600-series of "Traditional" operating cars — the 16617 C & N W from 1989 and the 16622 C S X from 1990 (both with ETDs) are examples. The classic boxcars were witness to a major innovation in 1990-1991 — the addition of RailSounds circuitry to the boxcars. Now, instead of remaining in stationary accessories, these realistic sounds can ride with the train.

19200 TIDEWATER SOUTHERN: 1987, boxcar; tuscan body; yellow lettering; yellow-orange feather logo; Symington-Wayne trucks. This boxcar marks the beginning of the fourth major boxcar series of the modern era as a successor to the 9200-, 9400- and 9700-series. — — — 18

19201 LANCASTER AND CHESTER: 1987, boxcar; blue lower sides and ends; white upper sides and roof; contrasting blue and white lettering and logo; Symington-Wayne trucks.

— — — 90

19202 P R R: 1987, boxcar; flat dark Brunswick green body; white lettering; white and red banner, logo and P R R keystone; Symington-Wayne trucks. — — — 45

19203 DETROIT & TOLEDO SHORE LINE: 1987, boxcar; yellow body; red lettering and square logo; number under- and over-scored; Symington-Wayne trucks. Same design as L C C A special boxcar of 1982 except for new colors.

— — — 15

19204 MILWAUKEE ROAD: 1987, boxcar; brown body; broad yellow stripe runs length of car through doors; contrasting yellow and brown lettering; red and white rectangular Milwaukee

B. Greenberg photograph

More 19200 boxcars. Note the change in truck styles on the last four — these are the ASF stong-arm trucks.
Top shelf: **19212 Pennsylvania.**
Second shelf: **19213 Spokane Portland and Seattle; 19214 Western Maryland.**
Third shelf: **19215 Union Pacific; 19216 Santa Fe.**
Bottom shelf: **19217 Burlington Route; 19218 New Haven.**

	GD	VG	EXC	MT

logo; Standard O trucks. Part of Milwaukee Road Fallen Flags set No. 2, whose components were offered only for separate-sale. — — — **40**

19205 GREAT NORTHERN: 1988, double-door automobile boxcar; dark green roof and ends; orange sides and doors; dark green lettering; number under- and over-scored; red and white circular goat logo; Standard O trucks. Part of Great Northern Fallen Flags set No. 3, whose components were offered only for separate-sale. — — — **40**

19206 SEABOARD SYSTEM: 1988, boxcar; black body and doors; gold lettering; gold and red double-"SS" logo; Symington-Wayne trucks. — — — **20**

19207 C P RAIL: 1988, double-door automobile boxcar; bright burnt-orange body and doors; black lettering; black and white Pac-man logo at right end of side; Symington-Wayne trucks. — — — **20**

19208 SOUTHERN: 1988, double-door automobile boxcar; tuscan body and doors; white lettering and D F logo; Symington-Wayne trucks. — — — **20**

	GD	VG	EXC	MT

19209 FLORIDA EAST COAST: 1988, boxcar; dark blue body and doors; yellow "Speedway" and "TO AMERICA'S /PLAYGROUND" lettering; number under- and over-scored; Symington-Wayne trucks. — — — **17**

19210 SOO: 1989, boxcar; white body; red doors; red stripe along bottom; large "SOO" logo in blue and silver; Symington-Wayne trucks; "BLT 1-89". — — — **17**

19211 VERMONT RAILWAY: 1989, boxcar; forest green body and doors; white lettering, number and mountain logo; Symington-Wayne trucks; "BLT 1-89". — — — **17**

19212 PENNSYLVANIA: 1989, boxcar; tuscan body and doors; white lettering; P R R keystone in black and white to right of doors; Symington-Wayne trucks; "BLT 1-89". — — — **20**

19213 SPOKANE PORTLAND AND SEATTLE R Y: 1989, double-door automobile boxcar; tuscan body and doors; large "S. P & S." logo in white; white lettering; Symington-Wayne trucks; "BLT 1-89". — — — **20**

19214 WESTERN MARYLAND: 1989, boxcar; brown body and doors; white lettering and W M logo; Standard O trucks; "BLT

The Lionel 90th Anniversary Set
Top shelf: 1900 (18502) Lionel Lines GP-9.
Second shelf: 19219 Lionel Lines with RailSounds; 19220 Lionel Lines.
Third shelf: 19221 Lionel Lines; 19222 Lionel Lines.
Bottom shelf: 19223 Lionel Lines; 19708 Lionel Lines bay window caboose.

A. Rudman Collection; B. Greenberg photograph

	GD	VG	EXC	MT

1-89". Part of Western Maryland Fallen Flags No. 4 set from 1989, whose components were all offered only for separate-sale.
— — — 30

19215 UNION PACIFIC: 1990, double-door boxcar; yellow body and doors; black lettering and U P logo to one side of doors, with "U.P." in hollow outline letters; multicolor "automated/rail way", "CUSHION RIDE" and map inside square black-outlined box"; ASF strong-arm trucks; "A 90-1 Lionel" substitutes for "BLT" date. This car has a left and right side. Map is to the left of door on one side and to the right on the other side.
— — — 18

19216 SANTA FE: 1990, boxcar; tuscan body and doors; white and yellow lettering; large Santa Fe cross logo in white to left of doors; ASF strong-arm trucks; "BLT 1-90".
— — — 18

19217 BURLINGTON ROUTE: 1990, boxcar; red body and doors; black and white lettering "BURLINGTON"; number under- and over-scored; black and white "Burlington/Route" logo to right

of doors; "EVERYWHERE/WEST"; ASF strong-arm trucks; "BLT 1-90".
— — — 18

19218 NEW HAVEN: 1990, boxcar; black body; bright orange doors; white lettering; large white "N" over white "H" to left of doors; number under- and over-scored; ASF strong-arm trucks; "BLT 1-90".
— — — 18

The 90th Anniversary Set

In 1990 Lionel celebrated its 90th birthday with a collector set of five matching boxcars capturing the ten most important events in the company's history. The set was headed by a GP-9 diesel and included a matching bay window caboose. When first issued, collectors thought the logos on the cars were poorly done. As it turned out, Lionel had applied an unusual antiquing to the electrocal to blur the edges of the images. An interesting footnote: the catalogue trumpeted the engine as including RailSounds, but

	GD	VG	EXC	MT

engineers could not fit the RailSounds circuit board into the GP, so they placed it in the 19219 boxcar.

19219 LIONEL LINES: 1990, boxcar with diesel RailSounds. This and the next four entries are part of the 11715 Lionel 90th Anniversary set, which also included the 18502 GP-9 diesel and the 19708 bay window caboose. Straw yellow sides; orange roof and ends; dark blue doors; black lettering; antiqued multicolor electrocals and several lines of descriptive text depicting the first gondola in 1900 and Standard Gauge in "1906"; doors are glued shut to deter tampering; RailSounds is muffled because the speaker is face down on the frame; Standard O trucks; "BLT 1-90". This car was one of the first to use a power pickup on the Standard O sprung trucks. A spring-mounted roller pickup is snapped into the truck, and a copper wiper strip spans the two axles to complete the ground. — — — 120

19220 LIONEL LINES: 1990, boxcar; straw yellow sides; orange roof and ends; dark blue doors; black lettering; antiqued multicolor electrocals and several lines of descriptive text depict Lionel events in 1926 and 1934; Standard O trucks; "BLT 1-90"; matches 19219. Part of 11715 Lionel 90th Anniversary set. — — — 25

19221 LIONEL LINES: 1990, boxcar; straw yellow sides; orange roof and ends; dark blue doors; black lettering; antiqued multicolor electrocals and several lines of descriptive text depict events at Lionel in 1935 and 1937; Standard O trucks; "BLT 1-90"; matches 19219. Part of 11715 Lionel 90th Anniversary set. — — — 25

19222 LIONEL LINES: 1990, boxcar; straw yellow sides; orange roof and ends; dark blue doors; black lettering; antiqued multicolor electrocals and several lines of descriptive text depict events at Lionel in 1948 and 1950; Standard O trucks; "BLT 1-90"; matches 19219. Part of 11715 Lionel 90th Anniversary set. — — — 25

19223 LIONEL LINES: 1990, boxcar; straw yellow sides; orange roof and ends; dark blue doors; black lettering; antiqued multicolor electrocals and several lines of descriptive text depict events at Lionel in 1979 and 1989; Standard O trucks; "BLT 1-90"; matches 19219. Part of 11715 Lionel 90th Anniversary set. — — — 25

19228 COTTON BELT: 1991, boxcar; tuscan Type X body and doors; white lettering; blue and white lightning streak logo to right; number under- and over-scored; ASF strong-arm trucks; "BLT 1-91". — — — 20

19229 FRISCO*: 1991, boxcar with diesel RailSounds; bright orange body and doors; silver roof; black lettering "Ship it in the Frisco!"; black and white shield logo to left; diesel RailSounds circuitry inside with volume control; bar code; Standard O trucks; "BLT 1-91". Part of Frisco Fallen Flags No. 5, whose components were only sold separately. — — — 150

19230 FRISCO*: 1991, double-door automobile boxcar; red body and doors; white and black lettering, with pattern similar to 19229; Standard O trucks; "BLT 1-91". Part of Frisco Fallen Flags Series No. 5, whose components were only sold separately. — — — 33

19231 T A G: 1991, double-door automobile boxcar; royal blue body and doors; yellow lettering "TENNESSEE, ALABAMA, & GEORGIA" and T A G logo; ASF strong-arm trucks; "BLT 1-91". — — — 20

19232 ROCK ISLAND: 1991, double-door automobile boxcar; tuscan body and doors; white lettering and Rock Island shield logo; number under- and over-scored; ASF strong-arm trucks; "BLT 1-91". — — — 20

19233 SOUTHERN PACIFIC: 1991, boxcar; dark green Type X body; black ends; red and black lettering (sometimes difficult to see black lettering); circular red S P logo; ASF strong-arm trucks; "BLT 1-91". — — — 20

19234 NEW YORK CENTRAL*: 1991, boxcar; light (robin's egg) blue body; Type X body mold with added rivet detail; light (canary) yellow door; colors of body and door are a reverse scheme from the 19235 Katy boxcar in this set; black lettering; NYC oval logo at upper right; "Pacemaker/FREIGHT/SERVICE" at upper left; number under-scored; Standard O trucks; "BUILT BY/LIONEL" (no date). Part of 11722 Girls' Train, a Collector set which was a modern revival of the famous 1957 Girls' set. — — — 40

19235 THE KATY*: 1991, boxcar; light (canary) yellow body; Type X body mold with added rivet detail; light (robin's egg) blue door; colors are a reverse scheme from 19234 boxcar; black lettering; "The Katy" in black script to upper right; Standard O trucks; "BLT 1-91". Part of 11722 Girls' Train, a Collector set which was a modern revival of the famous 1957 Girls' set. — — — 40

19800-SERIES BOXCARS

Lionel Trains, Inc. continues to remake the popular operating boxcars and refrigerator cars that were such postwar favorites. In fact, the milk car had not appeared at all in the modern era until LTI brought back the 19802 Carnation milk car in 1987, followed immediately by the 19810 Bosco car in 1988. The milk cars may be among the all-time action favorites of Lionel operators. The 19802 and 19810 modern milk cars are really refrigerator car bodies, so the reader will find their descriptions in that chapter.

There was a similar drought in production of the operating ice car during the modern era — only one car, the 6700 P F E, and its accompanying 2306 icing station, had been made from 1970 to 1986. LTI again sensed a pent-up demand and released the 19803 Reading ice car in 1987, the 19808 N Y R B ice car in 1988, the 19813 Northern Pacific ice car in 1989, and a new version of the icing station accessory (12703) in 1988. Although these cars are protypically refrigerator cars (of course!), Lionel has based its ice cars on 9700-style classic bodies with ice hatches in the roof, and a large opening panel in one side. So we have listed them here with the classic boxcars. Oddly enough, the three ice cars feature excellent rivet detailing on the car sides not seen on the classic boxcars themselves since the 1950s.

The 19800 numbering series includes all operating cars, so it will have boxcars, hoppers, smoking cabooses, cattle cars, etc., regardless of type of car. This section only lists operating versions of the classic boxcars.

Do not forget those old standbys — the plunger-operated men who appear when the door opens at the touch of a button. LTI has issued Santa Fe and Erie versions of that car.

Finally, a surprise in 1990: the brakeman car, absent from the Lionel line for 32 years, returned in Monon colors. The little man rides on the top here, and spends a lot of time on his stomach dodging the telltales. As with the giraffe cars, beware of place-

A selection of what Lionel calls "Special Series" cars.
Top shelf: **19901 I Love VA; 19903 1987 Christmas Car.**
Middle shelf: **19904 1988 Christmas Car; 19905 I Love CA.**
Bottom shelf: **19906 I Love PA; 19908 Season's Greetings.**

B. Greenberg photograph

	GD	VG	EXC	MT

ment on layouts, because larger rolling stock can get tangled in the telltales and trackside trips.

19803 READING LINES: 1987, icing station box/refrigerator car; white sides and doors; black roof and ends; body features excellent rivet detail; blue lettering and Reading diamond logo; number under- and over-scored; Standard O trucks; same construction as modern era 6700 and meant to accompany 2306 and postwar icing stations. — — — 50

19805 SANTA FE: 1987, operating boxcar; red body; white Santa Fe lettering; red and white Santa Fe cross logo; number under- and over-scored; blue man appears when plunger is activated; Standard O trucks. — — — 32

19808 N Y R B: 1988, icing station box/refrigerator car (New York Central); bright orange sides; red roof and ends; number under- and over-scored; blue and white "Early Bird" logo; Standard O trucks; "BLT 1-88". — — — 45

19809 ERIE LACKAWANNA: 1988, operating boxcar; red-brown-painted body; white lettering, number and EL logo; gray unpainted man tosses mail sack out of door when plunger is activated; Standard O trucks; operating couplers. — — — 35

19811 MONON: 1990, operating brakeman car; first brakeman car issued since 1958; blue man on top ducks as car approaches telltale; gray 9700-style body; red lettering; number under- and over-scored; red and white circle-M "Hoosier Line" decal to right; postwar die-cast bar-end trucks; "BLT 1-90". Comes with two telltales and trackside trip mechanism. — — — 60

19813 NORTHERN PACIFIC: 1989, icing station box/refrigerator car; uncatalogued; dark green body; black roof with ice hatch; ice car body with extensive rivet detail; opening side hatch; gold "AMERICAN/RAILWAY/EXPRESS" lettering; round N P Monad decal in white; black and red to left of doors; number is at both left and right side of car; Standard O trucks; "BLT 1-89". Comes with twelve-block ice load for operation with 12703 icing station. Offered in 1989 Holiday Collection flyer. — — — 50

19900 SPECIAL SERIES BOXCARS

Lionel set aside the 19900-series of numbers for "special series" cars, which so far have included the Toy Fair and Seasons Greetings Cars and a new group of cars in the "I Love"-State series. All these cars, nonetheless, are of the classic boxcar mold, from the 9700- and 19200-heritage. The "I Love"-State series began with the 9475 Delaware & Hudson "I Love New York" car in 1984. This car is often not identified with the "I Love"-State series because it was uncatalogued, and shows up as "Delaware & Hudson" in Collector guides. A 9486 Michigan car followed in 1986, then the series switched to five digits in 1987 with the 19901 Virginia. California, Pennsylvania and New Jersey followed each year thereafter. Will there eventually be 50 cars? What about Puerto Rico? At one per year, does Lionel plan to be around until 2033? Stay tuned!

19900 TOY FAIR: 1987, boxcar; uncatalogued; red body; silver roof and ends; red door; silver lettering; new red, white and blue "LIONEL" logo at right of door; "The Legend Lives On"; Symington-Wayne trucks; "BLT 1-87". — — — 150

Hi-Cube boxcars dating from 1976.
Top shelf: **9600 Chessie System; 9601 Illinois Central Gulf.**
Second shelf: **9602 Santa Fe; 9603 Penn Central.**
Third shelf: **9604 Norfolk and Western; 9605 New Haven.**
Bottom shelf: **9606 Union Pacific; 9607 Southern Pacific.**

R. Kaptur, R. LaVoie, and A. Rudman Collections; B. Greenberg photograph

	GD	VG	EXC	MT

19901 I LOVE VA: 1987, boxcar; yellow sides; blue roof and ends; pink "Virginia/is for lovers" in script; blue lettering; number under- and over-scored; Symington-Wayne trucks. Part of continuing annual "I Love"-State series.   —   —   —   35

19902 TOY FAIR: 1988, boxcar; uncatalogued; silver sides; black roof, ends and door; red, white and blue Lionel insignia and circle-L logo to right of door; black and gold Large Scale decals; black lettering "The Legend Lives On"; Symington-Wayne trucks; "BLT 1-88".   —   —   —   125

19903 LIONEL: 1987, Christmas car; uncatalogued; white sides; green roof and ends; red doors; red, white, blue and black Lionel insignia and circle-L logo; red and green lettering features "Merry Christmas" in five languages; plastic arch bar trucks; "BLT 1-87". Part of special year-end package for 1987, "Happy Lionel Holidays."   —   —   —   30

19904 LIONEL: 1988, Christmas car; uncatalogued; silver sides; red roof, doors and ends; red "Merry Christmas 1988" to left of door; black and green lettering; mistletoe and Christmas tree

electrocals; gold and black Lionel classics logo; Symington-Wayne trucks; "BLT 1-88".   —   —   —   35

19905 I LOVE CA: 1988, boxcar; medium blue sides; gold-painted roof and ends; yellow lettering and number; "CALIFORNIA/ THE GOLDEN STATE"; red heart logo; Symington-Wayne trucks; operating couplers. Part of continuing annual "I Love"-State series.   —   —   —   20

19906 I LOVE PA: 1989, boxcar; maroon or wine body; white and gold lettering; "I" and "PA" in white with red heart to left of doors; "You've Got a Friend/In Pennsylvania" in gold to right; number under- and over-scored; Symington-Wayne trucks. Part of continuing annual "I Love"-State series.
  —   —   —   20

19907 TOY FAIR: 1989, boxcar; uncatalogued; pale yellow body; dark green door; green lettering; "NEW YORK/TOY FAIR/1989" with large apple electrocal to right of door; "LIONEL SOUNDS GREAT" with train electrocal on left side; Symington-Wayne trucks; "BLT 1-89".   —   —   —   120

More Hi-Cube boxcars, a few repeats.

R. Kaptur, R. LaVoie, and A. Rudman Collections; B. Greenberg photograph

Top shelf: **9608** Burlington Northern; **9610** Frisco.
Middle shelf: **9626** Santa Fe; **9627** Union Pacific.
Bottom shelf: **9628** Burlington Northern; **9629** C&O Chessie System.

	GD	VG	EXC	MT

19908 SEASON'S GREETINGS: 1989, boxcar; uncatalogued; white sides; red roof and ends; silver door; red and gold Santa Claus electrocal to left of door; red, blue and gold "Season's Greetings from Lionel" with snowflakes on right side; gold lettering; Symington-Wayne trucks; "BLT 1-89". Available from 1989 Holiday Collection flyer. — — — **25**

19909 I LOVE N J: 1990, boxcar; dark green body; gold roof and ends; white and gold lettering; "I" and "N J" to left of doors with red heart; "Liberty and Prosperity" in gold script to right of doors; ASF strong-arm trucks; "BLT 1-90". Part of continuing annual "I Love"-State series. — — — **20**

19910 HAPPY HOLIDAYS: 1990, boxcar; uncatalogued; white sides; gold roof and ends; green door; green and gold lettering; "happy holidays 1990" in green on right side with red, white and blue Lionel logo; red, gold, yellow and green candle and menorah electrocal on left side; ASF strong-arm trucks; "BLT/1-90". In 1990, for the first time, Lionel also released Large Scale, Standard Gauge and American Flyer S Gauge versions of the Seasons Greetings cars, all decorated in the same fashion as the 19910 O Gauge boxcar. — — — **25**

19911 TOY FAIR: 1990, boxcar; uncatalogued; white sides; light blue roof and ends; red door; red and blue lettering; car has extensive graphics in red, blue and gold; gold 90th anniversary logo to left of door; "Celebrate with Lionel at Toy Fair 1990" to right side; ASF strong-arm trucks; "BLT 1-90". — — — **120**

19912 I LOVE OHIO*: 1991, boxcar; white body; red roof and ends; red and blue lettering; white door; "With God All Things are

Possible" in red script to right of door; "I" a red heart and "OH" to left of door; number under-scored; ASF strong-arm trucks. "BLT 1-91". Part of continuing annual "I Love" State series. — — — **23**

19913 SEASON'S GREETINGS*: 1991, boxcar. — — — **30**

19914 TOY FAIR*: 1991, boxcar. — — — **160**

80948 MICHIGAN CENTRAL: 1982, boxcar; L O T S; see Volume II, first edition.

HI-CUBE BOXCARS

In 1976 Fundimensions added another completely new boxcar to its growing roster of rolling stock reflecting modern prototype practices. This was the all-plastic "Hi-Cube" boxcar, derived from a 40-foot boxcar which is built 12 to 18 inches higher than the norm. Like their prototypes, Fundimensions' hi-cubes had no catwalks on the roof. They also featured extensive riveting detail along the car sides, going against the trend towards eliminating rivet detailing. The hi-cubes featured large sliding doors fastened in place by hooks at both top and bottom. In addition, an all-new plastic frame was created for them.

F. Stem Collection; B. Greenberg photograph

Mickey Mouse Express set including the locomotive and caboose. There are seven additional cars not shown: 9666-9672.
Top shelf: 8773 Mickey Mouse Express U36B engine; 9183 Mickey Mouse Express N5C porthole caboose.
Second shelf: 9660 Mickey Mouse; 9661 Goofy.
Third shelf: 9662 Donald Duck; 9663 Dumbo.
Bottom shelf: 9664 Cinderella; 9665 Peter Pan.

The hi-cubes were made in two distinct series. One featured real railroad names. There were fourteen of these, numbered from 9600 to 9608, plus a 9610 Frisco hi-cube which was only available as part of the 1977 Rocky Mountain set. After a gap of five years another set (9626 to 9629) appeared, repeating previous road names. A 9611 T C A "Flying Yankee" hi-cube was made for that association's 1978 national convention in Boston. (See entry 1018-1979 in the Volume II, first edition, for a good story about the conversion of this car to the T C A Mortgage Burning ceremony car.) The other class of hi-cubes was the Mickey Mouse series, colorful cars with Disney logos and characters. These cars ran from numbers 9660 to 9672. The last number is the extremely scarce Mickey Mouse 50th Birthday car from 1978. The hi-cube cars disappeared after 1984. Hi-cubes were produced for the Toy Train Operating Society's 1978 convention in Hollywood and a Pennsylvania car for the Lionel Operating Train Society in 1984. The latter, although produced outside of the factory, is very hard to obtain.

Most of the common issue hi-cubes are not in great demand; only the 9600 Chessie, the 9610 Frisco, and the special convention issues have aroused any real interest. Of the Disney cars, which are in considerably greater demand, the Pinocchio and Pluto cars are very hard to find. The 50th Birthday car and the Snow White car are true rarities.

Although the hi-cubes are colorful and contemporary, many operators complain that the rolling characteristics of these cars are poor. Because of their plastic frames and high center of gravity, they have a tendency to wobble or tip over unless weighted. Despite this problem, these cars show real effort by Lionel to add a contemporary flair to tinplate railroading. However, with the recent emphasis on the Standard O boxcars, it is not likely that any of these cars will again be produced in the foreseeable future.

All hi-cube boxcars have Symington-Wayne trucks with two operating couplers.

HI-CUBE BOXCAR LISTINGS

	GD	VG	EXC	MT

9600 CHESSIE SYSTEM: 1976-77, hi-cube boxcar; dark blue body; yellow letteringa and Chessie cat logo; yellow doors; Symington-Wayne trucks; two operating couplers.

(A) Thin door stop. — 7 9 20 25
(B) Thick door stop. — 7 9 20 25

9601 ILLINOIS CENTRAL GULF: 1976-77, hi-cube boxcar; orange body; black lettering; black and white I-beam logo; black doors; Symington-Wayne trucks; two operating couplers.
— 10 15 20 25

9602 SANTA FE: 1976-77, hi-cube boxcar; red body; white "ATSF" lettering; Santa Fe cross in white; number under- and over-scored; silver doors; Symington-Wayne trucks.
— 10 15 20 25
See Factory Errors and Prototypes chapter in Volume II, first edition.

9603 PENN CENTRAL: 1976-77, hi-cube boxcar; jade green body; white lettering and large P C logo; silver doors; Symington-Wayne trucks; two operating couplers. — 10 15 20 30

9604 NORFOLK AND WESTERN: 1976-77, hi-cube boxcar; black body; white lettering; silver doors; Symington-Wayne trucks; two operating couplers. — 10 15 20 25

9605 NEW HAVEN: 1976-77, hi-cube boxcar; orange body; white lettering; black "N" above white "H", each full-serifed; number under- and over-scored; black doors; Symington-Wayne trucks; two operating couplers. — 10 15 20 30

9606 UNION PACIFIC: 1976-77, hi-cube boxcar; yellow body; blue lettering; gray roof; red, white and blue U P herald to left of yellow doors; multicolor "automated/rail way", "CUSHIONED LOAD" and map inside square black-outlined box; Symington-Wayne trucks; two operating couplers.
(A) Light yellow. — 10 15 20 25
(B) Dark yellow. — 10 15 20 25

9607 SOUTHERN PACIFIC: 1976-77, hi-cube boxcar; red body and door; gray stripe arrow across body and doors; gray roof; white lettering; S P logo; "HY-CUBE"; Symington-Wayne trucks; two operating couplers. Available in a late 1976 dealer brochure, and catalogued in 1977. — 10 15 20 25

9608 BURLINGTON NORTHERN: 1976-77, hi-cube boxcar; green body and doors; white lettering and large B N logo; Symington-Wayne trucks; two operating couplers. Available in a late 1976 dealer brochure and catalogued in 1977.
— 10 15 20 25

9610 FRISCO: 1977, hi-cube boxcar; yellow body and doors; black lettering; Symington-Wayne trucks; two operating couplers. Came only in Rocky Mountain Limited set 1765. This car was shown in the set in the catalogue as 9609, but made as 9610.
— 12 20 30 50

9611 T C A: 1978, hi-cube boxcar; "The Flying Yankee"; see Volume II, first edition.

9626 A T S F: 1982-84, hi-cube boxcar; light and dark red body versions; number under- and over-scored; white lettering and doors; Symington-Wayne trucks; two operating couplers. Does not have the white-painted clearance warning on the car ends, unlike earlier hi-cube boxcars. Same as 9602 except a slightly darker red. J. Newaczyk comment. — — 15 20

9627 UNION PACIFIC: 1982-83, hi-cube boxcar; yellow body; red lettering; white doors; Symington-Wayne trucks; two operating couplers. Does not have the white-painted clearance warning on the car ends, unlike earlier hi-cube boxcars. Compare to 9606. J. Breslin Collection. — — 15 20

9628 BURLINGTON NORTHERN: 1982-84, hi-cube boxcar; Cascade green body; white lettering and doors; Symington-Wayne trucks; two operating couplers. Does not have the white-painted clearance warning on the car ends, unlike earlier hi-cube boxcars. Same as 9608 except this car is a brighter green and has white doors. — — 10 15

9629 C & O CHESSIE SYSTEM: 1983-84, hi-cube boxcar; dark blue body; yellow lettering and logo; dark blue doors; Symington-Wayne trucks; two operating couplers. Does not have the white-painted clearance warning on the car ends, unlike earlier hi-cube boxcars. T. Ladny Collection.
— — 15 20

> **Note:** *The Mickey Mouse Set consists of cars 9660-9671, plus an 8773 U36B engine, 9183 N5C porthole caboose, and the limited edition 9672 50th Anniversary boxcar.*

9660 MICKEY MOUSE: 1977-78, hi-cube boxcar; white body; yellow doors, roof and ends; Symington-Wayne trucks; two operating couplers; "BLT 1-77". 8 10 40 50

9661 GOOFY: 1977-78, hi-cube boxcar; white body; red doors, roof and ends; Symington-Wayne trucks; two operating couplers; "BLT 1-77". 8 10 40 45

9662 DONALD DUCK: 1977-78, hi-cube boxcar; white body; green doors, roof and ends; Symington-Wayne trucks; two operating couplers; "BLT 1-77". 8 10 40 50

9663 DUMBO: 1977-78, hi-cube boxcar; white body; red doors, roof and ends; Symington-Wayne trucks; two operating couplers; "BLT 1-77". Announced in a late 1977 dealer flyer and catalogued in 1978. 15 20 40 70

9664 CINDERELLA: 1977-78, hi-cube boxcar; white body; lavender doors, roof and ends; Symington-Wayne trucks; two operating couplers; "BLT 1-77". Announced in a late 1977 dealer brochure and catalogued in 1978. 15 20 55 75

9665 PETER PAN: 1977-78, hi-cube boxcar; white body; orange doors, roof and ends; Symington-Wayne trucks; two operating couplers; "BLT 1-77". Announced in a late 1977 dealer brochure and catalogue in 1978. 10 12 40 60

9666 PINOCCHIO: 1978, hi-cube boxcar; white body; blue doors, roof and ends; Symington-Wayne trucks; two operating couplers; "BLT 1-78". 40 75 125 200

9667 SNOW WHITE: 1978, hi-cube boxcar; white body; green doors, roof and ends; Symington-Wayne trucks; two operating couplers; "BLT 1-78". By far the hardest car to find in the regularly issued series. 150 175 350 500

9668 PLUTO: 1978, hi-cube boxcar; white body; brown doors, roof and ends; Symington-Wayne trucks; two operating couplers; "BLT 1-78". 30 75 150 200

9669 BAMBI: 1978, hi-cube boxcar; uncatalogued; white body; lime green doors, roof and ends; Symington-Wayne trucks; two operating couplers; "BLT 1-78". Announced in a late 1978 flyer. 10 30 60 100

B. Greenberg photograph

A group of interesting boxcars and stock cars.

Top shelf: **7901** Lionel Lines short boxcar with cop chasing hobo on spring-loaded elevated platform; **7904 San Diego Zoo** stock car with animated giraffe.

Second shelf: **7902 ATSF** short boxcar; **7910 C&O** Chessie System short boxcar with operating door. **Note the body style change in this car. It is a descendant of the postwar 6454 series.**

Third shelf: **7913** Turtle Shell Zoo stock car, with animated giraffe; **7926 Nickel Plate Road** short boxcar.

Bottom shelf: **7930 True Value** short boxcar; **7931 Town House TV and Appliances** short boxcar. **Both of these are uncatalogued special cars and quite hard to find.**

	GD	VG	EXC	MT

9670 ALICE IN WONDERLAND: 1978, hi-cube boxcar; uncatalogued; white body; jade green doors, roof and ends; Symington-Wayne trucks; two operating couplers; "BLT 1-78". Announced in a late 1978 flyer.   **10   30   50   75**

9671 FANTASIA: 1978, hi-cube boxcar; uncatalogued; white body; dark blue doors, roof and ends; Symington-Wayne trucks; two operating couplers; "BLT 1-78". Announced in a late 1978 flyer.   **10   30   30   40**

9672 HAPPY BIRTHDAY MICKEY: 1978, hi-cube boxcar; uncatalogued; white body; gold roof and ends; dull gold doors; Symington-Wayne trucks; two operating couplers; no "BLT" date. Limited edition. Announced in a late 1978 dealer bonus special brochure.   **—   225   395   500**

	GD	VG	EXC	MT

9678 T T O S: 1978, hi-cube boxcar; T T O S Hollywood Convention car; see Volume II, first edition.

121315 PENNSYLVANIA: 1984, hi-cube boxcar; L O T S Convention car; see Volume II, first edition.

O27 SHORT BOXCARS

Like their postwar predecessors, Fundimensions and Lionel Trains, Inc. have always made shorter inexpensive

A. Rudman Collection

7912 Toy's 'R Us Geoffrey's Star Car, a special operating giraffe car made for Toys 'R Us stores. Note the construction differences between this car, which used the new 7910 boxcar mold, and the regular-production giraffe cars. It is very hard to find.

boxcars for the Traditional sets and special department store promotional sets.

As mentioned earlier in this book, "O27" is a term meant to denote a "short" or "inexpensive" or "Traditional" Line, intended to distinguish these smaller boxcars from the larger Collector-style boxcars. The O27 short boxcars look rather silly next to the Standard O boxcars, and are not intended to run in the same trains. But a train of Alco engines pulling a set of small colorful boxcars can still look quite good, and can be had for a modest price. These little cars, sometimes referred to as "fixed door" boxcars because their doors for the most part are molded into the car body and do not operate, are probably the most neglected of all the boxcars because they lack the glamour of their larger cousins. Yet some of these cars are extremely hard to find; they represent a real opportunity for the beginning collector to get a scarce car at a reasonable price. Although most of these cars came in inexpensive Traditinal Line sets, an occasional straggler can be found for separate-sale. Some were also catalogued in inexpensive boxed "assortments."

By far, the scarcest are the special ones made for department stores such as J. C. Penney, Sears, True Value Hardware, Ace Hardware, Kiddie City and Toys 'R Us. There are, in fact, at least ten different Toys 'R Us cars, some with variations!

Often, these cars came as replacements for regular-issue boxcars in regular-issue traditional train sets (a kind of individualization of the set on behalf of the store). As such, most are uncatalogued.

Most of the O27 boxcars listed in this section are very much like their 6014 postwar predecessors, but they have a new molded plastic bottom piece in place of the metal frame used on the 6014 series. Most have one operating and one dummy coupler on Symington-Wayne trucks. Some have railroad markings, such as the Conrail, Erie Lackawanna and Santa Fe cars, while others have corporate markings such as Wheaties, Ford Motorcraft and Hershey's Chocolate.

The first of these short (8½ inch long) boxcars in the modern era was the 9040 Wheaties car in 1970. Hence, the reader may see references to the "9040-style" or its postwar predecessor "6014-style." Two types of bodies are found on the 8½-inch boxcars. The first is a postwar carry-over (Type IV) which featured partially complete rivet rows on the sides. Types I through III are described in *Greenberg's Guide to Lionel Trains (1945-1969), Volume I,* and outline a progressive process of rivet removal (to provide greater stamping area) which parallels that of the larger boxcars.

The Type V style completes the process by removing all the rivets — the sides are entirely smooth. The only cars to use the Type IV body are the 9040 Wheaties and the 9041 Hershey's — and some of these use Type V as well. After 1973, all the short boxcars used the Type V body, so the listings after that do not reference the body type.

There is really no rationale to explaining the various number groups in which one finds these cars, except to say that Lionel just placed them where numbers were available. Lately, the regular boxcars are placed in the 16200-series and the operating ones in the 16600-series.

In 1984, Lionel carried this obscure boxcar up a notch when it recreated the 9¼-inch 6454 boxcar of postwar fame. This is the second of the short boxcar styles listed in this section. The first new 6454-type car came in Chessie colors and appeared again for Toys 'R Us and True Value Hardware specials. The cars featured operating couplers, full rivet detail and an operating door. These cars add a touch of class to the smaller O27 train outfits.

Since very few collectors pay attention to these cars, the small O27 boxcars represent a wide-open field for the beginning collector. They are even available as throw-ins in collections of assorted junk. Still, these cars deserve far more attention than they have gotten to date. Some of them have skyrocketed in value because the sets in which they were included were not brisk sellers.

Note also that some of the short boxcars listed here have operating mechanisms. These include the Toys 'R Us Geoffrey Giraffe cars (similar to the giraffe stock cars) and the cop and hobo cars (on which a spring-loaded elevated platform supports a plastic cop or hobo figure, chasing the other figure stationed on a low-clearance bridge under which the car passes). So beware of running high equipment under that low bridge!

O27 SHORT BOXCAR LISTINGS

	GD	VG	EXC	MT

1987 MOPAR: 1987-88, short boxcar; see 16205.

6014-900 FRISCO: 1975, short boxcar; L C C A; see Volume II, first edition.

7901 LIONEL LINES: 1982-83, short operating cop and hobo boxcar; "HYDRAULIC/PLATFORM/MAINTENANCE/CAR"; dark red body; white lettering; dark blue cop; dark brown hobo; one figure moves from car platform to overhead trestle while other figure moves from trestle to car platform; Symington-Wayne trucks; one operating and one dummy coupler; "BLT 1-82". Somewhat hard to find recently. — — **20 25**

7902 A T S F: 1982-85, short boxcar; red body; white lettering; number under- and over-scored; large white cross logo to right;

A selection of early short boxcars.
Top shelf: 9035 Conrail; 9037 Conrail. These two cars are often substituted for each other in sets.
Second shelf: 9040 Wheaties; 9041 Hershey's Chocolate & Cocoa, the earliest of Lionel's short boxcars.
Third shelf: 9042 Autolite; 9043 Erie Lackawanna.
Bottom shelf: 9052 Toys 'R Us; 9339 Great Northern.

	GD	VG	EXC	MT

Symington-Wayne trucks; "BLT 1-82". Sold separately in 1982 and came with 1353 Southern Streak set in 1983-85.

	—	—	6	8

7903 ROCK: 1983, short boxcar; blue body; white lettering; Symington-Wayne trucks; one dummy and one operating coupler.

	—	—	6	8

7905 BLACK CAVE: 1982, short boxcar; 9040-type dark green body; luminous decals to be affixed by purchaser; "Acme Explosives Company"; ignited round bomb and "Acme TNT Company"; 7905 is not on car. Came with 1254 Black Cave Flyer set.

	—	—	7	10

7908 TAPPAN: 1982, short boxcar; uncatalogued; red body; white diagonal lettering "Good Cooking Begins With A Great Range" and "Tappan Is Cooking!"; "7908" horizontal in lower right corner; Symington-Wayne trucks; one operating and one fixed coupler; "BLT 9-82". Came as part of Tappan promotional set. Sponsored by Mike Moore of Town House Appliances. Reportedly

6000 made. Also came with black and white insert for billboard frame lettered diagonally "TAPPAN IS COOKING!" See article on Tappan and Town House sets in the second edition of *Greenberg's Guide to Lionel Trains (1970-1988)*. S. Hutchings, M. Samseli, J. Sawruk, and "Triple T" Collections.

	—	—	50	70

7909 LOUISVILLE & NASHVILLE: 1983-84, short boxcar; blue body; yellow lettering; Symington-Wayne trucks; two dummy couplers. Part of 1352 Rocky Mountain freight set.

	—	—	10	15

7910 C & O CHESSIE SYSTEM: 1985; short boxcar; 6454 style; dark blue body; yellow lettering; yellow Chessie cat logo; metal door guides with opening doors; mold resembles old 6454 mold but is different in some ways; Symington-Wayne trucks; one operating and one dummy coupler; "BLT 1-84". Catalogued 1984, but not produced until 1985. The reintroduction of the 6454 mold marks the first time modern Lionel has used this boxcar style,

	GD	VG	EXC	MT

which has not been produced since 1953. The rivet detail has been fully restored, and the boxcar's lettering has been rubber-stamped right over it. The body fastens to the frame with two Phillips screws instead of the single screw and slot system used on other boxcars, and instead of four plastic posts and screws used on the postwar version. The frame is the same one used on the Sheriff and Outlaw and Horse Transport cars; the large hole where the swinging mechanism would be is closed by a plastic plug. Actually, the special 7912 Toys 'R Us "Geoffrey's Star Car" was the first car to use this mold (see next entry below). R. LaVoie comment and Collection. — — **10** **15**

7912 TOYS 'R US GEOFFREY'S STAR CAR: 1982-84, short operating giraffe boxcar; uncatalogued; white 6454-mold boxcar body (see 7910 for details); orange "TOYS/R/US" logo to left of doors; number under- and over-scored: yellow and black "STAR/CAR" logo to right of doors; sliding doors with metal guides; orange giraffe with brown spots. This giraffe figure is far more elaborate than the one used in regular production. It has a larger nose and a nape on its neck. Car has operating Symington-Wayne trucks; one operating and one dummy coupler. The instruction sheet for the car is labeled "GEOFFREY CAR" instead of "GIRAFFE CAR". Came as part of special Toys 'R Us version of the Heavy Iron set, in which this car replaced the 9339 Great Northern car. R. Shanfeld Collection. — — **100** **125**

7914 TOYS 'R US GEOFFREY'S CARNIVAL: 1985-89, short operating giraffe boxcar; uncatalogued; similar to 7912 of 1982-83, but has Toys 'R Us logo to right of sliding doors and "GEOFFREY'S/CARNIVAL/CARRIER" to left; no "BLT" date. Came as part of special 1549 Toys 'R Us version of the Heavy Iron set, in which this car replaced the 9339 Great Northern car. It is interesting to note that the regular-issue Heavy Iron set was not available during these years; it last appeared in 1983. T. Wagner and J. Sawruk Collections. — — **100** **135**

7920 SEARS CENTENNIAL: 1985-86, short boxcar; uncatalogued; white body; black and blue lettering; "Sears New Century" to right of doors; "Centenial Celebration 1886-1986" to left of doors; note misspelling of word *Centenial*. Also made with "Centennial" spelled correctly; Symington-Wayne trucks; "BLT 1-85". Sold as part of Sears equivalent to Chessie set 1402 in 1985 and Sears equivalent to Lionel Nickel Plate Special set 1602 in 1986, in which this car replaced the boxcars in those sets. Reader comments on quantities of correctly spelled cars and how Lionel learned of the error would be appreciated.
(A) "Centenial", 1985 production. V. Gallo, Jr., J. Sawruk and "Triple T" Collections. — — — **50**
(B) "Centennial", 1986 production. R. Stidd Collection.
— — — **55**

7925 ERIE-LACKAWANNA: 1986-90, short boxcar; light gray body; maroon lettering; Symington-Wayne trucks; "BLT 1-86". Part of set 1615, the Cannonball Express. Appears identical to earlier 9043 except for number. — — **8** **12**

7926 NICKEL PLATE ROAD: 1986-91, short boxcar; yellow body; black lettering; number under- and over-scored; Symington-Wayne trucks; "BLT 1-86". Part of set 1602, the Nickel Plate Special. — — **8** **11**

7930 TRUE VALUE HARDWARE STORES: 1986, short boxcar; uncatalogued; white body; red and dark blue lettering; Symington-Wayne trucks; one dummy coupler; "BLT 1-86". Reader comments on sets containing this car are requested.
— — — **60**

7931 TOWN HOUSE TV AND APPLIANCES: 1986, short boxcar; uncatalogued; medium gray body; black Town House logo and number to left of doors; six appliance brand names in black to right of doors (brand names differ on each side); Symington-Wayne trucks; one operating and one dummy coupler; "BLT 1-86". Part of uncatalogued Town House set 1658. For more history on this car, see the article *Town House sets* in the second edition of *Greenberg's Guide to Lionel Trains (1970-1988)*. R. LaVoie Collection. — — — **50**
See Volume II, first edition.

7932 KAY BEE TOYS: 1986, short boxcar; uncatalogued; white body; "LIONEL" to left of doors; "KAY BEE / TOY STORES" and soldier logo to right of doors; Symington-Wayne trucks; one operating and one dummy coupler. Came in a special Kay Bee Toys version of the Freight Flyer (which was actually put out in 1978) in which this car replaced the 9035 Conrail boxcar. Reportedly, Lionel had many of these cars left over and so no further Kay Bee Specials were made. M. Salce comment. J. Sawruk and T. Wagner Collections. — — — **50**

9001 CONRAIL: 1986-89, short boxcar; blue body; white lettering; identical to 9035 except for number and "C R 9001" on one line instead of two; "BLT 1-86". Part of uncatalogued set 1687. Also sold separately in a rolling stock assortment in 1989 (9195). L. Bohn comment. — — **12** **15**

9035 CONRAIL: 1978-88, short boxcar; blue body; white lettering; Conrail logo in white to right of doors; Symington-Wayne trucks; one dummy coupler; "BLT 1-78". Came in many Traditional Line sets and rolling stock assortments.
— — **4** **8**

9037 CONRAIL: 1978-81, short boxcar; brown or blue; white lettering; Symington-Wayne trucks; one dummy coupler; "BLT 1-78". Identical to 9035 except for number and body color. This car would sometimes show up in sets and rolling stock assortments in place of the 9035.
(A) Brown. — — **4** **8**
(B) Blue. — — **4** **7**

9040 GENERAL MILLS: 1970-72, short boxcar; orange body; white lettering "WHEATIES/'Breakfast of/Champions'" to right of doors; large General Mills "G" in blue to left; MPC logo. Part of 1084 Grand Trunk set in 1970, 1055 Santa Fe twin diesel in 1971, and also came as separate-sale item in Type I boxes.
(A) Type V body; AAR trucks; one operating coupler; one dummy coupler; plastic wheels. — **5** **7** **10**
(B) Type IV body; Symington-Wayne trucks; one operating coupler; one dummy coupler; plastic wheels.
— **5** **7** **10**
(C) Type V body; Symington-Wayne trucks; one operating coupler; one dummy coupler; plastic wheels.
— **5** **7** **10**
(D) Type V body; Symington-Wayne trucks; one operating coupler; one manumatic coupler; metal wheels.
— **5** **7** **10**

9041 HERSHEY'S CHOCOLATE & COCOA: 1971-76, short boxcar; silver lettering; metal wheels; one operating coupler; one dummy coupler; "BLT 1-70"; MPC logo. This car was only sold separately (Type II box), never in a set.
(A) Type IV chocolate body; AAR trucks; plastic wheels; silk-screened lettering. S. Askenas Collection.
— **7** **10** **15**
(B) Type V dark chocolate body; Symington-Wayne trucks; plastic wheels. — **7** **10** **15**

Some of Lionel's most recent short boxcars. All are uncatalogued and difficult to find.
Top shelf: 7914 Carnival Carrier; 16209 Lionel Disney Magic.
Middle shelf: 16220 Ace Hardware; 16221 Macy's Parade of Toys.
Bottom shelf: 16207 True Value Hardware Stores; 16219 True Value Hardware Stores.

Courtesy of M. Braga of Lionel Trains, Inc.; B. Greenberg photograph

	GD	VG	EXC	MT
(C) Type V maroon body; Symington-Wayne trucks; two dummy couplers.	—	7	10	15
(D) Same as (C), but one operating coupler, one dummy coupler. S. Askenas Collection.	—	7	10	15
(E) Type IV chocolate body; Symington-Wayne trucks. C. Rohlfing Collection.	—	7	10	15

AUTOLITE FORD BOXCAR

(Reprinted with the permission of the Lionel Collectors Club of America, from its August 1990 newsletter, "The Lion Roars", by Ken Coates and Michael Wood.)

In 1971, Michael Wood was the Program Merchandising Specialist and program manager for the Autolite 9042 short O27 boxcar and the autoparts for which this commemorative car was created. As background, the Autolite-Ford Parts Division often used valuable merchandise to stimulate wholesale and retail demand for products. In late 1970, it was concluded that the Allegheny set, with a cast engine complete with a "new smoke generation concept," would be an ideal premium to merchandise Autolite Tune-

Up Kits. A Tune-Up Kit was a "peanut-type can" that contained six or eight Autolite spark plugs, Motorcraft ignition points, Motorcraft condenser, lubricant, a disposable point and plug gap measure tool, and instruction sheet.

After long negotiations, both internally and with MPC (Lionel), a plan was devised with strong benefits for both parties — Autolite-Ford (now called Ford Parts and Service Division, a Division of Ford Motor Company) and Lionel. Wood's best guess at production volume is about 50,000 sets. The parts wholesaler would buy a certain number of Tune-Up Kits and would be eligible to purchase one Allegheny set at a special price with two enclosed Tune-Up Kits. When the two enclosed Tune-Up Kits were sold at retail, the profit covered the acquisition price of the train set and it could then be given at no charge to the customer. This enabled a very satisfied customer — young or old — for the expense of the lost profit on two Tune-Up Kits (not to mention a happy and tuned Ford car).

Now the Autolite-Ford boxcar. First the set — it was an Allegheny set; however, it was special in three ways:

1. Each set contained the 9042 Autolite-Ford boxcar.

2. The train set carton/box had a special graphic design that pictured the Autolite-Ford boxcar.

3. The signs/billboards as part of the set had two unique inserts — one for Autolite spark plugs and the other for Autolite-Ford Tune-Up Kits.

The Lionel number assigned to the set was 1199. The train carton/box itself was the same size as the original Allegheny set. The cars, engine, and track were rearranged to enable packaging the Tune-Up Kits.

The 9042 special car was conceived early in the negotiations as a means to achieve lasting impact for the Autolite, Motorcraft and Ford brands — each very valuable, but in need of continual reinforcement in the highly competitive marketplace. Design for the car was begun at MPC Lionel after Wood provided a rough outline of desires: white car for impact uniqueness, color contrast for the special Autolite/Motorcraft orange, visibility of the Ford logo and overall pleasing tri-color combination; and non-similarity to other cars to avoid confusion. The Ford Corporate Identity Office provided design specifics as if the car were to be used on commercial railroads or the Ford Rough railroad to actually carry cargo.

"The final design, in other words, was created, designed and registered internally as if Ford were planning to use the car full scale (we did not; but if we had, it would have matched the Lionel car exactly)," said Wood. (Wood has the prototype version of this car — the MX9145 described in the Factory Errors and Prototypes chapter in Volume II, first edition.)

Other points of interest concerning the 9042 also are worthy of discussion. First, the MPC marketing of the Autolite-Ford car was limited by contract in that the car could not be sold separately until after the program was complete. "We wanted the 9042 car to be an exclusive until after we got 'full marketing pull' from our uniqueness. In other words, there could not be counterfeit Autolite-Ford sets. We also approved the numbers to be sold and the way they could be marketed — not in other sets, only as individual cars," according to Wood.

Another item of possible interest to collectors, but not related to the 9042 car, is the Autolite-Ford sales personnel demonstration kit. Each of the 400 or so Autolite-Ford field representatives was given a 24" x 8" x 8" metal tool box that contained the 8142 Allegheny engine, tender, and a transformer mounted on a walnut board. At the point of sale, the representative would "run" the smoking engine with its distinctive "choo-choo" sound. This was possible because the engine was mounted statically with elevated wheels and the motor was designed so it would not overspeed. MPC made these Autolite-Ford demonstrators as part of the overall marketing plan.

Further details on this engine are available under the 8142 entry in the Steam Engine chapter and in *Greenberg's Guide to Lionel Trains (1970-1988)*, second edition.

9042 AUTOLITE: 1971-72, short boxcar; Type V white body embossed with "Part 100-4-3" on the inside; black lettering; "Autolite" in orange; Symington-Wayne trucks; one operating coupler; one dummy coupler; metal wheels; MPC logo on car end; Ford logo to right; "BLT 1-71". This car was only included in one set, the uncatalogued 1199 Allegheny, produced specially for Ford in 1971, although it also came in a Type I box as a separate-sale item in 1972. The 1972 catalogue illustration shows the car with

	GD	VG	EXC	MT

a Ford logo on the upper right in a set on page 7, but with the logo overprinted in black on the separate-sale car on page 12. The production has the Ford logo. Although illustrated as part of the 1284 Allegheny set in 1972, it never came with that set, only in the 1199 set in 1971 and for separate-sale in 1972. Previous editions of this guide reported incorrectly that this car appeared in the 1284 set. See entry MX-9145 in the Factory Errors and Prototypes chapter (Volume II, first edition) for a description of the prototype for this car. In 1971 speculators bought stocks of sets with Autolite boxcars with the expectation that this car would be a limited-production item, but the car was catalogued in the next year. This also happened with the supposedly scarce white Cracker Jack refrigerator car. C. Weber and J. Brandon comment.

		GD	VG	EXC	MT
	—	5	8	12	

9043 ERIE LACKAWANNA: 1973-75, short boxcar; gray body; maroon lettering and E-diamond logo to right of doors; Type V body; Symington-Wayne trucks; plastic wheels; one operating coupler; one manumatic fixed coupler; no MPC logo. Some versions packaged in Type II boxes for separate-sale. Part of set 1385, the Blue Streak freight. Also part of quite a few Sears uncatalogued sets.　　　　　— 　4 　8 　12

9044 D & R G W: 1975-76, short boxcar; orange body; black lettering; Symington-Wayne trucks; one operating coupler; one manumatic fixed coupler; no MPC logo. Part of set 1582, The Yard Chief.　　　　3 　4 　6 　8

9045 TOYS 'R US: 1975, short boxcar; uncatalogued; white Type V body; orange and black lettering; number under- and over-scored; giraffe with hat to left of doors; Toys 'R Us logo to right; Symington-Wayne trucks; plastic wheels; one operating and one dummy coupler; no MPC logo. First of numerous Toys 'R Us special cars produced in the modern era. H. Holden Collection.
　　　　20 　30 　40 　50

9046 TRUE VALUE: 1976, short boxcar; uncatalogued; white body; red and black lettering; paint can in red, black and yellow to left of doors; True Value logo to right; Symington-Wayne trucks; metal wheels; one operating coupler; one dummy coupler. Part of special 1698 True Value version of the Rock Island Line set, in which this car replaced the 9033 P C gondola. H. Holden Collection.
　　　　20 　30 　40 　50

9047 TOYS 'R US: 1976, short boxcar; uncatalogued; white body; orange and black lettering; number under- and over-scored; giraffe with hobo sack to right of doors; Toys 'R Us logo to left; Symington-Wayne trucks; plastic wheels; one operating coupler; one dummy coupler; "BLT 1-76". Part of special 1693 Toys 'R Us version of the Rock Island Line set, in which this car replaced the 9033 gondola. H. Holden Collection.　　— 　20 　35 　50

9048 TOYS 'R US: 1976, short boxcar; uncatalogued; white body; orange and black lettering; number under- and over-scored; giraffe with lantern to right of doors; Toys 'R Us logo to left; Symington-Wayne trucks; plastic wheels; one operating coupler; one manumatic coupler; "BLT 1-76". Part of special 1694 Toys 'R Us version of the Black River Freight in which this car replaced the 9016 Chessie hopper. H. Holden Collection.
　　　　— 　20 　35 　50

9049 TOYS 'R US: 1977, short boxcar; uncatalogued; white body; orange-and-black-lettered "GEOFFREY POWER"; number does not appear on car. Part of a special Toys 'R Us version of the Steel Hauler set, in which this car replaced the 9016 Chessie hopper. G. Halverson Collection.　　— 　— 　35 　50

R. Kaptur, R. LaVoie, A. Rudman, and F. Stem Collections; B. Greenberg photograph

The unusual 9090 Mini-Max Railcar — one of the few four-wheel cars made by Lionel.
Top shelf: 9090 scarcer light blue version with orange-red and lime-green palletainers on either side.
Second shelf: Two dark blue 9090s with General Mills "G" placed in different panels. Note interior posts in the open car.
Third shelf: 16211 Hawthorne short boxcar, 16219 True Value short boxcar. These are hard to find uncatalogued specials.
Bottom shelf: 16222 Great Northern short boxcar.

	GD	VG	EXC	MT

9052 TOYS 'R US: 1977, short boxcar; uncatalogued; white body; orange and black lettering; number under- and over-scored; Geoffrey Giraffe and crossing signal to right of doors; Symington-Wayne trucks; plastic wheels; one operating coupler; one manumatic coupler; "BLT 1-77". — **20 30 40**

9053 TRUE VALUE: 1977, short boxcar; uncatalogued; green body with True Value yellow, black and red decals on right; paint can on left; blue and red lettering. Originally came in specially marked True Value bag within set; mint condition must include this bag. Part of special 1792 True Value version of the Rock Island Line set (see also 9046), in which this car replaced the 9033 PC gondola. G. Halverson and H. Holden Collections. — — **35 50**

9054 J C PENNEY: 1977, short boxcar; uncatalogued; orange body; black lettering; "75/Anniversary" logo to left of doors; J. C. Penney logo to right; Symington-Wayne trucks; one operating and one dummy coupler; "BLT 1-77". Came in special 1796 Penney's version of the Cargo King set, in which this car replaced the 9016 Chessie hopper. H. Holden Collection. — — **35 50**

9090 MINI-MAX RAILCAR: 1971, small hinged-side boxcar; blue roof and ends; white doors; dark blue lettering; four metal wheels; entire side panel is a door hinged at the top. Separate-sale cars came in Type I boxes. Light blue versions are harder to find. In the first and second editions of this Guide, Bill Meyer gave a detailed history and description of this intriguing little car, one of the few four-wheel Lionel cars and unlike anything made before or since. The reader is referred to these articles for detailed background. Critical variables are roof and end colors (light or dark blue); placement of General Mills "G" logo in the fourth panel from right or left; box packing (plain white or Type I); and box end stamping ("MINI-MAX/9090; "MINI-MAX/9090X with "X" in red; "9090/MINI-MAX" — note reversal of lines). The "X" version is

GD VG EXC MT

usually associated with the plain white box packing, which is probably the earliest production. There are other variations, including presence or absence of roof-to-floor struts inside the car, but this is no longer considered a critical variable. Lastly, there are variations in the small palletainers (orange-red, lime green, pale yellow) which come with the car. This is also not a major variable since the containers can be changed, and replacement ones are still available. We fully expect other variations to turn up. Reader comments invited. G. Halverson, R. LaVoie, and W. Meyer comments.

(A) Light blue roof and ends; "G" in fourth panel from left; three orange-red palletainers; plain white box with "MINI-MAX / 9090" stamped on both ends in purple with red-penned "X" after number; probably earliest production. R. LaVoie Collection.

20	25	50	75

(B) Dark blue roof and ends; "G" in fourth panel from left; three lime green palletainers; Type I box stamped "MINI-MAX / 9090" in black on both ends. R. LaVoie Collection.

10	15	50	75

(C) Dark blue roof and ends; "G" in fourth panel from right; three pale yellow palletainers; Type I box; "9090 / MINI-MAX" stamped in purple on both ends (note reversal of B). R. LaVoie Collection.

10	15	20	40

(D) Light blue roof and ends; "G" in fourth panel from right; Type I box; "MINI-MAX/9090" in block on both ends; palletainer color unknown. B. Kaiser Collection.

15	20	35	50

See also Factory Errors and Prototypes chapter in Volume II, first edition.

MX 9145 AUTOLITE: 1972; see Factory Errors and Prototypes chapter in Volume II, first edition.

9339 GREAT NORTHERN: 1979-83, 1986, short boxcar; green body; white lettering; Great Northern Railway logo; Symington-Wayne trucks; "BLT 1-79". Part of 1960 Midnight Flyer set (1979-81) and 1252 Heavy Iron set (1982-83). The car also appeared in a 1986 rolling stock assortment. C. Lang comment.

(A) 1979-81; one operating and one dummy coupler.

—	4	7	10

(B) 1982 and later; two operating couplers.

—	4	7	10

9359 NATIONAL BASKETBALL ASSN: 1979-80, short boxcar; uncatalogued; white body; red roof and ends; red and black lettering; N B A red, white and blue logo to left; N B A Championship trophy in gold to right; Symington-Wayne trucks; "BLT 1-79". Came in 1979 year-end special dealer package; many labels provided with car so that the purchaser could decide which individual team logo to place on car. C. Rohlfing Collection.

—	—	20	30

9360 NATIONAL HOCKEY LEAGUE: 1979-80, short boxcar; uncatalogued; white body; orange roof and ends; large silver Stanley Cup logo to right; N H L shield in orange and black to left; Symington-Wayne trucks; "BLT 1-79". Came in 1979 year-end special dealer package; many labels provided so that car purchaser could decide which individual team logo to place on car. C. Rohlfing Collection.

—	—	20	30

9361 NATIONAL FOOTBALL LEAGUE: Planned for 1980, this car was not produced, probably because the N F L wanted a fee, which Lionel did not want to pay, and production was canceled.
Not Manufactured

9362 MAJOR LEAGUE BASEBALL: 1979-80, short boxcar; uncatalogued; white body; dark blue roof and ends; black

lettering; World Series trophy in gold and black; Symington-Wayne trucks; "BLT 1-79". Came in 1979 year-end special dealer package; many labels provided with car, each for a different team, purchaser to decide which to place on car. C. Rohlfing Collection.

—	—	20	30

9365 TOYS 'R US: 1979, short boxcar; uncatalogued; white body; black lettering; number under- and over-scored; orange "TOYS/R/US" logo to left of doors; giraffe in engineer hat to right of doors; Symington-Wayne trucks; one operating and one dummy coupler; "BLT 1-81". Part of 1993 special Toys 'R Us version of the Midnight Flyer set, in which this car replaced the 9339 G N boxcar. G. Halverson Collection.

—	—	40	50

9376 SOO LINE: 1981, short boxcar; uncatalogued; white body; large black "SOO LINE" flanks doors; black lettering; number under- and over-scored; Symington-Wayne trucks; one operating and one dummy coupler; "BLT 1-81". Part of uncatalogued 1157 Wabash Cannonball set. Reader comments on set details are requested. G. Halverson Collection.

—	—	20	25

9388 TOYS 'R US: 1981, short boxcar; uncatalogued; white body; black lettering; number under- and over-scored; giraffe with engineer hat and crossing signal to left of doors; orange "TOYS/R/US" logo to right of doors; Symington-Wayne trucks; one operating and one dummy coupler. Part of 1159 special Toys 'R Us version of the Midnight Flyer set (see also 9365), in which this car replaced the 9339 G N boxcar. G. Halverson Collection.

—	—	40	50

16200 ROCK ISLAND: 1987-88, short boxcar; red body; white lettering and logo; arch bar trucks. Part of Rail Blazer set 11701.

—	—	—	10

16201 WABASH: 1988-91, short boxcar; dark blue body; white lettering and numbers; white Wabash flag emblem; Symington-Wayne trucks; two operating couplers; "BLT 1-88". Part of 11703 Iron Horse freight set.

—	—	—	10

16204 HAWTHORNE HOME APPLIANCES & ELECTRONICS: 1987, short boxcar; uncatalogued; white body; black lettering "Hawthorne/Competitive Prices Plus" to left of doors, "Plus" in red script; appliance manufacturers' logos in black to right of doors; Symington-Wayne trucks; two operating couplers; "BLT 1-87". From special Hawthorne Home Appliances promotional set; issued in the same fashion as earlier Town House car and set. The Hawthorne set box sticker matches the Town House set box sticker, except for the store name and decoration on the boxcar. This set came with 8902 A C L engine and caboose, and a free Lionel R R Club subscription. M. Salce comment.

—	—	—	75

16205 MOPAR: 1987-88, short boxcar; uncatalogued; gray body; red, white and blue lettering; three blue stripes; number not on car — "1987" is the only number on car; Symington-Wayne trucks; two operating couplers; "BLT 1-87". Part of 11757 Mopar Express Chrysler special promotion set in 1987 and 1988. L. Bohn Collection.

—	—	—	50

16207 TRUE VALUE HARDWARE STORES: 1988, short boxcar; uncatalogued; light blue body; dark blue, red and gold lettering; red "True Value" script logo to right of doors; gold 40th Anniversary logo to left; Symington-Wayne trucks; two operating couplers. Part of special True Value version of the Cannonball Express, the 11761 True Value 40th Anniversary set, in which this car replaced the usual 7925 Erie-Lackawanna car.

—	—	—	65

6232 Illinois Central; 6234 Burlington Northern

B. Greenberg photograph

	GD	VG	EXC	MT

16209 DISNEY MAGIC: 1988, short boxcar; uncatalogued; white body; blue and red lettering; Disney Magic logo to right of doors in blue and lavender; "Lionel" and circle-L to left of doors in red; catalogue number is not on the car; Symington-Wayne trucks; two operating couplers; "BLT 1-88". Came in set 11764, a special Sears version of the Iron Horse Freight, in which this car replaced the 16201 Wabash car. — — — **75**

16211 HAWTHORNE HOME APPLIANCES & ELECTRONICS: 1988, short boxcar; uncatalogued; virtually the same description as 16204, except appliance logos are rearranged and car carries "BLT 1-88" date. Came as part of 1988 Hawthorne special set 11756 whose contents, other than the boxcar, were the same as the 1987 set. R. LaVoie and M. Salnick Collections. — — — **70**

16213 SHOPRITE: 1988, short boxcar; uncatalogued; yellow body; red and black lettering "Shoprite/Does It Right" to left of doors; red and black circular Shoprite logo to right of doors; Symington-Wayne trucks; two operating couplers; "BLT 1-88". Came in 11767 special Shoprite version of the Freight Flyer, in which this car replaced the 9001 Conrail car. A first special for the Shoprite food store chain. Reportedly 1100 made. — — — **75**

16219 TRUE VALUE HARDWARE STORES: 1989, short boxcar; 6454-style; uncatalogued; yellow body; red script "True Value" to right of doors; black and red hammer logo to left of doors; other lettering in black and white; note improvement on earlier True Value cars by use of 6454-style boxcar — more rivet detail and operating doors. Symington-Wayne trucks; two operating couplers; "BLT 1-89". Came in special 11762 version of the Cannonball Express in which this car replaced the 7925 Erie-Lackawanna boxcar. — — — **65**

16220 ACE HARDWARE: 1989, short boxcar; uncatalogued; white body; large red "ACE" logo; "LIONEL" and L logo in black; black lettering; Symington-Wayne trucks; two operating couplers; "BLT 1-89". Part of 11774 special Ace Hardware version of the Cannonball Express, in which this car replaced the 7925 Erie Lackawanna car. Car has two unusual features for a store special: "LIONEL" is prominently displayed, and the 16220 number is not on the car. — — — **45**

16221 MACY'S: 1989, short boxcar; uncatalogued; white body; blue and red lettering — "macy's" to left in blue, "PARADE OF/TOYS" to right in red; no catalogue number on car; Symington-Wayne trucks; two operating couplers; "BLT 1-89". Came in special 11772 Macy's version of the Freight Flyer set, in which this car replaced the 9001 Conrail car. Reportedly less than 500 made. M. Salce comment. — — — **50**

16222 GREAT NORTHERN: 1990, short boxcar; light blue body; white lettering and G N goat logo; Symington-Wayne trucks;

two operating couplers; "BLT 1-89". Part of 16999 rolling stock assortment. — — — **12**

16224 TRUE VALUE: 1990, short boxcar; 6454-style; white body; black lettering; black Lawn Chief logo to right of door; black True Value logo on left side; ASF strong-arm trucks; "BLT 1-90". (Lawn Chief is a lawn products subsidiary of True Value.) Came with special 11781 True Value version of the Cannonball Express set, in which this car replaced the 7925 Erie-Lackawanna boxcar. T. Wagner comment. — — — **40**

16227 SANTA FE*: 1991, short boxcar; red body; white lettering and cross logo; "Ship and Travel/SANTA FE/–all the way"; ASF strong-arm trucks; two operating couplers; "BLT 1-91". Part of 11720 Santa Fe Special set. — — — **12**

16614 READING: 1989, short operating cop and hobo boxcar; yellow sides; green roof and ends; green lettering; Reading Lines yellow and green diamond to right of doors; green extension platform; blue cop chases light gray hobo on and off metal bridge; Symington-Wayne trucks; two operating couplers. Came with special large display box. — — — **30**

16624 NEW HAVEN: 1990-91, short operating cop and hobo boxcar; orange body and extension platform; white lettering; black "N" over white "H"; light blue cop chases black hobo on and off fixed gray metal bridge; number under- and over-scored; ASF strong-arm trucks; two operating couplers; "BLT 1-90". Came with special large display box. — — — **33**

16629 LIONELVILLE: 1990, short operating elephant boxcar; white 6454-style body with operating doors; red, orange, black and gray lettering; clown electrocal to right of doors, elephant to left; track trip mechanism similar to giraffe cars causes elephant head protruding from top of car to duck under telltales; ASF strong-arm trucks; two operating couplers; "BLT 1-90". Part of popular 11716 Lionelville Circus Special set. — — — **40**

16633 GREAT NORTHERN: 1991, short operating cop and hobo boxcar. Announced in Lionel's 1991 Book 1 catalogue, but not manufactured. **Not Manufactured**

16641 TOYS 'R US: 1990, short operating giraffe car; uncatalogued; white 6454-style body; "TOYS 'R US" and "KIDS 'R US" lettering in multi-colors to left of door; "GEOFFREY CAR" in blue to right of doors; Geoffrey giraffe in engineer's cap to far right of door; operating giraffe figure in orange with brown spots; track trip mechanism and telltale pole included; ASF stong-arm trucks; "BLT 1-90". Part of 11783 special Toys 'R Us version of the Heavy Iron set. — — — **50**

16642 GOOFY*: 1991, short 6454-style operating boxcar; pale green body with operating doors; multicolor Goofy electrocals; black lettering; blue, green and yellow Goofy figure pops out of

Standard O boxcars, all with the fine sprung trucks.
Top shelf: 9801 Baltimore & Ohio Sentinel; 9803 Johnson Wax
Middle shelf: 9806 Rock Island; 9808 Union Pacific Railroad.
Bottom shelf: 9826 Pittsburgh & Lake Erie.

R. Kaptur, R. LaVoie, and A. Rudman Collections; B. Greenberg photograph

                              GD   VG   EXC   MT

boxcar roof; track trips and telltale pole included; ASF strong-arm trucks; "BLT 1-91". Part of 11721 Mickey's World Tour train set.

                              —   —   —   35

STANDARD O BOXCARS

Lionel has maintained a steady momentum toward scale railroading in recent years, and nothing exemplifies this trend more than the handsome Standard O series of boxcars and rolling stock. "Standard O" is a phrase intended to designate scale length and dimensions, in conjunction with full car body detail and prototype lettering schemes. The booming market in scale-appearing rolling stock (even on Lionel's three-rail tubular track) forced Fundimensions' strong entry into the field in 1973, when it issued a remarkable group of box and

refrigerator cars which were the first rolling stock equipped with the excellent Standard O sprung trucks. The cars, based on the model railroading firm Rivarossi design, did not sell well in the first years, possibly due to a lack of scale engines or other equipment to match. With the scale Hudsons and SD-40s, however, the situation now is different, and the Standard O series is gaining new attention. The last five years have seen more boxcars, and other scale car styles, such as gondolas, flatcars, hoppers and woodsided cabooses. In 1990, Lionel released two entirely new Standard O tank cars.

The availability of the Standard O cars (boxcars and others) varies considerably. Common cars such as the 9803 Johnson's Wax and the 9809 Clark are easy to acquire at good prices. On the other hand, the 9806 Rock Island is very difficult to find. And Standard O boxcars in top Collector sets will always be difficult to find.

Standard O boxcars are distinguished from their illustrious 9400- and 9700-type relatives by a separate roof catwalk and greater length (11 inches vs. 10¼ inches long).

17200 Canadian Pacific; 17201 Conrail. Both are Standard O boxcars from Collector sets.

A variety of short and long stock cars.
Top shelf: 7302 Texas & Pacific; 7303 Erie.
Middle shelf: 7304 Southern; 7309 Southern.
Bottom shelf: 7401 Chessie System; 7404 Jersey Central Lines, an odd numbered boxcar produced as a companion to the 1986 Jersey Central FM Trainmaster.

A major new Standard O boxcar body style was released in 1991, a detailed model of the 50-foot ribbed double-door automobile boxcar. This huge 13-inch car marks yet another step in Lionel's steady march to scale.

STANDARD O BOXCAR LISTINGS

	GD	VG	EXC	MT

6232 ILLINOIS CENTRAL: 1986, Standard O boxcar; uncatalogued; orange body and catwalk; black and white I C logo; black lettering; Standard O trucks. Part of special direct-mail offer from Lionel in conjunction with the B & A Hudson. Very hard to find. — — 135 155

6234 BURLINGTON NORTHERN: 1985, Standard O boxcar; Cascade green body and doors; white lettering and large B N logo; black roof and catwalk; Standard O trucks. Part of 1552 Burlington Northern Limited set. One of few Lionel sets consisting of exactly matching rolling stock (a unit train). — — 30 40

6235 BURLINGTON NORTHERN: 1985, Standard O boxcar; matches 6234. From 1552 Burlington Northern Limited set. — — 30 40

6236 BURLINGTON NORTHERN: 1985, Standard O boxcar; matches 6234. From 1552 Burlington Northern Limited set. — — 30 40

	GD	VG	EXC	MT

6237 BURLINGTON NORTHERN: 1985, Standard O boxcar; matches 6234. From 1552 Burlington Northern Limited set. — — 30 40

6238 BURLINGTON NORTHERN: 1985, Standard O boxcar; matches 6234. From 1552 Burlington Northern Limited set. — — 30 40

6239 BURLINGTON NORTHERN: 1986, Standard O boxcar; matches 6234 through 6238; intended as add-on to Burlington Northern Limited set and sold separately as part of 1986 year-end "Stocking Stuffer" package. — — 30 40

9469 NEW YORK CENTRAL LINES: 1985, Standard O boxcar; red and gray paint scheme; number under-scored; white lettering; "Pacemaker/FREIGHT SERVICE"; Standard O trucks; "BLT 1-85". Shown with black-painted catwalk in catalogue, but came with catwalk in same red color as roof. Announced in the 1984 catalogue, but not made until 1985. F. Cieri and C. Rohlfing Collections. — — 110 125

9801 BALTIMORE & OHIO: 1973-75, Standard O boxcar; gray mold; silver and blue body; blue and white lettering; yellow and green signal logo to right of doors; Standard O trucks; "BLT l-73". First in the Standard O boxcar series.
(A) Light blue stripe. 15 20 35 50
(B) Dark blue stripe. 15 20 35 50
See Factory Errors and Prototypes chapter in Volume II, first edition.

9803 JOHNSON J. W. A. X.: 1973-75, Standard O boxcar; red, white and blue body; black and white lettering; red ends; blue

9221 operating Poultry Dispatch car (note "chicken sweeper" figure in door); **9224** Louisville operating horse car.

	GD	VG	EXC	MT

lower third of body; red top third; "Johnson" logo to right of doors; Standard O trucks.

(A) Painted red, white and dark blue.	10	20	30	40
(B) Painted red, white and light blue.	10	20	30	40

9806 ROCK ISLAND: 1975, Standard O boxcar; red mold; tuscan-painted body; white "ROUTE OF THE ROCKETS" lettering; large "ROCK/ISLAND" lettering to right of doors; Standard O trucks.

	30	40	75	100

9808 UNION PACIFIC RAILROAD: 1975-76, Standard O boxcar; yellow sides; silver roof and ends; black catwalk; black lettering; Union Pacific shield logo to left of doors; black-bordered multicolor map to right of doors; Standard O trucks; "BLT 1-75".

(A) White mold painted dark yellow; yellow door mold painted light yellow.	60	70	80	110
(B) Light yellow mold painted dark yellow; yellow door mold painted light yellow.	60	70	80	110

9826 PITTSBURGH & LAKE ERIE: 1976-77, Standard O boxcar; green body; white lettering; black catwalk; "NEW YORK/CENTRAL/SYSTEM" oval logo to left of doors; Standard O trucks; "BLT 1-76".

(A) Flat green; first run, 500 manufactured.	40	60	80	125
(B) Shiny green.	20	30	40	60

17200 CANADIAN PACIFIC: 1989, Standard O boxcar; silver sides and doors; black roof and ends; red lettering; C P beaver logo in orange, white and black to right of doors; Standard O trucks; "BLT 1-89". Part of 11710 C P Rail set.

	—	—	—	70

17201 CONRAIL: 1987, Standard O boxcar; tuscan body; white lettering and Conrail "wheel" logo; black catwalk; Standard O trucks. Part of 11700 Conrail Limited set. It is interesting that this car is numbered after the 17200 C P, but was produced two years earlier.

	—	—	—	60

17202 SANTA FE: 1990, Standard O boxcar; with diesel RailSounds; tuscan body; white and yellow lettering; number under- and over-scored; black and white Santa Fe cross logo to left of doors; Standard O trucks with power pickup; "BLT 1-90". This is the first Standard O boxcar to include RailSounds. Part of 11713 Santa Fe Dash-8 set. Catalogue indicates this car was to have an ETD, with the 17302 reefer having RailSounds, but in production these features were switched. The door of this car is sealed to deter tampering with the RailSounds circuitry.

	—	—	—	130

17203 COTTON BELT*: 1991, Standard O 50-foot double-door boxcar; entirely new highly-detailed automobile boxcar body style for the Standard O line; boxcar is 13 inches long with sides featuring heavy ribbed supports and new detailed door design; brown body; white and yellow lettering; "COTTON BELT" and

	GD	VG	EXC	M

"HYDRA-CUSHION"; operating doors; Standard O trucks; "BL 1-91".

	—	—	—	5

17204 MISSOURI PACIFIC*: 1991, Standard O 50-foot double-door boxcar; new detailed automobile boxcar body for the Standard O line; ribbed sides; 13 inches long; gray body with blu stripes on the upper and lower thirds of the sides; yellow door with gray central stripe; black and white lettering "Eagle MER CHANDISE SERVICE"; number under- and over-scored; operating doors; Standard O trucks; "BLT 1-91".

	—	—	—	5

17870 EAST CAMDEN & HIGHLAND: 1987, L C C A; se Volume II, first edition.

17876 COLUMBIA, NEWBERRY AND LAURENS: 198 Standard O boxcar; L C C A; see Volume II, first edition.

17884 COLUMBUS AND DAYTON: 1990, Standard O bo car; T T O S; see Volume II, first edition.

STOCK CARS

One of the most popular Lionel boxcar styles is the stoc (or "livestock") car, first introduced by postwar Lionel in 194 with the Armour operating cattle car. Though small in num ber (offering a good collector opportunity), these cars featur some unusual and fun action concepts. Some of the sma stock cars include animated horses or outlaws that bob in an out of the sides on hairsprings. Others use an ingenious tri mechanism which causes a giraffe to duck or raise his hea from the top of the car. Operators should be aware, however that the giraffe car uses a telltale pole and trackside cam fo operation, meaning larger engines or rolling stock could ru into them. Be wary of the placement of the operatin mechanism on layouts. And beware of running the giraff under bridges or tunnel portals!

The giraffe car had a long run in the postwar era — th 3376 from 1960 through 1969. The poultry dispatch car known irreverently as the "chicken-sweeper" car in which button activates a man and broom, appearing to sweep ou feathers, is a perennial favorite. There is certainly a strange color group of chickens on that car! The larger operating cattle and horse cars have been revived several times since 1970, and it is safe to say they have produced endless hours of fun fo kids and grown-up kids. It is forever a challenge to park th cars just right in front of the corrals to be sure the animal come out and in properly. By the way, Lionel recently im

B. Greenberg photograph

16605 Bronx Zoo stock car with animated giraffe.

roved the cattle and horse design by using a felt pad on the bottom of the figures rather than the small rubber fingers, which often as not had the animal going in circles, instead of the intended path.

In tallying the stock cars, do not forget the handsome collector versions in the 9400-, 9700-, 19500-, and 19800-series. We list them in this section, but the boxcar series collectors are after them as well (to complete their 9400- or 9700-series collections, etc.). In particular, the 9449 Great Northern is hard to find.

These cars are made in short (O27 type) and long-body versions. Four types of long-body cars exist, one for the operating horse and cattle cars, a second for the poultry cars, and a third for the (non-operating) Collector series. The latter can be distinguished by its split double-tier doors. The fourth style was a surprise 1991 introduction of a new single-door Collector stock car style in the Frisco Fallen Flags No. 5 set.

The short stock car bodies have three versions. The first is a standard stock car. The other two have cutouts in the roof (for the giraffe cars) or the sides (for the bobbing horse or outlaw cars). These cars fall near the bottom of the O27 line and often come with plastic wheels or dummy couplers.

STOCK CAR LISTINGS

	GD	VG	EXC	MT

989 SEARS CIRCUS: 1989, short-body horse car; see 16110.

301 N & W: 1982, long stock car; brown body; white lettering; white roof and ends; black split two-tier doors; Standard O trucks. From 1260 Continental Limited set. — — **40 50**

302 TEXAS & PACIFIC: 1983-84, short-body stock car; brown with white lettering; Symington-Wayne trucks; one dummy coupler. — — **10 15**

303 ERIE: 1984-85, long stock car; dull slate blue body; white lettering and Erie logo; blue split two-tier doors; Standard O trucks. From 1451 Erie-Lackawanna Limited set. — — **45 50**

304 SOUTHERN: 1983, long stock car; dark green body; tuscan roof and ends; tuscan split two-tier doors; white "SOUTHERN" and "7304" to right of doors; circular white Southern logo to left of doors; gold FARR Series 4 diamond insignia; Standard O trucks. Extra car meant to accompany

	GD	VG	EXC	MT

Famous American Railroad Series No. 4 Southern set but offered in year-end package for separate-sale. Hard to find. — — **60 75**

See Factory Errors and Prototypes chapter in Volume II, first edition.

7309 SOUTHERN: 1985-86, short stock car; tuscan body; white lettering; Symington-Wayne trucks; one dummy coupler. — — **10 15**

7312 WESTERN & ATLANTIC: 1986, short stock car; uncatalogued; tuscan body; yellow lettering and shield; plastic arch bar trucks; two operating couplers. Part of uncatalogued 1608 American Express set. T. Taylor Collection. — — **20 25**

7401 CHESSIE SYSTEM: 1984-85, short stock car; red body; white lettering; Symington-Wayne trucks; one operating and one dummy coupler. Part of 1402 Chessie System set. — — **10 15**

7808 NORTHERN PACIFIC: 1977, long stock car; brown body; silver roof; black split two-tier doors; silver lettering "PIG PALACE" electrocal on white plastic board glued to slats at right of doors; Symington-Wayne trucks; "BLT 1-77". Part of 1764 Heartland Express set. **20 25 50 65**

7812 T C A HOUSTON: 1977, long stock car; see Volume II, first edition.

7900 OUTLAW CAR: 1982-83, short operating stock car; orange body; black "Rio Grande" lettering; outlaw and sheriff move in and out of car windows as car moves (mechanism is like 9280 horse transport car); one set of figures is black, the other white; plastic arch bar trucks; plastic wheels; one operating coupler, one dummy coupler; "BLT 1-82". M. Solly Collection. — — **11 14**

7904 SAN DIEGO ZOO: 1983-84, short-body operating giraffe stock car; red plastic body; all-yellow giraffe; white lettering "SAN/DIEGO/ZOO" and "BLT 1-83 / LIONEL"; with telltale pole and cam device; Symington-Wayne trucks; one operating and one dummy coupler. Catalogue erroneously shows car numbered "7903". Rerun of postwar 3376 and 3386 from 1960s. C. Rohlfing comment. R. LaVoie Collection. — — **30 35**

7913 TURTLE BACK ZOO: 1985-86, short-body operating giraffe stock car; green body; plain yellow giraffe and cam follower piece; white lettering and logo; came with cam, mounting plate, and black pole with white telltales; Symington-Wayne trucks; one operating and one dummy coupler. — — **35 40**

9221 POULTRY DISPATCH: 1983-85, long stock car; dull brown-painted body; white lettering; unpainted gray doors; Symington-Wayne trucks; "BLT 1-83". Body is a modified stock

Some of Lionel's operating cars.

R. Kaptur Collection; B. Greenberg photogr

Top shelf: 19510 Pennsylvania; 19800 Circle L Ranch, operating cattle car that came with a corral.
Second shelf: 19801 Poultry Dispatch; 19808 NYRB, an operating ice car.
Bottom shelf: 19809 Erie Lackawanna, an operating car with man hidden inside; 19813 Northern Pacific, an operating ice car.

	GD	VG	EXC	MT

car with slats removed so three celluloid rows of chickens on way to market show through. Two bayonet-based light bulbs inside car provide illumination. When plunger is pulled down by remote control, door opens and gray man with broom mounted on delicate hair spring appears to be swinging back and forth, sweeping feathers out of car. Sometimes known as the "Chicken Sweeper" car. Reissue of postwar 3434 from 1959-60. T. Ladny and R. LaVoie Collections. **— — 35 40**

9224 LOUISVILLE K Y.: 1984-86, long-body operating horse stock car and corral; yellow sides and doors; tuscan roof, ends, and lettering; postwar bar-end metal trucks with one sliding shoe pickup for operation; "BLT 1-84". Horse corral has white frame and fencing and dark green corral chute and watering trough. Nine light brown horses are included. When car is on remote-control track and button is pushed, car doors drop down to meet corral platform and horses move into and out of car by vibrator action in car and corral. The word "CHURCHILL" is misspelled as "CHURCHHILL" on all cars, though the catalogue shows the correct spelling. Reissue of postwar 3356 car in new colors. Price for car and corral, boxed together. T. Ladny and R. LaVoie Collections. **— — 75 90**

9280 A. T. S. F.: 1978-80, short-body horse transport stock car; red body; white lettering and cross logo; two white horses bob in and out; Symington-Wayne trucks. **5 10 15 20**

9305 SANTA FE: 1980-82, short stock car; dark green car body; gold lettering; plastic wheels; plastic arch bar trucks; one operating and one dummy coupler. Bobbing tan plastic sheriff and outlaw figures; mechanism identical to 9280. From 1053 James Gang set. J. Sawruk Collection. **— — 15 20**

	GD	VG	EXC	M

9407 UNION PACIFIC: 1978-79, long stock car; gray- an yellow-painted yellow plastic body; black-painted black split two tier doors; number under- and over-scored; red lettering, "LIVE STOCK DISPATCH" and U P herald; "LIONEL" on right; Type mold; Type I frame; Symington-Wayne trucks. Catalogued i 1978; also shown in 1979 advance catalogue.
10 15 25 3

9408 LIONEL LINES: 1978, long stock car; uncatalogued white-and red-painted white plastic body; white-painted whit plastic split two-tier doors; red "LIONEL LINES" in box on left "CIRCUS CAR" in box on right; red-painted catwalk and hatche atop roof; Standard O trucks. Part of 1868 Minneapolis & St Louis Service Station set. Essentially a remake of the postwa 6376 model. Somewhat hard to find. R. Sigurdson comment.
15 20 30 4

9437 NORTHERN PACIFIC: 1981, long stock car; dar green body; black split two-tier doors; number under- an over-scored; white lettering and N P logo to right of doors; Stand ard O trucks; "BLT 1-81". From 1160 Great Lakes Limited set.
— — 30 5

9448 A T S F: 1981-82, long stock car; brown body; white letter ing; black split two-tier doors; Symington-Wayne trucks; "BL 1-81". From 1154 Reading Yard King set. It is interesting tha this "Western" stock car would be included in an Eastern railroa set. **— — 25 40 5**

9450 GREAT NORTHERN: 1981, long stock car; red sides black roof and ends; black split two-tier doors; white lettering an goat logo; FARR Series 3 diamond insignia in gold to far left Symington-Wayne trucks; "BLT 1-81". From Famous America

	GD	VG	EXC	MT

Railroad Series No. 3. Part of a year-end special and now somewhat hard to find. Although shown with the set in the 1981 catalogue, this car was not initially released with the other items (all sold separately). It was finally released through the 1981 Fall Collector brochure. — — **75 100**

9707 M-K-T THE KATY: 1972-75, long stock car; redpainted translucent plastic except (D); white lettering script "Katy" to left and "M-K-T" at right; frame stamped "6356-19"; yellow split two-tier doors; MPC logo; Symington-Wayne trucks; "BLT 1-72". Reissue of postwar 6556 from 1958. This car was sold separately and also came in the 1250 N Y C Hudson Service Station Special in 1972. C. Lang comment.

(A) Light yellow-painted light yellow doors; electrocal decoration. **6 8 15 25**

(B) Medium yellow-painted medium yellow doors, rubber-stamped lettering. **6 8 15 25**

(C) Same as (B), but heat-stamped lettering. **6 8 15 25**

(D) Dark red-painted red plastic; medium yellow-painted medium yellow doors. Reader confirmation requested. **NRS**

(E) Flat red-painted red body; unpainted yellow doors; dull white rubber-stamped lettering. R. LaVoie Collection. **8 10 20 25**

(F) Same as (E), but yellow-painted yellow doors. Came as part of 1388 Golden State Arrow set and the 1584 N & W Spirit of America set. G. Halverson Collection. **8 10 20 25**

9725 M-K-T KATY: 1973-75, long stock car; yellow-plastic body painted in several shade variations of yellow; black lettering "The Katy/SERVES THE SOUTHWEST" to left and "M-K-T" to right; black-painted black split two-tier doors; Type I frame; Symington-Wayne trucks. This car also came as part of the uncatalogued 1350 Canadian Pacific Service Station set in 1973. **10 12 15 20**

See Volume II, first edition.

9728 UNION PACIFIC: 1978, long stock car; L C C A; see Volume II, first edition.

9763 RIO GRANDE: 1976-77, long stock car; orange-painted orange plastic body; black-painted black plastic split two-tier doors; black lettering; Type I frame; Symington-Wayne trucks.

(A) Bright orange paint. **10 15 20 30**

(B) Dull orange paint. **10 15 20 30**

9773 N Y C: 1976, long stock car; black-painted black split two-tier doors; number under- and over-scored; black lettering and N Y C oval logo; Type I frame; Symington-Wayne trucks; "BLT 1-76". Came only in the 1665 Empire State Express set. C. Lang comment.

(A) Light yellow-painted yellow body. **12 15 25 35**

(B) Dark yellow-painted yellow body. **12 15 25 35**

16110 SEARS CIRCUS: 1989, short-body operating horse transport stock car; uncatalogued; orange body; white lettering "CIRCUS ANIMALS" and "1989"; two horses bob in and out on hairspring mechanism as car moves; Symington-Wayne trucks; two operating couplers; "BLT 1-89". Part of uncatalogued 1989 Sears Circus set 11770. — — — **25**

16603 DETROIT ZOO: 1987, short-body operating giraffe stock car; tuscan-painted body; white lettering and Lionel Lion logo; yellow giraffe with brown spots; includes cam, track plate, pole and telltale fringes; Symington-Wayne trucks; "BLT 1-87".

(A) One operating, one dummy coupler. — — — **25**

(B) Two operating couplers. M. Blacet Collection. — — — **25**

16605 BRONX ZOO: 1988, short-body operating giraffe stock car; blue car body; white lettering and number; yellow giraffe with brown spots; includes telltale, track clip, and cam plate; Symington-Wayne trucks; two operating couplers. Nearly a direct remake of the postwar 3376-3386 models. — — — **28**

16606 PHILADELPHIA ZOO: 1989, operating giraffe car; blue-painted short stock car body; white lettering and number; yellow giraffe with brown spots; Symington Wayne trucks; operating couplers. — — — **33**

16630 SOUTHERN PACIFIC: 1990-91, short-body operating outlaw stock car; yellow body with black lettering "LIONEL RANCH" on right side; ASF strong-arm trucks; "BLT 1-90". Black outlaw and white sheriff move in and out of car sides as it moves. Part of 11714 Badlands Express set. — — — **15**

16638 LIONELVILLE CIRCUS*: 1991, short operating stock car; red body; white lettering; lion, tiger, seal and zebra figures bob in and out of car sides on hairsprings; "KEEP HANDS AWAY FROM THE ANIMALS"; ASF strong-arm trucks; two operating couplers; "BLT 1-91". Add-on for Lionelville Circus set. — — — **27**

19510 PENNSYLVANIA: 1989, long stock car; tuscan body and split two-tier doors; white lettering and keystone logo; gold FARR Series 5 diamond insignia at left; Standard O trucks; "BLT 1-89". Car issued in year-end 1989 holiday collection to supplement Famous American Railroad Series No. 5 set from 1984. — — — **30**

19515 MILWAUKEE ROAD: 1990, long stock car; maroon/tuscan body and split two-tier doors; white lettering; white and red Milwaukee box logo to right of doors; Standard O trucks; "BLT 1-90". Offered in 1990 Stocking Stuffers catalogue as a supplement to the 1987 Milwaukee Road and Fallen Flags No. 2 set. — — — **30**

19519 FRISCO*: 1991, long stock car; brown-maroon body; brown single door (a change from previous body styles); white lettering and Frisco logo to right of door; Standard O trucks. Part of 18504 Fallen Flags No. 5 set from 1991. — — — **32**

19800 CIRCLE L RANCH: 1988, operating cattle car and corral; tan slatted sides; light gray roof and ends; black lettering "RAILWAY EXPRESS AGENCY"; "CIRCLE L RANCH" to left with "L" being the Lionel version, and "TEXAS LONGHORNS" to the right; postwar-style bar-end trucks (necessary because sliding shoe is needed to operate car) comes with medium orange and white cattle corral, and eight brown cattle; postwar rubber fingers removed from cattle undersides and replaced with felt (an old American Flyer trick) for better operation. When remote-control button is pressed, ramps on car drop and cattle move by vibration out of car, around the corral, and back into car. Similar in operation to postwar 3356 and modern horse car models. — — — **100**

19801 POULTRY DISPATCH: 1987, long-body poultry-style stock car; flat red stock car body; red doors; black lettering; two lights inside show celluloid strips of chickens on way to market; Symington-Wayne trucks; "BLT 1-87". Non-operating reissue of 6434 of postwar years and 9221 modern model. For operating version, see entry 9221 in this section of this chapter. — — — **35**

M. Solly Collection

Spirit of 76 Bicentennial set. These woodside boxcars have many variations.
Top shelf: **1776 Bicentennial Seaboard Coast Line U36B (see the Diesel chapter for listing).**
Second shelf: **7601 State of Delaware; 7602 State of Pennsylvania.**
Third shelf: **7603 State of New Jersey; 7604 State of Georgia.**
Bottom shelf: **7605 State of Connecticut; 7606 State of Massachusetts.**

WOODSIDE BOXCARS

This series of cars is distinctly different from the "classic" boxcar style. It is a combination of the 5700-series woodside reefer body with a standard boxcar door, and thus prompted some question as to whether it should be classified as a reefer or a boxcar. The cars, found principally in the 7600 Bicentennial and the 7700 Tobacco Road series, are nearly one-inch longer than the classic boxcars. They include detailed horizontal wood slat scribing, unlike the smooth sides of their classic boxcar brethren. A further difference is that they are made in two distinct large plastic pieces — the roof/ends combination, and the bottom/sides assembly — fastened by two screws recessed far into the base near the ends. (The classic boxcars are one body — roof, sides and ends — secured to a metal frame by a slot-screw arrangement.) All in all, the woodside boxcars closely resemble the 5700-series reefers, except for the doors.

There are a few other woodside boxcars that are not part of the Bicentennial or Tobacco series. These include the 7700 Uncle Sam car and the 7712 Santa Fe. Two very valuable and rare woodside boxcars were produced for the Toy Fair in 1976. No woodside boxcars have been made since 1980, but Lionel continues producing woodside reefers.

Woodside Boxcar Body Types

Type I: Black metal strip runs car length and is used to attach trucks. Underneath the strip at each end are square holes. A black metal strip is attached to the bottom of the car by one screw, with the trucks then attached to the black strip.

Type II: No-strip version with a round hole at each end on the bottom. Round holes are for the screws that hold the one-piece roof and ends to the car sides.

The remainder of the Spirit of 76 Bicentennial set.
Top shelf: 7607 State of Maryland; 7608 State of South Carolina.
Second shelf: 7609 State of New Hampshire; 7610 State of Virginia, the rarest of the cars in this series.
Third shelf: 7611 State of New York; 7612 State of North Carolina.
Bottom shelf: 7613 State of Rhode Island; 7600 Frisco N5C caboose.

M. Solly Collection; B. Greenberg photograph

WOODSIDE BOXCAR LISTINGS

THE BICENTENNIAL SERIES

The 7600 Bicentennial series of long woodside boxcars was produced from 1974 to 1976. These cars feature colorful markings for each of the thirteen original states, and many have variations. Each state's car names the state capital and portrays its flag, admission date, state flower, bird, tree and motto. At one time, Fundimensions may have had an ambitious plan to produce these colorful cars for the remaining 37 states, but this never happened. The Virginia and New York cars are highly prized in this set, but most of the rest are quite readily available in their Bicentennial boxes. The last six cars in the series, since they were made only in 1976, are slightly harder to find than the others.

7601 STATE OF DELAWARE: 1974-76, woodside boxcar; from Bicentennial series; Symington-Wayne trucks.

	GD	VG	EXC	MT
(A) Type I; light yellow body and doors painted light yellow; blue roof and ends painted blue; blue lettering; yellow-orange diamond in flag. D. Mitarotonda Collection.	—	10	15	20
(B) Same as (A), except cream-white body and doors painted light yellow. C. Lang Collection.	—	10	15	20
(C) Same as (A), except Type II body; and diamond is light gold. D. Mitarotonda Collection.	—	10	15	20

7602 STATE OF PENNSYLVANIA: 1974-76; woodside boxcar; from Bicentennial series; light blue body painted light blue; orange roof and ends painted orange; black or blue lettering; Symington-Wayne trucks.

	GD	VG	EXC	MT
(A) Type I; light blue doors painted light blue; black lettering.	—	10	20	30
(B) Type II body; cream-white plastic doors painted light blue.	—	10	20	30
(C) Type I cream-white body and doors painted light blue. J. Nowaczyk Collection.	—	10	20	30
(D) Same as (A), but unpainted light blue body. J. Nowaczyk Collection.	—	10	20	30

	GD	VG	EXC	MT

7603 STATE OF NEW JERSEY: 1974-76; woodside boxcar; from Bicentennial series; black lettering; Symington-Wayne trucks.

(A) Type I light green body and doors painted light green; gray roof and ends painted gold; yellow-orange flag. D. Mitarotonda Collection.	—	10	20	30
(B) Same as (A), but Type II body.	—	10	20	30
(C) Type II light green body and doors painted light green; clear white roof and ends painted gold; light gold flag. D. Mitarotonda Collection.	—	10	20	30

7604 STATE OF GEORGIA: 1975-76; woodside boxcar; from Bicentennial series; blue lettering; Symington-Wayne trucks.

(A) Type I light blue body painted light blue; clear white doors painted light blue; clear-white roof and ends painted red; red flag; yellow-gold bars and border stripes. D. Mitarotonda Collection.	—	10	20	30
(B) Type I cream-white body and doors painted light blue; red roof and ends painted flat red.	—	10	20	30
(C) Type II light blue body and doors painted light blue; red roof and ends painted dark red; dark red flag; lighter gold bars and border stripes. D. Mitarotonda Collection.	—	10	20	30
(D) Type II light blue body and doors painted light blue; red roof and ends painted glossy deep red.	—	10	20	30
(E) Same as (A), but cream-white roof and ends painted glossy red. J. Nowaczyk Collection.	—	10	20	30
(F) Same as (B), but cream-white roof and ends painted flat red. J. Nowaczyk Collection.	—	10	20	30

7605 STATE OF CONNECTICUT: 1975-76; woodside boxcar; from Bicentennial series; black lettering; Symington-Wayne trucks.

(A) Type I cream-white body and doors painted pale blue; blue roof and ends painted blue.	—	10	20	30
(B) Type II pale blue body and doors painted pale blue; dark blue roof and ends painted blue.	—	10	20	30
(C) Same as (A), but white roof painted blue. D. Mitarotonda Collection.	—	10	20	30
(D) Type I pale blue body painted pale blue; cream-white doors painted pale blue; cream-white roof painted blue. J. Nowaczyk Collection.	—	10	20	30

7606 STATE OF MASSACHUSETTS: 1975-76; woodside boxcar; from Bicentennial series; black lettering; Symington-Wayne trucks.

(A) Type I cream-white body and doors painted light yellow; cream-white roof and ends painted white; doors slightly more yellow-orange than sides.	—	10	20	30
(B) Type I cream-white body and doors painted medium yellow; cream-white roof and ends painted white; doors slightly more yellow-orange than sides. C. Weber comment.	—	10	20	30
(C) Type I shiny white body and doors painted dark yellow; cream-white roof and ends painted white; flag is bordered in dark gold; purple crest; light purple shadowing. D. Mitarotonda Collection.	—	10	20	30
(D) Type II shiny white body and doors painted very dark yellow; cream white roof and ends painted white; flag is bordered in yellow gold; dark blue crest; light blue shadowing. D. Mitarotonda Collection.	—	10	20	30
(E) Type II pale yellow body painted very dark yellow; pale yellow doors painted yellow; white roof and ends painted white. J. Nowaczyk Collection.	—	10	20	30

	GD	VG	EXC	MT

7607 STATE OF MARYLAND: 1975-76; woodside boxcar; from Bicentennial series; black lettering; Symington-Wayne trucks.

(A) Type I white body and doors painted light yellow; white roof and ends painted black; checkered quadrants of the flag are alternating gold and black squares; gold flagstaff is topped by a dark gold eagle. D. Mitarotonda Collection.	—	10	20	30
(B) Type II light yellow body and doors painted light yellow; yellow and black checkered flag quadrants; light gold cross tops flagstaff; black roof and ends painted black. D. Mitarotonda Collection.	—	10	20	30
(C) Type II cream-white body and doors painted mustard; cream-white roof and ends painted black.	—	10	20	30
(D) Type I cream-white body and doors painted dark yellow; cream-white roof and ends painted black.	—	10	20	30
(E) Type II light yellow body and doors painted light yellow; black roof and ends painted black; black and yellow alternating flag quadrant squares; white quadrants slightly shadowed; yellow-gold cross tops yellow-gold flagstaff. D. Mitarotonda Collection.	—	10	20	30

7608 STATE OF SOUTH CAROLINA: 1976; woodside boxcar; from Bicentennial series; black lettering; Symington-Wayne trucks.

(A) Type I dark yellow body and doors painted mustard; brown roof and ends painted chocolate brown. W. Mitchell and D. Mitarotonda Collections.	—	15	25	35
(B) Same as (A), but white doors painted darker mustard. D. Mitarotonda Collection.	—	15	25	35
(C) Type II dark mustard body and medium mustard doors painted dark mustard; mustard roof and ends painted chocolate brown; medium blue flag.	—	15	25	35
(D) Same as (A), but cream white doors painted mustard; cream-white roof and ends painted brown. C. Rohlfing Collection.	—	15	25	35
(E) Same as (D), but cream-white body painted mustard. J. Nowaczyk Collection.	—	15	25	35

7609 STATE OF NEW HAMPSHIRE: 1976; woodside boxcar; from Bicentennial series; black lettering; Symington-Wayne trucks. Harder to find than most of the series.

(A) Type I dark yellow body and doors painted dark yellow; light green roof and ends painted dark green.	—	30	35	45
(B) Type II dark yellow body painted dark yellow; dark yellow doors painted dark yellow; green roof and ends painted dark green; dark blue flag bordered in light gold with light gold leaves and printing on the flag. D. Mitarotonda Collection.	—	30	35	45
(C) Same as (A), but Type II body and white border around right side of map; half moon on map by star.	—	30	35	45
(D) Type I, dark yellow body painted dark yellow; white doors painted dark yellow; white roof and ends painted dark green; purple flag bordered in gold; gold leaves and printing on flag. D. Mitarotonda Collection.	—	30	35	45
(E) Same as (A), except white doors painted dark yellow. J. Nowaczyk Collection.	—	30	35	45

7610 STATE OF VIRGINIA: 1976; woodside boxcar; from Bicentennial series; black lettering; Symington-Wayne trucks. Rarest of the series, though nobody seems to know why fewer of these cars were produced. Some of the cars may have been

B. Greenberg photograph

Long woodside boxcars from the Tobacco Road series.
Top shelf: **7709 Salem; 7710 Mail Pouch.**
Bottom shelf: **7711 El Producto; 7712 A.T.S.F.** which was part of the Famous American Railroad Series No. 1.

	GD	VG	EXC	MT

distributed to the State of Virginia for promotion. J. Grzyboski and C. Lang comment.

(A) Type I cream-white body and doors painted orange; cream-white roof and ends painted dark ~~blue~~. **100 150 195**

(B) Type I orange body and doors painted orange; blue roof and ends painted blue; no quarter moon on map.
— **100 150 195**

(C) Same as (B), but Type II body. — **100 150 195**

(D) Same as (A), except dark blue roof and ends painted dark blue. D. Mitarotonda Collection. — **100 150 195**

(E) Same as (B), except cream-white roof and ends painted dark blue. J. Nowaczyk Collection. — **100 150 195**

7611 STATE OF NEW YORK: 1976; woodside boxcar; from Bicentennial series; black lettering; Symington-Wayne trucks. Harder to find than most other cars in the series, except the 7610.

(A) Type I cream-white body and medium yellow doors painted light yellow; dark blue roof and ends painted dark blue.
— **40 60 75**

(B) Type II cream body and medium yellow doors painted dark yellow; near perfect flag; dark blue roof and ends painted dark blue. — **40 60 75**

(C) Type II cream body and medium yellow doors painted dark yellow; flag with red border; dark blue roof and ends painted dark blue. — **40 60 75**

(D) Type II dark cream body and medium yellow doors painted dark yellow; flag with red and white border; dark blue roof and ends painted dark blue. — **40 60 75**

(E) Type II cream body and white doors painted medium yellow; flag with white border; dark blue roof and ends painted dark blue. — **40 60 75**

(F) Type I pale yellow body and medium yellow doors painted dark yellow (door darker than body); clear white roof and ends painted dark blue. D. Mitarotonda Collection.
— **40 60 75**

(G) Type I medium yellow body and medium yellow doors painted dark yellow (doors darker than body); clear white roof and ends painted dark blue. D. Mitarotonda Collection.
— **40 60 75**

(H) Type I medium yellow body and cream-white doors painted medium yellow; dark blue roof and ends painted dark blue. J. Nowaczyk Collection. — **40 60 75**

7612 STATE OF NORTH CAROLINA: 1976; woodside boxcars; from Bicentennial series; black lettering; Symington-Wayne trucks.

(A) Type I cream body painted dark mustard; yellow doors painted medium mustard; slight contrast between door and darker body; cream-white roof and ends painted black; flag heavily shadowed in blue tint; yellow letters consequently show green tint. D. Mitarotonda Collection. — **12 20 45**

(B) Type I white body and cream doors painted light mustard; cream-white roof and ends painted black.
— **12 20 45**

(C) Type II mustard body and doors painted dark mustard; no contrast between door and body; black roof and ends painted black; flag in light shadow; blue portion is dark blue. D. Mitarotonda Collection. — **12 20 45**

(D) Type II dark yellow body painted light mustard; yellow doors painted dark mustard; large contrast between darker door and body; black roof and ends painted black; flag in medium shadow; red portion is light red. D. Mitarotonda Collection.
— **12 20 45**

(E) Same as (A), but doors darker than sides. C. Weber Collection. — **12 20 45**

(F) Type I pale yellow body painted light mustard; pale yellow doors painted dark mustard; cream-white roof and ends painted glossy black. J. Nowaczyk Collection. — **12 20 45**

(G) Type I pale yellow body and doors painted mustard; cream-white roof and ends painted black; green tint in flag. J. Nowaczyk Collection. — **12 20 45**

7613 STATE OF RHODE ISLAND: 1976; woodside boxcar; from Bicentennial series; black lettering; Symington-Wayne trucks.

(A) Type I aqua-blue body and doors painted green; gray roof and ends painted gold. Very hard to find. J. Grzyboski Collection.
— **40 50 65**

(B) Type II green body and doors painted green; white roof and ends painted gold. — **20 25 30**

	GD	VG	EXC	MT

(C) Type I aqua-blue body painted dark green; dark green doors painted dark green; green roof and ends painted gold. D. Mitarotonda Collection. — — — **NRS**

(D) Same as (A), except green body and doors painted green. J. Nowaczyk Collection. — **20 25 30**

7700 UNCLE SAM: 1976; woodside boxcar; uncatalogued; white-painted body and doors; red-painted roof and ends; plastic top door guides with molded hook on bottom; white and black lettering; Uncle Sam pointing to left of doors; "UNCLE SAM WANTS YOU!" in red, white and blue to right. Offered only in a late 1975 dealer accessory promotion program.

(A) Opaque white plastic body and doors.
30 40 60 75
(B) Translucent, white plastic body. **30 40 60 75**

TOBACCO ROAD SERIES

The 7700 Tobacco Road series was produced from 1976 to 1978. These long woodside boxcars feature some of the biggest names in the tobacco industry and were obviously aimed at an adult audience. Nine of them were eventually produced (7701 through 7703, and 7706 through 7711). The El Producto and Mail Pouch cars are a little harder to find than the rest of the series, which are very common and readily available. Each car has a Type III door, as described in the introduction to the Classic boxcars section.

7701 CAMEL: 1976-77; woodside boxcar; from Tobacco Road series; yellow Type II body; brown, black and silver lettering; dark brown roof and ends; Camel and Pyramid logo to right of doors; Symington-Wayne trucks; "BLT 1-76".

(A) Opaque white body and doors painted medium yellow.
— **10 12 20**
(B) Same as (A), but medium dark yellow body and light yellow doors. — **10 12 20**
(C) Same as (A), but dark yellow body and doors.
— **10 12 20**
(D) Translucent white body painted light yellow; dark yellow doors. — **10 12 20**

7702 PRINCE ALBERT: 1976-77; woodside boxcar; from Tobacco Road series; red Type II body painted red and yellow; yellow doors; black roof and ends; yellow and white lettering; black and white oval electrocal to right of doors; Symington-Wayne trucks; "BLT 1-76". — **10 12 20**

7703 BEECH-NUT: 1976-77; woodside boxcar; from Tobacco Road series; opaque white body painted white; red roof and ends; blue doors painted blue; blue and red lettering; Beech-Nut sunrise electrocal to right of doors; Symington-Wayne trucks; "BLT 1-76". — **10 12 20**

TOY FAIR SERIES

Beginning in 1973 and each year since, Lionel has issued a special car marking the New York Toy Fair. This annual February event is a convention of toy manufacturers, including most model train makers. Lionel uses it to show its new prototype pieces, obtain an assessment of product sales projections and popularity, and release its consumer catalogue. Each year's Lionel Toy Fair Car is a very limited edition, fully uncatalogued car (i.e., not an-

nounced in any official Lionel flyers). In general these cars are quite hard to find, since they are produced in limited quantities. Unlike another annual series — the Seasons Greetings series which consists only of boxcars — the Toy Fair cars consist of woodside boxcars, regular ("classic") boxcars, and reefers. These cars cut across many numbering systems (including an odd reefer in 1981 numbered simply "512") and therefore are not found together in our listings. In earlier editions of this Guide Toy Fair cars were considered Special Production, but since they are Lionel products made for an annual train-related event, they have been moved here to the main listings.

The series started in 1973 and 1974 with two regular 9700-series cars overstamped for the Toy Fair (see the 9700-series listings in this chapter). Lionel had probably subcontracted out the overstamping, which is somewhat rough and not up to Lionel's usual standards. Possibly as a result, the firm started marketing fully dedicated (i.e., not overstamped regular issue) cars in 1975, with the scarce 9762 boxcar. In 1976, two excellent woodside boxcars were made, the 9704 for the United States Toy Fair and the 7705 for the Canadian Toy Fair. These are the two most valuable and sought-after cars in the series. In 1977 Lionel switched to classic-style boxcars in the 7800-series, then changed to reefers in 1981. The reader may refer to the Refrigerator Cars chapter for these Toy Fair reefer car descriptions. After 1986, Lionel returned to classic-type Toy Fair boxcars.

The Toy Fair cars are all very expensive and quite scarce. Here is the full list of the cars for our series collectors. Refer to the individual listings for details.

1973:	9708	boxcar, U.S. Mail, overstamped
1974:	9723	boxcar, Western Pacific, overstamped
1975:	9762	boxcar
1976:	7704	woodside boxcar
1976:	7705	woodside boxcar, Canadian Toy Fair
1977:	7807	boxcar
1978:	7815	boxcar
1979:	7816	boxcar
1980:	7817	boxcar
1981:	512	reefer
1982:	7519	reefer
1983:	7521	reefer
1984:	7523	reefer
1985:	7524	reefer
1986:	7525	boxcar
1987:	19900	boxcar
1988:	19902	boxcar
1989:	19907	boxcar
1990:	19911	boxcar

7704 TOY FAIR: 1976 (United States Toy Fair) woodside boxcar; uncatalogued; opaque white plastic body painted white; red roof and ends; translucent white doors painted red; blue and red lettering; plastic top door guides with molded hook on bottom; American flag logo and "LIONEL SALUTES AMERICA" to right of door; Symington-Wayne trucks; "BLT 1-76". C. Lang comment. — — **175 200**

	GD	VG	EXC	MT

7705 TOY FAIR: 1976 (Canadian Toy Fair) woodside boxcar; uncatalogued; opaque white plastic body painted white; red roof and ends; translucent white door painted red; red lettering in English and French to left of door; red Maple Leaf logo and numbers to right of door; plastic top on door guides with molded hook on bottom; Symington-Wayne trucks; "BLT 1-76". The hardest of all Toy Fair cars to obtain. "Triple T" Collection.

	—	—	300	400

(Tobacco Road listings continued)

7706 SIR WALTER RALEIGH: 1977-78; woodside boxcar; from Tobacco Road series; opaque white plastic body painted orange; blue roof and ends; translucent white doors painted gold; white and gold lettering; black and gold electrocals on each side of doors; Symington-Wayne trucks; "BLT 1-77".

	—	10	15	20

7707 WHITE OWL: 1977-78; woodside boxcar; from Tobacco Road series; opaque white plastic body painted white; brown roof and ends; translucent white doors painted gold; brown lettering; brown and white square electrocal to right of doors; Symington-Wayne trucks; "BLT 1-77".

	—	10	15	20

7708 WINSTON: 1977-78; woodside boxcar; from Tobacco Road series; red plastic body painted red; gold roof and ends; translucent white doors painted gold; white and red lettering; red and white square electrocal to right of doors; Symington Wayne trucks; "BLT 1-77".

	—	10	15	20

7709 SALEM: 1978; woodside boxcar; from Tobacco Road series; green-painted sides; gold roof, ends and doors; "tobacco/railroad" in script; square Salem electrocals to right of doors; Salem pack to right; Symington-Wayne trucks; "BLT 1-78".

	—	10	15	20

7710 MAIL POUCH: 1978; woodside boxcar; from Tobacco Road series; white-painted sides; red roof and ends; tuscan doors; red and tuscan lettering; "tobacco/railroad" in script; red, tuscan and white Mail Pouch electrocal to left of doors; green, yellow, black, gray, tuscan and white barn electrocal to right of doors; Symington-Wayne trucks; "BLT 1-78". C. Rohlfing Collection.

	—	10	25	30

7711 EL PRODUCTO: 1978; woodside boxcar; from Tobacco Road series; white sides; yellow doors; red roof and ends; red and black lettering; "tobacco/railroad" in script; cigar box to left; El Producto ramp to right; Symington-Wayne trucks; "BLT 1-78". C. Rohlfing Collection.

	—	10	25	30

7712 A. T. S. F.: 1979; woodside boxcar; yellow sides; silver roof; black "ship Santa Fe/all the way"; gold FARR Series 1 diamond insignia; Symington-Wayne trucks; "BLT 1-79". Part of Famous American Railroad Series No. 1, whose contents were sold separately.

	—	25	35	45

◆ CHAPTER 7 ◆
CABOOSES

It is ironic that Fundimensions is producing the best cabooses ever seen in tinplate just as these cars are being phased out on real railroads across the nation. The caboose is a car steeped in nostalgia. Who of us has not seen a picture of a train crew enjoying breakfast cooked over a coal stove in one of these way cars? For most of us, a freight train without a caboose is unthinkable. However, the caboose complicates switching assignments, and its need has been considerably lessened by detachable signal devices for the last car on the train and the commodious, air-conditioned cabs of the modern diesel locomotives. Real railroaders do not feel quite as romantically attached to the caboose; veterans of the rails would be quick to tell you that these cars were not all cozy little houses on rails. Unless the caboose was quite modern, it was drafty in winter despite the heat of the coal stove and, in summer, somewhere west of the Eternal Inferno. Thus, cabooses are becoming highly specialized or nonexistent in today's railroading.

Lionel has, for the first time in its history, bowed to the trend. In 1990 it issued a modern Santa Fe Dash-8 40B freight set including the 17302 reefer with an end-of-train light. This is the first freight set the firm has ever issued without a caboose.

This chapter is divided into the following categories of principal caboose types:

CATEGORY	PAGE
Bay Window	182
Extended Vision	188
N5C Porthole	191
Southern Pacific (SP)-type	197
Standard O Scale	202

Tinplate railroading, however, still demands cabooses for its trains, romantic or not, and in the modern era Lionel has responded with a fine variety of these cars. Some are modeled after their prewar predecessors, like the N5C porthole caboose, while others, such as the magnificent extended vision cabooses, are unique to the new breed of Lionel's train-makers.

BAY WINDOW CABOOSES

Lionel's postwar model of the bay window caboose was issued in only two regular production varieties — Lionel Lines and Erie. But when Fundimensions revived this handsome car, the firm produced a considerable number and variety of them. Nearly 40 have been made in the modern era so far.

The first Fundimensions bay window caboose came as part of the Empire State Express set of 1976 in green New York Central markings. There is a great story related to this particular caboose — the 9174 Peoria & Eastern. When it was issued, collectors thought Lionel had erred in lettering it "P & E". They presumed it should have been "P & LE" for the Pittsburgh and Lake Erie, a part of the New York Central System. Collector complaints flooded in and panic briefly ensued at Lionel until Dan Johns determined that the car was modeled after the Peoria and Eastern ("P & E") railroad, an obscure Midwest railroad also part of the N Y C. In fact, the car is a very close match for the P & E prototype. Lionel was correct after all.

Fundimensions' original intent was to limit the bay window caboose to special sets, but demand became so acute that it soon entered regular cataloguing and production.

Two examples of the bay window cabooses illustrate collector insistence upon matching locomotives and cabooses, no matter what the practice on the prototype railroad. In 1976

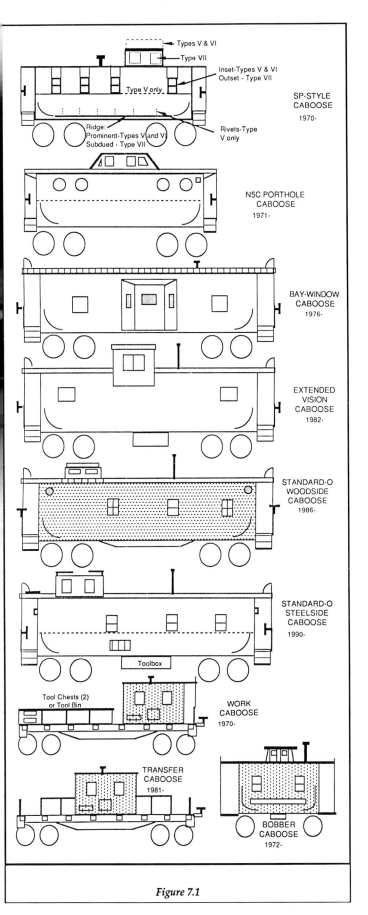

Figure 7.1

Fundimensions issued the Northern Pacific Service Station Special set with a black and gold Northern Pacific GP-9 locomotive and a green, silver and yellow Northern Pacific bay window caboose, true to the prototype. Collectors did not like the fact that the caboose was not a color match for the locomotive, so the company issued a black and gold Northern Pacific bay window caboose which did match the GP-9. Where the New York Central caboose had Symington-Wayne plastic trucks with long coupler extensions, both Northern Pacific cabooses had die-cast O27 passenger trucks. Since then, the bay window cabooses have come with both types of trucks.

Two years later, in 1978, history repeated itself. Fundimensions produced a magnificent Santa Fe SD-18 six-wheeled locomotive in blue and yellow freight colors. The bay window caboose meant to accompany this locomotive was made in red and black, just as the real railroad issued them. Once more, collectors howled that the caboose did not match the engines, so Fundimensions ceased making the 9274 red and black model in favor of a 9317 Santa Fe bay window caboose in blue and yellow colors. This means, of course, that the red and black caboose has become a real collector's item; reportedly, fewer than 3,000 were made.

It was not long before the bay window caboose became the dominant caboose of the Fundimensions lineup. Beginning in the late 1970s and through the early 1980s, several new issues turned up in every catalogue, and other new ones were used in limited edition sets. In recent years, these cabooses have been somewhat overshadowed in favor of the new extended vision and wood-sided cabooses.

The reasons for the popularity of the bay window caboose are not hard to understand. Its construction is excellent. It retains the stamped-metal frame of the postwar cabooses, and its metal ladder trim adds an authentic touch. The lighting system is a little curious, but effective. Clear plastic rods reach from the light bulb to the little red marker lights on the rear of the caboose, providing a fiber-optic pathway for the illumination. Earlier versions used the postwar spring clip and a No. 57 bayonet-based bulb, whether the trucks were plastic or die-cast. This practice continued until the 1978 Minneapolis and St. Louis model. The light bulb on 1978 and later versions of this caboose, and many other pieces of modern era Lionel rolling stock and locomotives, is a 12-volt plug-in clear lamp used in quite a few automotive applications. (Lamps designed for Chrysler Corporation side marker, instrument panel, and turn signal lights are exact duplicates of these light bulbs.) The windows in the central bay are shaded by black paper so that the clear plastic windows on the main body sides receive most of the light. Sometimes the paper is missing. The light bulb is located in the center.

All versions of these cabooses have two operating couplers, whether the trucks are plastic or die-cast. A strange fact about the bay window cabooses, with all their style and innovation, is that none of them have ever been equipped with smoke units. Since they are easily large enough to accommodate a smoke mechanism, and since Lionel is moving in that direction with many other types of rolling stock, perhaps we can look forward to this addition in the future.

Bay window cabooses from the late 1970s.

W. Dyson, R. Kaptur, R. LaVoie, A. Rudman, and F. Stem Collections; B. Greenberg photograph

Top shelf: **6401 Virginian; 6421 Joshua Lionel Cowen.**
Second shelf: **6425 Erie-Lackawanna; 6431 Southern.**
Third shelf: **6433 Canadian Pacific; 6439 Reading.**
Bottom shelf: **6441 Alaska Railroad; 6493 Lancaster and Chester.**

BAY WINDOW
CABOOSE LISTINGS

	GD	VG	EXC	MT

1990 LIONEL LINES: See 19708.

6401 V G N: 1981, (Virginian) bay window caboose; yellow sides with broad blue stripe through center, including bay; yellow and blue safety striping along lower side; "V G N" logo with yellow letters inside circular blue field surrounded by yellow and blue rings; blue, heat-stamped, sans-serif lettering; illuminated; Symington-Wayne trucks; "BLT 1-81". Matches 8950 Virginian Fairbanks-Morse. Also a good match for 8659 Virginian rectifier electric and Virginian SD-18 pair, 8071-8072. Brewer Collection.
— 15 35 40

6421 JOSHUA LIONEL COWEN: 1982, bay window caboose; uncatalogued; gold sides; tuscan roof; black lettering and number; electrocal of Cowen at right center; O27 die-cast passenger trucks; "BLT 1-82". Issued as a limited edition in the

"Spring Collector Series" and meant to match the Joshua Lionel Cowen commemorative Hudson and 9400-series commemorative boxcars.
— — 35 40

6422 DULUTH MISSABE: 1981-82, bay window caboose; tuscan body; yellow stripes; white lettering; illuminated; red, black and white "SAFETY FIRST" decal; Symington-Wayne trucks; "BLT 1-81". A good match for 8158-8159 Duluth diesels.
— — 20 25

6425 E: 1983-84, (Erie-Lackawanna) bay window caboose; gray body; maroon striping edged with yellow stripes; yellow lettering; illuminated; Symington-Wayne trucks; "BLT 1-83". Matches 8369 GP-20 and 8759 GP-9 diesels. R. LaVoie Collection.
— — 35 40

6431 SOUTHERN: 1983, bay window caboose; dark red sides and roof; white lettering; gold FARR Series 4 diamond insignia on sides; illuminated; die-cast O27 passenger trucks. Shown in catalogue with green sides. Part of Southern Famous American Railroad Series No. 4, whose components were all sold separately. L. Caponi and C. Rohlfing comments. — — 35 45

Bay window cabooses.

W. Dyson, R. Kaptur, R. LaVoie, A. Rudman, and F. Stem Collections; B. Greenberg photograph

Top shelf: 9174 P & E; 9177 Northern Pacific Railway.
Second shelf: 9184 Erie; 9188 Great Northern.
Third shelf: 9268 Northern Pacific Railway; 9231 Reading.
Bottom shelf: 9271 Minneapolis & St. Louis; 9272 New Haven.

	GD	VG	EXC	MT

6433 CANADIAN PACIFIC: 1981, bay window caboose; gray with maroon roof and lettering; illuminated; die-cast O27 passenger trucks; "BLT 1-87". Part of 1158 Maple Leaf Limited set.

— — 40 60

6438 GREAT NORTHERN: 1981, bay window caboose; dark orange and dark green body and ends; dark green roof; dark green stripe along bottom; black lettering in orange area; white number and built date; gold FARR Series 3 diamond insignia; yellow, black and white mountain goat logo; illuminated; Symington-Wayne trucks; "BLT 1-81". Part of G N Famous American Railroad Series No. 3, whose components were all sold separately.

— — 35 50

See Factory Errors and Prototypes chapter in Volume II, first edition.

6439 READING: 1984-85; bay window caboose; yellow and green body; green roof; yellow and green lettering; illuminated; Symington-Wayne trucks; "BLT 1-84". — — 20 30

See Factory Errors and Prototypes chapter in Volume II, first edition.

6441 ALASKA RAILROAD: 1982-83; bay window caboose; dark blue-painted blue body and roof; yellow lettering and Eskimo logo; illuminated; Symington-Wayne trucks; "BLT 1-82".

— — 25 30

	GD	VG	EXC	MT

6493 LANCASTER AND CHESTER: 1986-87, bay window caboose; medium blue body; gray-painted roof; white lettering and logo; illuminated; Symington-Wayne trucks; "BLT 1-86".

— — 20 25

9174 P & E: 1976, (Peoria & Eastern) bay window caboose; jade green sides; black roof; white lettering; "ROAD TO THE FUTURE"; black and white N Y C oval logo; illuminated; "BLT 1-76". Controversy arose when this car was released. Collectors insisted it should have been "P & L E" for Pittsburgh and Lake Erie. But Lionel was correct — the Peoria and Eastern is another Midwest branch of the New York Central. From Empire State Express set of 1976. Difficult to find.
(A) Symington-Wayne trucks. 40 50 75 90
(B) Die-cast O27 passenger trucks. M. Finney Collection.
50 60 90 100

9177 NORTHERN PACIFIC RAILWAY: 1976, bay window caboose; uncatalogued; silver roof; green and dark or medium yellow sides; yellow ends; black lettering; red and white N P Monad logo; illuminated; die-cast O27 passenger trucks; "BLT 1-76". From 1672 Northern Pacific Service Station Special set. This was the first bay window caboose to use die-cast trucks. C. Lang comment.
(A) Dark yellow sides. 9 15 25 35

Bay window cabooses.
Top shelf: 9273 Southern; 9274 Santa Fe.
Second shelf: 9316 Southern Pacific; 9317 Santa Fe.
Third shelf: 9323 Santa Fe; 9326 Burlington Northern.
Bottom shelf: 9328 W M Chessie System; 9355 D&H.

W. Dyson, R. Kaptur, R. LaVoie, A. Rudman, and F. Stem Collections; B. Greenberg photograph

	GD	VG	EXC	MT
(B) Medium yellow sides.	9	15	25	35

9184 ERIE: 1977-78, bay window caboose; red body; white lettering with lightning bolt; illuminated; Symington-Wayne trucks; "BLT 1-76". A reissue of postwar 6517-75, a very rare car, and one of only two bay window cabooses produced by postwar Lionel.

	10	12	20	30

9188 GREAT NORTHERN: 1977, bay window caboose; blue and white sides; black roof; white ends; white lettering and goat logo; illuminated; Symington-Wayne trucks; "BLT 1-77". From Rocky Mountain Special set.

	13	15	30	40

9231 READING: 1979, bay window caboose; green and yellow sides; yellow lettering; green roof; illuminated; Symington-Wayne trucks. Part of 1971 Quaker City Limited set.

	15	20	30	40

9259X SOUTHERN: 1977, bay window caboose; L C C A; see Volume II, first edition.

9268 NORTHERN PACIFIC RAILWAY: 1977, bay window caboose; uncatalogued; black and gold sides; yellow hash marks; red lettering; red, black and white Monad decal; gold ends and roofs; die-cast O27 passenger trucks; "BLT 1-77". Made in response to collector complaints that the 9177 Northern Pacific bay window caboose did not match the locomotive in the 1976 Service Station Special set. See 9274 entry for a similar situation.

	—	30	30	40

9269 THE MILWAUKEE ROAD: 1978, bay window caboose; dull orange sides; black roof; red logo; black lettering; die-cast O27 passenger trucks. Part of 1867 Milwaukee Limited Special set of 1978.

	—	35	35	60

9271 MINNEAPOLIS & ST. LOUIS: 1978-79, bay window caboose; red sides with large central white stripe; blue roof; white lettering; red and white "The/Peoria/Gateway" circle logo; illuminated; O27 die-cast passenger trucks; "BLT 1-78". Part of 1868 Minneapolis & St. Louis Service Station set of 1978, and catalogued the next year.

	12	15	20	30

9272 NEW HAVEN: 1978-80, bay window caboose; dark red body; white and black lettering; white serifed "N" over black "H" to right of window; illuminated; Symington-Wayne trucks; "BLT 1-78". Separate-sale only, not in sets.

	8	10	15	25

ecent bay window cabooses.
op shelf: **9361 C N W; 9368 Union Pacific.**
cond shelf: **9372 Seaboard; 9382 Florida East Coast.**
ottom shelf: **16506 Santa Fe; 16510 New Haven.**

W. Dyson, R. Kaptur, R. LaVoie, A. Rudman, and F. Stem Collections; B. Greenberg photograph

	GD	VG	EXC	MT

9273 SOUTHERN: 1978, bay window caboose; uncatalogued; green body with lower white stripe and gold accent stripes; gold roof and lettering; illuminated; die-cast O27 passenger trucks; "BLT 1-78". Intended to match 8774 GP-7 diesel. This mysterious caboose is not pictured in any Lionel flyers or brochures, and is listed only on two 1978-79 dealer order forms. The car was apparently planned to carry the number 9278 but this was changed before release. L. Bohn comment.

	10	20	40	55

9274 SANTA FE: 1978, bay window caboose; uncatalogued; black roof; red sides; white lettering and cross logo to left; illuminated; Symington-Wayne trucks; "BLT 1-78". Reportedly only 3,000 made because collectors complained that it did not match the 8872 Santa Fe SD-18 diesels made that year. In response, Fundimensions stopped making this caboose in favor of the blue and yellow 9317. Appeared in a late 1978 flyer with the number "9275", but made as 9274.

	40	50	60	90

9309 T P W: 1980-81, (Toledo, Peoria & Western) bay window caboose; orange body with silver roof and white lettering; white stripe near lower edge of body; illuminated; Symington-Wayne trucks. From 1072 Cross Country Express set. Shown in red in catalogue, but not made that way, although we have reports of a red example which may be a prototype. C. Lang, C. Rohlfing, and I. D. Smith comments.

(A) Orange body; silver roof; white lettering. G. Kline Collection.

	—	15	25	35

(B) Same as (A), but red body; possible prototype. Reader comments requested. W. Eddins Collection. **NRS**

	GD	VG	EXC	MT

9316 SOUTHERN PACIFIC: 1979, bay window caboose; uncatalogued; silver with black roof; black lettering; large orange "S" and "P"; illuminated; O27 die-cast passenger trucks; "BLT 1-79". From the Southern Pacific Limited set No. 1970. Pictured in the 1979 advance catalogue, but since the set was a sell-out it was not shown in the regular 1979 catalogue.

	—	—	60	85

9317 SANTA FE: 1979, bay window caboose; blue body; yellow roof and ends; yellow lettering and cross logo; illuminated; Symington-Wayne trucks; "BLT 1-79". Matches 8872 A T S F SD-18 locomotive. See entry 9274 for story behind this caboose.

	15	20	25	35

9323 SANTA FE: 1979, bay window caboose; tuscan body; black roof; white lettering; black and white Santa Fe cross logo; gold FARR Series 1 diamond insignia; illuminated; Symington-Wayne trucks; "BLT 1-79". From Santa Fe Famous American Railroad Series No. 1, whose components were only available for separate-sale.

	20	25	30	45

9326 BURLINGTON NORTHERN: 1979-80, bay window caboose; Cascade green-painted body; black roof; white lettering; B N logo to right; illuminated; "BLT 1-79".

	GD	VG	EXC	MT
(A) Symington-Wayne trucks.	12	15	20	25
(B) Die-cast O27 passenger trucks.	15	18	25	30

9328 W M CHESSIE SYSTEM: 1980, bay window caboose; yellow with silver roof; blue lettering and cat logo; illuminated; O27 die-cast passenger trucks; "BLT 1-80". From 1070 Royal Limited set.

	—	—	30	50

	GD	VG	EXC	MT

9355 D & H: 1980, (Delaware & Hudson) bay window caboose; dark blue body with lower gray stripe; thin yellow stripe between blue and gray areas; black and white lettering; white round D & H script logo; illuminated; Symington-Wayne trucks; "BLT 1-80". Matches 8050-8051 D & H U36C diesels.

— — 20 25

9361 C N W: 1980, bay window caboose; yellow sides; Brunswick green roof; black lettering; black, white and red "NORTH WESTERN" logos at each end; illuminated; bar code; Symington-Wayne trucks; no "BLT" date. Prior to the production of this caboose, several Midwestern train shops repainted other bay window cabooses into this color scheme. C. Rohlfing and R. LaVoie comments.

— 15 45 60

9368 UNION PACIFIC: 1980, bay window caboose; yellow with red roof and lettering; red, white and blue U P shield; FARR Series 2 diamond insignia; illuminated; Symington-Wayne trucks; "BLT 1-80". From U P Famous American Railroad Series No. 2, whose components were all sold separately.

— 15 30 45

9372 SEABOARD: 1980, bay window caboose; dark red body; black roof; white lettering; red, white and black circular Seaboard heart logo; illuminated; die-cast O27 passenger trucks; "BLT 1-80". From 1071 Mid Atlantic Limited set.

15 30 40

9382 FLORIDA EAST COAST: 1980, bay window caboose; red body; yellow lower section with silver stripe between red and yellow areas; red and yellow lettering; yellow, black and white circle decal to right; illuminated; Symington-Wayne trucks; "BLT 1-80". Matches 8064 and 8065 GP-9 diesels.

— — 25 35

9387 BURLINGTON: 1981, bay window caboose; red sides; white lettering; illuminated; die-cast O27 passenger trucks; "BLT 1-81". From 1160 Great Lakes Limited set.

— — 35 45

16506 SANTA FE: 1988, bay window caboose; blue body and roof; yellow ends; yellow Santa Fe lettering and cross logo; illuminated; Symington-Wayne trucks; "BLT 1-88". Appears to be identical to 9317 model made in 1979 except for number.

— — 25 30

16510 NEW HAVEN: 1989, bay window caboose; tuscan body; black roof and end platforms; black and white lettering; serifed black "N" over white "H" to right side; illuminated; Symington-Wayne trucks; "BLT 1-89".

— — — 30

16517 ATLANTIC COAST LINE: 1990, bay window caboose; red body and roof; black frame and platforms; white lettering; illuminated; ASF strong-arm trucks; "BLT 1-90". Issued in tandem with 18808 A C L SD-18 diesel engine.

— — — 26

16518 CHESSIE SYSTEM: 1990, bay window caboose; orange body; silver roof; yellow end platforms; black lettering and Chessie logo to left of window; illuminated ASF stong-arm trucks; "BLT 1-90". Part of 11717 C S X freight set. M. Daniels Collection.

— — — 35

16525 DELAWARE & HUDSON*: 1991, bay window caboose; red sides and ends; black roof; white lettering; illuminated; die-cast O27 passenger trucks; "BLT 1-91". Part of 11719 Coastal Freight Service Station Special set from 1991.

— — — 35

	GD	VG	EXC	M

16804 LIONEL RAILROADER CLUB: 1991, bay window caboose; see Volume II, first edition.

19708 LIONEL LINES 90TH ANNIVERSARY: 1990, bay window caboose; straw/light yellow sides; dark blue bay window; orange roof; gold lettering and 90th anniversary logo; "AND THE LEGEND LIVES ON", "1990" on bay window; catalogue number not on car; illuminated; die-cast O27 passenger trucks; "BLT 1-90". Part of 11715 Lionel 90th Anniversary set.

— — — 4

EXTENDED VISION CABOOSES

In 1982 Fundimensions issued a fine Collector train set in Norfolk and Western markings known as the Continental Limited. The handsome maroon SD-24 six-wheeled locomotive had an electronic horn, and the rolling stock was all of very high quality. However, the real surprise was reserved for the caboose, which was unlike anything ever seen in tinplate. The extended vision caboose is a large, scale-length square-cupola caboose which on the real railroads illustrates state-of-the-art caboose construction. Many collectors regard this caboose as the finest tinplate caboose ever produced. The extended vision cabooses produced to date have all been limited edition items.

The Lionel extended vision caboose has a stamped-metal frame with a black plastic battery box and brake cylinder piece attaching to the frame by means of a black plastic channel — on all except the initial 6900. All of these cabooses are equipped with O27 passenger-style or arch bar die-cast trucks with two operating couplers. The sides, ends and roof are molded in one piece with a large hole in the roof. A separately molded cupola piece is snapped onto the roof atop this hole; it is secured by projections in the body shell on the sides. Sometimes this separate cupola piece can lead to problems. On the 6905 Nickel Plate Road caboose, the lettering "Nickel Plate High Speed Service" goes across the top of the sides in such a way that one of the words is on the cupola. If the cupola is snapped onto the body in reverse, the sides will read "Nickel Speed High Speed Service" and "Nickel Plate High Plate Service". This is not a factory error — just an incorrectly installed cupola.

The sides of the extended vision cabooses are absolutely smooth except for molded grab-rails near the platform, two large square windows per side, and molded signal lamps at both ends. Inside the car, four clear plastic rods lead to the signal lamps for brighter illumination, and all the windows on the sides and on the cupola are lighted as well. Plastic snap-in end railing pieces and a tall plastic chimney complete the decor of the caboose — or do they? Some of these cabooses have been produced with slots cut into the ends of the roofs so that metal trim ladders can be attached as they are on the bay window cabooses. However, the extended vision cabooses have no roof catwalks! The 6900 Norfolk and Western and the 6901 Ontario Northland cabooses do not have these ladders but the 6903 Santa Fe does. In some cases the caboose is pictured in the catalogues without the ladders, but the produc

The first set of extended vision cabooses.
Top shelf: 6900 Norfolk and Western with no underbody detail or ladders — the first extended vision caboose; 6901 Ontario Northland.
Middle shelf: 6903 Santa Fe; 6904 Union Pacific.
Bottom shelf: 6905 Nickel Plate Road; 6906 Erie Lackawanna.

W. Dyson, R. Kaptur, R. LaVoie, A. Rudman, and F. Stem Collections; B. Greenberg photograph

tion pieces have them. In other cases the reverse is true. These now-you-see-them, now-you-don't ladders could make for some interesting variations. (We would like to hear from our readers about whether their samples have the ladders or not. It is quite possible that some pieces were made both ways!)

Because of their handsome scale appearance and high demand, most of the extended vision cabooses command substantial price premiums. The one exception seems to be the 6901 Ontario Northland caboose, which has not been in much demand. The 6910 New York Central Pacemaker extended vision caboose might become the scarcest of these cabooses because of extreme demand from scale Hudson, New York Central F-3, and New York Central GP-9 owners. The 6903 Santa Fe is also appreciating rapidly.

These cabooses are also magnificent matches for the new SD-40 scale diesels. Besides the Norfolk and Western, Ontario Northland, Nickel Plate, Santa Fe, and New York Central examples, extended vision cabooses in Union Pacific, Erie Lackawanna, and Burlington Northern colors have been made. A special "Miss Liberty" commemorative extended vision caboose was made in 1986 in Jersey Central colors.

Quite a few more followed in the LTI era, including several versions fitted with smoke units.

EXTENDED VISION CABOOSE LISTINGS

	GD	VG	EXC	MT

6900 NORFOLK AND WESTERN: 1982, extended vision caboose; dark red body; silver roof; white lettering and round "N & W" logo; no ladders to roof on ends; illuminated; die-cast O27-style passenger trucks; "BLT 1-82". Part of 1260 Continental Limited set; shown as "7301" in 1982 catalogue illustration. This was the first extended vision caboose. Unlike later versions, it lacks all underbody detail (battery box, air cylinder, etc.). It may have used a plain bay window caboose frame before detail was added for 6901 and subsequent numbers. We would like to learn of other observed examples. R. and R. Hunley comments and Collection. — — 90 120

6901 ONTARIO NORTHLAND: 1982, extended vision caboose; uncatalogued; yellow and dark blue body; blue and white lettering; dark blue roof and cupola sides; turquoise cupola roof; illuminated; dark blue "triple lightning" logo on sides; no ladders at ends; die-cast O27 passenger trucks; no "BLT" date. Separate-sale item from 1982 Fall Collector Center, not in a set. — — 50 75

W. Dyson, R. Kaptur, R. LaVoie, A. Rudman, and F. Stem; B. Greenberg photograph

Extended vision cabooses, all made since 1984 and all in high demand.
Top shelf: **6910 New York Central System; 6917 Jersey Central Lines.**
Second shelf: **19700 C&O Chessie System; 19703 Great Northern Railway,** note the change to die-cast arch bar trucks.
Third shelf: **19704 Western Maryland; 9706 (19706) Union Pacific.**
Bottom shelf: **19807 Pennsylvania with smoke.**

	GD	VG	EXC	MT

6903 SANTA FE: 1983, extended vision caboose; uncatalogued; blue and yellow body; yellow main roof; blue cupola sides and roof; illuminated; yellow lettering; blue cross logo; ladders at ends; black smokestack; O27 die-cast passenger trucks; "BLT 1-83". Separate-sale item from 1983 Collector Preview brochure. C. Rohlfing and R. LaVoie Collections.

— — **100 125**

6904 UNION PACIFIC: 1983, extended vision caboose; yellow body; red and white lettering; red, white and blue shield logo; red line along roof edge; silver main and cupola roofs; illuminated; black smokestack; O27 die-cast passenger trucks; "BLT 1-83". Came only in 1361 Gold Coast Limited set.

— — **100 150**

6905 NICKEL PLATE ROAD: 1983-84, extended vision caboose; uncatalogued; dark red body; black roof; white lettering on body side; gray stripe with black "Nickel Plate High Speed Service" lettering; "NICKEL PLATE/ROAD" in old fashioned white serif letters below cupola; number in white below lettering; illuminated; O27 die-cast passenger trucks; "BLT 1-83". Some cars came with cupolas installed incorrectly; these are not factory

errors in the usual sense, since reversing the cupola produces the correct lettering. Designed to match 8215 Nickel Plate Road 2-8-4 Berkshire locomotive. Separate-sale item from 1983 Fall Collector Center. LaVoie comment.

— — **75 100**

See Factory Errors and Prototypes chapter in Volume II, first edition.

6906 ERIE LACKAWANNA: 1984, extended vision caboose; gray body; yellow ends; maroon and yellow stripe on lower body; yellow lettering; maroon E-diamond logo; illuminated; O27 die-cast passenger trucks; "BLT 1-84". Part of 1451 Erie-Lackawanna Limited set.

— — **75 100**

6910 NEW YORK CENTRAL SYSTEM: 1984-85; extended vision caboose; uncatalogued; red upper sides and ends; gray lower sides ("Pacemaker" paint scheme); black roof; "NYC / 6910" in black on the gray area and New York Central oval in white on the red area; ladders; illuminated; O27 die-cast passenger trucks; "BLT 1-84". Separate-sale item from 1984 Spring Collector Center. This caboose is in demand because it matches the 8406 Hudson steam locomotive and the 8477 New York Central GP-9 diesel — not to mention numerous other New York Central

GD VG EXC MT

ocomotives produced in the past. R. LaVoie comment and Collection. — — 85 115

913 BURLINGTON NORTHERN: 1985, extended vision aboose; Cascade green body; yellow ends; gray roof; white B N ogo and lettering; illuminated; O27 die-cast passenger trucks; BLT 1-85". From 1552 Burlington Northern Limited Collector et of 1985. — — 85 115

917 JERSEY CENTRAL LINES: 1986; extended vision aboose; dark flat green body; cream lettering, logo and 1886/MISS/LIBERTY/1986" within circle of stars; illuminated; ream-painted cupola roof and car ends; ladders; die-cast O27 assenger trucks; "BLT 1-86". Made to match Jersey Central iberty Fairbanks-Morse and 7404 boxcar, but sold separately. — — 40 50

926 T C A NEW ORLEANS: 1986, extended vision caboose; ee Volume II, first edition.

706 UNION PACIFIC: See 19706.

19700 C & O CHESSIE SYSTEM: 1988, extended vision aboose; yellow sides; dark blue main and cupola roofs; dark blue ettering and logo; "C&O 19700" on cupola; O27 die-cast passenger rucks; "BLT 1-88". Catalogued with large vermilion stripe on ower half of caboose sides, but production pieces lack this stripe nd are solid yellow. Part of 11705 Chessie System unit train set. — — — 60

19703 GREAT NORTHERN RAILWAY: 1988, extended vision caboose; dark red body; black main and cupola roofs; white ettering; red, black and white goat logo; illuminated; die-cast arch ar trucks; "BLT 1-88". Part of G N Fallen Flags set No. 3, whose omponents were all sold separately. — — — 55

19704 WESTERN MARYLAND: 1989, smoking extended vision caboose; red body and cupola; black main and cupola roofs; white lettering and logo; illuminated; die-cast arch bar trucks; BLT 1-89". Part of Western Maryland Fallen Flags No. 4 set, vhose components were all sold separately. — — — 65

19705 C P RAIL: 1989, smoking extended vision caboose; yelow body; black roof and platform; white and black lettering; white nd black Pac-man logo at rear; illuminated; die-cast arch bar rucks; "BLT 1-89". Available only in 11710 C P Rail set. — — — 45

19706 UNION PACIFIC: 1989, smoking extended vision aboose; yellow body; red main and cupola roofs; black end platorms; red lettering; red "P" (not "UP") on cupola; black and white End of Train,/but Safety/Rolls On" decal; number is "9706", lropping the usual "1" at the front; illuminated; die-cast arch bar rucks; "BLT 1-89". Issued as a match for 18205 U P Dash-8 liesel. — — — 65

See Factory Errors and Prototypes chapter in Volume II, first dition.

19710 FRISCO*: 1991, smoking extended vision caboose; red ody; black end platforms; black and white lettering and Frisco hield logo; "Ship it on the Frisco!"; bar code; illuminated; die-cast rch bar trucks; "BLT 1-91". Part of Frisco Fallen Flags No. 5 set, vhose components were all sold separately. — — — 70

19807 PENNSYLVANIA: 1988, smoking extended vision aboose; tuscan body and roofs; black frame and platforms; gold ettering and number; number under- and over-scored; iluminated; die-cast arch bar trucks. Caboose is numbered in the

GD VG EXC MT

Collector sequence under "operating cars" because it was issued separately. Other cabooses of this type came in sets and are numbered in the 19700-series. — — — 65

N5C PORTHOLE CABOOSES

The N5C porthole caboose has been one of the mainstays of Lionel's modern era production, along with the bay window caboose. In real life, the N5C, which earned its name from its unique round porthole windows in its sides, was used only by the Pennsylvania Railroad, but that has not stopped Lionel from issuing this caboose in dozens of railroad names and colors. It did not stop Lionel in the postwar era either, when Virginian and Lehigh Valley cabooses were made. But modern Lionel has expanded the N5C line much further. Since all these cabooses are lighted and the design is very attractive, it is no wonder that they are so plentiful.

Production of the N5C has languished somewhat in recent years in favor of the bay window cabooses and the new extended vision cabooses — most of the modern lineup dates from the 1970s. Still, new N5Cs appear occasionally. In 1985 a good looking Pennsylvania porthole caboose was issued with the set of cars intended for the new 6-8-6 steam turbine locomotive, and for 1987 another one in a bronze paint scheme was issued to accompany a new bronze-finished GG-1. These particular examples marked a first in the N5C line because they used die-cast trucks (O27 passenger-type in the case of the 1985 caboose, and arch bar trucks starting in 1987) instead of the usual Symington-Wayne plastic trucks. This trend continued with the recent Milwaukee and Southern N5Cs. Of course, the caboose would look better with Standard O sprung trucks, but these trucks have only lately been adapted for a power roller pickup. Perhaps we will now see N5C cabooses with Standard O trucks. Unfortunately, the earlier (1970s) N5Cs had only one coupler for the most part, a strange shortcut on these handsome cabooses. After 1980, however, Lionel used two couplers for each.

One interesting and odd construction quirk about the porthole caboose is that it has an opaque white plastic insert within the shell to diffuse the interior light. Once in a while this insert will not be positioned properly and the jeweled marker lights cannot be installed on the sides. The marker lights also have a nasty tendency to get caught on the box when putting the caboose back inside.

The first of the N5C cabooses was the 9160 Illinois Central of 1971. This and the 9161 Canadian National are the only two N5Cs with the MPC logo, which disappeared from the Lionel line after 1973. Early production used AAR trucks with old postwar wheel sets, but these quickly changed to Symington-Wayne trucks and fast-angle wheels. Pennsylvania, Canadian Pacific, Chessie, and Santa Fe models were quick to follow, and in subsequent years these cabooses were produced in a considerable variety of road names. Special issues accompanied the Bicentennial, 75th Anniversary, and Disney sets, while others were made to match the available diesel locomotives in the new Lionel line.

In all, about 30 of these cabooses have been produced in one guise or another. Their availability is highly variable today. Even some of the regular issues have become hard to find, and the cabooses from the sets only turn up occasionally. The most difficult to find seems to be the red 9165 Canadian Pacific, which was only found in a Service Station set. Many others, such as the 9161 Canadian National, are quite common. These small, high-quality cabooses are bright additions to any collector's rolling stock. In recent years, they have fallen under the shadow of the bay window and extended vision cabooses, so they are usually available at good prices.

N5C Caboose Body Styles

Only three body types have been used on the N5C porthole caboose (see Figure 7.2): *Type I* is a postwar carry-over and was only used on the earliest production of the 9160 Illinois Central in 1971. *Type II* appeared quickly and persisted on most of the 9100-series cabooses into 1977. The change to *Type III* eliminated the prominent central ridge of rivets which divides the body horizontally, presumably to improve stamping for the graphics. This change occurred in 1977 and this style is in use through the present. Note: the shape of the cupola windows means there is a front and rear direction to the caboose.

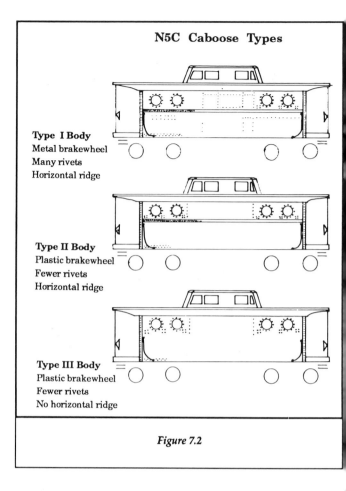

Figure 7.2

N5C PORTHOLE CABOOSE LISTINGS

	GD	VG	EXC	MT

1776 N & W: 1975, N5C caboose; white Type II body; red roof; blue ends and lower half of sides; gold lettering; illuminated; Symington-Wayne trucks; one operating coupler only. From 1584 N & W Spirit of America set. Car is catalogued 9170, but that number is not on car.

| (A) Flat red roof. | 10 | 20 | 30 | 35 |
| (B) Shiny, darker red roof. | 9 | 12 | 20 | 30 |

6449 WENDY'S OLD FASHIONED HAMBURGERS: 1981-82, N5C caboose; red body; yellow lettering; yellow roof; white, yellow and black Wendy's logo; illuminated; Symington-Wayne trucks; two operating couplers; "BLT 1-81". Part of Favorite Food set whose components were all sold separately.

| | — | — | 40 | 50 |

6908 PENNSYLVANIA: 1984-85, N5C caboose; deep maroon body; black main roof; yellow-painted cupola and cupola roof; white lettering including the words "LAKE REGION" under the number; white and black P R R keystone; gold FARR Series 5 diamond insignia; illuminated; O27 die-cast passenger trucks (the only N5C to be thus equipped to date); "BLT 1-84". Part of the Famous American Railroad set No. 5 (the last FARR set), whose components were all sold separately.

| | — | — | 65 | 95 |

7508 LIONEL 75TH ANNIVERSARY: 1975-76, N5C caboose; silver Type II body; black lettering; round "75th ANNIVERSARY" logo; illuminated; broad red stripe runs halfway across body; Symington-Wayne trucks; one operating coupler only; "BLT 1-75". Came with the 1585 Lionel 75th Anniversary Special set.

| | 7 | 11 | 20 | 30 |

7600 FRISCO: 1974-76, N5C caboose; red, white and blue Type II body; red roof; white lettering; illuminated; gold Seal of the United States; Symington-Wayne trucks; one operating coupler only; "BLT 1-74". From Spirit of '76 Bicentennial set with 1776 U36B and thirteen state cars, all components sold separately.

| (A) Flat red roof. | 10 | 20 | 30 | 40 |
| (B) Shiny red roof. | 10 | 20 | 30 | 40 |

See Volume II, first edition.

9160 ILLINOIS CENTRAL: 1971-72, N5C caboose; orange Type II body except for (B); black lettering "MAIN LINE OF MID-AMERICA"; illuminated; white "ic" in black circle except (C); no "BLT" date; MPC logo. This caboose appeared in the 1186 Cross Country set in 1971-72, and in the first modern era Service Station Special set — the Illinois Central in 1971; several versions of this set have been reported.

(A) Darker flat orange sides and roof; Symington-Wayne trucks; one operating coupler.	15	20	25	35
(B) Flat light orange sides and roof; AAR trucks; pre-1970 wheels; two operating couplers; Type I body. Earliest production; hard to find.	15	20	35	45
(C) Darker flat orange sides and roof; yellow "ic".	15	20	25	35
(D) Orange and white sides; white roof; white areas added by Glen Uhl, an Ohio Lionel dealer.	—	—	—	150
(E) Flat light orange roof; orange sides; Symington-Wayne trucks; one operating coupler; one dummy coupler.	15	20	25	35

See Volume II, first edition.

W. Dyson, R. Kaptur, R. LaVoie, A. Rudman, and F. Stem; B. Greenberg photograph

N5C porthole cabooses.
Top shelf: **6449** Wendy's Old Fashioned Hamburgers; **6908** Pennsylvania.
Second shelf: **7508** Lionel 75th Anniversary; **9160** Illinois Central, early version (B) with AAR trucks.
Third shelf: **9160** Illinois Central late version (A) with Symington-Wayne trucks; **9161** Canadian National.
Bottom shelf: **9162** Pennsylvania; **9163** A T S F.

	GD	VG	EXC	MT

9161 CANADIAN NATIONAL: 1972-74, N5C caboose; orange Type II body; white lettering; black roof; illuminated; Symington-Wayne trucks; one or two operating couplers; "BLT 1-72". Many examples have heavy blurred lettering, especially built date and MPC logo. Slight price premium (about $10) for crisp, clear lettering. Catalogued separately, not in sets.
(A) Orange body; black roof. **8 10 15 35**
(B) Lighter orange body and orange roof; same color as 9160. A. Adams Collection. **25 30 40 60**

9162 PENNSYLVANIA: 1973-76, N5C caboose; tuscan Type II body; white lettering; number under- and over-scored; includes green or red marker lights; illuminated; Symington-Wayne trucks; one operating coupler only; "BLT 2-53". Somewhat difficult to find. This caboose is unusual in that it actually has "N5C" printed on it, and has an unusual built date. Separate-sale only, not in sets. **10 20 35 45**

9163 A T S F: 1973-76, N5C caboose; red-painted gray Type II body with white lettering; illuminated; blue Santa Fe cross logo; Symington-Wayne trucks; one operating coupler only; "BLT 1-73".

Part of 1388 Golden State Arrow set of 1973; available as a separate-sale item thereafter. C. Lang comment.
6 8 15 25

9164 GREAT NORTHERN: 1970, N5C caboose; sky-blue body; white lettering and G N goat logo; AAR trucks. Catalogued to match 9206 boxcar but never manufactured. R. Hutchinson comment. **Not manufactured**

9165 CANADIAN PACIFIC: 1973, N5C caboose; uncatalogued; red Type II body with white lettering; illuminated; Symington-Wayne trucks; one operating coupler only. Came in 1350 Canadian Pacific Service Station Special set. Difficult to find. **15 20 25 40**

9167 C & O CHESSIE SYSTEM: 1974-76, N5C caboose; light yellow Type II body; silver roof; orange stripe along lower edge of body; blue lettering and cat logo; illuminated Symington-Wayne trucks; one operating coupler only; "BLT 1-74". Part of 1460 Grand National set of 1974; available as a separate-sale item thereafter. C. Lang Collection. **15 25 40 50**

9168 UNION PACIFIC: 1975-77, N5C caboose; yellow Type II body; red or green lettering; black roof; illuminated; Symington-

N5C porthole cabooses.

W. Dyson, R. Kaptur, R. LaVoie, A. Rudman, and F. Stem; B. Greenberg photograph

Top shelf: 9167 C&O Chessie System; 9165 Canadian Pacific.
Second shelf: 9168 Union Pacific; 9175 Virginian.
Third shelf: 9176 Bangor and Aroostook; 9180 The Rock.
Bottom shelf: 9181 Boston and Maine; 9182 N W.

	GD	VG	EXC	MT

Wayne trucks; one operating coupler only. Part of 1560 North American Express set in 1975, available as a separate-sale item thereafter.
(A) Red lettering. 10 15 20 30
(B) Green heat-stamped lettering; rare. Confirmation of authenticity requested. Three known to exist. G. Halverson Collection. **NRS**

9170 N & W: 1976; see 1776.

9175 VIRGINIAN: 1976-77, N5C caboose; dark blue Type II body; yellow roof; yellow lettering; illuminated; Symington-Wayne trucks; one or two operating couplers; "BLT 1-76". A handsome reissue of the postwar favorite 6427-60, except with a yellow roof. The postwar caboose is very hard to find.
(A) One operating coupler. 10 15 20 30
(B) Two operating couplers; factory production. R. LaVoie Collection. 10 15 20 30

9176 BANGOR AND AROOSTOOK: 1976, N5C caboose; uncatalogued; red, white and blue Type II body with red roof; red and white lettering; illuminated; Symington-Wayne trucks; one operating coupler only; "BLT 1-76". 1976 Bicentennial issue; came with 8665 Jeremiah O'Brien locomotive in one long box. An-

	GD	VG	EXC	MT

nounced only in a late 1976 flyer. Seldom sold separately from engine. 12 15 20 35

9180 THE ROCK: 1977-78, N5C caboose; blue sides; white roof; large black and white "R" logo; white lettering; illuminated; Symington-Wayne trucks; one operating coupler only; "BLT 1-76". Separate-sale only, not in a set.
(A) Type II body. 10 15 20 40
(B) Type III body. C. Rohlfing Collection. 10 15 20 40

9181 B M: 1976-77, (Boston and Maine) N5C caboose; blue body with black center stripe; white lettering; white logo centered on black stripe; illuminated; Symington-Wayne trucks; one operating coupler only; "BLT 1-76". Separate-sale only, not in a set. Appeared initially in a late 1976 dealer bonus special brochure.
(A) Type II body. 10 12 15 25
(B) Type III body. C. Rohlfing Collection. 10 12 15 25

9182 N W: 1976-77, (Norfolk and Western) N5C caboose; black body; white lettering and large N W logo; illuminated; Symington-Wayne trucks; one operating coupler only; "BLT 1-76". Separate-

W. Dyson, R. Kaptur, R. LaVoie, A. Rudman, and F. Stem; B. Greenberg photograph

N5C porthole cabooses.
Top shelf: 9183 Mickey Mouse Express; 9185 G T W.
Second shelf: 9186 Conrail; 9239 Lionel Lines.
Third shelf: 9270 Northern Pacific Railway; 9287 Southern.
Bottom shelf: 9288 Lehigh Valley; 19702 Pennsylvania.

	GD	VG	EXC	MT

sale only, not in a set. Appeared first in a late 1976 dealer bonus brochure.
(A) Type II body. — 10 12 15 35
(B) Type III body. C. Rohlfing Collection. — 10 12 15 35

9183 MICKEY MOUSE EXPRESS: 1977-78, N5C caboose; white Type III body; red-orange roof; large Mickey and lettering decal in yellow, black, red and blue; illuminated; Symington-Wayne trucks; "BLT 1-77". Part of separate-sale Mickey Mouse Express, a scarce set that is difficult to assemble.
(A) One operating coupler. — 20 25 35 50
(B) Two operating couplers. R. Paris Collection. — 20 25 35 50

9185 G T W: 1977, (Grand Trunk Western) N5C caboose; gray plastic body painted blue; orange ends; white lettering; illuminated; Symington-Wayne trucks; one operating coupler only; "BLT 1-77". Separate-sale only, not in a set.
(A) Type II body. — 10 12 20 35
(B) Type III body. C. Rohlfing Collection. — 10 12 20 35

9186 CONRAIL: 1976-78, N5C caboose; gray plastic painted blue; black roof; white lettering and Conrail wheel logo; illuminated; Symington-Wayne trucks; one operating coupler only; "BLT 1-76". Separate-sale only, not in a set. First appeared in a late 1976 dealer bonus brochure.
(A) Type II body. — 15 20 30 40
(B) Type III body. C. Rohlfing Collection. — 15 20 30 40

9239 LIONEL LINES: 1983, N5C caboose; uncatalogued; bright orange sides; dark blue roof; red, white and blue "L" circular logo centered on car side; "LIONEL LINES" in blue modern sans-serif letters, under- and over-scored by two blue stripes which run the length of the car; black railings, platforms and steps; number at lower right in blue; illuminated; Symington-Wayne trucks; one or two operating couplers; "BLT 1-83". Matches 8380 Lionel Lines SD-28 engine. Pictured only in the 1983 Fall Collector Center brochure. This caboose is considered part of the continuing Lionel Lines separate-sale set, whose components were offered beginning in 1982. R. LaVoie comment.
— 20 45 60 80

Some of the earliest SP cabooses.   W. Dyson, R. Kaptur, R. LaVoie, A. Rudman, and F. Stem; B. Greenberg photograph
Top shelf: 6485 Chessie System; 6918 B&O.
Second shelf: 9060 Nickel Plate Road; 9061 Santa Fe.
Third shelf: 9062 P C; 9063 G T W first version with orange Type V body.
Bottom shelf: 9063 G T W, later version with maroon Type VI body; 9064 C and O. Note the trucks changed also.

	GD	VG	EXC	MT

9270 NORTHERN PACIFIC RAILWAY: 1978, N5C caboose; orange-painted gray Type III body; white lettering "Main Street of the Northwest"; N P Monad logo under cupola; illuminated; Symington-Wayne trucks; no "BLT" date. Separate-sale only, not in a set.
(A) One operating coupler. C. Rohlfing Collection.

	10	12	15	20

(B) Two operating couplers.

	12	15	20	25

9287 SOUTHERN: 1977-78, N5C caboose; red-painted gray plastic Type III body; red roof; white lettering; red marker lights; illuminated; Symington-Wayne trucks; one operating coupler only; "BLT 1-77". Separate-sale only, not in a set. First announced in a 1977 dealer flyer with its matching 8744 Southern GP-7 diesel.

	10	12	15	25

9288 LEHIGH VALLEY: 1977-78, 1980, N5C caboose; red-painted gray plastic Type III body; yellow roof and lettering; yellow stripe through center; red marker lights; illuminated; Symington-Wayne trucks; one operating coupler only. Separate-sale only, not in a set. First announced in a 1977 dealer flyer with its matching 8775 Lehigh Valley GP-9 diesel.

	10	12	20	30

9289 CHICAGO & NORTH WESTERN: 1977-78, 1980, N5C caboose; gray plastic Type III body painted yellow; Brunswick green roof; black lettering; black, red and white North Western logo; red marker lights; illuminated; Symington-Wayne trucks. Separate-sale only, not in a set. First announced in a 1977 dealer flyer with its matching 8776 C N W GP-20 diesel.
(A) One operating coupler.

	10	15	20	30

(B) Two operating couplers; factory production. Dunn Collection.

	10	15	20	30

16504 SOUTHERN: 1987, N5C caboose; uncatalogued; red sides; yellow ends and railings; black roof and cupola; yellow Southern lettering and circular logo; illuminated; die-cast leaf-spring trucks. Part of 11704 Southern Freight Runner Service Station Special set.

	—	—	25	35

16522 LIONELVILLE CIRCUS: 1990-91, N5C caboose; yellow sides; red roof and ends; orange, gold and white tiger electrocal

GD   VG   EXC   MT

in center; black lettering; illuminated; ASF strong- arm trucks; "BLT 1-90". Part of 11716 Lionelville Circus Special.

—   —   —   35

19701 MILWAUKEE ROAD: 1987, N5C caboose; dull orange sides and ends; black roof and cupola; red and white rectangular Milwaukee logo; black lettering; illuminated; die-cast arch bar trucks; "BLT 1-87". Part of Milwaukee Road Fallen Flags set No. 2, whose components were all sold separately.

—   —   35   45

19702 PENNSYLVANIA: 1987, N5C caboose; bronze-painted body; purplish-black lettering and number; large red, white and black large P R R keystone centered on sides; illuminated; die-cast arch bar; "BLT 1-87". Made as a match for 18300 Pennsylvania GG-1.

—   —   40   50

19712 PENNSYLVANIA*: 1991, N5C caboose; light blue body; white lettering; number under- and over-scored; illuminated; die-cast arch bar trucks; "BLT 1-91". Remake of postwar 6427-500 caboose from the 1957 Girls' set. The modern car came in the modern version of the set, the 11722 Girls' Train from 1991.

—   —   —   60

THE SOUTHERN PACIFIC SQUARE-CUPOLA CABOOSES

The square-cupola Southern Pacific-style caboose has been produced from the first year of Lionel's modern era — 1970 — which is fitting, since this caboose was also the mainstay of postwar production. It is interesting to note that even though these are "Southern Pacific-style," none of the Fundimensions production actually bear that road name. This was also true for postwar production, though a few of those bore "SP" lettering above other names. Postwar square-cupola cabooses were dominated by (what else?) the Lionel Lines. The Fundimensions version of the SP-style caboose has a new plastic undercarriage which snaps onto the cab.

Nearly all of the SP cabooses have been used for inexpensive sets and are rarely offered just for separate-sale except in miscellaneous rolling stock assortments. A few (most notably ones in the 9100-series and several recent issues) have interior lighting and translucent white plastic window inserts. These "deluxe" cabooses are mostly found in early Collector sets and some, like the 9172 Penn Central and the 9173 Jersey Central, were offered for separate-sale. A few recent production models in the less expensive Traditional sets included "glow-in-the-dark" window inserts.

A good number of the early SP cabooses (from the 1970s) have only one coupler, unlike most other rolling stock and the larger cabooses. So the reader will note listings calling out one or two operating couplers. Remember, Lionel sought every means of reducing costs, and one less coupler meant one less assembly step. Most SP-type cabooses from the last decade do have two couplers, however. As with other rolling stock, the rectangular MPC logo appears on the early pieces (1970-1972) and disappears thereafter.

The most desirable of the SP-style cabooses are the ones from the sets, but none produced by Fundimensions or its successors can be considered truly rare. Some of the earliest unlighted SP cabooses marketed for Canadian distribution are in fact very difficult to find, but collectors have not shown too much interest in them — yet.

SP Caboose Body Styles

To the best of our knowledge, modern Lionel did not re-use molds I through IV of the S P caboose. It began production in 1970 with a new mold, Type V.

Several of the most important differences between postwar and modern Lionel S P cabooses:

Postwar	*Modern Era*
Steps molded as part of body piece	Steps part of separate end
No horizontal bar in windows	Horizontal bar in windows
Short cupola body only	Short and tall cupola bodies
Greater rivet detail	Less rivet detail

Type V can be recognized most easily by the continuous horizontal ridge at the center of the body running from front to back just below the windows. On later body types the ridge is broken under the cupola between the third and fourth windows, presumably to simplify graphics stamping. A more minor change between Types V and VI was the removal of small columns of three rivets along the lower body edge, apparently for the same reason. Type V was used on only four of the earliest MPC cabooses (9060, 9061, 9062 and 9063) and was phased out in 1970-1971. All four, therefore, still have the rectangular MPC logo. Type V only used tall-window cupolas and was modified quickly into Type VI.

Type VI is very similar to V except the horizontal ridge is now broken and the small rivet columns removed. Compare our picture of the 9063 Grant Trunk caboose, which switched from Type V to VI and changed color in the process. The Type VI style, again using only tall-window cupolas, was used on many 1970's vintage cabooses. It is possible, but not recorded, that this style was used after 1980. The last recognized use of the mold was on the 9381 Chessie in 1980, which has come in both Type VI and VII. It is also possible that the plentiful 9341 Atlantic Coast Line caboose, which continues to be produced today, could have been made as a Type VI after 1980. We encourage reader comments on SP cabooses (tall cupola) which may have been made after 1980.

Type VII has a short cupola, easily distinguishable from the tall cupolas of Types V and VII. It is of interest to note that postwar SP cabooses never used the tall cupola. Another difference is that Types V and VI have side window frames inset into the body (actually the ridges with rivets around the windows make it appear that way), whereas Type VII has plain window frames clearly set out from the body.

Still another noticeable difference is at the lower body edge, where a very prominent ridge, with a line of rivets atop it, is present in body types V and VI. This ridge is much more

SP CABOOSE BODY TYPE COMPARISON

Type V	Type VI	Type VII
Complete horizontal center ridge	Horizontal ridge broken under cupola	Horizontal ridge broken under cupola
Columns of 3 rivets along lower body edge	No columns of rivets along lower body edge	No columns of rivets along lower body edge
Inset window frames on 4 side windows	Inset window frames on 4 side windows	Window frame set out from body
Tall cupola	Tall cupola	Short cupola
Plain catwalk	Wood-grain catwalk	Plain catwalk
Prominent ridge on lower body edge with rivets on ridge	Prominent ridge on lower body edge with rivets on ridge	Subdued lower body edge ridge. Rivet line above ridge

subdued on Type VII, and the line of rivets is not on the ridge but on the body just above it. Compare the photo of the Type VI 9381 Chessie caboose with the Type VII 9341 A C L. One feature unique to Type VI is the wood-grain detail on the roof catwalk. This detailing is not present on body Types V or VII. Unfortunately this nice detail is not visible in most pictures.

Type VII was introduced as early as 1972 on the 9062 Penn Central caboose and persists as the dominant style of the SP caboose today. Several cabooses jumped from Type V to Type VII. Somewhere along the line the Type VII mold was reworked to bring out the rivet detail more clearly and thicken the cupola roof handrails. It is not known exactly when this change occurred (to what might be called Type VIIA), but it was probably in the early 1980s. The Type VII body style features the low (or short) cupola. The other differences — in the lower ridge, window frame and catwalk — are as described earlier under Type VI.

Previously, the number of rivets (2 vs. 2½) below the curved rib on the body side lower left and right corners was considered a body type discriminator. Recent investigation indicates this is not the case — 2 or 2½ rivets can be present, even on the same body, depending on how well the plastic fills the mold.

SP Caboose End Types

There are two types of end platform/step/ladder pieces used on the SP cabooses. The two are not associated with any particular body style, since the end pieces are separate and can be changed. In general, the Type I style is the older version:

Type I: Smooth walkway surface; 3-D metal brakewheel.
Type II: Rough walkway surface; flat plastic brakewheel.

SP-TYPE CABOOSE LISTINGS

	GD	VG	EXC	MT

1987 MOPAR EXPRESS: 1987-88; see 16507.

6430 SANTA FE: 1983-89, SP-type caboose; red Type VII body; gold lettering; Symington-Wayne trucks; "BLT 1-83". From 1352 Rocky Mountain freight set. Also appeared in 9195 rolling stock assortment in 1986-89.   —   —   6   8

6432 UNION PACIFIC: 1981-82, SP-type caboose; silver Type VII body; black roof; yellow lettering; red, white and blue shield logo; Symington-Wayne trucks; "BLT 1-81". Part of 1151 U P Thunder freight set.   —   —   10   12

6434 SOUTHERN: 1983-84, SP-type caboose; green Type VII body; white lettering; round S R logo under cupola; white stripe; unlighted; Symington-Wayne trucks. From 1353 Southern Streak set.   —   —   6   8

6478 BLACK CAVE: 1982, SP-type caboose; red Type VII body; no window inserts; luminous Black Cave Flyer decals to be installed by purchaser; no number on car; Symington-Wayne trucks; one operating, one dummy coupler. Part of 1254 Black Cave set. J. Sawruk Collection.   —   —   5   10

6482 NIBCO: 1982, SP-type caboose; uncatalogued; red unpainted plastic Type VII body; black plastic railings; silver and black "NIBCO EXPRESS" script logo between third and fourth side windows; unlighted, but with "glow-in-the-dark" windows; Symington-Wayne trucks; one operating coupler; no "BLT" date. Part of special 1264 promotional Nibco set 1264; see 8182 in Diesel chapter for background. Very hard to find. Raber Collection.   —   —   —   80

6483 NEW JERSEY CENTRAL: 1982, SP-type caboose; L C C A; see Volume II, first edition.

6485 CHESSIE SYSTEM: 1984-85, SP-type caboose; yellow plastic Type VII body with black trim; blue lettering and cat logo; Symington-Wayne trucks; one operating coupler only; "BLT 1-84". Part of 1402 Chessie System set.   —   —   —   10

6912 REDWOOD VALLEY EXPRESS: 1984-85, SP-type caboose; tuscan Type VII body; yellow lettering and logo; plastic arch bar trucks; one operating coupler only. Part of 1403 Redwood Valley Express set.   —   —   —   20

6918 B & O: 1986, SP-type caboose; dark blue Type VII body; yellow lettering and capitol logo; Symington-Wayne trucks; "BLT 1-86". Part of 1652 B & O freight set.   —   —   —   15

6919 NICKEL PLATE ROAD: 1986-91, SP-type caboose; red Type VII body; white lettering; Symington-Wayne trucks; "BLT 1-86". Part of 1602 Nickel Plate Special set.   —   —   —   10

6921 PENNSYLVANIA: 1986-90, SP-type caboose; red Type VII body; white lettering and large white P R R keystone; Symington-Wayne trucks; "BLT 1-86". Part of 1615 Cannonball Express set.   —   —   —   10

9057 C P RAIL: 1978-79, SP-type caboose; Type VII body; yellow unpainted sides; black roof; black lettering; black and white Pac-man logo at rear; Type II ends; Symington-Wayne trucks; one manumatic coupler, one dummy coupler. From 1866 Great Plains Express set.   5   7   9   11

9058 LIONEL LINES: 1978-79, SP-type caboose; orange unpainted Type VII body; black lettering and large square "L" logo;

	GD	VG	EXC	MT

Type II ends; Symington-Wayne trucks; plastic wheels; manumatic couplers; no "BLT" date. Part of 1864 Santa Fe double diesel and 1865 Chesapeake Flyer sets in 1978-79.

| | 3 | 5 | 6 | 8 |

9059 LIONEL LINES: 1979, SP-type caboose; uncatalogued; orange unpainted Type VII body; black lettering and square "L" logo; Type II ends; Symington-Wayne trucks; plastic wheels; two operating couplers; no "BLT" date. This car is identical to the 9058 except for the number. May have been included in 1979 versions of the 1864 Santa Fe double diesel and 1865 Chesapeake Flyer sets, instead of the 9058. We would like to hear from readers with this car or set. D. Cousins and D. Hundt Collections.

| | 3 | 5 | 8 | 10 |

9060 NICKEL PLATE ROAD: 1970-73, SP-type caboose; three shades of brown bodies; white lettering; Type I ends; tuscan or black frame; plastic AAR trucks; one operating coupler only; no "BLT" date; MPC logo. Part of the 1081 Wabash Cannonball set.
(A) Type V; light brown body; tall-window cupola. "Triple T" Collection.

| | 3 | 5 | 6 | 8 |

(B) Type VII light red-brown body; short-window cupola. R. LaVoie and "Triple T" Collections.

| | 3 | 5 | 6 | 8 |

(C) Type VII medium brown body; short-window cupola. "Triple T" Collection.

| | 3 | 5 | 6 | 8 |

9061 SANTA FE: 1970-76, SP-type caboose; red Type V or VII body; yellow lettering and cross logo; one operating coupler only; no "BLT" date; MPC logo. This caboose was part of many early 1970s sets.
(A) Type V light red body; tall-window cupola; AAR trucks; Type I ends. "Triple T" Collection.

| | 3 | 5 | 6 | 8 |

(B) Type VII medium red body; short-window cupola; Symington-Wayne trucks; one manumatic coupler only; Type II ends. "Triple T" Collection.

| | 3 | 5 | 6 | 8 |

(C) Same as (B), but with Type I ends.

| | 3 | 5 | 6 | 8 |

9062 P C: 1970-72, (Penn Central) SP-type caboose; jade green Type V or VII body; white lettering and interlocked P C logo under cupola; Type I ends; one operating coupler only; no "BLT" date. Part of 1083 Pacemaker, 1183 Silver Star, and several uncatalogued Sears sets.
(A) Type V body; MPC logo; tall-window cupola; AAR trucks.

| | 2 | 3 | 5 | 9 |

(B) Type VII body; short-window cupola; Symington-Wayne trucks; MPC logo. C. Lang Collection.

| | 2 | 3 | 5 | 9 |

(C) Same as (B), but no MPC logo. R. LaVoie Collection.

| | 2 | 3 | 5 | 9 |

9063 G T W: 1970-73, SP-type caboose; light orange or maroon Type V or VI body; white lettering and "GT" logo under cupola; Type I ends; AAR trucks; one operating coupler only; no "BLT" date; MPC logo. Somewhat hard to find. Came only in 1084 G T W set in 1970 and several Canadian sets in 1970-73.
(A) Type V orange body; tall-window cupola. "Triple T" Collection.

| | 10 | 15 | 20 | 25 |

(B) Same as (A), but dark orange body. R. LaVoie Collection.

| | 8 | 10 | 15 | 20 |

(C) Type VI maroon body; tall-window cupola; Canadian release. Quite hard to find. "Triple T" Collection.

| | 15 | 20 | 25 | 30 |

(D) Type VI brown-red body; Type II ends; one AAR and one Symington-Wayne truck. C. Rohlfing Collection.

| | 15 | 20 | 25 | 30 |

9064 C AND O: 1971-72, 1975-77, SP-type caboose; yellow Type VI or VII body; red stripe; blue lettering; "C AND/O/FOR/PROGRESS" under cupola; Type I ends; Symington-Wayne trucks; only one operating coupler; no "BLT" date; MPC logo. Came in the 1184 Allegheny set in 1971-72 and the Chesapeake Flyer set in 1975-77.
(A) Type VI body; tall cupola; light yellow body; light red stripe; light blue lettering.

| | 3 | 5 | 7 | 10 |

(B) Type VI body; tall cupola; medium light yellow; red stripe; blue lettering.

| | 3 | 5 | 7 | 10 |

(C) Type VI body; tall cupola; medium yellow; red stripe; blue lettering.

| | 3 | 5 | 7 | 10 |

(D) Type VII body; short cupola; medium light yellow; red stripe; blue lettering.

| | 3 | 5 | 7 | 10 |

9065 CANADIAN NATIONAL: 1971-73, SP-type caboose; maroon or dark red Type VI body; white lettering; "CN" logo under cupola; Type I ends; tall-window cupola; no "BLT" date; MPC logo; Symington-Wayne trucks; one operating coupler only. Canadian release only; somewhat hard to find. Mint condition for this and other Canadian production pieces must include original Type I Parker Brothers box. R. LaVoie Collection.

| | 10 | 15 | 20 | 25 |

9066 SOUTHERN: 1973-76, SP-type caboose; red Type VI or VII body; white lettering and circle S R logo; number on the car is "X9066"; Type I ends; Symington-Wayne trucks; one operating coupler only; "BLT 2-73"; no MPC logo. Part of 1384 Southern Express set.
(A) Red Type VII body; short cupola.

| | 5 | 6 | 8 | 10 |

(B) Very dark red Type VI body (almost maroon); tall cupola. C. Rohlfing Collection.

| | — | — | — | 75 |

9069 JERSEY CENTRAL LINES: 1973-74, SP-type caboose; brown Type VII body; white lettering and Statue of Liberty logo; Type I ends; Symington-Wayne trucks; one operating coupler only; "BLT 2-73". From 1385 Blue Streak set.

| | 3 | 5 | 6 | 8 |

9070 ROCK ISLAND: 1973-74, SP-type caboose; gray Type VII body; black and gray lettering; "ROUTE OF THE ROCKETS"; black "Rock Island" shield under cupola; Type I ends; Symington-Wayne trucks; one operating coupler only; "BLT 1-73". From 1386 Rockland Express set.

| | 6 | 8 | 10 | 15 |

9073 COKE: 1973-74, SP-type caboose; red Type VII body; white lettering and Wave logo; Type I ends; Symington-Wayne trucks; one operating coupler only; "BLT 1-74"; no MPC logo. Came as part of 1463 Coca-Cola switcher set.
(A) Light red body.

| | 3 | 5 | 10 | 15 |

(B) Medium red body.

| | 3 | 5 | 10 | 15 |

(C) Dark flat red body.

| | 3 | 5 | 10 | 15 |

9075 ROCK ISLAND: 1975, SP-type caboose; uncatalogued; red Type VII body; white lettering; Type I ends; Symington-Wayne trucks; one operating coupler only; "BLT 1-75"; no MPC logo. Part of uncatalogued 1594 Sears set. D. Alcorn Collection.

| | 6 | 10 | 10 | 15 |

9076 WE THE PEOPLE OF THE UNITED STATES: 1975, SP-type caboose; uncatalogued; white and red Type VII body; blue roof; white and blue lettering; American flag; Type I ends; Symington-Wayne trucks; one operating coupler only; no MPC logo. Came as part of 1577 Liberty Special set.

| | 8 | 12 | 20 | 40 |

9077 RIO GRANDE: 1976-83, SP-type caboose; orange body; black lettering and four stripes; Type II ends; Symington-Wayne trucks; one operating coupler only; "BLT 1-76"; no MPC logo. Part of the 1662/1963 Black River freight set and the 1252 Heavy Iron set which continues to be revived by Toys 'R Us to the present.

W. Dyson, R. Kaptur, R. LaVoie, A. Rudman, and F. Stem; B. Greenberg photograph

SP-type cabooses, tall and short cupolas, lighted and unlighted.
Top shelf: 9065 Canadian National; 9070 Rock Island.
Second shelf: 9166 Rio Grande; 9073 Coke.
Third shelf: 9169 The Milwaukee Road; 9171 Missouri Pacific Lines.
Bottom shelf: 9172 P C; 9187 Gulf Mobile & Ohio.

	GD	VG	EXC	MT
(A) Type VI body; tall cupola. C. Rohlfing Collection.	3	4	6	8
(B) Type VII body; short cupola.	3	4	6	8

9079 A T S F: SP-type caboose. Announced for 1979, but never made. **Not manufactured.**

9080 WABASH: 1977, 1979, SP-type caboose; red Type VII body; black roof; white lettering; Type II ends; Symington-Wayne trucks; one operating coupler only; "BLT 1- 77"; no MPC logo. Part of 1762/1962 Wabash Cannonball steam engine set.

	GD	VG	EXC	MT
	5	7	10	11

9166 RIO GRANDE: 1974-75, SP-type caboose; yellow Type VII body; silver roof and lower body edge; silver ends; black lettering and stripes; illuminated; stack; Type I ends; Symington-Wayne trucks; one operating coupler only; "BLT 1-74"; no MPC logo. Very similar to postwar 6657 (one of the best-looking SP-type cabooses made), and to later 9077. Part of the 1450 Rio

Grande Service Station Special in 1974, and offered for separate-sale the next year.

	GD	VG	EXC	MT
(A) Light yellow sides.	10	15	20	25
(B) Medium yellow sides.	10	15	20	25

9169 THE MILWAUKEE ROAD: 1975, SP-type caboose; uncatalogued; dull orange Type VII body; black roof; red lettering; illuminated; enclosed windows; Type I ends; Symington-Wayne trucks; one operating coupler only; "BLT 1-75". Part of 1529 Milwaukee Service Station set of 1975; but unlike the 9166 Rio Grande caboose from the previous year's set, never offered for separate-sale. Note: The previous edition of this Guide erroneously listed the car color as brown. A. Menken comment.

	GD	VG	EXC	MT
	10	15	15	20

9171 MISSOURI PACIFIC LINES: 1976-77, SP-type caboose; red sides and roof; white lettering and large round "Missouri Pacific Lines" logo; illuminated; Type I ends;

The recent SP-type caboose production.
Top shelf: **9341** Atlantic Coast Line; **9381** B&O Chessie System.
Middle shelf: **16501** Lehigh Valley; **16515** Lionel Lines.
Bottom shelf: **16516** Lehigh Valley.

	GD	VG	EXC	MT

Symington-Wayne trucks; one operating coupler only; "BLT 1-76". This and the next two entries were unusual practice for the SP caboose — they were offered only for separate-sale, and were not in sets.

	GD	VG	EXC	MT
(A) Type VI body; tall cupola.	6	8	15	20
(B) Type VII body; short cupola.	6	8	15	20

9172 P C: 1976-77; SP-type caboose; black Type VII body and roof; white lettering and interlocked P C logo; illuminated; Type I ends; Symington-Wayne trucks; one operating coupler only; "BLT 2-76". Separate-sale only, not in a set.

	10	15	25	35

9173 JERSEY CENTRAL: 1976-77, SP-type caboose; red Type VI or VII body and roof; white lettering; broad white stripe with red lettering under cupola; illuminated; Type I ends; Symington-Wayne trucks; one operating coupler only; "BLT 1-76". Separate-sale only, not in a set.

	GD	VG	EXC	MT
(A) Type VI body; tall cupola.	8	10	15	20
(B) Type VII body; short cupola.	8	10	15	20
(C) Same as (A), but Type II ends. C. Rohlfing Collection.	8	10	15	20

9178 ILLINOIS CENTRAL GULF: 1976, SP-type caboose; light or dark orange Type VII body; silver roof; black lettering; white "IC"; Type II ends; illuminated; Symington-Wayne trucks; two operating couplers; "BLT 1-76". Part of 1664 Illinois Central Gulf freight set, and never offered for separate-sale.

	GD	VG	EXC	MT
(A) Light orange.	10	15	20	25
(B) Dark orange.	10	15	20	25

9187 GULF MOBILE & OHIO: 1977, SP-type caboose; red-painted gray plastic Type VII body; black roof; white lettering and logo; Type II ends; illuminated; Symington-Wayne trucks; one operating coupler only; "BLT 1-77". From 1764 Heartland Express set and not offered for separate-sale. C. Rohlfing Collection.

	10	15	15	30

9276 TEXAS & PACIFIC: 1980, SP-type caboose; dark blue body; white lettering; catalogued with a 1980 Texas & Pacific freight set but not made. **Not manufactured**

9341 ATLANTIC COAST LINE: 1979-82, 1986-90, SP-type caboose; red with white lettering; glow-in-the-dark windows (1979-80 only); Symington-Wayne trucks; "BLT 1-79". From 1960 Midnight Flyer set and many others. This caboose and its 8902 locomotive have been resurrected many times since the original production run for department store and other low-priced special sets. R. LaVoie comment.

	GD	VG	EXC	MT
(A) Type VI body; tall cupola.	—	—	6	8
(B) Type VII body; short cupola.	—	—	6	8

9346 WABASH: 1979, SP-type caboose; uncatalogued; dark red Type VII body; white lettering; black roof. From 1991 Wabash Deluxe Express. Further details on this car and set are requested from our readers. Young Collection.

	—	—	6	10

	GD	VG	EXC	MT

9380 NEW YORK, NEW HAVEN & HARTFORD: 1980-81, SP-type caboose; silver-painted Type VII body; black roof and cupola; black New Haven script lettering; Symington-Wayne trucks; two operating couplers; "BLT 1-80". Came with 1050 New Englander set. J. Zylstra Collection. — — **10 12**

9381 B & O CHESSIE SYSTEM: 1980, SP-type caboose; yellow sides and ends; silver roof; blue lettering and cat logo; Symington-Wayne trucks; two operating couplers; no "BLT" date. From 1052 Chesapeake Flyer set.
(A) Type VI body; tall cupola. — — **8 10**
(B) Type VII body; short cupola. — — **8 10**

16501 LEHIGH VALLEY: 1987, SP-type caboose; yellow Type VII body; silver roof; black frame and end rails; black lettering; illuminated; Symington-Wayne trucks; two operating couplers; "BLT 1-87". Part of Black Diamond set 11702.
— — **15 20**

16505 WABASH: 1988-91; SP-type caboose; red Type VII body; white lettering, logo and numbers; Symington-Wayne trucks; one operating coupler. Part of 11703 Iron Horse freight set.
— — **8 10**

16507 MOPAR EXPRESS: 1987-88, SP-type caboose; uncatalogued; red Type VII body; black frame, platforms and railings; white lettering "ME 1987" and "MOPAR EXPRESS"; catalogue number not on the car; Symington-Wayne trucks; two operating couplers; "BLT 1-87". From 11757 uncatalogued Mopar sets made for Chrysler in 1987-88. L. Bohn comments.
— — — **50**

16508 LIONEL LINES: 1989, SP-type caboose; uncatalogued; orange Type VII body; black lettering; large circle-L logo under cupola; Symington-Wayne trucks; no "BLT" date. Part of 11771 Microracers Special set made for K-Mart in 1989.
— — — **20**

16509 DENVER & RIO GRANDE: 1989, SP-type caboose; uncatalogued; yellow Type VII body; black striping, logo and lettering; illuminated; die-cast arch bar trucks; two operating couplers; "BLT 1-89". Part of 11758 Denver & Rio Grande Western "Desert King" Service Station Special set in 1989.
— — — **30**

16513 UNION PACIFIC: 1989, SP-type caboose; silver Type VII body; black roof, platforms and railings; red lettering "Safety is the Golden Rule in Action"; illuminated; Symington-Wayne trucks; "BLT 1-89". — — — **22**

16515 LIONEL LINES: 1989, SP-type caboose; gray Type VII body; dark blue roof, platform and railings; white lettering; Lionel circle-L logo under cupola; illuminated; Symington-Wayne trucks; two operating couplers; "BLT 1-89". Intended to go with 33000 Lionel RailScope engine. — — — **25**

16516 LEHIGH VALLEY: 1990, SP-type caboose; red Type VII body; black frame and platforms; white lettering with "A" in front of "16516"; black and white L V diamond logo; bar code to right; illuminated; ASF strong-arm trucks; "BLT 1-90". Designed to match 18807 Lehigh Valley RS-3 diesel.
— — — **24**

16520 SEARS CIRCUS: 1989, SP-type caboose; uncatalogued; red body; white lettering "Welcome to the Show" and yellow tiger electrocal under cupola; Symington-Wayne trucks; "BLT 1-89". Catalogue number is not on the car. Part of uncatalogued 11770 Sears Circus Train set. — — — **22**

	GD	VG	EXC	M

16521 PENNSYLVANIA: 1990, SP-type caboose; tuscan Type VII body; white lettering; white P R R keystone; Symington Wayne trucks; two operating couplers; "BLT 1-89" on caboose, bu issued in 1990 as part of 16999 rolling stock assortment.
— — — **1**

16523 ALASKA*: 1991, SP-type caboose; blue Type VII body yellow main and cupola roofs; yellow lettering and eskimo figure illuminated; ASF strong-arm trucks; two operating couplers "BLT 1-91". Similar to postwar 6027. Intended as a match for 18811 Alaska SD-9 diesel issued in 1991.
— — — **2**

16524 ANHEUSER-BUSCH: 1989, SP-type caboose; un catalogued; red Type VII body; white lettering; white eagle-A logo "BLT 1-89/LIONEL" is the only lettering on the car (no number) Symington-Wayne trucks; two operating couplers. Part of un catalogued set 11775, the Anheuser-Busch Beer set, available only through a 1989 Anheuser-Busch gift catalogue.
— — — **4**

16526 KANSAS CITY SOUTHERN*: 1991, SP-type caboose maroon Type VII body; white lettering; large octagonal KCS logo in white under cupola; illuminated; ASF strong-arm trucks; two operating couplers; "BLT 1-91". Catalogued for separate-sale as a match for the 18812 Kansas City Southern GP-38 diesel. This road name was never before used on a Lionel caboose.
— — — **2**

16529 A T S F*: 1991, SP-type caboose; red Type VII body white lettering; not lighted; ASF strong-arm trucks; two operating couplers; "BLT 1-91". Part of 11720 Santa Fe Special set.
— — — **1**

16530 MICKEY'S WORLD TOUR '92*: 1991, SP-type caboose; red Type VII body; yellow lettering; "1001" in large numerals on body; multicolor Mickey's World Tour shield logo under cupola; not lighted; ASF strong-arm trucks; two operating couplers; "BLT 1-91". Part of 11721 Mickey's World Tour train set. — — — **15**

THE STANDARD O SCALE CABOOSES

Wood-Sided

Back in the late 1930s, Lionel introduced a beautifully executed scale model wood-sided caboose to accompany its fine scale switchers of the period. Collectors have always regarded this caboose with awe and respect, for it is a fine scale model. They paid large sums of money for any surviving cabooses of this type because they did not have a modern version available to them — until late 1986, that is.

In that year, Lionel introduced two new reproductions of this fine wood-sided caboose as part of an extremely limited direct-mail offer. One was an exceedingly handsome New York Central model slightly dressed up over its antique predecessor. This caboose had dark brown coloring offset by black main and cupola roofs. The other caboose was plain brown, but it had the same life-like detail and was a direct match for the 8606 Boston and Albany Hudson with its crisp

W. Dyson, R. Kaptur, R. LaVoie, A. Rudman, and F. Stem; B. Greenberg photograph

Outstanding Standard O scale cabooses, all in great demand.
Top shelf: **6907 New York Central System; 6920 B&A.**
Second shelf: **17600 N.Y.C.; 17601 Southern, with high cupola.**
Third shelf: **17602 Conrail; 17603 Rock Island.**
Bottom shelf: **17604 Lackawanna; 17605 Reading.**

white B & A markings. To be sure, some of the fine detail work of the prewar version had to be sacrificed because its cost was too prohibitive, but Lionel made up for that in another way — a new form of die-cast truck.

The new die-cast truck, unlike the excellent Standard O trucks, could be adapted for illumination rollers — and these two cabooses were indeed lighted. The sides and roofs were expertly wood-scribed, the metal ladders were present, and there were the same highly detailed square windows as the prewar piece. Collectors were very happy with this design, but the cabooses were in very short supply.

For the next year, the news was even better for Lionel fans. Another version of the wood-sided caboose, also in New York Central markings, was produced to match the new gun-metal gray New York Central Hudson; this one had a lighter, plain brown color, and the front marker lights of the first two were eliminated (making the two rear ones light better).

In addition, the first variation of this caboose was produced for the Conrail Limited set for 1987. This was a fine development for the wood-sided caboose. Since Lionel uses a "plug-in" design for the cupola, all the firm had to do was to design a new high-window cupola, plug it onto the wood-sided caboose's roof, and — presto, a new high-cupola wood-sided caboose was born! This one came in bright Conrail blue with white lettering, and it was a scale dead-ringer for the old Canadian National wooden cabooses of the early years of this century. Conrail actually gave some of these ancient cabooses a new paint job and used them in its early years. This one looks magnificent; it has drawn praise from collectors and is in hot demand. Rock Island and Southern versions of this caboose have since been made, and a Lackawanna version was made as a match for the 18003 Lackawanna Northern in 1988.

Steel-Sided

In late 1990 Lionel introduced a major new revision to the Standard O wood-sided caboose. Although the new caboose retains the size and form of its wood-sided predecessors, there are several major body style differences. The first is that the new version has no wood-sided slats — it is in fact a steel-sided caboose with rivet detail (on the sides *and* roof), matching anything made since the 6464 boxcars. In addition, the new cabooses have smoke units and flashing rear warning lights similar to the ETDs on boxcars. The action of the smoke unit was improved for this release by adding a piston/cam device to the wheel so that the smoke puffs are synchronized to the wheel speed, as with the steam engines.

Other more subtle differences between the steel-sided and wood-sided cabooses are changes in the window pattern, cupola design (Lionel seems to enjoy altering cupolas on its cabooses!), the door shape at the rear, the addition of separate grab-rails on the side and ends (an excellent detail) as opposed to molded grab-rails on the wood-sided versions, and placement of an opening toolbox on the underside. Two versions of the steel-sided caboose were introduced in 1990, including one in New York Central — meaning four of the thirteen Standard O cabooses made are lettered for N Y C. The action and lights are bound to make these new cabooses favorites among collectors and operators. A Chessie version was released in 1991 to match the 18011 Chessie T-1.

All the Standard O cabooses have been made as matches for Lionel's best locomotives. Expect Lionel to keep going with a winner and produce new models of this fine caboose in the next few years, and perhaps it will issue road names other than New York Central.

In fact, since Lionel Trains, Inc. has dedicated a full number series to the scale Standard O cabooses (all have been made since 1986), it is appropriate to also give them the "17600-series" label.

STANDARD O CABOOSE LISTINGS

GD   VG   EXC   MT

6907 NEW YORK CENTRAL SYSTEM: 1986, Standard O scale wood-sided caboose; uncatalogued; tuscan body; black main roof and on low cupola; ladders; tall stack; marker lights at all four corners; white lettering; black and white N Y C oval logo; illuminated; new die-cast arch bar trucks; "BLT 1-86". A new design for Lionel in the modern era and the first production of this caboose since prewar years. Available only as part of a direct mail-ordering package from Lionel, associated with the 784 B & A Hudson and the 6920 caboose.   —   —   150   200

6920 B & A: 1986, (Boston & Albany) Standard O scale wood-sided caboose; uncatalogued tuscan body and roof; low cupola; ladders; tall stack; marker lights at all four corners; white lettering; black and white N Y C oval logo (the B & A was a subsidiary of the New York Central); illuminated; die-cast arch bar trucks; "BLT 1-86". Available only as part of a direct mail-order offer from Lionel, associated with the 784 B & A Hudson and the 6907 caboose.   —   —   125   175

17600 N. Y. C.: 1987, Standard O scale wood-sided caboose; uncatalogued; light brown body and roof; low cupola; white lettering and number; black ladders, end rails and cupola roof rails; pictured with marker lights only at rear instead of at all four corners as on earlier models; illuminated; die-cast arch bar trucks; "BLT 1-87". Sold as a match for 18002 gun-metal New York Central Hudson in year-end "Happy Lionel Holidays!" package.   —   —   75   95

GD   VG   EXC   M

17601 SOUTHERN: 1988, Standard O wood-sided caboose; re body; high cupola; black main and cupola roofs; yellow letterin and S R circular logo; illuminated; die-cast arch bar trucks; "BL 1-88". Made to compliment 18301 Southern Fairbanks-Mors diesel.   —   —   70   8

17602 CONRAIL: 1987, Standard O wood-sided caboose bright blue body; high cupola; white striping, lettering and Conrai logo; black roof and cupola roof; low-window wood-sided cupol used on earlier releases of this caboose replaced by new high-win dow version; marker lights only at rear; illuminated; die-cast arc bar trucks; "BLT 1-87". Part of Conrail Limited set 11700.   —   —   70   8

17603 ROCK ISLAND: 1988, Standard O wood-sided caboose dark maroon body (shown as tuscan in catalogue); high cupola black trim pieces; white number and Rock Island logo; il luminated; die-cast arch bar trucks. Compliments 18001 Roc Island Northern from 1987.   —   —   60   7

17604 LACKAWANNA: 1988, Standard O wood-sided caboose low cupola; dark brown body; black trim pieces; white letterin and logo; illuminated; die-cast arch bar trucks; "BLT 1-88". Issue to match 18003 Lackawanna Northern steam locomotive.   —   —   6

17605 READING: 1989, Standard O wood-sided caboose; re body; low cupola; black main and cupola roofs; white lettering yellow railings on end platforms and cupola roof; illuminated die-cast arch bar trucks; "BLT 1-89". Issued to accompany th 18004 Reading steam locomotive.   —   —   —   6

17606 NEW YORK CENTRAL: 1990, Standard O steel sided caboose; gray body with red stripe at top of sides; catalogu pictures it as black but made in red/gray "Pacemaker" scheme; re high cupola; black main and cupola roofs and end platforms; whit lettering; catalogue shows "17006" on car but actually numbere "17606"; number under-scored; opening toolbox; illuminated flashing rear warning light similar to boxcar ETDs (light is light-emitting diode); cam-operated smoke unit (Lionel advise the caboose should be kept moving, or the smoke unit may bur out); die-cast arch bar trucks; "BLT 1-90". First Standard (caboose with smoke unit. New body style includes fine rivet an catwalk detail and separate grab-rails. Released late 1990.   —   —   —   7

17607 READING: 1990, Standard O steel-sided caboose; tus can body and high cupola; black frame and platforms; whit lettering; opening toolbox; illuminated; truck axles include a ne cam device to improve smoke unit operation (Lionel advises th caboose should be kept moving, or the smoke unit may burn out) new body with fine rivet and catwalk detail and separate grab rails; has a flashing rear light similar to boxcar ETDs; die-cas arch bar trucks; "BLT 1-90."   —   —   —   7

17608 C & O CHESSIE SYSTEM*: 1991, Standard O steel sided caboose with smoke; tuscan-red body and high cupola; blacl frame and platforms; white "C/AND/O/FOR/PROGRESS" letter ing; opening toolbox; illuminated; axle-driven cam-activite smoke unit; flashing rear warning light; die-cast arch bar trucks "BLT 1-91". Intended as a match for 18011 Chessie T-1 steam locomotive.   —   —   —   8

17610 WABASH*: 1991, Standard O steel-sided caboose medium red body and high cupola; black frame and end platforms white lettering; opening toolbox; separate grab-rails; illuminated axle-cam operated smoke unit; flashing rear warning light; die cast arch bar trucks; "BLT 1-91".   —   —   —   8

GD VG EXC MT

7611 NEW YORK CENTRAL: 1990-91, Standard O wood-sided caboose; brown body and high cupola; white lettering "C. C. C. & St. L/6003" and large black and white N Y C oval in center; illuminated; die-cast arch bar trucks; "BLT 1-90". This caboose was originally planned to be an Ontario & Western, as it was pictured in the 1990 Stocking Stuffers brochure with the 18009 Mohawk locomotive. When collector pressure forced a road name change on the Mohawk back to New York Central, the caboose was changed as well. As a result, it is the fourth Standard O caboose (out of thirteen produced) thus far lettered for New York Central. Regularly catalogued in 1991.   —   —   —   **70**

7880 DENVER & RIO GRANDE: 1990, scale wood-sided caboose; L C C A; see Volume II, first edition.

WORK, TRANSFER AND BOBBER CABOOSES

Postwar Lionel issued many work cabooses, mostly variations on a Delaware, Lackawanna and Western road name, which have not been re-released by modern Lionel. Both the postwar and modern work cabooses have three variations: a version with two tool chests (on the flatcar forward of the cab), another with one large bin replacing the two tool chests, and a two tool chest car with a searchlight mounted between them. (There are many other minor variations.)

Several work cabooses (also sometimes called "wrecker" cabooses) have been issued for the modern Lionel Traditional series ever since the first years of the company, beginning with the 9021 Santa Fe in 1970. This little caboose featured a "convertible" cab which could be taken off so that the car could be used as a simple flatcar. There followed a similar D T & I model in 1971 and a Soo Line work caboose in 1975. Other work cabooses have been made for the Trains n' Truckin', and Working on the Railroad sets of 1977 and 1978. One example, the 6916 New York Central, was produced in 1985 as part of the Yard Chief steam switcher work train, followed by a work caboose for the 1986 Santa Fe work train Service Station Special which even had Standard O trucks — perhaps a case of overkill! Most of these cabooses do not attract much attention, except for a few early varieties of the 9021 Santa Fe and that curio Santa Fe with the Standard O trucks.

However, recently Lionel has dramatically upgraded this plain caboose with two pieces that have attracted considerable attention. The 19709 Pennsylvania was released in 1989 as a companion to the B-6 switcher. It is a handsome tuscan version with die-cast trucks and includes the first smoke unit and interior illumination installed on a modern era work caboose. The next year Lionel took that same design and added an old-fashioned pivoting searchlight with metal housing between the tool chests. This is the 19707 Southern Pacific, and is a revival of the 2420 and 6420 postwar favorites. It is a match for the 18503 Southern Pacific NW-2 switcher, and follows Lionel Train, Inc.'s obvious trend toward higher end scale/Collector pieces with nostalgic revivals of old-time favorites. Both cabooses are numbered in the Collector series, the first work cabooses to reach that level.

The four-wheeled bobber caboose was first made for the Kickapoo Valley and Northern set of 1972. It is an all-plastic car, completely new with Fundimensions production. Although it looks small and it has been used only on lower-priced sets, it is surprisingly faithful to its prototype, some of which can be seen on the Strasburg Railroad in Strasburg, Pennsylvania. It is one of the few four-wheeled cars in the modern Lionel repertoire. It has been made in Chessie, Santa Fe, Rock Island, and Reading colors over the years; the Reading in green was even available for separate-sale. A version with extra trim pieces was produced as part of a Santa Fe dockside switcher set, the Midland Freight, in 1985. Another one in bright red forms the tail of the 1987 Rail Blazer set. These whimsical, rather cute cabooses are interesting additions to a collection, although as part of the lower-priced lines they do not attract much collector attention.

Finally in 1981, a new type of caboose emerged with the production of the Reading Yard King set. This was the transfer caboose, sometimes called the maintenance caboose. Lionel has used both terms. Essentially, this caboose consists of a flatcar with pipe-style railings on both sides leading to a small square cab — or "shanty" — mounted at the center of the flatcar. Another version of the Reading caboose was produced for separate-sale, with the green and yellow colors reversed from the one included with the Yard King set.

Several other transfer cabooses have emerged in recent years, among them Chicago & North Western, Burlington Northern, Erie-Lackawanna, and New York Central. As with the work cabooses, LTI has nudged the quality on this caboose up a notch, installing interior illumination on the 16519 Rock Island. Despite the fact that this caboose design is of relatively recent vintage, it has an old-time look about it which looks very good with a string of wood-sided reefers in a train. The separate-sale Reading and the Burlington Northern are the easiest ones to acquire, but the collector can expect several more examples of this caboose in the Traditional series in years to come.

One last note: We include the strange 6506 L. A. S. E. R. security car in these listings simply for lack of a better place to put it. It was the trailing car in the unusual L. A. S. E. R train of 1981-1982, but is really a flatcar with large housing attached and two "laser guns" mounted atop. The cab housing is derived from the equally strange postwar 520 boxcab electric.

WORK, TRANSFER AND BOBBER CABOOSE LISTINGS

GD VG EXC MT

6420 READING: 1981-82, transfer caboose; dark yellow shanty on flatcar with dark green base; yellow lettering on car; green lettering and logo on shanty; Symington-Wayne trucks; "BLT 1-81". Available only as part of 1154 Reading Yard King freight set.   —   —   **15**   **20**

Transfer and work cabooses.

W. Dyson, R. Kaptur, R. LaVoie, A. Rudman, and F. Stem; B. Greenberg photograph

Top shelf: 6420 Reading Lines; 6426 Reading Lines. Reverse color scheme.

Second shelf: 6435 U.S.; 6491 Erie Lackawanna.

Third shelf: 6916 New York Central System; 9025 D T & I.

Bottom shelf: 9085 Santa Fe; 19709 Pennsylvania, a dramatically updated work caboose with lights, smoke unit and die-cast trucks.

	GD	VG	EXC	MT

6426 READING: 1982-83, transfer caboose; dark green shanty centered on yellow flatcar; yellow Reading diamond logo; reverse color scheme from 6420 Yard King set caboose; Symington-Wayne trucks; BLT 1-82". — — **10 12**

6427 BURLINGTON NORTHERN: 1983-84, transfer caboose; green flatcar body and shanty; black roof and railings; white and green B N logo and lettering on shanty; Symington-Wayne trucks; "BLT 1-83". — — **10 15**

6428 CHICAGO & NORTH WESTERN: 1983-85, transfer caboose; dark green wood-scribed flatcar body; dark green or black plastic pipe-style handrails; yellow center shanty; white flatcar lettering; black lettering and C N W logo on shanty; Symington-Wayne trucks; one dummy coupler; "BLT 1-83". Part of 1314 Northern Freight Flyer set.
(A) Dark green flatcar body. — — **12 15**
(B) Black flatcar body with yellow lettering. E. Lazar and C. O'Dell Collection. **NRS**

6435 U.S.: 1983-84, transfer caboose; olive drab with two railings on one side of shanty and dual gun on other; Symington-Wayne trucks with plastic wheels; two dummy couplers. Part of

1355 Commando Assault set. Came without lettering on car; decals furnished with set. — — — **20**

6491 ERIE LACKAWANNA: 1985-86, transfer caboose; black flatcar body and handrail piping; dark red cab; black roof and stack; white lettering and diamond logo; Symington-Wayne trucks; "BLT 1-85". — — — **12**

6494 ATCHISON, TOPEKA & SANTA FE: 1985-86, bobber caboose; uncatalogued; blue body; silver frame, end rails and stack; yellow "ATCHISON, TOPEKA & SANTA FE" lettering; no number on car; two dummy couplers; no "BLT" date. From 1501 Midland freight set. — — **8 10**

6496 A T S F: 1986, work caboose; black plastic base with white lettering; red cab with yellow cross logo and number; red tool bin; short stack; ladder; Standard O trucks (the first and only work caboose so equipped); "BLT 1-86". From 1632 Santa Fe Work Train Service Station Special. This and the 9085 are similar to the postwar 6120. J. Kouba Collection. — — — **30**

6506 L. A. S. E. R.: 1981-82, security car with gun; black flatcar base with white "L.A.S.E.R."; chrome-finished cab with blue "L.A.S.E.R" lettering; no other lettering or numbers; lighted

W. Dyson, R. Kaptur, R. LaVoie, A. Rudman, and F. Stem; B. Greenberg photograph

Bobber cabooses.
Top shelf: **Three versions of the 9067 Kickapoo Valley & Northern.**
Bottom shelf: **9068 Reading; 9179 Chessie System.**

	GD	VG	EXC	MT

radioactive waste canister; Symington-Wayne trucks. Part of 1150 L. A. S. E. R. train set. This car is technically a flatcar with a large building attached, but since it acts as a caboose for the L. A. S. E. R. train, it is included here. This car is like nothing else in the Lionel line, and most resembles the 3535 security car of the postwar years, except the L. A. S. E. R. car is in chrome and includes a radioactive waste canister rather than searchlight. The cab is actually derived from the odd 520 postwar boxcab electric engine. — — **15 30**

6916 NEW YORK CENTRAL SYSTEM: 1985-86, work caboose; black flatcar base; gray cab and tool bin; black N Y C oval logo; white lettering on flatcar; Symington-Wayne trucks; one operating and one dummy coupler; "BLT 1-85". From 1502 Yard Chief set. — — **12 15**

9021 SANTA FE: 1970-74, work caboose; black frame with yellow lettering; red cab and toolbox except (D); yellow cab lettering and cross logo; caboose converts into "wood" deck flatcar when cab is removed; no "BLT" date. Car appears in several early 1970-74 sets and the Timberline set in 1978.
(A) Medium red cab; light red tool bin; "9021" on frame; AAR trucks; plastic wheels; one manumatic coupler; one dummy coupler. (Note: A "manumatic" coupler can be hand-operated; but it does not have the thumb tack pressed into the armature shaft so that a remote track will pull it down. Obviously, any manumatic coupler can be quickly made into a remote-control coupler.) **5 8 10 15**
(B) Same as (A), but light red cab; two manumatic couplers. **5 8 10 15**
(C) Dark glossy red cab and tool bin; Symington-Wayne trucks; one operating coupler; one dummy coupler; "9021" not on frame. Packed in plain white box with number typed on box. C. Lang Collection. **5 8 10 15**
(D) Same as (A), but orange cab. Came in early sets; somewhat difficult to find. **12 15 20 30**
(E) Same as (A), but "9022" on frame. C. Rohlfing Collection. **7 10 15 20**

9025 D T & I: 1971-74, (Detroit, Toledo & Ironton) work caboose; black frame with white lettering; orange cab with black lettering and D T & I "bulls eye" logo; orange tool bin; Symington-

Wayne trucks; operating coupler in front; dummy rear coupler; no "BLT" date. Came with 1182/1382 Yardmaster sets and may have appeared in 1978 in the Logging Empire or Timberline sets. **4 6 8 10**

9027 SOO LINE: 1975, work caboose; black frame with white lettering; red cab with white lettering and SOO logo; dark red tool bin; caboose converts into flatcar with stakes; Symington-Wayne trucks with plastic wheels; one manumatic coupler in front; "BLT 1-75". Appeared in the 1582 Yard Chief set. **4 6 8 10**

9067 KICKAPOO VALLEY & NORTHERN: 1972, bobber caboose; black plastic frame; four plastic wheels; gold lettering; no numbers on car; frame stamped "9067-10"; one dummy coupler, fastened to frame with screw (for a total of three metal parts). Came only in the Kickapoo Valley and Northern set of 1972. This is the first regular issue of this new style inexpensive caboose.
(A) Red body. **3 5 7 10**
(B) Yellow body. **3 5 7 10**
(C) Green body. **3 5 7 10**

9068 READING: 1973-75, bobber caboose; green body; yellow lettering; black plastic frame stamped "9067-10"; four plastic wheels; one dummy coupler. Came as separate-sale item in Type II box, and also as part of 1380 U.S. Steel industrial switcher set. **3 5 6 8**

9071 A. T. & S. F.: 1974-75, 1977-78, bobber caboose; red body; white lettering; black plastic frame stamped as on 9067; four plastic wheels; one dummy coupler. Part of Sears set 79N96178C (Sears catalogue number) and catalogued set 1760 from 1977-78, the Steel Hauler. Also part of set 1790, Lionel Leisure Steel set, sold by Kiddie City stores. J. R. Hunt Collection. **5 6 8 10**

9072 BALTIMORE & OHIO: 1972-73, SP Type VII; blue body; yellow lettering; Type I ends. **3 5 6 9**

9078 ROCK ISLAND: 1976-78, bobber caboose; red body; white lettering; no numbering on car except "9067-10" stamped under black plastic frame; four plastic wheels; one dummy coupler. Included in 1661 Rock Island Line set. **3 5 6 8**

	GD	VG	EXC	MT

9085 A T S F: 1979-82, work caboose; red cab with yellow number and cross logo; plain black flatcar; Symington-Wayne trucks; plastic wheels; one operating coupler; one dummy coupler; no "BLT" date. Very similar to earlier 9021 except no lettering on flatcar. Part of 9195 rolling stock assortment.

	3	4	5	6

9179 CHESSIE SYSTEM: 1976, bobber caboose; yellow body; blue lettering; black frame; four plastic wheels. Same description as 9067 Kickapoo. Came in 1660 Yard Boss set. It is not clear why this car is numbered in the 9100-series, rather than the 9000-series.

	3	5	6	10

9357 SMOKEY MOUNTAIN LINE: 1979, bobber caboose; one-piece plastic cab and roof; frame underside stamped as on 9067; black unpainted plastic frame; two black unpainted plastic end railing units; four plastic wheels; one dummy coupler; no "BLT" date. Came with set 1965 the Smokey Mountain Line set. Same color variations as on 9067 except a logo was added to the sides.
(A) Unpainted red plastic body; white lettering. G. Halverson Collection.

	2	4	8	10

(B) Unpainted green plastic body; black lettering; black heat-stamped "SML" logo between windows.

	2	4	8	10

(C) Unpainted yellow plastic body; black "SML" lettering. C. O'Dell Collection.

	5	10	15	20

16500 ROCK ISLAND: 1987-88, bobber caboose; bright red body; white lettering; gray frame, end rails and stack; otherwise the same description as 9067. Part of 11701 Rail Blazer set.

	—	—	—	25

16503 NEW YORK CENTRAL SYSTEM: 1987, transfer caboose; black flatcar body and railings; white lettering on flatcar; medium gray cab with black number and black and white NYC oval logo; Symington-Wayne trucks; two operating couplers; "BLT 1-87".

	—	—	—	12

16511 PENNSYLVANIA: 1988-89, bobber caboose; tuscan body; gold lettering; frame and railings; BLT 1-88". Part of 11708 Midnight Flyer set in 1989 and uncatalogued 11708 Toys 'R Us Pennsy set (same components) the year before.

	—	—	5	7

16519 ROCK ISLAND: 1990, transfer caboose; black flatcar body; blue shanty with white Rock Island shield; white lettering on flatcar; illuminated with opaque window insert (first transfer caboose to be lighted); ASF strong-arm trucks; "BLT 1-90". Intended to accompany 18610 0-4-0 Rock Island steam switcher.

	—	—	—	22

16503 New York Central System work caboose.   *B. Greenberg photos*

	GD	VG	EXC	MT

16645 AMTRAK*: 1991, work caboose with searchlight; light gray flatcar body; orange cab; black logo and lettering on cab; white flatcar lettering; catalogued as 19816 but made as 16645; illuminated; operating searchlight in place of tool chests or bins; ASF strong arm trucks; "BLT 1-91". The unusual number on this caboose stems from the fact that Lionel classified it as an operating car (16600-series) rather than a caboose. Part of the 11723 Amtrak Maintenance Train set.

	—	—	—	45

19707 SOUTHERN PACIFIC: 1990, work caboose; light gray flatcar body; medium red cab and tool chests; illuminated with opaque window insert; smoke unit; yellow railing on front and rear; white lettering on cab and flatcar; small operating searchlight on pivot between tool chests; searchlight has old-style metal housing; brakewheel on raised post; die-cast arch bar trucks; "BLT 1-90". This car, a remake of the postwar 6420 except for the road name, is expected to be in demand with its added new features. Issued as a match to 18503 Southern Pacific NW-2 switcher.

	—	—	—	85

19709 PENNSYLVANIA: 1989, 1991, work caboose; maroon-tuscan cab and tool chests; black roof; black flatcar body; gold lettering on cab and frame; metal handrails; brakewheel on raised post; smoke unit; illuminated; die-cast arch bar trucks; "BLT 1-89". Issued as a match for 18000 scale B-6 steam switcher. This car marks several firsts in the work caboose series and is expected to be in demand.

	—	—	—	80

19816 AMTRAK: 1991; see 16645.

CHAPTER 8

CRANE AND DERRICK CARS

Crane cars have been staples on Lionel layouts since before World War II, and few operating cars more typify Lionel's trademark action philosophy. It was important enough that the 6560 crane car was one of the few transition pieces which bridged the turbulent changes between the faltering postwar Lionel Corp. and the fledgling MPC/Fundimensions era (leading to endless confusion and controversy over the 6560!).

Since then, Fundimensions and its successors have made several different crane cars. The first major crane car did not emerge until 1979, when two were produced, both with Standard O trucks. The first one was a handsome Reading crane in green and yellow included with the Quaker City Limited set; the other was designated (apparently at the last minute) as the sixth car of the Santa Fe Famous American Railroads set. It carries the diamond-shaped F A R R logo (of which many collectors seem unaware), and was a separate-sale item. This was the attractive blue and yellow 9348 Santa Fe crane car.

The next crane cars sported a significant innovation: the six-wheel die-cast passenger trucks which had been introduced on the Blue Comet passenger cars in 1978. First of these was the 9329 Chessie crane in the usual bright yellow and blue Chessie "Cat" paint scheme. It was part of the Royal Limited Collector set of 1980. From this point on, most of the crane cars were made for special Collector sets. The next one came in the maroon and gray colors of the Canadian Pacific as part of the Maple Leaf Limited set of 1981. A 6510 Union Pacific crane was made in 1982; it was a separate-sale item, but it was also a great match for the Gold Coast Limited set. An attractive Erie model came out in 1984 for the Erie-Lackawanna Limited set. For 1985 a New York Central crane in black with white lettering was issued as part of the New York Central steam switcher set; unlike the others, this crane had Symington-Wayne plastic trucks. A special Illinois Central Gulf crane was made for the L C C A in 1985. In 1986, a red and black Santa Fe model was made as part of the Santa Fe Service Station Special; it had Standard O trucks instead of the six-wheel versions. Both the Great Northern model

produced for the Fallen Flags set No. 3 in 1988 and a bright green Southern car in 1991 marked a return to the six-wheel die-cast trucks.

The Fundimensions derrick car is a sort of baby crane car without the cab; it is modeled after a postwar Lionel car (the 6670). This car has a standard long Type II (6511-2) flatcar as its base, and the derrick assembly is riveted to the car. The derrick is collapsible and snaps into position when raised. It operates with a hand crank and swivels. In the modern era versions, the outrigger mechanism used on some postwar versions has been omitted.

In 1980 a version just like the postwar derrick in Lionel markings with a red flatcar was scheduled for a Texas and Pacific set headed by an Alco diesel, but the set was never made. Instead, the Lionel car came out the next year as part of the Reading Yard King set. The next derricks both came out in 1983. One was a Chicago & North Western, which was part of the Northern Freight Flyer set; the other was a yellow 9235 Union Pacific, which was available for separate-sale in that year and in 1984. Production of a black and orange Illinois Central derrick was set for 1985, but canceled after appearing in the catalogue. Apparently, advance orders did not justify its production. The only further derrick car since that time was the 16603 Lehigh Valley model of 1987.

Mention should also be made of several often ignored short crane cars, one of which — the 9364 N & W — may have launched Fundimensions on the road to reviving all the crane cars including the Collector versions which followed. The 9364 was actually a four-wheel small flatcar body with snap-in crane cab and boom which originated with 1978's Timberline set. Two later versions (with regular trucks) appeared in the Redwood Valley set and the Midland Freight.

Together, Lionel's modern cranes are a colorful consist and most of them are desirable pieces. This should remain the case because not many have been made and only two new ones have appeared in the last five years. They add an element of

---

* *Asterisk found in listings indicates that the information within that listing was derived from Lionel catalogue only.*

The best of the crane cars. Many came in Collector sets.

R. Kaptur, R. LaVoie, and F. Stem Collections; B. Greenberg photograp

Top shelf: 6508 Canadian Pacific; 6524 Erie.
Second shelf: Two versions of the maddening 6560 crane car. The crane on the left is variation (A) with AAR trucks; the right is variation (D) with Symington-Wayne trucks.
Third shelf: 6579 New York Central; 6593 Santa Fe.
Bottom shelf: 9329 Chessie System; 9332 Reading.

realism and play value to any layout, especially when combined with work cabooses and gondolas.

CRANE AND DERRICK CAR LISTINGS

6325 NEW YORK CENTRAL: Crane car; see 6579.

6508 CANADIAN PACIFIC: 1981, crane car; maroon base and boom with white letters; gray cab with maroon lettering and "Canadian Pacific" logo; maroon roof and stack; die-cast six-wheel

	GD	VG	EXC	MT

passenger trucks; "BLT 1-81". Part of 1158 Maple Leaf Limited set. — — 45 70

6510 UNION PACIFIC: 1982, crane car; yellow cab with gray roof; gray plastic base; red "UNION PACIFIC" lettering; tall stack; notched boom at high end; die-cast six-wheel passenger trucks; "BLT 1-82". Separate-sale item, but is a good match for the 1361 Gold Coast Limited set or the Famous American Railroad No. 2 set. Weisblum, R. Sigurdson, N. Banis and T. Ladny Collections.
— — 50 75

6524 ERIE: 1984, crane car; yellow base with maroon logo and lettering; maroon cab with white "ERIE" lettering and "ERIE" logo; gray cab roof and boom; die-cast six-wheel passenger trucks; "BLT 1-84". From 1451 Erie-Lackawanna Limited set.
— — 45 70

6560 CRANE: *The carry-over 6560 Bucyrus Erie crane has always been a very difficult piece to define and describe accurately. Lionel's Dan Johns says that the crane was thrown together rather haphazardly from postwar and early Fundimensions pieces, and that even some completely-postwar versions went out in Fundimensions boxes! From what we have been able to reconstruct, only original factory-installed Symington-Wayne trucks can absolutely define any given 6560 as Fundimensions and not postwar (produced in Hagerstown, Maryland). There are, however, several other distinguishing features which will likely mark a crane as Fundimensions, but since parts were mixed and interchangeable, there is never full certainty. The history of this thoroughly frustrating car is a great deal more complicated than originally supposed. Readers are encouraged to write and describe their boxed cranes to assist us in more precisely defining the production history.*

	6560: MPC/ FUNDIMENSIONS	6560: POSTWAR HAGERSTOWN, MD
CAB	Darker translucent unpainted red	Lighter red
BOOM	Black	Very dark blue
BASE	Dark blue	Black
RIVET AT BOOM TOP	Chromed with black felt washer	Black or bronzed with metal washer or no washer

	GD	VG	EXC	MT

6560 LIONEL LINES: 1971, crane car; very dark blue base (best seen from underside); black boom; translucent red plastic cab (darker than Hagerstown postwar examples); white lettering on cab, "BUCYRUS ERIE" and "LIONEL LINES"; solid crank wheels; white lettering on base sides; small chromed rivet with black felt washer holds wire assembly at top of boom; blackened or bronzed U-shaped rivet holds boom crank at base of boom; open AAR trucks; postwar wheels which turn on axles; two operating couplers.
(A) As described above; came in Fundimensions Type I box with red lettering on box end label and picture of car. Mint value must include this box. P. Catalano, C. Rohlfing, and R. LaVoie comments. G. Halverson Collection. **75 100 125 150**
(B) Canadian distribution; came in Type I box with smaller cellophane window and Parker Brothers black-printed logo. One example observed in Montreal. We would like to know if there are any differences between this version and the one assembled for American production. G. Halverson comment. One recently observed version had a black base. C. O'Dell Collection. **NRS**
(C) Black boom and base; chromed rivet; lettering rubber-stamped instead of heat-stamped; authenticated as original in Fundimensions Type I box. H. Powell Collection. **75 100 150 175**

	GD	VG	EXC	MT

(D) Same as (A), but factory-installed (metal rivet) Symington-Wayne trucks. R. LaVoie Collection. Further reader confirmation requested. **75 100 150 175**
(E) Same as (A), but with blue boom and unplated rivet at top of boom. C. Rohlfing Collection. **75 100 125 150**

6567 ILLINOIS CENTRAL GULF: 1985, crane car; L C C A; see Volume II, first edition.

6574 REDWOOD VALLEY EXPRESS: 1984-85, short crane car; short Type II yellow flatcar base with dark brown lettering; tuscan plastic cab with yellow logo; gray boom; plastic arch bar trucks. Part of 1403 Redwood Valley Express set. **— — — 15**

6576 SANTA FE: 1985-86, short crane car; dark blue scribed short Type II flatcar body; dark blue cab; gray boom; gray log cradle (hanging from boom) and gray cab attachment piece; yellow lettering and "Santa Fe" cross logo; Symington-Wayne trucks; dummy couplers. From 1501 Midland Freight set. **— — — 12**

6579 NEW YORK CENTRAL: 1985-86, crane car; black base, cab and boom; white lettering and white "New York Central System" oval logo; Symington-Wayne trucks with one dummy coupler; "BLT 1-85". Part of 1502 N Y C Yard Chief Switcher set. Car was catalogued as 6325, but made as 6579. Lionel changed several numbers in this set between catalogue and production. **— — 30 50**

6593 ATCHISON TOPEKA SANTA FE: 1986, crane car; red cab; black base with white lettering; yellow "A.T.S.F." lettering and cross logo on cab; black boom; Standard O trucks; "BLT 1-86". Part of 1632 Santa Fe Work Train Service Station Special set. **— — 35 50**

6670: See 9378.

9235 UNION PACIFIC: 1983-84, derrick car; yellow flatcar base with black derrick; red lettering; Symington-Wayne trucks; "BLT 1-83". Separate-sale item. **— — 10 15**

9236 CHICAGO & NORTH WESTERN: 1983-85, derrick car; black flatcar base with yellow derrick; Symington-Wayne trucks. Sold as part of 1354 Northern Freight Flyer set. **— — 15 20**

9245 ILLINOIS CENTRAL: Announced for 1985, derrick car; black flatcar base with white lettering and logo; bright orange swiveling boom riveted to flatcar; Symington-Wayne trucks. Canceled from dealer order sheets in September 1985. **Not Manufactured**

9325 N & W: See 9364.

9329 CHESSIE SYSTEM: 1980, crane car; blue base; yellow cab with silver roof; Chessie cat logo on cab rear; yellow lettering on base; die-cast six-wheel passenger trucks; "BLT 1-80". Came with the 1070 Royal Limited set. **— — 45 70**

9332 READING: 1979, crane car; dark green base; yellow cab; green roof; yellow boom; yellow and green "READING LINES" logo on cab; Standard O trucks; "BLT 1-79". From 1971 Quaker City Limited set. **— — 40 55**

9348 A. T. S. F.: 1979, crane car; uncatalogued; blue base with yellow lettering; blue cab with yellow "Santa Fe" cross logo; gold FARR Series 1 diamond insignia on cab; yellow boom; Standard O trucks; "BLT 1-79"; came in special Type III box. Announced in a late dealer brochure as an extra car for the first Famous American Railroads set of 1979. R. LaVoie Collection. **— 45 55 70**

Two crane car and two derrick cars — "a poor man's crane car."
Top shelf: 9348 A.T. & S.F.; 19402 Great Northern.
Bottom shelf: 9235 Union Pacific; 16609 L V. Both are derrick cranes.

W. Dyson, R. Kaptur, R. LaVoie, A. Rudman, and F. Stem Collections; B. Greenberg photograph

	GD	VG	EXC	MT

9364 N & W: 1978, small crane car; black short Type II, four-wheel flatcar base; four plastic wheels; yellow snap-on cab and boom pieces; part of No. 1860 Logging Empire set. Base of car has "9325" number, but came in box marked "9364", which distinguishes this car from its dumping car companion. J. Sawruk Collection. — — 8 10

9378 LIONEL: 1981, red flatcar with yellow derrick; pictured as 6670 in catalogue, but produced as 9378; Symington-Wayne trucks. From 1154 Reading Yard King set. R. DuBeau and W. Barnes comments. — — 15 20

16609 L V: 1987, (Lehigh Valley) derrick car; green flatcar body; white lettering and diamond logo; yellow derrick; Symington-Wayne trucks. Part of Black Diamond set 11702. Note: The previous edition of this guide erroneously numbered this car 16302. — — 20 25

16644 AMTRAK*: 1991, crane car; gray frame; orange cab; black boom; black number and "Amtrak" on cab; white lettering on frame; ASF strong-arm trucks (used because the car came in a Traditional Line set); "BLT 1-91". Part of 11723 Amtrak Maintenance Train set. — — — 45

19402 GREAT NORTHERN: 1988, crane car; black frame and boom; bright orange cab; dark green "GN" lettering on cab; red, white and green circular "goat" logo; die-cast six-wheel passenger trucks. Part of Fallen Flags set No. 3.
— — — 50

19405 SOUTHERN: 1991, crane car; green cab and frame; silver boom; silver cab roof; yellow lettering and S R logo on cab; S R circle logo on boom; die-cast six-wheel passenger trucks; "BLT 1-91". Intended as a match for 11704 Southern Freight Runner Service Station Special set or the Southern Famous American Railroad set No. 4. — — — 60

F<small>LATCAR</small>S

*D*uring the postwar years, the Lionel Corporation made the flatcar its most versatile freight carrier. The long and short plastic flatcars were used to haul just about everything under the sun, from submarines and helicopters to transformers and Christmas trees. If the load could not be put on the flatcar directly, Lionel saw to it that the car was adapted to the purpose. Some cars were fitted with bulkheads to hold pipes or gas containers. Another "depressed-center" body was created to carry taller loads (like the transformer!) under low-slung layout overpasses.

In the modern era, Lionel has not made the flatcar nearly the all-around performer it was in the 1950s and 1960s, principally because the company has expanded its production of hoppers and other rolling stock more suited to colorful graphics. Still, the modern flatcar has seen good use.

The last edition of this Guide listed three different flatcar bodies. New research has expanded the total now to ten uniquely identifiable flatcars used during the modern era. Four are new molds developed by Fundimensions, and the other six are postwar carry-overs. See Figure 9.1 for illustrations of these body types.

Lionel's use of the flatcar in the modern era has been to give an up-to-date realistic look to the freight line rather than serve as a "do-it-all" platform. Very few of the flatcars are scarce, so they represent an excellent collecting opportunity and can form an important part of the hobbyist's freight consist.

F<small>LATCAR</small> B<small>ODY</small> T<small>YPES</small>

LONG DEPRESSED CENTER is a die-cast, extra-long flatcar reminiscent of the 6418 car from 1957. It has four die-cast O27-style passenger trucks — the only modern era Lionel freight car so equipped. It is the only die-cast flatcar and has

two post-mounted brakewheels. This huge car (15 inches long) has been used for only two pieces in the modern era, a girder carrier and a transformer carrier.

SHORT DEPRESSED CENTER has been resurrected only in the last few years after a long run in the postwar era. This 8-inch-long car has been used in three road names to carry cable reels, and once as a small transformer carrier, which was a postwar favorite. Like its long brother, this style has two post-mounted brakewheels.

STANDARD-O SERIES flatcars were created in the 1970s, beginning with the 9823 Santa Fe. These cars, meant to accompany the Standard O boxcars, gondolas, reefers and wood-sided cabooses in realistic-looking scale trains, certainly rank near the top of any list of fine tinplate flatcars. One of them, the 6233 Canadian Pacific from 1986, was part of a limited direct-mail offer from Lionel and is quite hard to find. Standard O cars are 11 inches long and have been outfitted with crate loads, logs or just stakes. The stakes were metal on the 9823 Santa Fe and the 6521 New York Central cars, and plastic stakes were supplied with later issues.

RAISED CENTER is a unique flatcar designed specially for the 6519 Allis Chalmers car in 1958, and reissued by Fundimensions on the same car as 9232 in 1980. It has not been used on any other modern era cars, but appeared in postwar years as a missile-firing car and a Mercury capsule car.

FOUR-WHEEL is once again an entirely unique style to the 9019 all-purpose flatcar used on the Timberline set in 1978. Lionel attempted a new tack with this set in a clever effort to reduce costs — it supplied the basic flatcar with kits which the user assembled to make a small crane car, a boxcar, a log dump car or work caboose. The flatcar itself is four-wheeled with simulated eight-wheel trucks molded into the frame. Interestingly, Lionel later offered some of them as assembled cars

* Asterisk found in listings indicates that the information within that listing was derived from Lionel catalogue only.

boxed for separate-sale under separate numbers. While this marketing scheme has not been used since, this flatcar, sans the simulated wheels and fitted with regular four-wheel trucks, was developed into the Short Type II flatcar described in the following section.

SHORT flatcars, are found in three types — all 8 to 8½ inches long:

Type I (9020-style) was one of the first cars out of the block when MPC Lionel started operations in 1970. It was a new design, as compared to the old stamped-metal postwar version. As introduced first on the 9020 Union Pacific, it had a wood-scribed deck top and bottom, and sixteen plastic stakes which fit into molded holes around the perimeter. The 9020, which came in countless inexpensive sets in Fundimensions' early years, may well be the most numerous car made in the modern era. The style was copied in a sequence of 9000-series flatcars in Santa Fe, C & O, M K T, and Republic Steel markings during the period from 1972 to 1980. Like the U P, they populated a multitude of Traditional Line sets. Some of these cars were equipped with logs or bulkheads, which will seldom be found with the car for sale today, but can still be obtained from parts dealers. The scarcest Short Type I is the black 9020 with AAR trucks — probably from the earliest stages of production. The Short Type I style gave way to Type II around 1980, though it had an unexplained encore in 1986 as the 6515 U P in a rolling stock assortment. The short Type I car is most easily distinguished from its two short brethren by the eight stake pockets along the top of each side.

Type II (9325-style) started life as the Four-Wheel style described earlier, then became a more normal flatcar (with eight wheels!) on the 9325 Norfolk and Western in 1979-1980 as a part of the uncatalogued Wabash Deluxe Express set. Once again a new flatcar style to the modern era, this car has now taken over for Short Type I in Lionel's Traditional Line sets. Its distinguishing features are six stake hole pockets (instead of eight) on each side, which are more prominent than on Type I and also are used to support fences, which were never used on Short Type I cars; a lack of steps on the frame (this feature positively distinguishes it from Type I and III); and a more prominent lip on the tapered lower side beams. Otherwise, it has a nice wood-grained floor and an upward-facing brakewheel like the Short Type I car. After its debut on the 9325 (it has a 9325 mold number stamped on the bottom), this car appeared in a Marines set, in the Redwood Valley set, in Pennsylvania colors with many Traditional sets during the 1980s, and made its most recent appearance in Southern Pacific markings for 1990's Badlands Express set. With fences, it will often be found with horses corralled for transport. A last note of interest here: this flatcar body is used as the base for some of Lionel's transfer and work cabooses (see the Caboose chapter).

Type III (1877- or General-style) gets its number reference from a postwar 1877 flatcar in a set pulled by the General locomotive. It has an 1877 mold number on the bottom. In size and style, this car very much resembles the Short Type II (9325) from a distance, especially when outfitted with fences and horses. But there are several major differences up close. The Short Type III flatcar has not been used extensively in the modern era — it appeared first as a 9553 in the reissue of the 1877 General engine and cars in 1978. It then had a fun run in Santa Fe colors as part of the James Gang set. Its latest (and last) appearance was with a 1986 uncatalogued American Express rerun of the General.

LONG flatcars emerged in 1971. MPC brought back a handsome 9121 Louisville and Nashville car with bulldozer or scraper, using the car precisely as the old Lionel Corporation did before. From there, this car has become the most common of the modern flatcars (in diversity, if not quantity), although it has yet to achieve the tremendous variety of applications used by postwar Lionel. Long flatcars used two nearly identical molds, both developed in the postwar era. Of the two types, the 424-11 is by far the most common. The other, 6511-2, has appeared mostly on the track maintenance and

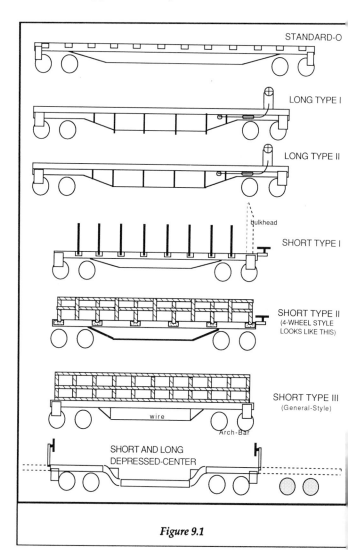

Figure 9.1

Comparison Between Short Type II and Type III Flatcars		
	TYPE II	*TYPE III*
Steps	No	Yes
Underframe	Sloped beam with lip	No beam—wire rails under deck
Brakewheel	Yes	No
Stake Pockets	Six large	None—fences snap into holes in deck
Wheel Sets	Symington-Wayne mostly	Old-style arch bar

searchlight cars. Long flatcars are 10 inches in body length, and 11 inches coupler to coupler.

TYPE I (6424-type), the most common of the long flatcars, takes its name from the stamped mold number underneath. This car body is nearly identical to the Type II (6511) mold except for two things: additional stiffeners are included on the inside surface of the two main tapered support beams under the car, so that when a Type I car is viewed from the side the additional stiffeners create four downward protrusions relative to the profile of the Type II. The second difference involves underside molding not visible from the top — the Type I car has extra plastic clumps at the intersections of the under-deck support beams, relative to the Type II. The Type I car has appeared on a large number of modern Lionel pieces: it is the base for all the Trailers-On-Flatcars (TOFCs) produced since 1970 (see the TOFC subheading in this chapter) except the T T U X articulated cars; it is the base for all the barrel ramp cars issued since 1987; and it saw several odd applications such as carrying missiles and helicopters in the L. A. S. E. R. set, carrying huge steam shovels and cranes recreating two postwar favorites, and even supporting lighted radioactive waste containers. For this, two rails are laid the length of the car and the canisters are clipped to the rails, and as it rides along, the canisters blink red warning lights. Scarcely romantic (and certainly not prototypical!), but a definite curiosity.

One note of importance here: the steam shovel and Harnischfeger crane-carrying cars came as kits to be assembled by the purchaser. These, as well as the bulldozer and scrapers supplied on the 9121, will command a premium nearly equal to the car itself if found in good and complete condition.

TYPE II (6511-type) is the less-common version of the long flatcar, without the protruding vertical stiffeners. It has been used principally for the revival of the Track Maintenance cars beginning in 1987 and for searchlight cars. The crane and steam shovel cars (9157 and 9158) also had variations which appeared on this body. The number "6511-2" is stamped on the bottom. There are mold die variations on both the Type I and Type II long flatcars

having to do with stake hole and other hole locations for various superstructures and other items which go on top. We will not detail them here, but the reader is referred to a brief discussion of them in *Greenberg's Guide to Lionel Trains 1945-1969, Volume I, eighth edition and Volume II, second edition.*

Comparison Between Long And Short Flatcars		
	SHORT	*LONG*
Length	8"	10"
Brakewheel	Upward-facing at deck level, or none	Single side-facing on post at one end
Vertical Stiffeners	None	Found on two tapered support beams under car; printing must be applied between and around them
Deck Surface	Wood-scribed	Wood-scribed; has two square areas at each end molded as floor treads

FLATCAR LISTINGS

              GD   VG   EXC   MT

6233 CANADIAN PACIFIC: 1986, Standard O flatcar; uncatalogued; black body; white lettering; 24 black plastic stakes; Standard O trucks; "BLT 1-86". Available only as part of a direct-mail offer from Lionel associated with the B & A Hudson. Hard to find.   —   —   **135**   **155**

6500 LIONEL TRANSFORMER CAR: See 9233.

Note: *The following four entries, with the 8161 gas turbine, made up an unusual "L. A. S. E. R." set reminiscent of the military and space cars produced by postwar Lionel in the 1960s.*

6504 L. A. S. E. R.: 1981-82, short Type II flatcar; has helicopter; black body; white "L. A. S. E. R." lettering; no number on car. From 1150 L. A. S. E. R. set.   —   —   **12**   **30**

6505 L. A. S. E. R.: 1981-82, long Type I flatcar; satellite tracking car; black body; white lettering; no number on car; light blue housing similar to superstructure used on postwar 3540. From 1150 L. A. S. E. R. set.   —   —   **12**   **30**

6506 L. A. S. E. R.: 1981-82, security car which uses long Type I flatcar base; see Caboose chapter.

6507 L. A. S. E. R.: 1981-82, long Type I flatcar; with air-launched cruise missile; black body; white lettering; no number

Two long depressed-center flatcars and several attractive Standard O flatcars.
Top shelf: **9233 Lionel Transformer Car.**
Second shelf: **6509 Lionel depressed-center flatcar with bridge girders.**
Third shelf: **6233 Canadian Pacific; 6521 N Y C.**
Bottom shelf: **9823 A T S F; 17501 Conrail.**

R. Kaptur Collection; B. Schwab photograph

	GD	VG	EXC	MT

on car; gruesome looking white missile. From 1150 L. A. S. E. R. set.   —   —   **12**   **30**

6509 LIONEL: 1981, long depressed-center flatcar; gray-painted die-cast body; two maroon bridge girders with white "LIONEL" attached to car by rubber bands; no lettering on car; two brakewheel posts; four sets of die-cast O27-style passenger trucks; bottom has "6418-4" mold number. Offered for separate-sale (another long depressed-center die-cast car — the 9233 Transformer — was offered the same year, but only in a set). One of the first cars to be packaged in a Type IV collector box. C. Lang comment. W. Barnes Collection.   —   —   **60**   **75**

6515 UNION PACIFIC: 1986, short Type I flatcar; identical to 9020 except for number; yellow body; blue lettering; sixteen black plastic stakes; Symington-Wayne trucks; one operating and one dummy coupler. Came in a 1986 rolling stock assortment (9195). J. Sawruk Collection.   —   —   —   **10**

6521 N Y C: 1984-85, Standard O flatcar; tuscan body; scribed floor; white lettering and N Y C oval logo; "BLT 1-85"; 24 metal stakes supplied with car to fit into holes around car perimeter; no load included; Standard O trucks.
     —   —   **55**   **70**

> **Note:** *Another unusual Traditional Line set with flat-cars is the 1355 Marines Commando Assault Train from 1983-1984, which consisted of the following three entries and a 6435 Marines transfer caboose pulled by an 8377 Marine switcher. The set also came with a large number of Marine figures and decals so that the user could decorate the pieces as desired — all the rolling stock originally came unlettered, and a mint price for the set requires the unused decal sheet. 1984 was apparently Lionel's "Year of the Marines" — a 5726 bunk car, 6526 searchlight car, and an 8485 NW-2 switcher were issued that year, in addition to this set.*

	GD	VG	EXC	MT

6561 U. S. MARINES: 1983-84, short Type II flatcar; with cruise missile; unlettered; olive drab body; Symington-Wayne trucks with two dummy couplers. From 1355 Commando Assault Train.   —   —   —   **25**

6562 U. S. MARINES: 1983-84, short Type II flatcar; crates and six barrels; unlettered; olive drab body; Symington-Wayne

W. Dyson, R. Kaptur, R. LaVoie, A. Rudman, and F. Stem Collections; B. Schwab photograph

Some unusual small flatcars.
Top shelf: **6561** U.S. flatcar with cruise missile; **6564** U.S. flatcar with two tanks.
Second shelf: **6562** U.S. flatcar with crates and barrels. These three U.S. cars were part of a Marines Command Assault set; **9020** Union Pacific early production flatcar with AAR trucks.
Third shelf: **9020** Union Pacific flatcar, perhaps the most common car made by modern Lionel; **9022** A.T.S.F.
Bottom shelf: **9023** M K T; **9325** Norfolk and Western.

	GD	VG	EXC	MT

trucks with two dummy couplers. From 1355 Commando Assault Train. — — — 25

6564 U. S. MARINES: 1983-84, short Type II flatcar; unlettered; olive drab body and two tanks; Symington-Wayne trucks with two dummy couplers. From 1355 Commando Assault Train. — — — 25

6575 REDWOOD VALLEY EXPRESS: 1984-85, short Type II flatcar; tuscan body with yellow lettering; no number on car; yellow fences around car perimeter; crate loads; plastic arch bar trucks. Part of Redwood Valley set 1403. — — — 15

6582 PORTLAND: 1986, flatcar with lumber load; T T O S; see Volume II, first ediiton.

6585 PENNSYLVANIA: 1986-90, short Type II flatcar; black body; white lettering; logs; yellow fencing; Symington-Wayne trucks; "BLT 1-86". Part of Cannonball Express set 1615. — — — 10

6587 WESTERN & ATLANTIC: 1986, General-style Type III flatcar; uncatalogued; tuscan body; yellow lettering and fencing; included one black and one white horse; arch bar trucks. Part of uncatalogued American Express set 1608. T. Taylor Collection. — — 20 30

9014 TRAILER TRAIN: 1978-79, short Type I flatcar; yellow body; black lettering and stakes; Symington-Wayne trucks with plastic wheels; manumatic couplers. From 1864 Santa Fe double diesel set. — — 4 6

9019 LOGGING EMPIRE: 1978, four-wheel short flatcar; used as a base for a superstructure of a box or crane car, work caboose or log loader; unlettered black flatcar base; fixed dummy couplers. Came as part of 1862 Logging Empire or 1860 Timberline sets. This is actually a four-wheel car with eight-wheel trucks simulated on the sides of the base, similar to Marx practice of many years ago. See other notes under 9325. J. Sawruk comment. — — 3 4

9020 UNION PACIFIC: 1970-77, short Type I flatcar; woodgrained floor; sixteen stakes; some versions have bulkheads;

	GD	VG	EXC	MT

Symington-Wayne trucks with plastic wheels (except H, I and J below); one manumatic coupler, one fixed coupler. This car is found in a multitude of inexpensive sets from the early Fundimensions period, and may be the most plentiful car made in the modern era.

(A) Medium yellow body; black lettering.

	GD	VG	EXC	MT
	2	3	4	5

(B) Light yellow body; light blue lettering.

	2	3	4	5

(C) Dark yellow body; dark blue lettering.

	2	3	4	5

(D) Medium yellow body; blue lettering.

	2	3	4	5

(E) Medium light yellow body; blue lettering.

	2	3	4	5

(F) Medium yellow body; blue lettering.

	2	3	4	5

(G) Medium light yellow body; blue lettering.

	2	3	4	5

(H) 1970-71; early production; unpainted tuscan plastic; heat-stamped; yellow-lettered; "BLT 1-70"; AAR trucks; one fixed, one disc-operating coupler. Came as part of early MPC set, the 1083 Pacemaker and in a 1092 Sears set. T. Durbin, C. Anderson, R. LaVoie, and Wolf Collections.

	—	—	15	20

(I) Same as (H), but dark red body; no wood-graining on floor. C. Rohlfing Collection.

	—	—	15	20

(J) 1970; first production: black body with yellow lettering; AAR trucks. Very hard to find. "Triple T" Collection.

	—	20	30	45

9022 A. T. S. F.: 1971-72, 1975-77, short Type I flatcar; yellow lettering; black plastic stakes; bulkheads; four unstained dowel-cut logs; Symington-Wayne trucks with metal wheels; one dummy coupler; no "BLT" date. Part of 1184-1284 Allegheny and 1586 Chesapeake Flyer freight sets.

(A) Red body; wood-grained floor.	3	4	8	15
(B) Red body; plain floor.	3	4	8	15
(C) Black body.	3	4	8	15

9023 M K T: 1973-74, 1978, short Type I flatcar; black body; white lettering; sixteen black plastic stakes; bulkheads; four unstained dowel-cut logs; Symington-Wayne trucks with metal wheels; one operating coupler; one fixed coupler; no "BLT" date. Part of 1386 Rock Island Express freight set.

	4	6	8	12

9024 CHESAPEAKE & OHIO: 1973-75, short Type I flatcar; yellow body; blue lettering; sixteen plastic stakes; Symington-Wayne trucks with plastic wheels; two fixed couplers; no "BLT" date. This car came in several sets during the 1973-75 period.

	2	3	4	6

9026 REPUBLIC STEEL: 1975-80, short Type I flatcar; blue body; white lettering; wood-grained floor; Symington-Wayne trucks with plastic wheels; sixteen stakes; bulkheads; one manumatic coupler, one dummy coupler. Part of 1582 Yard Chief and 1662 Black River freight sets.

(A) Medium blue body.	2	4	6	8
(B) Dark blue body.	2	4	6	8
(C) Very dark blue/purple body. T. Rollo Collection.	4	6	8	10

9029 BALTIMORE & OHIO: 1976, blue body; yellow lettering; plastic wheels; fixed couplers.

	1	2	4	5

9121 L & N: 1971, 1974-76, 1978-79, long Type I flatcar; with yellow dozer and scraper kit; white lettering, MPC logo and "BLT 1-71". Prices shown are for flatcars only; add $15 for both dozer

and scraper kits intact and in complete condition, and $30 if these kits are still sealed and unbuilt. There appear to be occasions when other flatcars (see 9122 N P and 9124 P C in this chapter) would be substituted for this car in various sets.

(A) 1971; brown body; white lettering; AAR trucks; came in Type I box with yellow dozer and scraper kits. Also offered in early sets. R. Loveless Collection.

	8	10	15	20

(B) Same as (A), but maroon flatcar body. This version somewhat hard to find. G. Halverson and R. LaVoie Collections.

	15	20	35	45

(C) Same as (A), but without "BLT 1-71" and MPC logo under "LIONEL". R. Loveless and K. Wills Collections.

	8	10	15	20

(D) Same as (A), but Symington-Wayne trucks. This is the most common version. C. Lang comment.

	8	10	15	20

(E) Same as (C), but MPC logo is missing while built date is still present. R. Loveless Collection.

	8	10	15	20

(F) 1974-76, 1978-79, brown body; Symington-Wayne trucks. Came in special Type II box when offered for separate-sale; included both kits. Part of 1866 Great Plains Express (1978-79). Also part of 1460 Grand National set in 1974 and 1560 North American set in 1975. Kaiser Collection.

	6	10	15	20

(G) Same as (A), but yellow lettering. This is possibly a chemically altered version. Reader comments invited. C. Lang Collection.

				NRS

See Factory Errors and Prototypes chapter in Volume II, first edition.

9124 PENN CENTRAL: 1973-75, 1978, long Type I flatcar; uncatalogued; green unpainted body; white lettering; large "P & L E" letters; small P C logo; comes with three logs; two black plastic ribs; plastic arch bar trucks; one operating coupler with plastic semi-disc for manual operation (known as manumatic coupler); one fixed coupler; "BLT 1-73". Reader comments are invited as to lettering variations on this car, as well as on sets in which it may have come.

(A) As described above. Part of uncatalogued 1392 and 1492 Sears sets in 1973-75. Cunningham and Ristau Collections.

	—	8	10	15

(B) Same as (A), but dozer kit instead of logs; Symington-Wayne trucks. Came as part of 1866 Great Plains Express set, although not catalogued with it. Apparently this flatcar substituted for the 9121 in some Great Plains sets. Somewhat rare. C. Rohlfing Collection.

	—	—	30	40

(C) Same as (A), but two white vans. Rare. Reader comments as to sets in which this car came are invited.

	—	—	—	50

9157 C & O: 1976-78, 1981, long Type I or II flatcar; blue body; yellow lettering; unassembled P & H yellow crane kit; Symington-Wayne trucks. Hard to find with crane kit intact. Car comes with "BLT 1-76/LIONEL" or just "BLT 1-76". No change in value. R. Stidd comment.

(A) Flatcar only.	5	10	15	20
(B) Flatcar with crane in excellent condition.	—	—	35	40
(C) Flatcar with crane kit unbuilt and sealed.	—	—	—	60

9158 P C: 1976-77; 1980, (Penn Central) long Type I or II flatcar; green body; white lettering; unassembled steam shovel kit; Symington-Wayne trucks. Hard to find with steam shovel kit intact.

W. Dyson, R. Kaptur, R. LaVoie, A. Rudman, and F. Stem Collections; B. Schwab photograph

op shelf: Two variations of the 9121 L&N flatcar with yellow dozer and scraper kit. Left is maroon; right is brown.

cond shelf: Box showing the 9157 flatcar with construction crane; box showing the 9158 flatcar with steam shovel.

ird shelf: 9234 Lionel; 9389 Lionel. Two strange radioactive waste cars.

ttom shelf: 9232 Allis-Chalmers; W. & A.R.R. short Type III General-style flatcar with fence and horses.

	GD	VG	EXC	MT
(A) Flatcar only.	5	10	15	20
(B) Flatcar with steam shovel in excellent condition; black treads on steam shovel.	—	—	35	40
(C) Same as (B), but with gray treads on steam shovel.	—	—	45	50
(D) Flatcar with steam shovel kit unbuilt and sealed; black treads on steam shovel.	—	—	—	60
(E) Same as (D), but with gray treads on steam shovel.	—	—	—	70

9232 ALLIS-CHALMERS: 1980-81, raised-center flatcar; with gray atomic reactor condenser load; orange base; blue lettering; Symington-Wayne trucks; "BLT 1-80". Rerun of postwar 6519 from 1958-61; part of 1072 Cross Country Express set.

| | | 35 | 60 |

9233 LIONEL TRANSFORMER CAR: 1980, long depressed-center flatcar; tuscan-painted die-cast body; no lettering; red transformer with white insulators; sign lettered "LIONEL/TRANSFORMER/CAR" in yellow; two brakewheel posts; four die-cast O27 passenger trucks. Part of 1071 Mid Atlantic Limited set. Originally scheduled as number 6500, but 9233 was the actual production number and appears on the transformer, not the car. T. Ladny Collection.

| | | 60 | 85 |

9234 LIONEL: 1980, long Type I flatcar; with "RADIOACTIVE/WASTE" containers; red body with white lettering; two rails run car length; two removable energy containers with flashing red lights; die-cast O27 passenger trucks with roller pickup; no "BLT" date. Part of 1070 Royal Limited set. C. Lang comment. T. Ladny Collection.

| | | 30 | 45 |

9306 A T S F: 1980-82, short Type III General-style flatcar; brown body and fences; gold lettering; two brown horses; plastic arch bar trucks; plastic wheels; "BLT 1-80". Part of 1053 The James Gang set. J. Sawruk Collection. — — 15 20 See also Factory Errors and Prototypes chapter in Volume II, first edition.

Note: *The 9325 flatcar is joining ranks with the 6560 crane and the 9853 Cracker Jack reefer with respect to the level of confusion it has engendered among Lionel historians and collectors. We are asking original owners of the 9325 flatcar and the 9019 flatcar to assist us in sorting out the facts of this story. In particular, we are interested in the relationship between the 9019 (unlettered) flatcar and the 9325 N W flatcar, and their relationship to the Working on the Railroad Logging Empire set, the Wabash Deluxe Express set, and the rolling stock assortments in the 1978-79-80 time period. We also encourage reader confirmation of our hypothesis that the 9325 came in boxes marked "9363" and "9364" with dump and crane superstructures, respectively. Readers with these sets and cars are encouraged to send comments.*

	GD	VG	EXC	MT

9325 NORFOLK AND WESTERN: 1979-81, short Type II flatcar; black plastic body; heat-stamped white letters on side; "BLT 1-79/N & W 9325/NORFOLK/AND/WESTERN/LIONEL"; underscored number; simulated wood-grained floor; upward-facing plastic brakewheel; two-rung tan plastic fencing around floor perimeter; Symington-Wayne trucks with plastic wheels; one manumatic and one dummy coupler. Bottom stamped "9325-T-5A LIONEL MT. CLEMENS MICH. 48045". This is the first Type II short flatcar, derived from the 9019 Logging Empire car. Came in box marked "LIONEL O27 GAUGE FLAT CAR WITH FENCES 6-9325". Part of uncatalogued Wabash Deluxe Express set in 1979, and several versions of the 9195 rolling stock assortment. Note: two other "9325" cars were issued separately as an N & W coal dump car (came in a box marked "9363") and an N & W small crane car (box marked "9364"), using this car as a base. B. Smith and Runft Collections. — 3 5 10
See Log and Coal Dump Cars, and Crane and Derrick Cars chapters.

9379 LIONEL: Catalogued in 1980 as part of Texas and Pacific diesel set, but never made; flatcar with derrick.
Not Manufactured

9389 LIONEL: 1981-82, long Type I flatcar; with "RADIOACTIVE/WASTE" containers; maroon body; white "LIONEL" lettering and number; two rails run car length; two removable tan energy containers with flashing red lights; O27-style die-cast passenger trucks with roller pickup; no "BLT" date. Separate-sale item in Type III box similar to 9234 set car except for number and flatcar color. R. LaVoie comment. W. Berresford Collection. — — 30 40

9553 W. & A. R. R.: 1978-80, (Western & Atlantic) short Type III General-style flatcar; brown base and fence; yellow "W. & A.R.R." and "BLT 1-77"; six horses; plastic arch bar trucks with metal wheels and operating couplers. Part of separate-sale only set with 8701 General engine and two 9500-series General-style passenger cars.
(A) As described above. — — 15 20
(B) Same as (A), except yellow fencing; hard to find. G. Halverson Collection. — — 35 45

9823 A T S F: 1975-76, Standard O flatcar; tuscan body; white lettering; two sets of tan plastic crates; 24 black metal stakes

	GD	VG	EXC	MT

supplied with car fit into holes around car perimeter; Standard O trucks. Very hard to find. 30 50 80 125

16300 ROCK ISLAND: 1987-88, short Type II flatcar; red body; white lettering "ROCK ISLAND" and "BLT 1-87"; black fencing; gray crates; arch bar trucks. Part of Rail Blazer set 11701. — — 6 8

16301 LIONEL: 1987, barrel ramp car; dark blue flatcar body; yellow lettering and number; white superstructure (same structure was used for ramp of postwar culvert loader and unloader accessories); eight small varnished wooden barrels; Symington-Wayne trucks; Type VI box. Reissue of postwar 6343; no "BLT" date. R. LaVoie Collection. — — — 15

16306 SANTA FE: 1988, barrel ramp car; red flatcar body and barrel ramp; white lettering; eight stained barrels; Symington-Wayne trucks. — — — 15

16315 PENNSYLVANIA: 1988-89, short Type II flatcar; white lettering; black fences and twenty-piece crate load; Symington-Wayne trucks; "BLT 1-88". Part of uncatalogued 11708 Toys 'R Us Pennsy set in 1988, and catalogued 11708 Midnight Shift set in 1989. — — — 15

16317 PENNSYLVANIA: 1989, barrel ramp car; tuscan body and barrel ramp; gold lettering; gold P R R keystone logo on ramp; eight barrels; Symington-Wayne trucks; "BLT 1-89". — — — 16

16318 LIONEL LINES: 1989, depressed-center flatcar; maroon body; white lettering; two gray cable reels embossed "LIONEL" with wire cable; Symington-Wayne trucks; "BLT 1-89". Reissue of postwar 6561. — — — 20

16320 GREAT NORTHERN: 1990, barrel ramp car; green body with yellow lettering; orange ramp with circular G N goat logo in green; comes with eight stained barrels; ASF strong-arm trucks; "BLT 1-90". — — — 16

16324 PENNSYLVANIA: 1990, depressed-center flatcar; black body; white lettering; two tan cable reels embossed "LIONEL"; ASF strong-arm trucks; "BLT 1-90". — — — 20

16325 MICRORACERS: 1989, barrel ramp car; uncatalogued. Very unusual alteration of barrel ramp car to carry four small die-cast "Microracer" autos — red, yellow, green and blue. Red unpainted plastic flatcar body and ramp with white lettering and "BLT 1-89"; large black and white sign reading "MICRO-RACERS EXHIBITION" affixed to ramp; comes with a black canister labeled "MICRORACERS OIL" in white; Symington-Wayne trucks. Part of uncatalogued 11771 Microracers set available only through K-Mart. R. LaVoie Collection. — — — 35

16326 SANTA FE*: 1991, depressed-center flatcar; light gray body; white lettering; two blue cable reels embossed "LIONEL" with wire cable; ASF strong-arm trucks; "BLT 1-91". — — — 21

16329 SOUTHERN PACIFIC: 1990-91, short Type II flatcar; brown body; white lettering; tan fences (catalogued as white) with two horses; ASF stong-arm trucks; "BLT 1-90". Part of 11714 Badlands Express set. — — — 16

16331 SOUTHERN: 1991, barrel ramp car. Announced in Lionel's 1991 Book 1 catalogue, but not manufactured.
Not Manufactured

16332 LIONEL*: 1991, depressed-center flatcar; light blue body; white lettering and white "TRANSFORMER CAR" lettered on the upper levels of the car sides; gray transformer with four

Lionel's newest flatcars.

W. Dyson, R. Kaptur, R. LaVoie, A. Rudman, M. Solly, and F. Stem Collections; B. Schwab photograph

Top shelf: **16301** Lionel barrel ramp car; **16324** Pennsylvania depressed-center flatcar with two cable reels.
Second shelf: **16317** Pennsylvania barrel ramp car; **16610** Lionel track maintenance car.
Third shelf: **16318** Lionel Lines depressed-center flatcar with two cable reels; **17500** Canadian Pacific Standard O flatcar.
Bottom shelf: **17502** A.T.S.F. flatcar with single trailer, the first Standard O flatcar outfitted with a trailer.

	GD	VG	EXC	MT

white electrodes and sign reading "DANGER/1,000,000/VOLTS"; ASF strong-arm trucks; "BLT 1-91". Reissue of short 6461 postwar transformer car in new colors. — — — **24**

16333 FRISCO*: 1991, long Type I flatcar with bulkheads and lumber load; tuscan body; white lettering and Frisco shield logo; two bulkheads; three simulated lumber pallets; ASF strong-arm trucks; "BLT 1-91". Sold separately, but a good match for the Frisco Fallen Flags No. 5 set also offered in 1991.
— — — **24**

16340 AMTRAK*: 1991, long Type I flatcar with stakes; black body; white lettering; black plastic stakes; ASF strong-arm trucks; "BLT 1-91". Part of 11723 Amtrak Maintenance Train set.
— — — **22**

16610 LIONEL: 1987-88, long Type II track maintenance flatcar; gray body; black lettering and number; bright blue two-deck superstructure with white lettering; two yellow men, one on each deck; hand-operated crank raises and lowers platform about one inch; Symington-Wayne trucks. Remake of postwar 6812.
— — — **20**

16618 SANTA FE: 1989, long Type II track maintenance flatcar; red body; white lettering; gray superstructure with black "TRACK MAINTENANCE" lettering; two yellow men, one on car, one on platform; hand-operated crank raises and lowers the platform about 1"; Symington-Wayne trucks; "BLT 1-89".
— — — **20**

16620 C & O: 1990-91, long Type II track maintenance flatcar; black body; white "CHESAPEAKE AND OHIO" lettering; translucent unpainted yellow superstructure with black lettering "TRACK MAINTENANCE" (lettering not pictured in catalogue); two blue men; hand-operated crank raises and lowers platform about one inch; ASF strong-arm trucks; "BLT 1-90". Some collectors do not like the "toy" appearance of the unpainted yellow plastic on this car, questioning Lionel's decision to skip the paint step. L. Caponi comment. — — — **20**

16635 C P RAIL: 1991, long Type II track maintenance flatcar. Announced in Lionel's 1991 Book 1 catalogue, but not manufactured. **Not Manufactured**

17500 CANADIAN PACIFIC: 1989, Standard O-series flatcar; black body; white lettering; comes with 24 black plastic stakes

	GD	VG	EXC	MT

and three large dowel-logs restrained by chains; Standard O trucks; "BLT 1-89". Part of 11710 C P Rail Limited set.

| | — | — | — | 55 |

17501 CONRAIL: 1987, Standard O-series flatcar; brown flatcar body; white lettering and logo; 24 black plastic stakes; Standard O trucks. Part of Conrail Limited set 11700.

| | — | — | — | 40 |

19409 SOUTHERN*: 1991, long Type I flatcar with stakes; black body; white lettering; Standard O trucks; "BLT 1-91". This interesting car, listed in the Collector Line, is not a Standard O flatcar body, but has the deluxe sprung trucks nonetheless. Pictured as a companion to the 19405 Southern crane car.

| | — | — | — | 25 |

TRAILERS ON FLATCARS

Although modern era Lionel may not have made as much use of the flatcar carrying loads, it has certainly eclipsed the postwar output in the area of Trailers on Flatcars (TOFC).

The most frequent use of the long flatcar in the modern era has been the TOFC flatcar with trailers. These 10-inch-long cars all use the Type I (mold 6424-11) long flatcar body with its single brakewheel post. There are several die variations to the 6424-11 mold (which originated in the postwar era) involving locations of stake holes. Remember, the flatcar was originally developed to support stakes or fence posts. The reader is referred to a brief discussion on the mold variations in *Greenberg's Guide to Lionel Trains 1945-1969, Volume I, eighth edition.*

Since 1970, the company has issued approximately 25 of these cars (sometimes called "piggyback" cars), and they are in keeping with Lionel's desire to use its graphic capabilities well. Until 1988, Lionel produced these flatcars with two small vans. The Burlington Northern car that year saw the first production of a single long van, which looks much better on the flatcar. The real TOFC cars can be used both ways.

The first of the TOFC cars was the 9120 Northern Pacific in 1970, one of the first cars issued by the new company. This car was green with white lettering, and it had two white vans with corrugated sides and no markings. The trailers were constructed a little differently from their postwar predecessors. The postwar trailers had a separate metal tongue riveted to the underside of the trailer which held the plastic prop wheels. This metal piece was riveted to the trailer. Fundimensions cast the trailer body in one plastic piece, including the tongue support. The flatcar had plug-in side slip barriers, just as the postwar originals did, and the trailers were all single-axled and double-wheeled. It is not too unusual to find leftover postwar trailers on some of the earliest production. Once again, that is efficient use of existing stock.

One of the scarcer TOFC flatcars was issued in early 1972. It was another Northern Pacific TOFC car with the same color scheme as the 9120, but with the number 9122 and a 1972 built date. This car came in a Type II box, whereas its predecessor had a Type I box. The plastic cover for the trailer axles on the 9120 was black; on the 9122, the axle was green.

Very early in the production run, the colors of the 9122 were changed to a tuscan flatcar and gray trailers. As a result, the green 9122 is one of the scarcer TOFC cars.

By 1976, Fundimensions had made the decision to expand its line of TOFC cars to add a modern look to its rolling stock. To dress up the car, the firm made the trailers smooth sided instead of corrugated; this allowed the use of bright modern railroad logos on the trailers. The first of these cars was the Cascade green 9133 Burlington Northern. It was quickly followed by cars in C P Rail, I C Gulf, Great Northern, Southern Pacific, North Western, and Union Pacific markings among several others. With the 1987 production of the Pennsylvania TOFC, Lionel Trains, Inc. learned a lesson. In the early production run, collectors complained that the gold lettering on the dark maroon vans was too dull. Lionel corrected that by triple-stamping every one of the trailers in the late part of the run, and the lettering is noticeably brighter. Curiously, all the flatcars themselves have dull gold lettering; they were probably run off before the change was made.

One of the more interesting TOFC flatcars is the one made in 1976 for the Lionel Collectors' Club of America (L C C A) convention in Atlanta, Georgia. This trailer car is not on a regular flatcar, but on a newer tri-level automobile car without the racks. The trailers themselves are not Lionel and are much larger than the style Lionel uses. Fundimensions inadvertently sent the whole shipment to the LCCA with only one side of the flatcars stamped. The club offered to have members' cars restamped on demand, but on the whole, the version with one side stamped is still more common. This car is entirely unique in the Lionel line.

Another note of interest to collectors is that some of the earlier TOFC flatcars were issued with and without vans. These are simply variations of the same car. This happened with the 9122 N P, the 9124 P C, and the 9133 B N.

Recent production has included road names like Nickel Plate Road, Wabash, Western Maryland, Santa Fe, M K T Katy, and naturally, Lionel Lines. This last car, the 16323, may eventually become hard to find, as collectors add it to the separate-sale Lionel Lines set started in 1982. The Nickel Plate car introduced a new-style short trailer to the TOFC with squared-off ends and four wheels, instead of the two used on previous cars. These new vans have been used on each of the two-trailer TOFC cars produced since 1988.

A major departure from the TOFC designs used previously by Lionel occurred in 1990. An entirely new body mold appeared — a long, three-truck, central-pivot double flatcar with realistic detailing was issued with Trailer Train markings. It can be separated into two individual flatcars with the extra truck included in the box, and comes with two long vans in Sea Land colors. Another nice detail is the new stanchion supporting the front of the trailer. Each car is separately numbered, but they are meant to run as a three-truck articulated unit. This car is certainly a unique first in Lionel's continuing march to scale realism.

Yet another odd fact about the TOFC cars is that Lionel rarely catalogued them in sets. Only the first 9120 N P (also sold separately), the 9285 I C Gulf, and the 16311 Mopar were sold in sets. The 19404 Western Maryland was part of a Fallen Flags set, but all the set components were only sold separately.

W. Dyson, R. Kaptur, R. LaVoie, A. Rudman, M. Solly, and F. Stem Collections; B. Schwab photograph

A near complete collection of the regular production TOFC flatcars.
Top shelf: **6531 U.S. Mail; 9120 N P.**
Second shelf: **Two variations of the green 9122 N P. The left car has the two gray vans; the right car has two white vans.**
Third shelf: **Another version of the 9122 N P, the tuscan flatcar with two gray vans; 9133 B N with the two matching Burlington Northern vans.**
Bottom shelf: **9149 C P Rail; 9222 L&N, tuscan body.**

All told, the TOFC flatcars are a good area for the collector. They offer a great variety of colors and markings, coupled with a manageable quantity. Only the uncatalogued 16311 Mopar Express and the very scarce 17871 T T O S Kodak/Xerox cars can be considered truly hard to find. Together, these cars make a wonderfully colorful "unit" train. But be quick about it — the prices on these cars are moving upward now with the recent issue of the Intermodal Crane, giving countless Lionel pikes a "reason" for dispatching trains full of TOFC cars!

TOFC LISTINGS

0781 LIONEL RAILROADER CLUB: 1983, TOFC flatcar; see Volume II, first edition.

1987 MOPAR EXPRESS: 1987-88, TOFC flatcar; see 16311.

6531 U.S. MAIL: 1985-86, TOFC flatcar; blue body; white "NEXT DAY SERVICE" lettering; two blue vans with orange

	GD	VG	EXC	MT

roofs, white lettering and orange and white "EXPRESS MAIL" logo; Symington-Wayne trucks; "BLT 1-85".

	GD	VG	EXC	MT
	—	—	15	25

9120 N P: 1970-71, (Northern Pacific) TOFC flatcar; green body; white lettering; white vans with corrugated sides and no lettering; Symington-Wayne trucks; two operating couplers; "BLT 1-70".
(A) AAR trucks; MPC logo; no side slip barriers on flatcar. Some examples have vans with postwar body shells and Fundimensions roofs. G. Halverson comment.

	GD	VG	EXC	MT
	15	30	40	50

(B) Same as (A), but later production; Symington-Wayne trucks; no MPC builder's logo; with side slip bars.

	GD	VG	EXC	MT
	15	30	40	50

9122 N P: 1972-75, TOFC flatcar (except (E); white lettering and MPC logo; Symington-Wayne trucks; "BLT 2-72".
(A) Green body; white unlettered vans with corrugated sides; black axle covers; Symington-Wayne trucks; identical to 9120 except for number and built date; came in early Type II box. Somewhat hard to find. R. LaVoie Collection.

	GD	VG	EXC	MT
	15	30	40	55

(B) Same as (A), but vans are gray. R. LaVoie Collection.

	GD	VG	EXC	MT
	15	30	40	50

W. Dyson, R. Kaptur, R. LaVoie, A. Rudman, M. Solly, and F. Stem Collections; B. Schwab photograph

Some of the more recent TOFC flatcars.
Top shelf: **9226 D&H; 9282 Great Northern.**
Second shelf: **9285 Illinois Central Gulf; 9333 Southern Pacific.**
Third shelf: **9352 Chicago & North Western Trailer Train; 9383 Union Pacific.**
Bottom shelf: **16303 Pennsylvania; 16307 Nickel Plate Road.**

	GD	VG	EXC	MT
(C) Tuscan flatcar body; unlettered gray vans with corrugated sides and green axle covers.	15	30	40	50
(D) Same as (B), but vans are postwar leftover pieces. G. Halverson Collection.	15	30	40	50

(E) Tuscan flatcar with yellow grader kit (no dozer kit); part of 1560 North American set in which apparently this car car body sometimes replaced the 9121 L & N. J. Breslin Collection.

	1∂	30	40	50

9133 B N: 1976-80, (Burlington Northern) TOFC flatcar; green body; white lettering and logo; Symington-Wayne trucks; "BLT 1-76".

(A) Two matching green Burlington Northern vans with smooth sides and white B N logo.

	10	20	30	50

(B) No load; apparently produced in 1976, when it was shown with corrugated-sided B N vans. Vans are not known to have been made that way. Reader comments invited.

	5	10	12	15

	GD	VG	EXC	MT

9149 C P RAIL: 1977-78, TOFC flatcar; red body; white lettering; silver, white and black vans with white letters and Pac-man logo; Symington-Wayne trucks; "BLT 1-77".

(A) Light red flat.	10	15	20	40
(B) Dark red flat. J. Nowaczyk comment.				
	10	15	20	40

9212 L C C A: 1976, TOFC long flatcar; see Volume II, first edition.

9212 SEABOARD COAST LINE: 1976; long TOFC flatcar; with vans; L C C A; see Volume II, first edition.

9222 L & N: 1983-84, TOFC flatcar; two gray vans with black lettering; "L & N" in red; Symington-Wayne trucks; "BLT 1-83".

(A) Tuscan body with white lettering. C. Lang Collection.	—	—	15	25
(B) Maroon body with pale yellow lettering. C. Lang Collection.	—	—	15	25

W. Dyson, R. Kaptur, R. LaVoie, A. Rudman, M. Solly, and F. Stem Collections; B. Schwab photograph

Top shelf: **16308** Burlington Northern; **16314** Wabash.
Bottom shelf: **16323** Lionel Lines; **19404** Western Maryland Trailer Train.

	GD	VG	EXC	MT

9226 D & H: 1984-85, (Delaware & Hudson) TOFC flatcar; bright blue body with yellow lettering and logo; gray vans with black lettering; black and yellow D & H logo on vans; vans have "9226" on them, unusual for TOFC cars; Symington-Wayne trucks with one fixed coupler; "BLT 1-84". — — **20 30**

9282 GREAT NORTHERN: 1978, 1981-82, TOFC flatcar; orange body; green lettering; Symington-Wayne trucks; "BLT 1-78"; green vans with gold lettering and red, white and black goat logo.
(A) Trailer undersides marked "LIONEL" with "MPC 1000"; van has hole for tractor and tractor lift. **10 20 30 45**
(B) Same as (A), but vans marked "LIONEL 80 / MT. CLEMENS MICH / MADE IN U. S. A." H. Edmunds Collection.
10 20 30 45

9285 ILLINOIS CENTRAL GULF: 1977, TOFC flatcar; black body; white lettering; silver vans with black lettering; I C orange and black pig-on-wheels logo on van sides; Symington-Wayne trucks; "BLT 1-77". Came as part of 1785 Rocky Mountain Special set and never offered for separate-sale. C. Lang comment. R. LaVoie Collection. **15 20 50 65**

9333 SOUTHERN PACIFIC: 1979-80, TOFC flatcar; uncatalogued; tuscan body; white lettering; two white vans with black wheels and black "SOUTHERN PACIFIC" lettering on sides with large red "S" and "P" and red stripe; Symington-Wayne trucks; "BLT 1-79". This car appeared only in a late 1979 Collector's Accessory Center brochure. D. Griggs Collection.
— — **40 50**

9352 TRAILER TRAIN: 1980, (Chicago & North Western) TOFC flatcar; Brunswick green body with yellow "TRAILER TRAIN" lettering; two yellow vans lettered "FALCON SERVICE" in green with bird logo and red and white "NORTH WESTERN" logo; Symington-Wayne trucks; "BLT 1-80".
— **20 60 85**

9383 UNION PACIFIC: 1980, TOFC flatcar; dark gray body with white lettering; light yellow vans with red lettering and stripe and red, white and blue U P shield logo; gold FARR Series 2 diamond insignia; Symington-Wayne trucks; "BLT 1-80". This was the extra freight car marketed separately to supplement the Union Pacific Famous American Railroads No. 2 set. Announced in the Fall 1980 Collector Center brochure. C. Rohlfing and C. Lang comments. R. LaVoie Collection.

— **20 30 40**

16303 PENNSYLVANIA: 1987, TOFC flatcar; tuscan body; gold lettering and numbers; two tuscan vans with gold lettering and keystone logo; Symington-Wayne trucks; "BLT 1-87".
(A) Dull gold lettering on both flatcar and vans, early production run. — — **30 40**
(B) Same as (A), but flatcar has dull gold lettering and vans have much brighter gold lettering; later production run. R. LaVoie comment. — — **30 40**

16307 NICKEL PLATE ROAD: 1988, TOFC flatcar; bright blue body with white lettering; two silver-painted trailers with blue logo and lettering; Symington-Wayne trucks; "BLT 1-88". The trailers are a new design; they have two axles each instead of one, and the front ends are squared off rather than rounded.
— — — **20**

16308 BURLINGTON NORTHERN: 1989, TOFC flatcar; first regular production TOFC car with a single van; green body; white lettering and number; one new-design large trailer painted silver with green lettering and large green B N logo. The van is also numbered "298224", another unusual feature for this car, and it has silver wheel hubs; Symington-Wayne trucks; operating couplers. This is apparently the same trailer design as the separate-sale 12725 Lionel tractor and trailer. Most collectors feel that the new trailer looks much more realistic than the two diminutive postwar carry-over trailers offered up to this time. Scheduled for 1988, but not made until 1989.
— — **30 40**

16311 MOPAR EXPRESS: 1987-88, TOFC flatcar; uncatalogued; blue body; white lettering "ME 1987" and "BLT 1-87"; no number on flatcar; two white trailers with red, blue and black lettering "CHRYSLER MOTORS GENUINE PARTS/MOPAR"; blue stripes on vans; Symington-Wayne trucks. Part of special Chrysler 11757 Mopar Express set. L. Bohn Collection.
— — — **70**

GD VG EXC MT

16314 WABASH: 1989, TOFC flatcar; blue body; white lettering; two new-style square-ended trailers with four wheels each; a shade lighter blue than the flatcar; broad diagonal white stripe and red, white and blue Wabash flag; white lettering on trailers; Symington-Wayne trucks; "BLT 1-89". — — — 20

16321 SEA LAND: 1990, TOFC articulated flatcar; see description for 16322 for details. *Price for 16321 / 16322 combination only.* — — — 60

16322 SEA LAND: 1990, TOFC articulated flatcar; all-new Lionel flatcar body modeled after T. T. U. X. Trailer Train cars common on American railroads; detailed narrow I-shaped center body painted mustard yellow; two trays flank the center beam to support trailer wheels; trailer front fits into orange plastic fifth-wheel stanchion; white and black "TRAILER TRAIN" and "T. T. U. X. 16322"; "BLT 1-90" on one side only. The car comes in a single box (labeled "16322") assembled to 16321 with three ASF strong-arm wheel sets between them, resulting in an articulated flatcar with vans 21 inches long. A unique brass shoulder screw arrangement, along with removable end platform pieces and center triangular pivot pieces, allows the user to run two separate cars (with extra truck provided), the two together, or add more cars for a train of any desired length. One brakewheel on post on each car. Long-style silver van similar to B N van of 1989; black and red "Sea Land" lettering and "S L" logo. Vans are made in Mexico. Has been a brisk seller. *Price for 16321 / 16322 combination only.* — — — 60

16323 LIONEL LINES: 1990, TOFC flatcar; light gray body with black lettering; two dark blue new-style trailers with white "LIONEL LINES" lettering and blue, orange and white Lionel circle logo; ASF strong-arm trucks; "BLT 1-90". Expected to be in demand as collectors add this car to the separate-sale Lionel Lines set beginning in 1982. — — — 25

16330 M K T*: 1991, TOFC flatcar; red body with white lettering; two gray/white new-style trailers with red and black lettering; "Katy" in red script; ASF strong-arm trucks; "BLT 1-91". — — — 24

16335 NEW YORK CENTRAL*: 1991, TOFC flatcar, black flatcar body with white lettering and NYC oval logo; single long gray and red van in Pacemaker paint scheme; white NYC oval logo on van and white "Pacemaker/ FREIGHT SERVICE" lettering; "BLT 1-91". Part of 11719 Coastal Freight Service Station Special set. — — — 35

16337 CHICAGO & NORTH WESTERN*: 1991, TOFC articulated flatcar; yellow plastic flatcar body similar to 16332;

see 16332 entry for construction and operating details; comes as a set within a single box with 16338 and two vans; white and black flatcar lettering; white van(s) with black "FALCON SERVICE" and Falcon logo; red, white and black CNW logo on vans; four ASF strong-arm trucks come with the set; "BLT 1-91". Price for 16337/16338 combination only. — — — 65

16338 CHICAGO & NORTH WESTERN*: 1991, TOFC articulated flatcar; yellow plastic flatcar body similar to 16332; see 16332 entry for construction and operating details; comes as a set with in a single box with 16337 and two vans; white and black flatcar lettering; white van(s) with black "FALCON SERVICE" and Falcon logo; red, white and black CNW logo on vans; four ASF strong-arm trucks come with the set; "BLT 1-91". Price for 16337/16338 combination only. — — — 65

17502 A. T. S. F.: 1990, TOFC flatcar; with single van; Standard O-series flatcar body; first TOFC car to use a Standard O car; black flatcar body with snap-in fifth-wheel stanchion and retention chock; white lettering; silver-painted long van; red "Santa Fe" and cross logo; van also numbered "549"; Standard O trucks; "BLT 1-90". Part of 11713 Santa Fe Dash-8 set.
— — — 80

17871 KODAK/XEROX: 1987, TOFC flatcar; T T O S; see Volume II, first edition.

17887 CONRAIL: 1991, TOFC flatcar; L C C A; see Volume II, first edition.

17888 CONRAIL: 1991, TOFC flatcar; L C C A; see Volume II, first ediition.

17889 SOUTHERN PACIFIC: 1991, TOFC flatcar; T T O S; see Volume II, first edition.

19404 TRAILER TRAIN: 1989, (Western Maryland) TOFC flatcar; deep red body; white lettering "TRAILER TRAIN" and logo; two new-style trailers painted silver with yellow "WESTERN MARYLAND" lettering; Standard O trucks; "BLT 1-89". Part of Western Maryland Fallen Flags Series No. 4, whose components were all offered for separate-sale. Car is numbered in this way because it is part of a "Collector" set, though it is not different than other (16300-series) TOFC cars, except for the trucks.
— — — 30

81487 KODAK/XEROX: 1987, TOFC flatcar; T T O S; see 17871.

298224 BURLINGTON NORTHERN: 1989; see 16308.

◆ CHAPTER 10 ◆
GONDOLAS

On real railroads, no piece of rolling stock takes as much steady abuse as the gondola car. Big loads of scrap steel, 55-gallon drums, machine parts, crushed automobiles, and other assorted refuse of our highly industrialized society are routinely dropped with a bang into these decidedly non-glamorous cars with nary a thought for the car's appearance or shape. One never sees gondolas in new condition, it would seem. Instead, they are observed in varying stages of abuse and decay; some have rusted sides, and some are dented beyond belief. But somehow all of them keep rolling on the rails and doing their jobs.

In a way, the Lionel gondolas were subjected to their own kind of abuse in the postwar period. Innumerable New York Central gondolas were made in black, red, green and blue versions. Because these cars were meant to be loaded and played with, they probably took more abuse at the hands of young railroaders than any other cars. Look through a tinplate junkpile at a train show, and chances are that most of the junk cars are gondolas. Not only that, but the cars were cheapened as the years went by. The postwar gondolas began with impressive metal frames and trucks, and finished with absolutely bare undersides, plastic trucks, and cheap non-operating couplers.

In recent years, Lionel may have reversed that trend by bringing some style back to the lowly gondola car. Several of its later gondola issues have been equipped with the magnificent Standard O trucks. Some have even been offered as separate-sale limited production items, such as the 6208 B & O meant to complete the Royal Limited set. Coal loads have been added. New colors and rail markings have brightened the car considerably. Even the less expensive short gondolas have at least been made in brighter colors than their postwar predecessors.

Body Types

Three types of gondola bodies have been used by Fundimensions and its successors, one of which is a completely new design. The first one is the reissue of the short 6142 type of the postwar years. One example is the 9032 Southern Pacific gondola of 1975. Like all the new Lionel versions of the gondola, this car has molded brakewheels on each side, rather than the older practice of separately installed metal ones or no brakewheels at all.

The second gondola is also a short car, but it is a version which is new with modern era Lionel. The 9033 Penn Central of 1977 represents a fine example. If you look closely, you can distinguish this car from the earlier carry-over model by the thick rim on the long sides of the car and the smaller molded brakewheel on the car sides. Like the other short gondola, this car has been used frequently in inexpensive sets. Many short gondolas are found in both body styles.

The third type of gondola is by far the most numerous — the long 6462-type gondola. This car shows several construction variations from its later postwar predecessors. The modern Lionel car has molded brakewheels, where the older car either had metal ones or none at all. In the later postwar cars the bottom was absolutely smooth and devoid of all ornamentation. Fundimensions added girder and rivet work to the bottom of its 6462-type gondolas, and they look much better as a result.

Close inspection of the bottom of the newer Lionel gondolas reveals a circle with the numbers "6462-2" and either "1" or "2" under the part number. This marking was present on the postwar cars as well. The presence of "1" and "2" numbering does not mean that a separate mold was used. It refers to the side of the mold from which the car emerged after the plastic injection process. The mold for the 6462-type cars was made in such a way that two cars were made at a time (gang molds). The "1" and "2" merely indicate from which mold cavity a particular car came.

---

* Asterisk found in listings indicates that the information within that listing was derived from Lionel catalogue only.

The first of the early long gondolas was the 9140 Burlington model of 1970. This car was made in at least three shades of green, all of equal scarcity. However, there is one version of the 9141 Burlington Northern from 1971 which is genuinely rare. Most of the 9141 production was green, but a few were made in tuscan. This car is highly prized. So is the 9143 Canadian National gondola made for Canadian sets distributed by Parker Brothers in 1971. This car is also very hard to find. Two Santa Fe gondolas of similar design can cause confusion as well. One of them, the 9284, was available in 1977 and 1978 in some sets; this car had a red and yellow body in a "half-and-half" paint configuration. In 1980 a black and yellow 9379 Santa Fe gondola of the same design was made for the Cross Country Express set. The black and yellow one is harder to find, although neither is really scarce. To add to the confusion, Republic Steel models have been made in different numbers in yellow, blue and green cars, all with the same Republic Steel logos and markings. All of these are fairly common, though the yellow 9055 model is less frequently seen.

As with other types of Lionel rolling stock, the reader will note a reference to the "MPC logo" appearing on some of the cars prior to 1972-1973. The logo disappears thereafter. Another interesting feature on some of the gondolas is the presence of under- and over-scoring around the number and/or a road name abbreviation on the side of the car. This is especially noticeable on the gondolas and hoppers, and some boxcars have them, too. Sometimes, variations exist where the top line, the bottom line, or both are missing.

Since the Quaker City Limited Collector set of 1979, most of the Collector sets have included a long gondola in colorful markings with Standard O (sprung) trucks. Many of these gondolas, and some more common ones, have included round canisters like those of the postwar era. These canisters can be found in many colors. A few cars have the square radioactive waste canisters without the lighting apparatus. The 19408 Frisco gondola from 1991 introduced an interesting twist — coil covers over the entire gondola body, decorated to match the car. Loads for the short gondolas have included the canisters and, recently, two cable reels, with or without wire "cable" (similar to those found on the depressed-center flatcars).

Other gondolas have appeared in the modern era Lionel lineup from time to time, some of them quite remarkable. Scale-size Standard O series gondolas were first produced in 1973. These cars were scale-length with the sprung trucks typical of the series, and they also included a highly realistic simulated coal load. They came in Wabash, Southern Pacific, Grand Trunk, and New York Central markings. In the case of the Wabash, two examples of the car have been reported in gray rather than in black. Needless to say, these are probably factory prototypes and are extremely rare. Another Standard O gondola, again in New York Central markings (the 6209), was produced in 1985. A colorful Railgon version (6231) was made in 1986 as part of a special direct-mail offer, and for 1987 there is a Standard O Conrail gondola (17401) as part of the Conrail Limited set. C P Rail and Santa Fe Standard O gondolas have followed, as Lionel now appears to be in the mode of releasing one Standard O set each year.

At the other end of the spectrum is the pint-sized 9030 Kickapoo gondola from 1972, one of the few four-wheel pieces produced by Lionel. The Kickapoo set, wth its equally unusual four-wheel coal dump bin car, bobber caboose and tiny Dockside switcher, is easily the smallest, and probably least expensive, Lionel set made in the modern era.

Some gondolas were made to operate, using as models two highly successful operating cars from the postwar era. The 9307 Erie animated gondola is a direct remake of the 3444 model of the postwar era. In this amusing and colorful car, the pull of a lever sets off a vibrator motor which turns a length of 16 mm film around two spools. Attached to the film by little metal clips are figures of a policeman and a hobo. The film and spools are cleverly concealed by a load of crates, making it appear that the policeman is chasing the hobo around and around the crates. A less expensive version of this car came in Union Pacific markings. This car (the 6201) used a rubber band drive rather than a vibrator motor, and it would only work when the car was in motion.

The other operating gondola, the 9290 Union Pacific model issued in 1983 as part of the Gold Coast Limited Collector set, is a revival of the popular operating barrel car. A vibrator mechanism sends six wooden barrels up a chute built into the car. At the top of the chute, a workman kicks them off the car into a bin (or onto the postwar barrel ramp, which has not been reissued). This car was made in black and yellow Union Pacific markings. A tuscan Conrail barrel car was scheduled for 1984 production, but it was delayed until September 1985. Both of these barrel cars feature the old postwar bar-end metal trucks because these are the only trucks which can be equipped with the sliding shoe contacts needed for the car's operation.

Unfortunately, the Union Pacific version is quite scarce. The handsome Conrail barrel car, however, is readily available. Both barrel cars had a strange and unanticipated problem. Lionel equipped them with varnished barrels instead of the postwar plain wooden barrels. The varnished barrels are so slippery that the vibration of the car cannot send them up the ramp very easily. Unvarnished postwar barrels correct the problem handily, of course, even though the varnished barrels look much better.

The modern era Lionel production of the gondola has added some much-needed color and attractiveness to this usually humdrum piece of rolling stock. The special collector series cars and some of the scarce variations in the earlier production are well worth a search by the Lionel collector.

Attempts to decipher the numbering system of Lionel's gondolas are hopeless — gondola number groups also contain many other types of rolling stock. The Standard O series gondolas were placed in the 9800-series (along with reefers), and the long-bodied gondolas came in the 6200-, 9100-, 9200- and 9300-series. Short ones are found in the 9000-series, along with nearly every other kind of O27 rolling stock, and also in the 9300-series.

One can only hope this much-abused little car at last finds a home in the five-digit numbers that Lionel Trains, Inc. has assigned: 16300 for short gondolas, 16600 for operating versions, 17400 for Standard O gondolas, and 19400 for the long-body types.

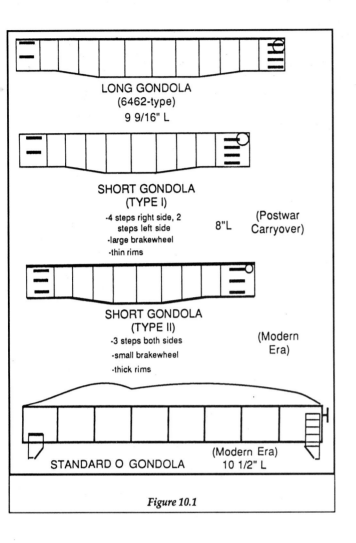

LONG GONDOLA
(6462-type)
9 9/16" L

SHORT GONDOLA
(TYPE I)
-4 steps right side, 2
steps left side
-large brakewheel
-thin rims
8"L
(Postwar Carryover)

SHORT GONDOLA
(TYPE II)
-3 steps both sides
-small brakewheel
-thick rims
(Modern Era)

STANDARD O GONDOLA
(Modern Era)
10 1/2" L

Figure 10.1

GONDOLA LISTINGS

	GD	VG	EXC	MT

1987 MOPAR EXPRESS: 1987-88, long gondola; see 16310.

6200 F. E. C.: 1981, long gondola; orange body; yellow numbers and letters; three silver-finished plastic canisters; Symington-Wayne trucks. Part of 1154 Reading Yard King set.

| | | 15 | 30 |

6201 UNION PACIFIC: 1982-83, operating long gondola; cop and hobo car; yellow body; tan crates; red lettering; animated car with rubber-band belt drive from axle; railroad cop chases hobo around crates only when car is moving; Symington-Wayne trucks. See 9307 for vibrator motor version.

| | | 25 | 35 |

6202 WESTERN MARYLAND: 1982, long gondola; black body; white lettering; black plastic coal load; Standard O trucks; "BLT 1-82". Part of 1260 Continental Limited set. This was the first regular-issue gondola equipped with a coal load. C. Lang comments.

| | | 35 | 45 |

6203 BLACK CAVE: 1982, short gondola; orange Type II body; small molded brakewheel; luminous individual letters "DANGER"; Symington-Wayne trucks; dummy couplers. Part of Black Cave Flyer set.

| | | 6 | 8 |

	GD	VG	EXC	MT

6205 CANADIAN PACIFIC: 1983, long gondola; dark brown body with white lettering; under- and over-scored number; C P beaver electrocal; two gray canisters; Standard O trucks; "BLT 1-83". Sold as a separate-sale item only, not in a set.

| | | 25 | 30 |

6206 C & I M: 1983-85, (Chicago & Illinois Midland) long gondola; red Type II body with white lettering; two gray atomic energy-type canisters without lights and lettering; Symington-Wayne trucks. Part of 1354 Northern Freight Flyer set.

| | 8 | 10 | 15 |

6207 SOUTHERN: 1983-85, short gondola; black Type II body with white lettering; two red or white canisters; Symington-Wayne trucks. Part of 1353 Southern Streak set.

| | | 6 | 8 |

6208 B & O CHESSIE SYSTEM: 1983, long gondola; un-catalogued; dark blue body; yellow "B & O" and "6208" at left of car; yellow Chessie cat logo at center, and yellow "Chessie System" at right; two gray canisters; Standard O trucks; "BLT 1-83". Designed to supplement the Royal Limited set from 1980. Shown in 1983 Fall Collector Center brochure. R. LaVoie comment.

| | | 25 | 30 |

6209 NEW YORK CENTRAL SYSTEM: 1984-85, Standard O-series gondola; black body; white lettering; N Y C oval to right; under- and over-scored number; simulated coal load; Standard O trucks; "BLT 1-85". Issued with a group of N Y C Standard O rolling stock intended to go with the 783 Hudson.

| | | 50 | 75 |

6210 ERIE LACKAWANNA: 1984-85, long gondola; black body; white lettering and Erie logo; two gray unlettered atomic energy containers; Standard O trucks; "BLT 1-84". From 1451 Erie-Lackawanna Limited set.

| | | 20 | 30 |

6211 CHESAPEAKE & OHIO: 1984-85, long gondola; un-painted black body; yellow lettering and logo; two yellow canisters; Symington-Wayne trucks; "BLT 1-84". From 1402 Chessie System set.

| | | | 10 |

6214 LIONEL LINES: 1984, long gondola; uncatalogued; orange body and interior; last four outer panels on right painted dark blue; "LIONEL / LINES" in dark blue across orange panels; red, white, and blue circular "L" herald on blue area; car number under- and over-scored; Symington-Wayne trucks. This car is considered part of the Lionel Lines set headed by the 8380 diesel, whose components were all offered for separate-sale beginning in 1982. Shown only in the 1984 Spring Collector Center brochure.

| | | 25 | 40 |

6231 RAILGON: 1986, Standard O series gondola; un-catalogued; black body; yellow lower edge and ends; yellow logo and lettering; "Nationwide gondola pool"; Standard O trucks. Available only through special direct-mail offer from Lionel associated with the 784 B & A Hudson. Quite hard to find.

| | | 140 | 200 |

6254 NICKEL PLATE ROAD: 1986-91, long gondola; black body; yellow lettering; two silver canisters; Symington-Wayne trucks. Part of Nickel Plate Special set 1602.

| | | 10 | 12 |

6258 A T S F: 1985-86, short gondola; dark blue body; yellow lettering and cross logo; Symington-Wayne trucks; dummy couplers. Part of 1501 Midland freight set. C. Rohlfing Collection.

| | | | 6 |

X6260 NEW YORK CENTRAL SYSTEM: 1985-86, long gondola; gray body; black lettering and oval N Y C logo; two black

W. Dyson, R. Kaptur, A. Rudman, and F. Stem Collections; B. Schwab photograph

A selection of long and Standard O gondolas from the mid-1980s. Many came in sets.
Top shelf: 6201 Union Pacific, an operating gondola; 6202 Western Maryland.
Second shelf: 6208 B & O Chessie System; 6205 Canadian Pacific.
Third shelf: 6209 New York Central System, a Standard O gondola; 6210 Erie Lackawanna, a hard-to-find item.
Bottom shelf: 6211 Chesapeake & Ohio; 6231 Railgon.

	GD	VG	EXC	MT

canisters; Symington-Wayne trucks; one dummy coupler; "BLT 1-85". Part of 1502 Yard Chief switcher set.

	—	—	15	18

6272 A T S F: 1986, long gondola; uncatalogued; red body; pale yellow lettering and cross logo; three gray canisters; Standard O trucks. The set box also had two black cable reels, apparently an attempt to reduce overstock. Part of 1632 Santa Fe Work Train Service Station Special set. J. Kouba and J. Arman Collections.

	—	—	20	25

9017 WABASH: 1978-81, short gondola; Type II body; red with white lettering; under- and over-scored number; three canisters; Symington-Wayne trucks. Part of 1865 Chesapeake Flyer set.

	—	—	4	5

9030 KICKAPOO VALLEY AND NORTHERN: 1972, half-size gondola; black base; car has no lettering at all. One of the very few Lionel pieces with four wheels — plastic ones at that. Part of 1280 Kickapoo set.

(A) Green top.	2	3	5	7
(B) Red top.	1	2	3	4
(C) Yellow top; also used later as part of the Smokey Mountain set 1965.	2	3	4	6

	GD	VG	EXC	MT

9031 NICKEL PLATE ROAD: 1974, 1979, 1983, short gondola; brown body; white lettering; Symington-Wayne trucks; dummy couplers on 1974, 1979 versions; operating couplers on 1983 version, which came as part of 1253 Heavy Iron set.

(A) Type I body — large brakewheel.	2	3	5	7
(B) Type II body — small brakewheel.	2	3	5	7

9032 SOUTHERN PACIFIC: 1975, 1978, short gondola; red body; white lettering and circular S P logo; Symington-Wayne trucks; dummy couplers; "BLT 1-75". Appeared in the 1581 Thunderball freight set.

(A) Light red Type I body.	1	2	3	4
(B) Dark red Type II body.	1	2	3	4

9031 Nickel Plate Road.

W. Dyson, R. Kaptur, A. Rudman, and F. Stem Collections; B. Schwab photograph

Several early gondolas and one odd numbered gondola.
Top shelf: X6260 New York Central System from the Yard Chief set of 1985, all the pieces in this set had their numbers changed from the catalogue picture; 9033 P C short gondola.
Second shelf: 9055 Republic Steel; 9131 Rio Grande.
Third shelf: 9136 Republic Steel; 9140 Burlington, the dark green version.
Fourth shelf: Two more variations of 9140 Burlington; light green, medium green. All of this car's variations are pictured here.
Bottom shelf: 9030 Kickapoo Valley and Northern, a pint-sized piece from the unusual Kickapoo Valley set.

	GD	VG	EXC	MT
(C) Medium red Type I body.	1	2	3	4

9033 P C: 1977-90, (Penn Central) short gondola; light green body; white lettering; Symington-Wayne trucks; dummy couplers; "BLT 1-76". This car has appeared in a multitude of inexpensive Traditional Line sets in the last fourteen years.

(A) Type I body.	1	2	3	4
(B) Type II body.	1	2	3	4

9049 REPUBLIC STEEL: 1978, long gondola; never made; see 9055. **Not Manufactured**

9032 Southern Pacific

	GD	VG	EXC	MT

9055 REPUBLIC STEEL: 1978-81, long gondola; uncatalogued; yellow body; dark blue lettering; three silver canisters; Symington-Wayne trucks with plastic wheels; one dummy coupler; one manumatic coupler; "BLT 1-78". This car appeared in a one-page dealer flyer in 1978, numbered "9049" and shown without canisters in a rolling stock assortment. It is not known to have been made that way. Later in 1978 a dealer accessory brochure announced the 9055 gondola in the same rolling stock assortment. For some reason, Lionel changed the number of the car. The number 9049 was given to a Toys 'R Us O27 boxcar in 1979. Either way, the 9049/9055 Republic Steel gondola is not regularly catalogued. L. Bohn comment.

	4	6	10	12

9131 RIO GRANDE: 1973-77, long gondola; orange body; black lettering; two unpainted white plastic canisters; Symington-Wayne trucks; one operating coupler, one dummy coupler; "BLT 1-73". Part of 1386 Rock Island Express and 1586 Chesapeake Flyer sets.

(A) Light orange.	1	2	5	8

These are among Lionel's most interesting gondolas.

W. Dyson, R. Kaptur, A. Rudman, and F. Stem Collections; B. Schwab photograph

Top shelf: Two variations of the 9141 Burlington Northern; tuscan, green. The tuscan car is quite scarce and was only sold in Canada.
Second shelf: 9143 Canadian National; 9144 Rio Grande, a Service Station Special item from 1974.
Third shelf: 9225 Conrail operating barrel car, the first modern remake of a postwar favorite; 9284 Santa Fe.
Bottom shelf: 9290 Union Pacific operating barrel car; 9307 Erie operating long gondola with cop and hobo.

	GD	VG	EXC	MT
(B) Medium orange.	1	2	5	8
(C) Dark orange.	1	2	5	8

9136 REPUBLIC STEEL: 1972-79, long gondola; blue body; white lettering; Symington-Wayne trucks with plastic wheels; one manumatic coupler, one dummy coupler; "BLT 2-72"; MPC logo.

(A) Light blue.	2	4	8	10
(B) Medium blue.	2	4	8	10
(C) Dark blue.	2	4	8	10

(D) Dark blue; MPC logo dropped; post-1972 production. C. Rohlfing comment.

	2	4	8	10

9137 PENNSYLVANIA: 1973-75, tuscan long body; white lettering; Symington-Wayne trucks; fixed couplers.

	4	6	8	10

9140 Burlington

	GD	VG	EXC	MT

9140 BURLINGTON: 1970-89, long gondola; green body; white lettering; Symington-Wayne trucks with plastic wheels (except (A)); one manumatic coupler, one dummy coupler.

(A) 1970; medium green body; AAR trucks with metal wheels; flat surface brakewheel; MPC logo. C. Lang Collection.

	4	6	10	12

(B) 1971 and later; light green body; no MPC logo. Part of 1662 Black River freight set of 1976 and an uncatalogued Sears set 6594 from 1975. This car, with or without three gray canisters, has also appeared in many inexpensive sets and was available as late as 1989 in a rolling stock assortment.

	4	6	8	10

(C) 1971; dark green body; no MPC logo.

	4	6	8	10

See Factory Errors and Prototypes chapter in Volume II, first edition.

9141 BURLINGTON NORTHERN: 1970-72, long gondola; green body; white lettering and B N logo at center; flat surface brakewheel; Symington-Wayne trucks (except (C)); metal wheels; one manumatic coupler, one dummy coupler; "BLT 1-70"; MPC logo. This car came in several early Fundimensions sets — the Wabash Cannonball, the Yard Boss, the Santa Fe Express freight, the Santa Fe twin diesel, and the Allegheny. It was often used interchangeably with the 9140 and the 9136.

(A) Light green body.

	2	4	6	8

Some handsome and some hard-to-find gondolas.
Top shelf: **9315 Southern Pacific; 9336 C P Rail.**
Second shelf: **9370 Seaboard; 9379 Santa Fe.**
Third shelf: **9385 Alaska Railroad; 9820 Wabash.**
Bottom shelf: **9821 Southern Pacific; 9822 Grand Trunk Western.**

W. Dyson, R. Kaptur, A. Rudman, and F. Stem Collections; B. Schwab photograph

	GD	VG	EXC	MT

(B) Medium green body; three yellow canisters. T. Durbin Collection. **2 4 6 8**

(C) Dark green body; AAR trucks. C. Rohlfing comment. **4 8 10 12**

(D) Tuscan body; Canadian production only. Very hard to find. Sold separately in Parker Brothers Type I box with small cellophane window and black Parker Brothers logo. Mint condition must include the box. G. Halverson, R. LaVoie, "Triple T", and R. Bryan Collections. **50 100 150 200**
See Factory Errors and Prototypes chapter in Volume II, first edition.

9142 REPUBLIC STEEL: 1971, long gondola; green body; white lettering; Symington-Wayne trucks; plastic wheels; one manumatic coupler, one dummy coupler; "BLT 1-71"; MPC logo. Very similar to 9136 except for body color.
(A) Dark green body. **2 4 6 8**
(B) Medium green body; recessed brakewheel. C. Rohlfing Collection. **2 4 6 8**
(C) Same as (B), but metal wheel sets. H. Edmunds Collection. **2 4 6 8**
See Factory Errors and Prototypes chapter in Volume II, first edition.

9143 CANADIAN NATIONAL: 1971-73, long gondola; maroon body; white lettering; Symington-Wayne trucks; metal

	GD	VG	EXC	MT

wheels; one manumatic coupler, one dummy coupler; "BLT 1-71"; MPC logo. Sold primarily in Canada and shown only in Canadian catalogues. Somewhat hard to find. Mint requires Parker Brothers box. **20 30 40 50**

9144 RIO GRANDE: 1974-76, long gondola; black body; yellow lettering; two yellow canisters; Symington-Wayne trucks; metal wheels; two operating disc couplers; "BLT 2-74". Came as part of 1450 Rio Grande Service Station Special set in 1974. Catalogued separately in 1975-76. **2 4 6 8**
See also Factory Errors and Prototypes chapter in Volume II, first edition.

9225 CONRAIL: 1984-85, operating barrel car; dark brown body; black chute; white lettering and Conrail "wheel" logo; blue man with flesh-colored hands and face; six varnished barrels; postwar bar-end trucks with sliding-shoe power pickup; includes black dump tray. See 9290 for more details.
— 30 35 50

9283 UNION PACIFIC: 1977, long gondola; yellow body; red lettering; U P shield to right; three silver-gray canisters; Symington-Wayne trucks. Part of 1764 Heartland Express set. C. Rohlfing Collection. **2 5 8 10**

9284 SANTA FE: 1977-78, long gondola; red and yellow body; last five panels to right painted yellow; yellow and red lettering;

Lionel's most recent gondola production.
Top shelf: **9824 New York Central System; 17400 C P Rail.**
Second shelf: **17401 Conrail; 17402 A T S F.**
Third shelf: **19400 The Milwaukee Road with two black cable reels; 19401 Great Northern.**
Bottom shelf: **19403 Western Maryland.**

W. Dyson, R. Kaptur, A. Rudman, and F. Stem Collections; B. Schwab photograp

	GD	VG	EXC	MT

two unpainted red canisters; Symington-Wayne trucks; "BLT 1-77". Part of 1762 Wabash Cannonball set.

	10	12	20	25

9290 UNION PACIFIC: 1983, operating barrel car; blue man "unloads" barrel as vibrator mechanism pushes six varnished wooden barrels up chute at center of car; black body; yellow lettering; came with unloading bin; postwar bar-end trucks were used with sliding-shoe pickup to activate the operating mechanism; "BLT 1-83". Reissue of 3562-type car from 1954-58 although with new road name. Only available as part of 1361 Gold Coast Limited set. However, there has been no modern era release of the postwar 362 barrel loader with which this car is intended to operate. Thus, the postwar version must be used. C. Lang comment.   —   50   55   85

9307 ERIE: 1980-84, operating long gondola; cop and hobo car; red body; white lettering and Erie logo; O27-style die-cast passenger trucks with power pickup roller; "BLT 1-80"; the motor causes blue cop to chase gray hobo around crates. Remake of postwar 3444 Erie gondola. We have had reports of many variations of this car: figure painting (partially-painted hobo, fully-painted one-color figures, detailed cop and hobo with flesh-colored hands and face); crate color (tan or gray); lettering on crates (absent, one side or both sides). The car with fully-painted figures and with tan crates lettered on both sides appears to be the most

common. Add 20% premium for other variations. Further reader comments invited. M. Kowalski, C. O'Dell, J. Glockley, J. Timmerman, and E. Lazar comments.   —   30   40   60

See Factory Errors and Prototypes chapter in Volume II, first edition.

9315 SOUTHERN PACIFIC: 1979, long gondola; uncatalogued; brown body painted brown; white lettering; Southern Pacific decal with white letters on black background; built-in small brakewheel; Standard O trucks; "BLT 1-79". Part of the 1970 Southern Pacific Limited set, which sold out after its appearance in the 1979 advance catalogue, and so this set is not regularly catalogued.   —   12   20   30

9336 C P RAIL: 1979, long gondola; red body; white lettering; black and white Pac-man logo appears at end opposite brakewheel; Standard O trucks; "BLT 1-79"; came in Type IV box; 6462 mold designation on underside. From 1971 Quaker City Limited set. Miller and J. Breslin observations.
—   15   20   25

9340 ILLINOIS CENTRAL GULF: 1979-82, short gondola; Symington-Wayne trucks with plastic wheels; "BLT 1-79".
(A) Orange Type II body with black lettering; yellow canisters. Part of regular issue 1960 Midnight Flyer set.
—   —   5   10

	GD	VG	EXC	MT

B) Red body with white lettering; no canisters. Part of 1159 Midnight Flyer set made for Toys 'R Us. G. Kline Collection.
— — **15 20**

C) Same as (B), but with two gray canisters. Came with uncatalogued Tappan set in 1982. C. Rohlfing Collection.
— — **20 25**

9370 SEABOARD: 1980, long gondola; tuscan body with yellow lettering; three silver-finished plastic canisters; black and red Seaboard heart logo to right; Standard O trucks; "BLT 1-80". From 1071 Mid Atlantic Limited set. — **15 20 25**

9379 SANTA FE: 1980-81, long gondola; black and yellow body; two gray plastic radioactive waste containers; black and white lettering and cross logo; Symington-Wayne trucks; "BLT 1-80". Came with 1072 Cross Country Express set.
— **15 25 35**

9385 ALASKA RAILROAD: 1981, long gondola; yellow body with black lettering; four unpainted white canisters; under-scored number; Standard O trucks. Part of 1160 Great Lakes Limited set. A remake of the postwar 6162-60, one of the few postwar gondolas not lettered for N Y C, Pennsy or Lionel Lines.
— **20 30 40**

9820 WABASH: 1973-74, Standard O-series gondola; simulated coal load; white lettering; under- and over-scored number; Standard O trucks; "BLT 1-73".
(A) Black body. **20 25 40 50**
(B) Brown body; no trucks or truck mounting holes. Produced by Lionel on special order for O Scale modelers to mount own trucks; originally sold by dealer Andrew Kriswalus. These cars have flat underfloors (no details). C. Lang Collection. **NRS**
(C) Same as (B), but black body. C. Lang Collection. **NRS**
See Factory Errors and Prototypes chapter in Volume II, first edition.

9821 SOUTHERN PACIFIC: 1973-75, Standard O-series gondola; brown or black body; white lettering and S P circle logo; simulated coal load; Standard O trucks; "BLT 1-73".
(A) Brown body. **20 25 40 50**
(B) Brown body; no trucks or truck-mounting holes. See 9820(B) for details. C. Lang Collection. **NRS**
(C) Black body. Hard to find. — — **275 350**
See Factory Errors and Prototypes chapter in Volume II, first edition.

9822 GRAND TRUNK WESTERN: 1974-75, Standard O-series gondola; blue body; white lettering and large "GT" to right side; simulated coal load; capacity data under- and over-scored; Standard O trucks; "BLT 1-74". **20 25 40 50**

9824 NEW YORK CENTRAL SYSTEM: 1975-76, Standard O-series gondola; black body; white lettering and N Y C oval; simulated coal load; Standard O trucks.
20 40 60 85

16304 RAIL BLAZER: 1987-88, short gondola; red or orange body; white number and lettering; two black cable reels; plastic arch bar trucks; "BLT 1-87". Part of 11701 Rail Blazer set.
(A) 1988 production; red Type I body; two operating couplers.
— — — **6**
(B) 1987; orange Type I body; one dummy coupler. Probably earliest production. Lionel changed to red bodies in mid-run so car would match rest of set. R. Weidinger and F. Wilkins Collections. — — — **10**
(C) Same as (B), but Type II body. R. Weidinger Collection.
— — — **10**

16309 WABASH: 1988-91, long gondola; medium brown body; white lettering and numbers; two unlettered white canisters; Symington-Wayne trucks; operating couplers. Part of 11703 Iron Horse freight set. — — **5 7**

16310 MOPAR EXPRESS: 1987-88, long gondola; uncatalogued; tuscan body; white lettering; came with two canisters in 1987; 16310 does not appear on car — "1987" is only number on car; Symington-Wayne trucks; "BLT 1-87". Came only in 11757 Chrysler Mopar Express set. C. O'Dell and L. Bohn Collections. — — — **20**

16313 PENNSYLVANIA: 1988-89, short gondola; green Type I body; white lettering and P R R logo; two black cable reels; Symington-Wayne trucks; "BLT 1-88". Part of uncatalogued 11708 Toys 'R Us Pennsy set in 1988, which later became the catalogued 11708 Midnight Shift set in 1989.
— — **5 7**

16327 SEARS CIRCUS: 1989, short gondola; uncatalogued; yellow body; blue lettering "The Big Top"; 16327 is not on the car; two canisters labeled "Elephant Food"; Symington-Wayne trucks; "BLT 1-89". Part of uncatalogued 11770 Sears Circus set. — — — **20**

16328 NICKEL PLATE ROAD: 1990, short gondola; light gray Type I body; yellow lettering; Symington-Wayne trucks; "BLT 1-89". Came with two black cable reels; no wire. Came in a 1990 rolling stock assortment. Probably will appear in future Traditional Line sets. — — — **8**

16339 MICKEY'S WORLD TOUR '92*: 1991, long gondola; dark blue/black body; magenta lettering; two yellow canisters; ASF strong-arm trucks; "BLT 1-91". Part of 11721 Mickey's World Tour train set. — — — **20**

16628 LIONELVILLE CIRCUS: 1990-91, operating gondola; cop and hobo car, similar to 9307; bright blue Type I body; yellow lettering "LAUGHTER" in large block letters on side panels; tan crate load with light blue lettering; ASF strong-arm trucks; "BLT 1-90"; car motion causes green cop to chase white hobo carrying a brown sack around the crates. Lionel created a simple mechanism using wheel motion to activate the animation on this car. A worm-gear attached directly to the axle rotates a shaft connected to the cop and hobo figures. This assembly replaces the temperamental vibrator motor used earlier, and in fact, the crates in the car still have a slot where the motor switch lever used to be. In recent years, the painting detail on figures such as these has improved considerably over the earlier Fundimensions era. In this case, both cop and hobo are highlighted with red and blue polka dots! Part of 11716 Lionelville Circus set. — — — **40**

17400 C P RAIL: 1989, Standard O-series gondola; dark red body; white lettering "CP RAIL" to right; Pac-man in black and white on left side; simulated coal load; Standard O trucks; "BLT 1-89". Part of 11710 C P Rail set. It is not clear why this car is numbered ahead of the 17401 Conrail, which was made two years earlier. — — — **40**

17401 CONRAIL: 1987, Standard O-series gondola; brown-painted body; white lettering and "wheel" logo; coal load; Standard O trucks; "BLT 1-87". Part of 11700 Conrail Limited set. — — **35 50**

17402 A T S F: 1990, Standard O-series gondola; brown body; white lettering; coal load; Standard O trucks; "BLT 1-90". Part of 11713 Santa Fe Dash-8 set. — — — **45**

	GD	VG	EXC	MT

19400 THE MILWAUKEE ROAD: 1987, long gondola; brown body; white lettering; red and white rectangular Milwaukee logo; under- and over-scored number; Standard O trucks; "BLT 1-87"; two black cable reels. Part of Milwaukee Fallen Flags set No. 2, whose components were all offered for separate-sale.

— — — 30

19401 GREAT NORTHERN: 1988, long gondola; black body; white slanted lettering; red and white Goat circular logo; simulated coal load; Standard O trucks; "BLT 1-88". Part of Fallen Flags set No. 3, whose components were all offered for separate-sale.

— — — 40

19403 WESTERN MARYLAND: 1989, long gondola; tuscan/brown body; white lettering; simulated coal load; under- and over-scored number; Standard O trucks; "BLT 1-89". Part of

Fallen Flags set No. 4, whose components were all offered for separate-sale.

— — — 2?

19408 FRISCO: 1991, long gondola; black body; white lettering; two new-style coil covers, decorated to match car, included as loads — first gondola so equipped; Standard O trucks; "BLT 1-91". Part of Fallen Flags set No. 5, whose components were all offered for separate-sale.

— — — 3?

19410 NEW YORK CENTRAL*: 1991, long gondola; pink body; blue lettering; NYC oval logo; number under- and over-scored; four unpainted white plastic canisters with black lettering; Standard O trucks; "BUILT BY LIONEL" (no date). An exact remake (except number and trucks) of the pastel pink 6462 gondola from the famous 1957 Girls set. The modern car came in the modern revival of that set, the 11722 Girls Train.

— — — 3?

H $\diamond$ CHAPTER 11 $\diamond$ OPPER S

With all the variety shown in its freight car lines, it is interesting that Lionel used only two basic types of hopper cars in the modern era until quite recently. Perhaps this is because the company was able to make good use of the two existing types without resorting to new dies. In 1986 Lionel did respond to frequent collector requests by issuing the first of several fine models of the A C F center-flow hoppers. Just prior to that, Lionel came out with a nice model of the little iron ore cars so common on America's bulk ore carriers today. So it now appears that new Lionel is moving into new directions with its hopper cars.

SHORT HOPPERS

The first hopper issued by Fundimensions was the 9010 Great Northern short hopper car of 1970, essentially a revised version of the very common postwar 6456 Lehigh Valley hopper cars.

The only difference between the Fundimensions car and the postwar car (aside from the usual change of trucks) was the presence of a molded brakewheel on one end of most of the Fundimensions cars. The Fundimensions short hopper, which is 8½ inches long, has been used almost universally in inexpensive production since the beginning. It has been issued in Chessie, Reading, D T & I, Canadian National, and many other railroad markings. Some of the earlier cars have color variations which are quite scarce. For example, there is a very rare 9011 Great Northern in a dark royal blue color and two 9012 T A & G color variations which are hard to find. Some cars have lettering variations, too, which mark them as scarce variations, notably another T A & G hopper with yellow lettering instead of white. Collectors, however, should beware of chemical alterations on cars such as this. Chemically altered fakes are easy to produce, especially cars with white/yellow lettering variations.

In 1981 the short hopper was modified to reproduce the operating hopper car of postwar years. It is somewhat curious that seven versions of this car have been produced, but the coal ramp to make these cars work has not been reissued to date! The postwar version is, however, readily available. The only trouble is that the coupler release at the top of the ramp will not work with a disc-operating coupler; perhaps that is what has held up the reintroduction of this accessory. A metal plate is attached to the bottom of the hopper car, and the square bin ports are punched out of the car. A plunger is attached to the plate which, when pulled down by an electromagnet, opens the bins and releases the coal. These cars are also equipped with Standard O sprung trucks, perhaps a bit of overkill on such O27 short hoppers. Lionel has put this car out in Great Northern, Reading, Chesapeake & Ohio, Erie, New York Central, Wabash, and Pennsylvania markings thus far.

Another fun fact about the hopper cars, large and small, is the presence of under- and over-scored lines around the road abbreviations and numbers on some of them — a good example is the 9117 Alaska. As on other rolling stock, particularly the gondolas, the presence or absence of the lines can provide a source of variation.

As with other freight cars, the reader will note that some listings include a reference to the MPC diagonal logo, which disappeared from the trains around 1973.

LARGE QUAD HOPPERS

A second type of hopper car frequently issued in the modern era has been the big, 11-inch-long, handsome "quad" hopper which first appeared in the postwar years in Lehigh Valley markings. This car has come at various times with and without hatched covers, with and (mostly) without a metal center spreader bar, and with metal or plastic plates holding the trucks to the car. The latest versions of this car have come with coal loads instead of hatched covers. Some versions have been produced with rectangular builder's plates molded into the car sides at the lower left; others have lacked them. Some cars come both ways. The removal of the builder's plate from the mold appears to have occurred around 1976. Similarly, the quad hopper cars through 1984 carried a hole at the top center of the sides into which the spreader bar was inserted. The hole disappears after 1984. The 6111 L & N car comes both ways. The early cars produced before 1976-1977 have a metal plate holding the truck to the car. Thereafter a plastic plate is used instead. Technically, these changes constitute changes in body types; but since we can identify them in time, this book simply lists the feature, or lack of it, rather than inserting body type entries in each listing. Many, many versions of this car have been produced in both railroad and corporate markings, beginning with the blue uncovered 9130 B & O hopper of 1970. The roofs on the covered ones have twelve hatches which actually open, but they are a bit fragile.

Tom Rollo, a frequent contributor to Greenberg guides, has pointed out a curious construction feature of this car. If you look at the car's interior, you will see a large drum-shaped projection at the bottom center of the car where the mold mark is. From underneath, there is a deep recess with two bracket slots on each side. Just adjacent to the outer edge, there are two holes which look like receptacles for screws. Mr. Rollo's conjecture is that at one time an operating mechanism was considered for this car, but it was never produced.

The same construction feature shows up on the postwar cars right from the beginning. (Other collectors have arrived at this conclusion independently.) Even more fascinating is the conjecture that this opening was meant to accommodate a radio receiver such as those designed for the Electronic Radio Control sets produced from 1946 to 1949. It should be noted that the first quad hoppers were not produced in the postwar era until 1954. We would like to hear from our readers about this bit of speculation, for which there is strong circumstantial evidence. It is even more interesting that the Fundimensions, Kenner-Parker, and Lionel Trains, Inc. versions of these hopper cars retain this odd feature so many years later.

Another oddity about these modern era hoppers is that there are frequently differences between the cars offered as part of sets and the same cars offered for separate-sale. For example, the 9111 Norfolk and Western hopper in sets is an unpainted medium brown color. The same car in separate-sale boxes is frequently, although not always, tuscan-painted brown plastic. The normal 9135 Norfolk and Western hopper is navy or royal blue with white lettering. In the late example included with the Spirit of America set, produced in 1975, the lettering on the car is gray instead of white. The separate-sale 9117 Alaska hopper has a black cover; reportedly, some versions included in a Service Station set had orange covers (A. J. Conto Collection). There are several other examples of this phenomenon, especially in the early production of these hopper cars. But the reader should beware of strange cover variations — quad hopper covers are easily changed.

Another interesting quad hopper fact: unlike the engines and other rolling stock, New York Central and Santa Fe do not dominate Lionel's quad hopper roster. The reason is these were not typically coal-carrying railroads. In fact, only one N Y C hopper has been released, and a short one at that. On the other hand, five Reading hoppers and thirteen B & O/C & O/Chessie/C S X hoppers have departed Mt. Clemens. These railroads were major coal-carrying lines.

The great majority of the postwar quad hoppers were produced, in quite a few body colors, lettered for the Lehigh Valley. Modern Lionel has not reissued the long or short hoppers in this road name (except for two probable carry-overs in 1970), preferring instead to apply its excellent graphics capabilities to other road names. Fundimensions did reissue four popular postwar quad hoppers in other names: Alaska, Alcoa, Detroit & Mackinac, and Minneapolis St. Louis. And of course, the 6446-25 Norfolk & Western, literally identical to the postwar version, was reissued in 1970 for Glen Uhl.

There seem to be three levels of value attached to the quad hoppers. The most common seem to be the ones with corporate logos, such as Domino Sugar, Planters Peanuts, and Sun-Maid Raisins. (A noteworthy exception is the Ralston Purina car, which is very hard to find.) Most of the cars with railroad names are a little more desirable and scarce, such as the Pennsylvania, Virginian, Illinois Central, and some of the early B & O and Norfolk and Western cars. The scarcest cars are the club convention cars, those available only in special sets, and some variations of the earliest cars. Examples of these are the gray-lettered 9110 B & O, the L C C A Corning car, the Alcoa, and the Southern cars. Most hopper cars are relatively easy to find, and the beginning collector can amass quite a few of them readily at reasonable prices. None can be considered as truly rare, but they add a nice look to an operating layout, especially the cars with railroad markings and full covers.

ACF Center-Flow Hoppers

In 1986 a new and extremely attractive hopper car emerged from Lionel in the form of a scale model of the A C F center-flow hopper car. This car has the wide, chunky appearance of the real thing, and collector reaction to it has been very favorable. Unfortunately, the ones produced so far have been severely limited in production because they have been part of limited edition sets. In 1986, two of them, a Burlington Northern and a Chicago & North Western, were issued as part of a special, direct-from-Lionel mail order promotion. A gray Conrail A C F hopper was part of the Conrail Limited set of 1987. In early 1988 Lionel produced a Chessie unit train with a beautifully detailed "stretched" three-bay A C F center-flow hopper. With their highly detailed tops and rails, their great bellied sides, and their Standard O trucks, these cars look wonderful on anyone's layout.

No doubt more of these cars will be produced eventually, and the next edition of this Guide will probably require a separate chapter devoted to them, since they are sufficiently different from the quad and two-bay hoppers.

48-FOOT THREE-BAY HOPPERS

The 1990s have found Lionel proceeding headlong down the road toward scale modeling. In 1991 the corporation introduced (among many other new body styles of rolling stock) a near-scale model of the 48-foot ribbed-sided, open-top, three-bay hopper common on United States railroads today. This wonderfully detailed hopper is even longer (12 inches) than the quad hopper, and is a great match for the Standard O ribbed 50-foot boxcars also introduced in 1991.

NUMBERING SYSTEMS

Finally, a note about the numbering systems for the hoppers. In the early 1970s, Lionel numbered its short hoppers in the 9000-series and its quad hoppers in the 9100-series. As it ran out of numbers there, the hoppers were switched (long and short) to the 9200- and 9300-series. In the early 1980s, these series, too, ran short. So the company switched to the 6100-series for both long and short hoppers. In the LTI five-digit era, Lionel has set the 16400-series for its "Traditional" Line hoppers (quad and short), the 17000-series for its "Standard O" (ACF and 48-foot) versions, the 19300-series for "Collector" (mostly quad) hoppers, and the 19800-series for the operating versions — so far, only the short ones.

In closing, it is interesting to guess whether Lionel has other new designs of hopper cars in the works. Whatever the case, the modern era hoppers once more illustrate the ability of the firm to make the most of its existing resources.

Figure 11.1

HOPPER CAR LISTINGS

	GD	VG	EXC	MT

0784 LIONEL RAILROADER CLUB: 1984, quad hopper; see Volume II, first edition.

6076 LEHIGH VALLEY: 1970, short hopper; uncatalogued; black body with white lettering; Symington-Wayne trucks, one operating and one dummy coupler. Possible postwar carry-over equipped with Fundimensions trucks and included in an early set. A number were sold by New York Lionel dealer Andy Kriswallus. Further reader comments invited. C. Lang Collection.

	10	15	20	25

6076 SANTA FE: 1970, T T O S convention car; see Volume II, first edition.

6100 ONTARIO NORTHLAND: 1981-82, covered quad hopper; blue sides and cover; yellow trim; white and yellow lettering; yellow "triple lightning" logo; Symington-Wayne trucks; "BLT 1-81".

		—	—	30	40

6101 BURLINGTON NORTHERN: 1981-82, covered quad hopper; green sides and cover; white lettering and B N logo to right; Symington-Wayne trucks; "BLT 1-81".

		—	—	15	25

	GD	VG	EXC	MT

6102 GREAT NORTHERN RAILWAY: 1981, covered quad hopper; tuscan body and cover; white lettering; under- and over-scored number; gold FARR Series 3 diamond insignia; black and white goat logo; Symington-Wayne trucks; "BLT 1-81". From Great Northern Famous American Railroad Series No. 3, whose components were only offered for separate-sale.

		—	—	35	50

6103 CANADIAN NATIONAL: 1981, covered quad hopper; gray body with dark red lettering; maroon cover; "CN" in large letters to right; under- and over-scored number; Standard O trucks; "BLT 1-81". Part of 1158 Maple Leaf Limited set. C. Rohlfing Collection.

	—	—	25	35

6104 SOUTHERN: 1983, quad hopper with coal load; dark green body; black coal load; gold lettering and FARR Series 4 diamond insignia; "BLT 1-83". Part of Southern Famous American Railroad Series No. 4, whose components were only available for separate-sale. This was the first quad hopper to include a simulated coal load. C. Lang comment.

		—	—	75	85

A colorful quad hopper selection from the early 1980s.

Top shelf: 6100 Ontario Northland; 6101 Burlington Northern.
Second shelf: 6102 Great Northern Railway; 6103 Canadian National.
Third shelf: 6104 Southern; 6105 Reading.
Bottom shelf: 6106 Norfolk and Western; 6107 Shell Chemical Plastics.

W. Dyson, R. Kaptur, R. LaVoie, A. Rudman, and F. Stem Collections; B. Schwab photograph

	GD	VG	EXC	MT

6105 READING: 1982, short operating hopper; tuscan body; white lettering and logo; red, black and white Reading Lines decal on right; under- and over-scored number; Standard O trucks; "BLT 1-82". — — **55** **65**

6106 NORFOLK AND WESTERN: 1982, covered quad hopper; gray body with black lettering; black cover; Standard O trucks; "BLT 1-82". Part of 1260 Continental Limited set. — — **35** **45**

6107 SHELL CHEMICAL PLASTICS: 1982, covered quad hopper; yellow body and cover; black lettering; red shell logo; Symington-Wayne trucks; "BLT 1-82". — — **15** **20**

6109 CHESAPEAKE & OHIO: 1983, operating short hopper; opening bins; black body; white lettering; under- and over-scored number; Standard O trucks; "BLT 1-83". — — **25** **40**

6110 MISSOURI PACIFIC LINES: 1983-84, covered quad hopper; black body and cover; white lettering; under- and over-scored number; white "Route of/THE/Eagles" script and "buzzsaw" logo; Symington-Wayne trucks; "BLT 1-83".
(A) With spreader bar holes. — — **15** **25**
(B) Without spreader bar holes. — — **15** **25**

	GD	VG	EXC	MT

6111 L & N: 1983-84, covered quad hopper; gray body and cover with red lettering; "L & N" to left and "THE DIXIE LINE"; Symington-Wayne trucks; "BLT 1-83". This car spans the period when the spreader bar hole in the sides was removed.
(A) With spreader bar hole. — — **15** **25**
(B) Without spreader bar hole. — — **15** **25**

6112 COMMONWEALTH EDISON: 1983, quad hopper with coal load; L C C A; see Volume II, first edition.

6113 ILLINOIS CENTRAL: 1983-85, short hopper; black with white lettering "Main Line of Mid-America" in script; Symington-Wayne trucks; "BLT 1-83". Part of 1354 Northern Freight Flyer set. — — **10** **15**

6114 CHICAGO NORTHWESTERN SYSTEM: 1983, covered quad hopper; dark green body and cover; pale yellow lettering and logo; Standard O trucks; "BLT 1-83". Available only as part of 1361 Gold Coast Limited set. The boxes for the 6114 cars were mislabeled "6114 Norfolk & Western." Car is decorated for Chicago & North Western. C. O'Dell comment. — — **105** **125**

6115 SOUTHERN: 1983-86, short hopper; gray with red lettering; Symington-Wayne trucks. Sold as part of 1353 Southern Streak set and a 1986 rolling stock assortment. — — **10** **20**

W. Dyson, R. Kaptur, R. LaVoie, A. Rudman, M. Solly, and F. Stem Collections; B. Schwab photograph

More good-looking hoppers, many from sets. The two short hoppers have plunger-operated opening doors.
Top shelf: 6109 Chesapeake & Ohio operating short hopper; 6110 Missouri Pacific Lines.
Second shelf: 6111 L&N; 6114 Chicago North Western System.
Third shelf: 6117 Erie operating short hopper; 6118 Erie.
Bottom shelf: 6123 Pennsylvania; 6124 Delaware & Hudson.

	GD	VG	EXC	MT

6117 ERIE: 1984-85, operating short hopper; black body; white lettering; yellow Erie diamond logo; Standard O trucks; "BLT 1-84". Plunger opens bins when activated by remote-control track.
— — **25 35**

6118 ERIE: 1984-85, covered quad hopper; light gray body and cover; black lettering; black diamond Erie logo; Standard O trucks; "BLT 1-84". From 1451 Erie-Lackawanna Limited set.
— — **45 50**

6123 PENNSYLVANIA: 1984-85, covered quad hopper; gray body and cover; black lettering; white and black P R R keystone; gold FARR Series 5 diamond insignia; Standard O trucks; "BLT 1-84". From Pennsylvania Famous American Railroad set No. 5, whose components were only available separately. Reportedly, fewer of these hoppers were produced than the other cars, but the tank car and the N5C caboose are regarded as the most desirable cars from this particular set. — — **45 55**

6124 DELAWARE & HUDSON: 1984-85, covered quad hopper; bright red body and cover; yellow lettering and logo; yellow and black D & H shield at upper right; Symington-Wayne trucks; "BLT 1-84". — — **15 25**

	GD	VG	EXC	MT

6131 ILLINOIS TERMINAL: 1985-86, covered quad hopper; yellow body and cover; red lettering "Illinois/Terminal" with oversized "I" and "T"; Symington-Wayne trucks; "BLT 1-85". Erroneously listed as Illinois Central on some dealer lists.
— — **17 25**

6134 BURLINGTON NORTHERN: 1986, A C F two-bay center-flow hopper; uncatalogued; Cascade green body; white lettering and logo; Standard O trucks; "BLT 1-86" with bar code; new hopper style. Available only as part of a direct-mail campaign from Lionel, associated with the B & A Hudson. Hard to find.
— — **150 200**

6135 CHICAGO NORTH WESTERN SYSTEM: 1986, A C F two-bay center-flow hopper; uncatalogued; medium gray body; black and yellow North Western logo; yellow lettering; Standard O trucks; "BLT 1-86" with bar code. Available only as part of a direct-mail campaign from Lionel, associated with the B & A Hudson. Hard to find. R. LaVoie Collection.
— — **150 200**

6137 NICKEL PLATE ROAD: 1986-91, short hopper; gray body; black lettering; Symington-Wayne trucks. Part of set 1602, the Nickel Plate Special and a rolling stock assortment in 1988-89.
— — **10 15**

Three of the five hopper body styles are shown here.   *W. Dyson, R. Kaptur, R. LaVoie, A. Rudman, and F. Stem Collections; B. Schwab photograph*

Top shelf: 6131 Illinois Terminal; 6134 Burlington Northern, an ACF center-flow hopper. The first Lionel car of this type. It is very hard to find.
Second shelf: 6135 Chicago North Western was released with 6134 and is also scarce; 6138 B&O.
Third shelf: 6446-25 Norfolk and Western, a special made for Glenn Uhl; 7504 Lionel 75th Anniversary.
Bottom shelf: 9010 Great Northern; 9013 Canadian National.

	GD	VG	EXC	MT

6138 B & O: 1986, quad hopper with coal load; light gray body; black lettering and capitol logo at center; under- and over-scored number; Symington-Wayne trucks with one dummy coupler; "BLT 1-86". Part of 1652 B & O freight set.

| | — | — | 20 | 30 |

6150 A T S F: 1985-86, short hopper; dark blue body; yellow lettering and cross logo; Symington-Wayne trucks; dummy couplers. Part of 1501 Midland freight set. C. Rohlfing Collection.

| | — | — | 10 | 15 |

6177 READING: 1986-90, short hopper; tuscan body; yellow lettering and diamond logo; number under- and over-scored; Symington-Wayne trucks. Part of set 1615, the Cannonball Express. Appears to be identical to earlier 9015 except for new number.

| | — | — | 20 | 25 |

6446-25 NORFOLK AND WESTERN: 1970, covered quad hopper; uncatalogued; special production by Fundimensions with postwar number for Glen Uhl, an Ohio Lionel dealer. Royal blue body and cover; Type I unlabeled box; under- and over-scored number; AAR trucks. This car has many more plastic lap (or "knit") lines than usual; these are formed as the styrene plastic

cools in the mold. Reportedly, only 450 were made. M. Schoenberg, T. Rollo, and G. Halverson Collections.

| | — | — | 150 | 175 |

6476-135 LEHIGH VALLEY: 1970-71, short hopper; uncatalogued; yellow body; black lettering and L V diamond logo; no number on car other than under- and over-scored "LV 25000". This is a postwar-leftover hopper apparently used by MPC-Fundimensions on some early sets in 1970-71 when other hoppers were not available. Symington-Wayne trucks; two dummy couplers; no "BLT" date; came in Type I box. Verified as Fundimensions production. R. LaVoie Collection.   **NRS**

7504 LIONEL 75th ANNIVERSARY: 1975-76, covered quad hopper; dark blue body; red cover; no builder's plate; electrocals depicting Lionel accessories and 75th Anniversary logo; Symington-Wayne trucks; no "BLT" date. Only available in set 1585, the Lionel 75th Anniversary Special.

| | — | 10 | 20 | 25 |

9010 GREAT NORTHERN: 1970-71, short hopper; light blue body; white lettering; plastic brakewheels; metal wheels; one manumatic coupler, one dummy coupler; MPC logo. This car was

W. Dyson, R. Kaptur, R. LaVoie, A. Rudman, and F. Stem Collections; B. Schwab photograph

Some of Lionel's short hopper cars.
Top shelf: **Two versions of the 9012 T. A. & G. Ry. Co.**
Second shelf: **9015 Reading; 9016 B & O Chessie System.**
Third shelf: **9038 B&O Chessie System; 9079 Grand Trunk Western.**
Bottom shelf: **25000 (6476-135) Lehigh Valley, a leftover postwar car apparently used in some 1970 sets.**

	GD	VG	EXC	MT

present in four of the first five sets produced by MPC-Fundimensions in 1970.

(A) Medium blue body; AAR trucks; "BLT 1-70".

	GD	VG	EXC	MT
	3	4	6	8

(B) Light blue body; AAR trucks; "BLT 1-70".

| | 3 | 4 | 6 | 8 |

(C) Medium light blue body; AAR trucks; "BLT 7-70".

| | 3 | 4 | 6 | 8 |

(D) Light blue body; Symington-Wayne trucks; "BLT 1-70".

| | 3 | 4 | 6 | 8 |

See Factory Errors and Prototypes chapter in Volume II, first edition.

9011 GREAT NORTHERN: 1970-72, 1975-83, short hopper; medium blue body; white lettering; white goat logo; Symington-Wayne trucks; plastic wheels; one manumatic coupler, one dummy coupler; "BLT 7-70". This car was uncatalogued from 1970-72, when it appeared in several department store sets. Then from 1975-81, it appeared in four different Traditional Line sets and a rolling stock assortment from 1979-83.

	GD	VG	EXC	MT

(A) Externally-mounted brakewheel; MPC logo.

| | 3 | 4 | 6 | 8 |

(B) Molded-in brakewheel; MPC logo.

| | 3 | 4 | 6 | 8 |

(C) Molded-in brakewheel; no MPC logo.

| | 3 | 4 | 6 | 8 |

(D) Same as (A), but AAR trucks. C. Rohlfing Collection.

| | 3 | 4 | 6 | 8 |

(E) Deep royal blue mold. Very rare. C. Lang Collection.

| | — | — | 120 | 165 |

(F) Same as (C), but navy blue mold; same color as 9012 navy hopper. P. Mark Collection.   **NRS**

9012 T. A. & G. R. Y. CO.: 1971-72, short hopper; blue body; white lettering; molded-in brakewheel; Symington-Wayne trucks; plastic wheels; one manumatic coupler, one dummy coupler; "BLT 1-71"; MPC logo. Came with the 1085 Santa Fe twin diesel set, the 1184/1284 Allegheny set, several Canadian sets, and was also available for separate-sale.

(A) Dark blue body (navy).

| | 2 | 3 | 5 | 7 |

(B) Medium blue.

| | 2 | 3 | 5 | 7 |

W. Dyson, R. Kaptur, R. LaVoie, A. Rudman, M. Solly, and F. Stem Collections; B. Schwab photograph

The earliest quad hoppers and the start of the billboard hopper series.

Top shelf: Two versions of the 9110 B&O. The white-lettered version at left is standard issue (cover added later by owner). The gray-lettered car at right is scarce.

Second shelf: 9111 Norfolk and Western; 9112 Rio Grande.

Third shelf: 9113 Norfolk and Western; 9114 Morton Salt.

Bottom shelf: 9115 Planters; 9116 Domino Sugar.

	GD	VG	EXC	MT

(C) Bright blue body (royal blue). This model reportedly came only in Canadian sets. Also has been found in 1972 Cross Country Express set, but may be a post-factory changeout. Further comments are requested from readers who have this car in this set.

—	—	—	65

(D) Same as (C), but yellow lettering. Confirmation requested.

NRS

9013 CANADIAN NATIONAL: 1972-76, short hopper; red body; white lettering and large "CN" to right; molded-in brakewheel; under- and over-scored number; Symington-Wayne trucks; plastic wheels; one manumatic coupler, one fixed coupler; "BLT 1-72"; MPC logo. Part of several Canadian distribution-only sets in 1972, and quite a few regularly catalogued United States sets in the 1970s. Also available for separate-sale.

	GD	VG	EXC	MT
(A) Dark red body.	2	3	4	5
(B) Medium red body.	2	3	4	5
(C) Light red body.	2	3	4	5

9015 READING RDG.: 1973-75, short hopper; tuscan body; yellow lettering and Reading Lines diamond logo; molded-in brakewheel; under- and over-scored number; Symington-Wayne trucks; metal wheels; one disc coupler, one dummy coupler; "BLT 1-73"; no MPC logo. Has been sought after in Middle Atlantic

states for use in unit trains by operators. Came in 1386 Rock Island Express set, and for separate-sale. R. LaVoie comment.

	GD	VG	EXC	MT
	7	12	20	25

9016 B & O CHESSIE SYSTEM: 1975-79, 1987-89, short hopper; yellow body; blue lettering and Chessie Cat logo; molded-in brakewheel; Symington-Wayne trucks; metal wheels; one operating coupler, one fixed coupler; "BLT 1-75"; no MPC logo. Part of 1586 Chesapeake Flyer and other sets.

	GD	VG	EXC	MT
(A) Yellow body.	2	3	4	6
(B) Light yellow body.	2	3	4	6

(C) Same as (A), but with two operating couplers. Part of 1987-89 rolling stock assortment. C. Massey Collection.

	GD	VG	EXC	MT
	3	4	5	7

9018 D T & I: 1978-82, short hopper; yellow body; black heat-stamped lettering very large "D T & I"; plastic brakewheel; Symington-Wayne trucks; one manumatic coupler, one dummy coupler; "BLT 1-78". Part of 1864 Santa Fe double diesel, 1151 U P Thunder freight, and 1865 Chesapeake Flyer sets.

	GD	VG	EXC	MT
	2	3	5	8

9025 D T & I: 1978, short hopper; uncatalogued. Came with 1864 Santa Fe double diesel set as an optional insert. The exist-

More quad hoppers from the mid-70s.
Top shelf: 9117 Alaska Railroad; 9119 Detroit & Mackinac.
Second shelf: 9130 B&O, note the stress mark at the lower center; 9134 Virginian.
Third shelf: Two versions of the 9135 Norfolk and Western; flat navy and royal blue.
Bottom shelf: 9213 M St L; 9240 New York Central System, an operating short hopper.

W. Dyson, R. Kaptur, R. LaVoie, A. Rudman, and F. Stem Collections; B. Schwab photograph

	GD	VG	EXC	MT

ence of this car has been questioned. Further reader comments are requested.

(A) Yellow body with black lettering. Forst Collection.

| | — | — | 5 | 7 |

(B) Orange body with black lettering. Forst Collection.

| | — | — | 5 | 7 |

9034 LIONEL LEISURE: 1977, short hopper; uncatalogued; white body; red, blue and orange lettering; brown, blue and orange Casey Kangaroo logo; Symington-Wayne trucks; "BLT 1-77". Made for Kiddie City retail outlet as part of special 1790 Steel Hauler set in 1977. Hard to find. G. Halverson comment and Collection. — — 35 50

9038 B & O CHESSIE SYSTEM: 1978, 1980-81, short hopper; blue body with yellow lettering; Symington-Wayne trucks with plastic wheels; one operating and one dummy coupler; "BLT 1-78". Except for the number, this is an exact reverse color scheme to the 9016. Appeared in 1052 Chesapeake Flyer set. Not catalogued in 1978-79, it may have been included in place of the 9016 in some sets or in a rolling stock assortment. 2 3 8 10

9079 GRAND TRUNK WESTERN: 1977, short hopper; deep blue body; white lettering and large "GT" at right; molded-in

brakewheel; under- and over-scored number; Symington-Wayne trucks; metal wheels; one dummy coupler; "BLT 1-77". Came only in the 1762 Wabash Cannonball set. Somewhat hard to find. 8 10 15 20

9110 B & O: 1971, quad hopper; not covered; black body; metal plate holding trucks; "BLT 2-71"; builder's plate; B & O capitol and MPC logos to right. Only sold separately, not in a set.

(A) Gray lettering; Symington-Wayne trucks; reportedly only 1,000 made. — — 40 70
(B) White lettering; postwar die-cast bar-end trucks. 10 20 25 35

9111 NORFOLK AND WESTERN: 1972-75, quad hopper; not covered; white lettering; builder's plate; metal plate holding trucks; under- and over-scored number; Symington-Wayne trucks; "BLT 2-72"; MPC logo. Versions found with an unpainted brown body came only in sets; those with painted tuscan bodies came with sets such as the 1388 Golden State Arrow (1973-75) and the 1186 Cross Country Express (1972), and were also sold separately (1972). C. Rohlfing, R. LaVoie, and G. Halverson comments.

(A) Unpainted brown body; center spreader bar. R. LaVoie Collection. 5 7 10 20

	GD	VG	EXC	MT

(B) Painted tuscan body; center spreader bar; came with set 1388, the Golden State Arrow. G. Halverson Collection.

	7	10	15	30

(C) Same as (B), but unpainted tuscan body. C. Rohlfing Collection.

	7	10	15	30

(D) Same as (A), but lighter unpainted brown body. C. Rohlfing Collection.

	5	7	10	20

See Factory Errors and Prototypes chapter in Volume II, first edition.

9112 RIO GRANDE: 1973-75, covered quad hopper; orange body; black lettering; orange cover; builder's plate; metal plate holding trucks; Symington-Wayne trucks; "BLT 1-73". Sold only separately, not in a set.
(A) Light orange body; deep heat-stamped lettering.

	7	10	12	20

(B) Light orange body; flatter heat-stamped lettering.

	7	10	12	20

(C) Darker orange body; flatter heat-stamped lettering.

	7	10	12	20

9113 NORFOLK AND WESTERN: 1973, quad hopper; not covered; uncatalogued; gray body; black lettering; center spreader bar; under- and over-scored numbers; lettering is same as on 9111, except for colors; builder's plate; metal plate holding trucks; Symington-Wayne trucks; "BLT 3-73". From 1973 Canadian Pacific Service Station set 1350. In the early 1970s the Service Station sets were not described in any official Lionel flyers, so this car and all the set components are considered uncatalogued. T. Wagner comments.

	10	20	25	40

9114 MORTON SALT: 1974-76, covered quad hopper; navy blue body; white and yellow lettering; girl logo in yellow, purple and white; yellow cover; builder's plate; metal plate holding trucks; Symington-Wayne trucks; "BLT 2-74". First of a series of "billboard" hoppers depicting corporations and products, rather than railroad names. These were generally sold separately, not in sets, although the 9114 did come with the 1460 Grand National set in 1974. Many 9800-series reefers were also decorated in such "billboard" fashion.

	6	8	15	25

9115 PLANTERS: 1974-76, covered quad hopper; dark blue body; yellow lettering; yellow and black Mr. Peanut logo; yellow cover; builder's plate; metal plate holding trucks; Symington-Wayne trucks; "BLT 2-74". Sold separately, not in a set. "Billboard Hopper" series.

	6	8	15	25

9116 DOMINO SUGAR: 1974-76, covered quad hopper; gray body; blue lettering; navy blue cover; builder's plate; metal plate holding trucks; Symington-Wayne trucks; "BLT 1- 74". Sold separately, not in a set. "Billboard Hopper" series.

	6	8	15	25

9117 ALASKA RAILROAD: 1974-76, covered quad hopper; black body; black cover; Symington-Wayne trucks; "BLT 1-74". Reissue of postwar 6636 from 1959. From 1974 Rio Grande Service Station set No. 1450. Also sold separately in 1975-76.
(A) Orange-yellow lettering; builder's plate.

	10	12	15	25

(B) Light yellow lettering; builder's plate.

	10	12	15	25

(C) Light yellow lettering; no builder's plate.

	10	1	15	25

(D) Orange unpainted cover instead of black; came with some of the Service Station set production. Hard to place a value upon since covers are easily switched. Sample observed came from mint set. G. Halverson observation; A. J. Conto Collection.   **NRS**

9118 CORNING: 1974, covered quad hopper; L C C A; see Volume II, first edition.

9119 DETROIT & MACKINAC: 1975, covered quad hopper; uncatalogued; red body; white lettering; shiny red cover; no builder's plate; metal plate holding trucks; under- and over-scored number; Symington-Wayne trucks; "BLT 1-75". Reissue of postwar 6736 from 1962. From 1579 Milwaukee Service Station set in 1975. Also sold separately.

	8	10	25	30

9130 B & O: 1970-71, quad hopper; not covered; medium royal blue paint on gray body; white lettering; center spreader bar; MPC logo; builder's plate; AAR trucks; "BLT 1-70". Some examples came in Type I long boxes with a 9110 label which had the 9110 number crossed out in blue marker ink and the number 9130 reprinted on the label. Incredibly, the picture of the car is numbered 9130! It is also curious to note that this car was produced before the 9110, not afterward. The stress marks on the sides are very visible on this car. See 9135 entry. Lionel also catalogued this car in two 1970 sets which were not made. R. LaVoie Collection.
(A) Plastic plate holding trucks.

	8	10	15	20

(B) Metal plate holding trucks.

	10	12	15	25

(C) Large "B & O" letters; no Capitol dome logo, as shown in 1970 poster catalogue. Confirmation requested.   **NRS**

9134 VIRGINIAN: 1976-77, covered quad hopper; silver body; blue lettering and circular V G N logo; blue cover; plastic plate holding trucks; number under- and over-scored; Symington-Wayne trucks; "BLT 1-76". Sold separately, not in a set.
(A) No builder's plate.

	12	15	20	25

(B) Builder's plate.

	12	15	20	25

See Factory Errors and Prototypes chapter in Volume II, first edition.

> **Note:** *All quad hoppers produced until mid-1973 have a bell-shaped stress mark in the plastic sides, exactly in the center just above the lower frame. The mark is easily seen when the car is held at a sharp angle to the light, and is especially noticeable on dark plastic cars — for example, the 9135 N & W, the 9130 B & O, the 6446 Uhl hopper, and the 9111 N & W. Sometime in 1973, Lionel reworked the die, and the stress mark disappeared. This is of special significance to the 9135 because it was reissued in 1975 in the "Spirit of America" set, meaning there are versions with and without the stress mark. The set car never came in its own box — only in the set.*

9135 NORFOLK AND WESTERN: 1971, 1975, quad hopper; blue or purple body; white lettering; royal blue cover; under- and over-scored number; builder's plate (except (A); metal plate holding trucks; Symington-Wayne trucks (except (D); "BLT 9-70"; MPC logo. From 1584 N & W Spirit of America set in 1975, and sold separately in 1971.
(A) Royal blue body; no builder's plate.

	8	10	15	20

(B) Royal blue body.

	8	10	15	20

(C) Purple body; light gray lettering; 3,000 manufactured.

	15	20	30	40

(D) Light blue body; AAR trucks.

	8	10	12	15

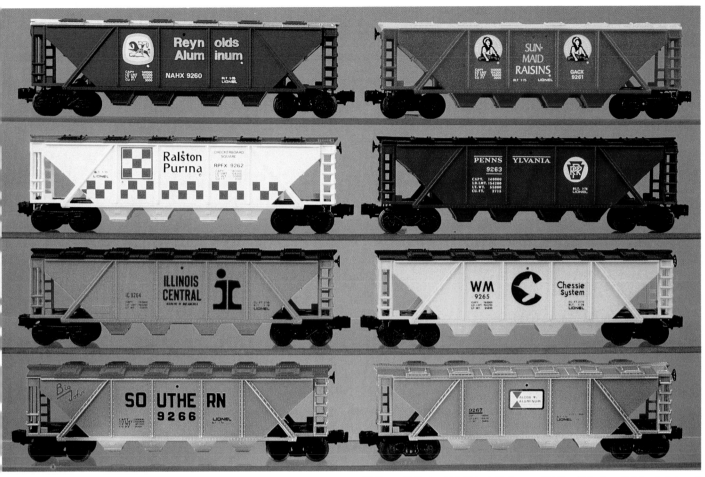

The billboard hoppers hit their stride.
Top shelf: **9260 Reynolds Aluminum; 9261 Sun Maid Raisins.**
Second shelf: **9262 Ralston Purina; 9263 Pennsylvania.**
Third shelf: **9264 Illinois Central; 9265 WM Chessie System.**
Bottom shelf: **9266 Southern; 9267 Alcoa Aluminum.**

W. Dyson, R. Kaptur, R. LaVoie, A. Rudman, and F. Stem Collections; B. Schwab photograph

	GD	VG	EXC	MT

(E) Same as (D), but covers glued on by factory. Reader comments requested; this would be a most unusual manufacturing technique. **8 10 12 15**

(F) Flat navy blue-painted blue plastic body; glossy unpainted dark blue cover; light gray lettering instead of white. It is possible that this particular version was issued in 1975 as part of the "Spirit of America" diesel set. Reader comments invited. G. Halverson comment. R. LaVoie and G. Halverson Collections.
— — 35 50

9213 M ST L: 1978, covered quad hopper; bright red body and cover; white lettering; Standard O trucks; "BLT 1-78". Reissue of postwar 6536 hopper from 1963. Part of 1868 M & St. L Service Station set from 1978. **— — 25 35**

9240 NEW YORK CENTRAL SYSTEM: 1986, short hopper; white lettering and NYC oval; under- and over-scored number; "BLT 1-85".

(A) Operating version; tuscan body; black metal operating mechanism; Standard O trucks. **— — 30 40**

(B) Non-operating version; light brown body; Symington-Wayne trucks; black plastic plate glued over bin holes; Type VI box. Found in many toy stores as part of 9195 rolling stock assortment. Unusual practice for Lionel Trains, Inc. Apparently Service Sta-

tions performed many such alterations of this car. R. LaVoie, M. Sabatelle, and L. Caponi Collections. **— — 25 30**

9260 REYNOLDS ALUMINUM: 1975-76, covered quad hopper; royal blue body; silver lettering; blue, silver and white knight logo; metal plate holding trucks; silver cover with blue hatches; Symington-Wayne trucks; "BLT 1-75". Sold separately and in 1560 North American Express set. Considered a "Billboard Hopper," but this one did come in a set.

(A) No builder's plate. **8 10 12 20**
(B) Builder's plate. **8 10 12 20**

9261 SUN-MAID RAISINS: 1975-76, covered quad hopper; red body; yellow and white lettering; yellow cover; yellow, green and white Raisin Lady logo; no builder's plate; metal plate holding trucks; Symington-Wayne trucks; "BLT 1-75". Announced in Fall 1975 brochure and catalogued in 1976. Sold separately, not in a set. "Billboard Hopper" series. **10 12 15 20**

9262 RALSTON PURINA: 1975-76, covered hopper; white body; red and white checkerboard design; red and black lettering; red cover with black hatches; no builder's plate; metal plate holding trucks; Symington-Wayne trucks; "BLT 1-75". Announced in 1975 Fall brochure. Catalogued in 1976. "Billboard

Hoppers from the late 1970s and early 1980s.

W. Dyson, R. Kaptur, R. LaVoie, A. Rudman, and F. Stem Collections; B. Schwab photograph

Top shelf: 9276 Peabody Coal Company; 9286 Bessemer & Lake Erie Railroad.
Second shelf: 9322 Santa Fe; 9330 Kickapoo Valley half-size coal dump car (see listing in Log and Coal Dump Cars chapter.
Third shelf: 9338 Pennsylvania Power & Light Company; 9366 Union Pacific.
Bottom shelf: 9371 Lantic Sugar; 9374 Reading.

	GD	VG	EXC	MT
Hopper" series. Sold separately, not in a set. Somewhat hard to find.				
(A) As described. C. Rohlfing Collection.	20	50	60	90
(B) Same as (A), but plastic plate holding trucks. P. Sudhoff Collection.	20	50	60	90

9263 PENNSYLVANIA: 1976-77, covered quad hopper; tuscan body; white lettering and P R R keystone logo; black cover; no builder's plate; Symington-Wayne trucks; "BLT 1-76". Sold separately, not in a set. A few boxes were mislabeled Penn Central, but the cars inside were labeled properly.

	GD	VG	EXC	MT
(A) Metal plate holding trucks.	10	25	30	40
(B) Plastic plate holding trucks.	10	25	30	40

9264 ILLINOIS CENTRAL: 1976-77, covered quad hopper; bright orange body; black lettering; large black I C I-beam logo; black cover; Symington-Wayne trucks; "BLT 1-76". Sold separately, not in a set.

	GD	VG	EXC	MT
(A) Metal plate holding trucks; no builder's plate.	15	20	25	30
(B) Same as (A), but plastic plate holding trucks.	15	20	25	30
(C) Same as (A), but builder's plate.	15	20	25	30

	GD	VG	EXC	MT
(D) Plastic plate holding trucks; builder's plate.	15	20	25	30

9265 WM CHESSIE SYSTEM: 1976-77, covered quad hopper; yellow body; blue lettering and Chessie cat logo; blue cover; no builder's plate; Symington-Wayne trucks; "BLT 1-76". Sold separately, not in a set.

	GD	VG	EXC	MT
(A) Metal plate holding trucks.	10	20	25	30
(B) Plastic plate holding trucks.	10	20	25	30

9266 SOUTHERN: 1976, covered quad hopper; gray body painted silver; black lettering; red cover; plastic plate holding trucks; red "Big/John" script logo; Symington-Wayne trucks; "BLT 1-76". Came with the top-of-the-line set in 1976 — the 1665 NYC Empire State Express — and is very sought after now.

	GD	VG	EXC	MT
(A) Builder's plate.	—	40	50	85
(B) No builder's plate.	—	40	50	75

9267 ALCOA ALUMINUM: 1976, covered quad hopper; uncatalogued; silver-painted gray body; blue lettering; silver cover; no builder's plate; under-scored number; bright Alcoa Aluminum decal; Standard O trucks; "BLT 1-76". A reissue of postwar 6346 hopper from 1956. From 1672 Northern Pacific Service Station Special set.

	GD	VG	EXC	MT
	15	20	30	40

9276 PEABODY COAL COMPANY: 1978, quad hopper; not covered; yellow body; dark green lettering "PEABODY/COAL

W. Dyson, R. Kaptur, R. LaVoie, A. Rudman, M. Solly, and F. Stem Collections; B. Schwab photograph

Top shelf: 9384 Great Northern, an operating short hopper; 16402 Southern.
Second shelf: 17002 Conrail; 17003 Dupont Alathon Polyethylene (there is an unusual variation of this car).
Third shelf: 17100 C&O Chessie System; 17101 C&O Chessie System.
Bottom shelf: 17102 C&O Chessie System; 17103 C&O Chessie System.

	GD	VG	EXC	MT

COMPANY/power for progress"; Standard O trucks; "BLT 1-78". Part of 1867 Milwaukee Limited set. — **15 25 35**

9286 BESSEMER & LAKE ERIE RAILROAD: 1977, covered quad hopper; orange body; black lettering; black and white I-beam decal logo (one of the few instances where Lionel has used decals); black cover; no builder's plate; plastic plate holding trucks; Symington-Wayne trucks; "BLT 1-77". Came only with the 1765 Rocky Mountain Special set. **8 12 15 25**

9322 SANTA FE: 1979, covered quad hopper; red body painted red; red cover; white lettering; black and white Santa Fe cross logo; gold FARR Series 1 diamond insignia; plastic brakewheel; center brace holes; Symington-Wayne trucks; "BLT 1-79". Part of Santa Fe Famous American Railroad Series No. 1, whose components were all sold separately. — **40 70 80**

9338 PENNSYLVANIA POWER & LIGHT COMPANY: 1979, quad hopper; tuscan body; yellow lettering; no cover; Standard O trucks; "BLT 1-79". From 1971 Quaker City Limited set.

This car is an excellent copy of the Bethlehem Steel Corporation prototype. Hard to find because some operators have used large numbers of them for unit trains. C. Rohlfing and R. LaVoie comments. — — **50 75**

9358 SAND'S OF IOWA: 1980, covered quad hopper; L C C A; see Volume II, first edition.

9366 UNION PACIFIC: 1980, covered quad hopper; silver-painted gray body; black cover; red, white and blue Union Pacific shield logo; gold FARR Series 2 diamond insignia; Symington-Wayne trucks; "BLT 1-80". From Union Pacific Famous American Railroad Series No. 2, whose components were all sold separately. — — **25 35**

9371 ATLANTIC SUGAR REFINER UNLIMITED: 1980, (Seaboard) covered quad hopper; yellow sides and cover; red logo with white "Lantic/Sugar" lettering; black lettering; under- and over-scored number; Standard O trucks; "BLT 1-80". Type IV box is labeled "SEABOARD COAST LINE COVERED HOPPER", but

The most recent of the big center-flow and quad hoppers.
Top shelf: **17104** C&O Chessie System; **17107** Dupont Sclair Polyethylene.
Second shelf: **17108** Santa Fe; **19302** Milwaukee Road.
Third shelf: **19303** Lionel Lines; **19304** Great Northern.
Bottom shelf: **19309** Seaboard; **19312** Reading.

W. Dyson, R. Kaptur, R. LaVoie, A. Rudman, and F. Stem Collections; B. Schwab photograph

	GD	VG	EXC	MT

that lettering does not appear on the car; from 1071 Mid-Atlantic Limited set. — — **25 35**

9374 READING: 1980-81, covered quad hopper; black sides and cover; white lettering; red and black Reading diamond logo; under- and over-scored number; Symington-Wayne trucks; "BLT 1-80". From 1072 Cross Country Express. A popular car that is somewhat hard to find now. — — **60 75**

9384 GREAT NORTHERN: 1981, operating short hopper; dark green body; white lettering; red, black and white mountain goat logo; bins open by remote control; under- and over-scored number; Standard O trucks; "BLT 1-81". From 1160 Great Lakes Limited set. — — **55 75**

16400 PENNSYLVANIA: 1988-89, short hopper; gray body; black lettering, number and P R R keystone logo; Symington-Wayne trucks; "BLT 1-88". Part of 11708 Midnight Shift set in 1989 and uncatalogued Toys 'R Us version of the same set the year before. — — — **25**

16402 SOUTHERN: 1987, quad hopper with coal load; uncatalogued; gray body; black lettering and number; Standard O trucks; "BLT 1-87". Part of 11704 Southern Freight Runner Service Station Special set. — — **30 40**

16406 C S X: 1990, quad hopper with black coal load; black body; yellow lettering; large "CSX" under-scored at upper right; ASF strong-arm trucks; "BLT 1- 90". Part of 11717 C S X Freight set. — — — **30**

16407 BOSTON & MAINE*: 1991, covered quad hopper; gray body; black lettering and logo; Standard O trucks; "BLT 1-91". Part of 11719 Coastal freight Service Station Special set. — — — **25**

17002 CONRAIL: 1987, A C F two-bay center-flow hopper; light gray body; black lettering and logo; Standard O trucks; "BLT 1-87" with bar code. Part of 11700 Conrail Limited set. — — **90 110**

17003 DUPONT ALATHONT POLYETHYLENE RESIN: 1990, A C F two-bay center-flow hopper; medium red body; white

W. Dyson, R. Kaptur, R. LaVoie, A. Rudman, M. Solly, and F. Stem Collections; B. Schwab photograph

19804 Wabash; 19806 Pennsylvania. Two short operating hoppers.

	GD	VG	EXC	MT

lettering; large white rectangle at center with red DuPont logo and black "ALATHON"; Standard O trucks; "BLT 1-90". Came only with 11713 Santa Fe Dash-8 set. Original production had the word "POLYETHYLENE" under "ALATHON" spelled without the first E. This can be seen on the prototype in the catalogue. Lionel corrected it on later pieces by painting black strip over the error and reprinting the correct word in white.
(A) "POLYETHYLENE". — — — 80
(B) "POLYTHYLENE". — — — 140

17004 MKT*: 1991, ACF two-bay center-flow hopper; green body; yellow lettering; large "MKT" at center; Standard O trucks; "BLT 1-91". — — — 38

17100 C & O CHESSIE SYSTEM: 1988, three-bay A C F center-flow hopper; new "stretched" design based on two-bay models introduced in 1986. Bright yellow body; dark blue lettering and Chessie cat logo; Standard O trucks; "BLT 1-88" with bar code. Part of 11705 Chessie System unit train. This and the Burlington Northern Limited set from 1985 were Lionel's first real forays into the "unit" freight train concept.
 — — — 50

17101 C & O CHESSIE SYSTEM: 1988; matches 17100 above. Part of 11705 Chessie System unit train.
 — — — 50

17102 C & O CHESSIE SYSTEM: 1988; matches 17100 above. Part of 11705 Chessie System unit train.
 — — — 50

17103 C & O CHESSIE SYSTEM: 1988; matches 17100 above. Part of 11705 Chessie System unit train.
 — — — 50

17104 C & O CHESSIE SYSTEM: 1988; matches 17100 above. Part of 11705 Chessie System unit train.
 — — — 50

17107 DUPONT SCLAIR POLYETHYLENE: 1989, three-bay A C F center-flow hopper; orange body; broad diagonal white stripe with overstamped black lettering "sclair" and "DUPONT POLYETHYLENE" — see 17003 entry for a related story; "DOCX 17107" to lower left; catalogued as 17000, but made as 17107; extensive decals with chemical data to right. Came only with 11710 C P Rail freight set. Bright orange of this car is a strange combination with the dark red of other set components; Standard O trucks; "BLT 1-89". — — — 80

17108 SANTA FE: 1990, three-bay A C F center-flow hopper; brown body; white lettering; large "Santa Fe" letters at center; extensive capacity, load and operation data; Standard O trucks; "BLT 1-90". Came only with 11713 Santa Fe Dash-8 set.
 — — — 75

	GD	VG	EXC	MT

17109 NORFOLK AND WESTERN*: 1991, ACF three-bay center-flow hopper; gray body; black lettering; Standard O trucks; "BLT 1-91". — — — 40

17110 UNION PACIFIC*: 1991, 48-foot three-bay Standard O hopper with coal load; new detailed near-scale model of prototype three-bay hopper with ribbed sides; Lionel car has a brown body; white lettering; detailed coal load; Standard O trucks; "BLT 1-91". The heavily-ribbed sides of this 12-inch-long hopper make it a good match for the ribbed Standard O boxcars also released for the first time in 1991. — — — 42

17111 READING*: 1991, 48-foot three-bay Standard O hopper with coal load; new design model of prototype three-bay ribbed-sided hopper; this model has a black body; white lettering; detailed coal load; Standard O trucks; "BLT 1-91". A good match for the ribbed Standard O boxcars also released in 1991.
 — — — 42

19302 MILWAUKEE ROAD: 1987, quad hopper with coal load; yellow body; black lettering "America's/Resourceful/Railroad"; Standard O trucks; "BLT 1-87". Part of Milwaukee Fallen Flags set No. 2, whose components were all sold separately.
 — — — 30

19303 LIONEL LINES: 1987, quad hopper with coal load; uncatalogued; blue body with bright orange sides; blue ends, upper quarter panels and bottom; red, white and blue Lionel "L" logo; dark blue lettering; Symington-Wayne trucks; "BLT 1-87". Part of year-end package for 1987. Two shades of blue have been observed on the "L" decal. The first run was dark blue; the second was light blue. We do not know which version is scarcer. Reader comments requested. Car is considered part of separate-sale "Lionel Lines" set, whose components were issued beginning in 1982. — — 50 70

19304 GREAT NORTHERN: 1988, covered quad hopper; light gray body and cover; black lettering; red and white circular "goat" logo; Standard O trucks; "BLT 1-88". Part of Fallen Flags set No. 3, whose components were all sold separately.
 — — — 40

19309 SEABOARD: 1989, covered quad hopper; light gray body and cover; black lettering; Symington-Wayne trucks; "BLT 1-89". — — — 20

19310 LANCASTER & CHESTER: 1989, quad hopper with black coal load; light blue body; wide white stripe at top; blue and white lettering; detailed oval L & C logo in center; Symington-Wayne trucks; "BLT 1-89". — — — 20

19311 SOUTHERN PACIFIC: 1990, covered quad hopper; light gray body; red lettering; "SOUTHERN PACIFIC" in large letters at right; red S P Lines circle logo to left; ASF strong-arm trucks; "BLT 1-90". — — — 20

	GD	VG	EXC	MT

19312 READING: 1990, quad hopper with black coal load; black body; white lettering; large "READING" at top center; red, white and black Reading Lines logo at upper right; under- and over-scored number; ASF strong-arm trucks; "BLT 1-90". Similar to 9374. — — — 20

19316 WABASH*: 1991, covered quad hopper; gray body; red lettering; large "WABASH" letters at top center; red, white and blue Wabash flag logo at top right; under- and over-scored number; ASF strong-arm trucks; "BLT 1-91". — — — 22

19317 LEHIGH VALLEY*: 1991, quad hopper with coal load; lilac (light purple) body; black lettering; number under- and over-scored; Standard O trucks; "BUILT BY LIONEL" (no date). Reissue of postwar 6436-57, which was part of the infamous Girls'

	GD	VG	EXC	MT

set in 1957. The modern car was part of the 1991 reincarnation of that set — the 11722 Girls' Train. — — — 4

19804 WABASH: 1987, operating short hopper; black body white/gray lettering and Wabash flag logo; black operating mechanism; Standard O trucks; "BLT 1-87".
— — — 3

19806 PENNSYLVANIA: 1988, operating short hopper car light gray body; black operating mechanism; black lettering and keystone logo at upper right; Standard O trucks; "BLT 1-88".
— — — 3

25000 LEHIGH VALLEY: See 6476-135.

◆ CHAPTER 12 ◆
LOG AND COAL DUMP CARS

*T*he Lionel modern era log dump car is modeled after the late postwar Lionel Corporation examples, especially the 3361. It is an all-plastic car with an open flatcar body (6362 mold) and a central log cradle released by a spring-loaded plunger. When the magnet in an operating track pulls down the plunger, the cradle tilts and dumps three wooden dowels serving as logs. The mechanism works well, but the logs sometimes flip off the cradle on sharp curves during operation.

Over the years, Lionel has produced its log cars in quite a few railroad markings. The first one catalogued was a tuscan Louisville and Nashville car in 1970, which was never produced. The first of the log cars was a green 9300 Penn Central, which ran from 1970 through 1974, and again in 1977. In 1974 the car was changed to yellow Union Pacific markings as the 9303 — or 9305 (car plus remote-control track). This car ran from 1974 through 1978, and again in 1980. A red Santa Fe model appeared in 1979 through 1983, and for 1984 a Northern Pacific model in dark forest green was made. A Pennsylvania log dump car in tuscan was produced in 1985, followed by a B & O version for 1986, a New York Central version in 1987, and another Santa Fe version in 1988 — this time with real logs made of tree limbs. All the log dump cars since 1988 have come with the life-like logs. Recent production has included log dump cars in Soo, Alaska, and Rio Grande markings. Another, in C S X colors, came only in the C S X freight set in 1990.

The modern era Lionel coal dump car is essentially a modified log dump car with a tilting coal bin attached to the cradle. It is a bit ungainly and does not interest collectors much. Some people had complaints about the coal supplied with the car; it was made of PVC plastic pellets which would pick up static electricity and stick to everything on the layout, including the operator when he/she tried to put the coal back in the car.

Another operating problem is that the hinge on the side of the dump bin which opens is very fragile, subject to breakage. The car bears little resemblance to, and does not

operate as well as, the die-cast black postwar 3469. Thousands of 3469s can still be found, a fact which may explain the lukewarm reception the new cars received.

The first of the newly designed coal dump cars came out in 1974 with a dark blue color scheme and yellow Chesapeake and Ohio lettering. This car ran from 1974 through 1978, after which it was replaced by a yellow Union Pacific model running from 1979 through 1982. In 1983 a coal dump car was included as part of the Northern Freight Flyer; this car had a black flatcar body with a gray bin and white Chicago & North Western lettering. It was not offered for separate-sale. The separate-sale car for 1983 and 1984 was a tuscan Pennsylvania car with gold lettering. A New York Central coal dump car was produced for 1985; although it was an obvious match for the Yard Chief switcher set of that year, it was not part of the set and was sold separately. The New York Central car continued into 1986, and for 1987 an Erie-Lackawanna version was issued. One 1987 coal dump car, the Southern, was part of the Service Station Special for that year. Unlike the others, it had Standard O trucks. An Illinois Central version appeared in 1988, followed by Katy, Wabash, and Western Maryland, one per year.

As with hopper and crane cars, there were also two very short versions of the dump car used in the most inexpensive Traditional Line sets. This car used a short flatcar body with a hand-operated bin. One came as a snap-together four-wheeler in the Logging Empire set of 1978. The car was lettered 9325 N & W (see Flatcar chapter) but came in a box numbered 9363. A second short dump car came with the Redwood Valley Express set in 1984, and this one included logs. These cars certainly demonstrate Lionel's interest in operating fun even with the bottom-of-the-line Traditional sets.

The log and coal dump cars do not, as a rule, interest collectors too much. There are a few scarce factory errors in the group, and the 1988 L O T S Milwaukee log car is a true rarity. Still, Lionel continues to pour out dump cars with

---

Asterisk found in listings indicates that the information within that listing was derived from Lionel catalogue only.

Coal dump cars. All came with simulated coal and trackside bin. The hinge pins on these cars are easily broken.
Top shelf: **6251 N Y C; 9304 C&O.**
Second shelf: **9398 Pennsylvania; 16600 Illinois Central.**
Third shelf: **16602 E L; 16613 M K T.**
Bottom shelf: **16619 Wabash.**

surprising regularity — there are more of them than most collectors realize, and two or three have been released every year since 1987. Perhaps a reissue of the operating coal- or log-loading accessories will spark new interest in them.

Log And Coal Dump Car Listings

	GD	VG	EXC	MT

6251 N Y C: 1985-86, coal dump car, black body; grating pieces added to car ends (earlier varieties did not have these pieces); black bin; white lettering; white N Y C oval logo; Symington-Wayne trucks; one dummy coupler; "BLT 1-85". Came with simulated coal and trackside bin. Sold separately, intended to supplement the 1502 New York Central Yard Chief set. R. LaVoie Collection. — — **15 20**

6573 REDWOOD VALLEY EXPRESS: 1984-85, short log dump car; Type II flatcar with log dump bin; tuscan body; yellow lettering; no number on car; gray bolsters and hand-operated lo, bin; three brown-stained logs; plastic arch bar trucks. Part o Redwood Valley set 1403. — — — 1

9238 NORTHERN PACIFIC: 1984, log dump car; dark fores green body and log cradle; white lettering; three stained woode logs and green trackside bin included; Symington-Wayne trucks one dummy coupler; "BLT 1-84". — — **15 2**

See Factory Errors and Prototypes chapter in Volume II, firs edition.

9241 PENNSYLVANIA: 1985-86, log dump car; tuscan body grating pieces added to ends of car; gold lettering Symington-Wayne trucks; one dummy coupler; "BLT 1-85". Cam with three stained large logs and tuscan dumping bin. — — **15 2**

9300 P C: 1970-74, 1977, log dump car; green body; whit lettering; MPC logo; two operating couplers; no "BLT" date. Thi car was present in many early MPC/Fundimensions sets.
(A) 1970; Type I box without cellophane; no dumping bi enclosed; MPC logo; AAR trucks; Type I armature (magnet ce mented to disc); two operating couplers; three unstained dowels

B. Greenberg photograph

Log dump cars.
Top shelf: **9238 Northern Pacific; 9241 Pennsylvania.**
Second shelf: **9300 P C; 9303 U.P.**
Third shelf: **9335 Baltimore and Ohio; 16604 N Y C.**
Bottom shelf: **16611 Santa Fe; 16612 Soo Line. Note the more realistic log loads on these two.**

	GD	VG	EXC	MT

Car has no mold number or molded rivet rows as on most later dump cars. R. LaVoie Collection.   **8   10   15   20**
(B) Same as (A), but with silver-painted wooden helium tanks instead of logs. R. Hutchinson Collection.
10   15   20   25
(C) 1971 and later, Type II larger box with dumping bin; Symington-Wayne trucks; three unstained wooden dowels; molded rivet rows; embossed "6362-2" mold number on center bar of platform. Common production. R. Hundt comment.
5   7   10   15

9303 U. P.: 1974-80, log dump car; yellow body; red lettering; Symington-Wayne trucks; one dummy coupler; "BLT 1-74". Appeared in the 1560 North American Express set, the 1460 Grand National set, and also sold separately.   **4   6   10   15**

9304 C & O: 1974-78, coal dump car; dark blue body and dump bin; yellow lettering; coal and trackside bin included; Symington-Wayne trucks; one dummy coupler; "BLT 1-74".
(A) White "coal" from raw plastic pellets.
4   5   10   12
(B) Black "coal."   **4   5   10   12**

	GD	VG	EXC	MT

See Factory Errors and Prototypes chapter in Volume II, first edition.

9305: This number refers to a package which included the 9303 U. P. car and a remote-control track. Add $4 to values of 9303 for presence of track in original package.

9306: This number refers to a package which included the 9304 C & O car and a remote-control track. Add $4 to values of 9304 for presence of track in original package.

9310 A T & S F: 1978-82, log dump car; red body; yellow lettering; three dowels about six inches long, 5/8-inch diameter, and trackside bin included; Symington-Wayne trucks; one dummy coupler; "BLT 1-78".   **5   7   10   15**

9311 UNION PACIFIC: 1978-82, coal dump car; yellow body and dump bin; red lettering; simulated coal and trackside bin included; Symington-Wayne trucks; one dummy coupler; "BLT 1-78".   **5   7   10   15**

9325 N & W: See 9363.

9330 KICKAPOO VALLEY: 1972, half-size coal dump car; four plastic wheels; black frame; no lettering or number, except "9330" molded into bottom of car; two dummy couplers. Part of

	GD	VG	EXC	MT

1280 Kickapoo Valley set, and issued again in 1979 as part of 1965 Smokey Mountain Line set. These two sets represent perhaps the most inexpensive sets Lionel has produced in the modern era.

		GD	VG	EXC	MT
(A)	Green bin.	1	2	3	8
(B)	Red bin.	1	2	3	8
(C)	Yellow bin.	1	2	3	8

9335 BALTIMORE AND OHIO: 1986, log dump car; tuscan body; white lettering; three stained wooden dowels and trackside bin included; Symington-Wayne trucks; one dummy coupler; "BLT 1-86". Part of 1652 B & O freight set. — — 15 20

9363 N & W: 1978, short log dumping car; black short Type II flatcar base; four plastic wheels; blue snap-on body. Part of Logging Empire set 1862; numbered "9325" on car, but came in box marked "9363". J. Sawruk Collection.

— 3 5 8

9398 PENNSYLVANIA: 1983-84, coal dump car; tuscan frame and bin; gold lettering; rubber-stamped keystone on dump bin; trackside bin and simulated coal load included; Symington-Wayne trucks; one dummy coupler. — — 20 25

9399 CHICAGO & NORTH WESTERN: 1983-85, coal dump car; black frame; gray bin; Symington-Wayne trucks; one dummy coupler. Part of 1354 Northern Freight Flyer set.

— — 15 20

16600 ILLINOIS CENTRAL: 1988, coal dump car; back flatcar base with white lettering; orange dump bin and bulkheads; white I-beam logo on bin; dumping bin and simulated plastic coal load included; Symington-Wayne trucks with two operating couplers; "BLT 1-88". Catalogue hints at a brown body, but it was made black. — — — 20

16602 E L: 1987, (Erie Lackawanna) coal dump car; gray flatcar and bin; gray grating pieces; maroon lettering and logo; coal and 2160 dumping bin included; Symington-Wayne trucks; two operating couplers — a first since the 9300 (all later coal/log cars have two working couplers); "BLT 1-87".

— — — 18

16604 N Y C: 1987, log dump car; black flatcar, cradle, and grating pieces; white "N Y C" lettering, logo, and number; three large stained dowels and 2160 trackside bin included; Symington-Wayne trucks; "BLT 1-87". Separate-sale item, but matches rolling stock in 1502 Yard Chief set. — — — 18

16607 SOUTHERN: 1987, coal dump car; uncatalogued; black body and grating pieces; dark green dump bin; gold lettering on car body and gold Southern herald on bin; Standard O trucks (a first for this car). Part of 11704 Southern Freight Runner Service Station Special set. — — — 25

16611 SANTA FE: 1988, log dump car; blue flatcar body with white lettering; yellow log cradle (one of the few cases in which the cradle is a different color than the body); dumping bin; three real logs (this treatment has not been seen on a Lionel car since the 6361 log carrier car of 1962); Symington-Wayne trucks; catalogued in 1988, but "BLT 1-89". The logs are available separately (accessory 12740). — — — 20

16621 Alaska Railroad.   *B. Greenberg photograph*

	GD	VG	EXC	MT

16612 SOO LINE: 1989, log dump car; light brown body and log cradle; white lettering "SOO LINE"; three wood dowels and dump bin; Symington-Wayne trucks; "BLT 1-89".

— — — 20

16613 M K T: 1989, coal dump car; black body and dump bin with white lettering; "The Katy" in script on bin; simulated coal and trackside bin included; Symington-Wayne trucks; "BLT 1-89".

— — — 20

16619 WABASH: 1990, coal dump car; dark gray body; brown coal bin with white Wabash flag logo; simulated coal and 2160 trackside bin; ASF strong-arm trucks. — — — 20

16621 ALASKA RAILROAD: 1990, log dump car; translucent unpainted yellow body and cradle; black lettering "ALASKA RAILROAD" and round A R R logo; three wood logs and trackside bin included; ASF strong-arm trucks; "BLT 1-90". Some collectors dislike the "toy" appearance of the bright yellow plastic which results from Lionel skipping the paint step. L. Caponi comment.

— — — 21

16627 C S X*: 1990, log dump car; dark blue flatcar and log cradle; white lettering "CSX"; three wood logs and trackside bin included; ASF strong-arm trucks; "BLT 1-90". Part of 11717 C S X freight set. — — — 21

16634 WESTERN MARYLAND*: 1991, coal dump car; brown body with white "WM" logo; red-orange coal bin with "WESTERN MARYLAND" in white; simulated coal and trackside bin included; ASF strong-arm trucks; "BLT 1-91".

— — — 22

16636 RIO GRANDE*: 1991, log dump car; orange body and log cradle; black lettering "Rio Grande"; three wood logs and trackside bin included; ASF strong-arm trucks; "BLT 1-91".

— — — 22

16643 AMTRAK*: 1991, coal dump car; black body with white lettering, number and "Amtrak" logo; orange coal dump bin; simulated "ballast" load (Lionel calls this a "ballast dump car" because there would be no reason for Amtrak to haul coal around!); trackside bin included; ASF strong-arm trucks; "BLT 1-91". Part of 11723 Amtrak Maintenance Train set.

— — — 25

17874 MILWAUKEE: 1988, log dump; L O T S; see Volume II, first edition.

O • CHAPTER 13 • S
ORE CARS

Introduction by Mike Solly, Bill Meyer and Philip Smith

The introduction of a new small hopper car style in 1984 was noteworthy in that it demonstrated modern Lionel's intent to move into new areas and designs with its freight cars, rather than simply standing pat with tools and dies inherited from the postwar corporation.

The stubby little ore car which appeared that year in Soo and Penn Central colors is remarkably similar to its full-size prototype, and features a wealth of molded details on its body exceeding that of most other Lionel cars.

Ore cars look (and are) much shorter than standard coal hopper cars, and for a good reason: ore is much heavier than coal. If a full-sized coal hopper was loaded with ore, the weight would exceed its limits, working woe on the sides, trucks and draft gear. Railroads did sometimes use coal hoppers for ore service, but only loaded them about two-thirds full.

The Soo was a good name for Fundimensions to model, as it was a major Michigan ore carrier — huge trains of up to 135 cars were commonly seen on the line. Since 1984, many other roads have been represented, including Canadian National, Northern Pacific, Lehigh Valley (also a major ore carrier), Pennsylvania, Milwaukee, B & L E, and Great Northern. Unfortunately, one of the recent issues, the 19315 Amtrak, represents a passenger railroad with no need for ore-carrying cars! Amtrak does use versions of a two-bay hopper for ballast maintenance-of-way.

The Lionel ore car is a fine model of the real thing, and is very similar to the Atlas/Rivarossi scale O cars which have been in use for some time. Collectors have noted, however, that Lionel's ore cars ride somewhat too high on their Symington-Wayne trucks and the new ASF trucks produced since 1990.

The majority of these cars have been produced since the corporate hand-over to Lionel Trains, Inc. in 1986 — the in-

tent is clearly to make these cars an important constituent of Lionel's freight line.

The ore cars have been brisk sellers for several very good reasons: they are inexpensive, prototypical, and collectors have bought whole fleets of them for unit trains (consists less than 135 cars were also common!). This has led to an increase in value of some of the cars, but most are still readily available, meaning they are still a good opportunity for beginners and experienced collectors alike. Ore loads have been sold to add to the earlier cars, and the recent ones have come with loads.

One last note: several ore cars were made for the train clubs and are thus somewhat harder to find. This includes a wonderful series produced for the T T O S in support of its fund raisers for a new museum in Tucson, Arizona. Each car was lettered for real mining companies in Arizona, and all were made in very limited quantities. As a result, this set is very hard to find now and is appreciating rapidly in value. See Volume II, first edition for further details.

ORE CAR LISTINGS

	GD	VG	EXC	MT

6116 SOO LINE: 1984-85, ore car; tuscan body; white lettering; Symington-Wayne trucks; "BLT 1-84". First of the new-style freight cars produced by Lionel, a shortened hopper with open framework on car ends. Erratic availability because many operators bought whole fleets of these cars for unit trains.
— — **35 45**

6122 P C: 1984-85, (Penn Central) ore car; black body; white "PC" lettering and logo; Symington-Wayne trucks; "BLT 1-84"; open framework on car ends. Same comments as those for 6116 above.
— — **35 45**

6126 CANADIAN NATIONAL: 1986, ore car; light brown body; white lettering; Symington-Wayne trucks; "BLT 1-85". This

---

Asterisk found in listings indicates that the information within that listing was derived from Lionel catalogue only.

W. Dyson, R. Kaptur, R. LaVoie, A. Rudman, M. Solly, and F. Stem Collections; B. Schwab photograph

Pictured here is the complete collection of Lionel's regular production ore cars through 1990. There are five other special production ore cars listed in Volume II.

Top shelf: **6116 Soo Line; 6122 P C; 6126 Canadian National.**
Second shelf: **6127 Northern Pacific; 16305 Lehigh Valley, the hardest of the group to obtain; 19300 Pennsylvania.**
Third shelf: **19301 The Milwaukee Road; 19305 B&O Chessie System; 19307 B.& L.E.**
Bottom shelf: **19308 Great Northern; 19313 B&O.**

	GD	VG	EXC	MT

and the 6127 may have been delayed in release due to Lionel's Mexico production problems. — — **25 30**

6127 NORTHERN PACIFIC: 1986, ore car; black body; off-white lettering and circular N P logo; Symington-Wayne trucks; "BLT 1-85". — — **30 35**

16305 L V: 1987, (Lehigh Valley) ore car; gray body; black lettering and diamond logo; Symington-Wayne trucks; "BLT 1-87". Came only in set 11702, the Black Diamond. Only ore car issued so far in a set. Hard to find. — — **40 70**

16800 LIONEL RAILROADER CLUB: 1986, ore car; see Volume II, first edition.

17872 ANACONDA: 1988, ore car; T T O S; see Volume II.

17878 MAGMA: 1989, ore car; T T O S; see Volume II, first edition.

17881 PHELPS-DODGE: 1990, ore car; T T O S; see Volume II, first edition.

17886 CYPRUS: 1991, ore car; T T O S; see Volume II, first edition.

19300 PENNSYLVANIA: 1987, ore car; tuscan body; white lettering; white P R R keystone logo; Symington-Wayne trucks; "BLT 1-87". — — — **22**

19301 THE MILWAUKEE ROAD: 1987, ore car; red oxide-orange body; white lettering; Symington-Wayne trucks; "BLT 1-87". Separate-sale item, but may increase in value because it can be used with the Milwaukee Fallen Flags set No. 2. — — — **20**

19305 B & O CHESSIE SYSTEM: 1988, ore car; black ore car body; yellow lettering, number and Chessie cat logo; Symington-Wayne trucks; no "BLT" date. — — — **18**

19307 B. & L. E.: 1989, (Bessemer & Lake Erie) ore car; light brown body; white lettering and Bessemer I-beam logo to right

	GD	VG	EXC	MT

side; came with copper-colored simulated ore load, first ore car equipped with a load; Symington-Wayne trucks; "BLT 1-89".

—	—	—	17

19308 GREAT NORTHERN: 1989, ore car; tuscan body; white lettering; copper-colored ore load; Symington-Wayne trucks; "BLT 1-89".

—	—	—	17

	GD	VG	EXC	MT

19313 B & O: 1990-91, ore car; black body; white lettering; large "B & O" at center; light brown ore load; ASF strong-arm trucks; "BLT 1-90".

—	—	—	18

19315 AMTRAK*: 1991, ore car; orange body; black lettering; gray ore load; ASF strong-arm trucks; "BLT 1-91". Amtrak, principally a passenger line, is an unusual road name for an ore car.

—	—	—	20

◆ CHAPTER 14 ◆
PASSENGER CARS

One of the real pleasures of tinplate railroading has always been to start up a train layout, turn off all the lights, and watch the lighted layout by "night." If the layout were well-equipped, street and signal lights would shine, searchlights would beam onto the platform, and the locomotive would come flying around a curve, its headlight reflecting off the tracks. If the operator looked at the train coming at him at eye level, he could watch the locomotive speed past him, followed by a long string of lighted passenger cars, possibly with small silhouettes of people in the windows.

Obviously, tinplate doth not live by freight cars alone. That is why Fundimensions tried to respond as quickly as possible to repeated requests for a new passenger car series.

There are five major types of passenger cars made by modern Lionel: long, extruded aluminum cars based on the postwar 2500-series; short streamlined O27 cars based on the postwar 2400-series; old-time passenger cars designated as "General" style; long heavyweight 1920s-style passenger cars similar to the postwar Madison cars, and short versions of the Madison cars which we call 9500-series. Unfortunately, the 9500-series also contains other passenger car types, but the majority are short Madison-style cars, so we use 9500 to identify them.

All of these cars were part of, or were later additions to, passenger train sets, many of which have snappy names like "The Blue Comet," the Southern Pacific "Daylight," or the Burlington "Zephyr." We have included brief descriptions of the sets and the common features and graphics on the cars of which they are comprised.

THE 9500-SERIES "SHORT MADISON" PASSENGER CARS

In 1973 Fundimensions began the production of its 9500-series passenger cars with the Milwaukee Special set. In this set, an 8305 4-4-2 locomotive in Milwaukee Road markings pulled three dull orange Milwaukee passenger cars with maroon roofs and gold lettering. These cars were excellent models of the heavyweight cars used during the 1920s on almost every American passenger railroad. They were lighted and highly detailed, with little vents in the clerestories, detailed closed vestibules, and translucent window inserts. The only sore points about the cars were their length (it did not quite match the length of the classic pre- and postwar Madison cars) and their couplers. The couplers were non-operating and mounted directly onto the car bodies; if the track was not level or had rough spots, the cars could easily uncouple accidentally. Some operators went so far as to put twist-ties around the coupler knuckles to keep them together! In addition, if for any reason the coupler broke off and took the screw hole in the car with it, the operator was out of luck.

The Milwaukee Special was followed during the next two years by a Broadway Limited set with Pennsylvania cars in tuscan and black with gold lettering, and a Capitol Limited with Baltimore and Ohio cars in blue and gray with gold lettering. Unfortunately, the color of the B and O cars did not match the 8363 B and O F-3 diesels, which were a lighter shade of blue. The three set cars soon had several stablemates. In 1975 separate-sale Pullman cars were produced to match all three sets. In the next year, full baggage cars were introduced. And the end of 1976 saw many observation cars made into the Campaign Special series with Presidential posters, bunting and an American flag decorating the cars in all three road names. One Milwaukee car, the 9511 Minneapolis, was offered as part of a coupon deal. In all, there

---

* *Asterisk found in listings indicates that the information within that listing was derived from Lionel catalogue only.*

were eleven Milwaukee cars, ten Pennsylvania cars, and nine Baltimore and Ohio cars when production was complete. Diner cars were produced for all three sets in 1988 and 1989 — twelve years after the original production!

As problems arose with these cars, attempts were made to solve them. It was found that the lights in the cars shone through the car roofs. At first, Fundimensions tried silver paint on the tops of the light bulbs in the cars, but that cut down the illumination too much. Eventually, cardboard inserts were placed into the roofs, and that solved the problem handily. Getting at the light bulbs to change them was a horrendous problem never fully solved. The roof and translucent window pieces were made of one casting which snapped into the car bodies. At first, there were tabs on the car bottoms, but these actually had to be cut off to remove the roof. Later, the tabs were eliminated in favor of projections in the translucent window inserts which snapped into the window frames. Even with this arrangement, getting the roofs off these cars has always been a job to tax the most patient of people.

Another less significant design quirk has led to several variation reports from collectors. The surface of the car body around the windows is inset from the surfaces above and below, making painting in this region more difficult (Lionel has often painted the window strip a lighter color than the remaining body on the 9500-style cars). As a result, some cars have incomplete painting in this area.

In 1977 the cars were issued in a different railroad scheme, this time with operating couplers. A baggage car, a combine, two Pullman coaches, and an observation car were made in green and gold Southern markings to match the 8702 Southern 4-6-4 Hudson. These made up the Southern Crescent set (though the items were always sold separately, not as a complete set — also true for all later releases of 9500-series passenger cars). Amazingly, it took ten years until Lionel Trains, Inc. produced a diner car to match these cars. Coincidentally, these cars also matched the Southern F-3 diesel pair produced in 1975. The next year, the cars were produced in the Blue Comet set with a significant improvement — the die-cast six-wheel passenger trucks. Several changes were made to the casting of the car underside to accommodate these trucks, and unfortunately earlier cars cannot be retrofitted with them. The same five-car scheme was used for the Chessie Steam Special set in 1980 and the Chicago and Alton set of 1981. In 1986 and 1987, Lionel Trains, Inc. made diner cars to match all four of these sets. So far, the Chessie and Alton diners have become very scarce and, unfortunately, expensive items.

Over the years, several of these cars were also made as T C A Special cars in dark Brunswick green. Another similar set in yellow was made for the Toy Train Operating Society. See the Volume II, first edition for photos of these cars. In 1986 Lionel Trains, Inc. issued a set of six 9500-style Wabash cars in handsome dark blue and gray "Bluebird" colors pulled by a matching 4-6-2 Pacific steam engine. These cars were the first entries in the new "Fallen Flags" Series of special Collector sets.

THE LONG HEAVYWEIGHT "MADISON" PASSENGER CARS

From 1973 through 1990, Lionel had been content to model the long heavyweight passenger cars of the 1920s (also known in Lionel-land as "Madison" cars) with somewhat shortened versions of the famous Madison cars produced by postwar Lionel immediately before and after World War II. The story goes that the original dies for the cars had been lost, so that Lionel/Fundimensions was forced to create its own dies in 1973 in order to produce new passenger cars. The new ones, however, were 3 or 4 inches shorter than the originals. Still, the modern company got great mileage out of their "short Madison" passenger car sets — eight sets were produced, all quite successful.

But all through this period, Lionel had been under competitive pressure from other manufacturers to produce longer more scale-length versions of the heavyweight passenger cars, and collectors had been clamoring for a rerun of the original full-length Madison cars. They got their wish in 1991. Clearly, given the time needed to make new dies, Lionel must have been planning this event for some years.

The modern set, in the same handsome tuscan colors as the 1940s versions, even included the Sager Place observation car that had been catalogued, but never made, in the postwar era. The new cars were made in phenolic plastic, to simulate the heavy "Bakelite" plastic from which the originals were made, and which gave them their "heavyweight" nickname. There is nothing in all of Lionel railroading quite like seeing a scale Hudson pulling a set of heavyweight Madison cars. Now, many modern Lionel hobbyists will have new opportunities to witness this spectacle.

SHORT O27 STREAMLINED PASSENGER CARS

In 1976 Fundimensions reissued the short O27 streamlined passenger cars of the postwar period as the Lake Shore Limited set. These cars, modeled on the old 2400-series of postwar years but without some of the detailing of the originals, were pulled by an Alco in Amtrak markings with four matching cars. Later on, three more cars were added as separate-sale items to expand the set. They had the same plastic wooden beam-style trucks as the earlier 9500 cars (odd, since these were archaic trucks for cars of a modern design) and were illuminated. These cars were produced in coach, vista dome, and observation configurations. They have also been used for a T C A Bicentennial set and the Quicksilver Express set of 1982. Since taking over in 1986, Lionel Trains, Inc. has expanded this line considerably. In 1987 LTI produced a handsome set of Pennsylvania 2400-series cars in authentic tuscan and black with gold lettering. To make sure that the lettering was bright and crisp, Lionel's factory workers stamped each side of every car three times, using the

Tampo process — six operations per car! New Amtrak cars were made in 1988 as part of a "Silver Spike" set; and combines, baggage cars and diners were made later for both sets.

In 1989, a six-car set of O27 passenger cars was made in two-tone New York Central gray, meant to go with the 18606 N Y C 2-6-4 Atlantic steam engine. This set was popular despite some problems with the engine. Another O27 set in attractive forest green was released in 1990, this time lettered for the Northern Pacific. Still another set followed in 1991, decorated in the orange and brown of the Illinois Central.

In 1990 the Service Station Special set featured four Lionel Lines passenger cars in gray, green and yellow, trailing another good looking 18611 2-6-4 Lionel Lines Atlantic steamer. The cars, named for Michigan cities significant to modern Lionel, have helped make this set a big seller.

"General" - Style Passenger Cars

In 1978 Fundimensions revived the "General" style baggage and coach cars to accompany its reissue of the "General" engine the year before. This old-time car has also been used in Rock Island and Peoria three-car sets, Baltimore and Ohio cars, and one straggler as part of the James Gang set (which also included other freight cars). In 1986 two more cars identical to the 1978 versions, except for their numbers, were produced as part of a special set available only through American Express. These cars were faithful reproductions of the postwar issues. The 1988 Service Station set, the "Dry Gulch," features three of these cars in Virginia and Truckee markings. Another single baggage/mail car appeared in 1990's "Badlands" set, and T C A got into the act with a handsome General-style car issued for its 1990 Atlanta convention.

Long Extruded Aluminum Passenger Cars

Nice as these cars were, they were not the passenger cars everyone was waiting for. Those emerged in 1979 with the reissue of the big extruded aluminum cars from the fabled Congressional Limited in beautiful Pennsylvania markings. Instead of the flat finish of the postwar issues, the new Lionel cars had a polished aluminum finish which looked great behind the Pennsylvania F-3 twin-motored diesels also produced in that year. A baggage car, two passenger coaches, a vista dome car and an observation car formed the original set, but Fundimensions later added a diner car, a combine, and an extra passenger car to the set. These cars were an outstanding success for Fundimensions, and it was inevitable that more would follow.

That is exactly what happened in 1980. A startling Burlington Zephyr set was produced with chrome-plated twin F-3 diesels and the same five basic cars with authentic Zephyr-style lettering. As with the Pennsylvania cars, the extra cars were soon produced. Perhaps the most breath-taking set of all came the next year, when Fundimensions issued the "J"-class Norfolk and Western steam engine and six stunning aluminum Powhatan Arrow passenger cars painted deep maroon with black roofs and gold lettering and striping. Many collectors believe this set to be the most beautiful passenger set ever produced in tinplate. Unfortunately, the quality was reflected in the stiff price exacted for the cars, especially the diner, which was produced later in extremely limited quantities.

The follow-up to the Powhatan Arrow set was impressive, too. In 1982 Fundimensions produced the long-awaited Southern Pacific Daylight set. This set was originally pulled by an F-3 pair of diesels, but in 1983 the "J"-class die was used to produce a terrific model of the Gs4 Daylight steam engine. A nearly identical steam engine (a Gs2 rather than Gs4) was made in 1991. The passenger cars were done in bright red, orange and black colors made famous by the elite West Coast train of the 1940s. As before, separate-sale cars came out later. Unfortunately, Southern Pacific fans noted deviations in the color schemes from the original. Like the Norfolk and Western set, the Daylight set has attracted a big following because of its beautiful color scheme. Today, in fact, this is the single most valuable set made by modern Lionel, partly because of the very limited quantities (and high premiums) of the diner and dome cars, as well as for the F-3 B units and the Gs4 steam engines.

By this time Fundimensions was really on a roll, producing set after beautiful set of these passenger cars in colors and styles no postwar aluminum set could hope to match. In 1983, however, Fundimensions changed the style of the cars. All of the previous aluminum cars had been made with stylish fluted sides and roofs, just as their postwar predecessors were. With the New York Central cars of 1983, Fundimensions eliminated the scribed sides and roofs and produced the cars with smooth sides and roofs. To be sure, the cars were still very attractive, but collectors soon voiced complaints about them. For one thing, the smooth-sided cars would fingerprint very easily, and the fingerprints were difficult to remove. Worse than that, the paint on the cars would chip all too easily, leaving unsightly aluminum marks through the paint. This was, of course, one way Fundimensions could keep the cost of these very expensive cars down, but for many collectors the New York Central set represented a distinct decline in quality. As before, the cars were accompanied by New York Central F-3 diesels, and separate-sale cars were added to the set.

The 1984 set, in Union Pacific Overland Limited colors, sparked vehement complaints. Two distinctly different shades of yellow were used for the locomotives, and more often than not they did not match. Collectors would thus have to hunt through many boxes to find locomotive units with colors properly matching. Worse, the plastic doors used on the passenger cars did not match the color of the paint used on the cars, and there were even two shades of yellow paint. The observation cars did not match the rest of the set. In addition, collectors complained that the red striping on the cars was very poorly applied, giving the smooth-sided cars a rather cheap look. Lionel was, in fact, having production problems at the time, and it is unfortunate that such a fine set fell victim to the difficulties the factory was experiencing. These sets have sold somewhat poorly as a result.

For 1985 Lionel rectified the error somewhat, but at the cost of repeating a successful formula until it wore out its welcome. That year saw the production of a smooth-sided set in brown and orange Illinois Central "City of New Orleans" colors. This time, at least, the quality was right; the colors looked very good and the set, pulled by a great-looking Illinois Central A-B-A trio, was very impressive. So was the price! This was the sixth set issued as aluminum passenger cars pulled by F-3 premium diesels. The tremendous expense of these sets raises the question of how extensive the resources of modern era collectors really are.

Whether for that reason or because of the turmoil created by the management changeover, Lionel gave passenger car collectors a brief rest. Then in 1989 a new set in Amtrak colors appeared, and this time the extruded bodies returned to the fluted side and roof designs of their pre-1983 predecessors. 1989 also saw the introduction of a new style body, the full-length vista dome, which looked much more realistic than the partial vista dome cars used earlier. In 1991 a stunning new Santa Fe set came out, 30 years after the last Santa Fe passenger cars disappeared from the postwar Lionel line. The new set marks several interesting firsts — the cars include the first use of silver-painted trucks, the F-3 diesels pulling the cars carry the first RailSounds electronics used in a passenger set, and the rear car is a very interesting new body style — a combination observation/vista dome design.

As befits a top-of-the-line product, Lionel's long aluminum passenger cars all contain the best features: illumination with silhouette window strips (except the baggage cars) and die-cast trucks with operating couplers. And, of course, each set is pulled by the best of Lionel's massive steam and diesel engines. All extruded aluminum passenger cars were available for separate-sale only, never in a set box. However, one operator caution: these cars, and several of the longer diesels, cannot negotiate O27 switches.

One must admit that these aluminum cars have formed the consist of some truly magnificent sets which illustrate the apex of tinplate achievement.

Overall, modern era Lionel has met the challenge of producing passenger cars extremely well. The beginning collector can secure quite a few passenger cars (aside from the aluminum ones) without severe damage to the wallet. The earliest Pennsylvania, Milwaukee, and Baltimore and Ohio 9500-series cars are readily available, except for the full baggage cars, which are very scarce items. The 1987 Pennsylvania 2400-type cars are quite inexpensive, and Lionel Trains, Inc. has even produced a good looking little 4-4-2 Columbia steamer to pull them. This engine and the Pennsylvania cars make a very handsome train at a modest (for Lionel) cost.

With such sets, you too can return to an apparently much more innocent day than ours, when miniature passenger trains ran without a care or a schedule on a tinplate layout. The power to enthrall is still there.

Passenger Car Numbering System

Lionel reserved the 9500-series numbers for its passenger cars from 1973 to 1984, when it began running out of numbers. It then switched to the 7200-series which also absorbed some of the add-ons to earlier sets.

One exception was the short O27 streamlined style, which began its modern era career with the Lake Shore Limited set in 1976, numbered in the 6400-series. Lionel appeared to have plans to make more of these cars or sets, but the next set with these cars did not appear until 1982 — the Quicksilver Express — and was numbered in the 7200-series.

In the post-1986 five-digit era, Lionel has apparently decided to number its long extruded aluminum cars (considered Collector pieces) in the 19100-series. The smaller O27 streamlined cars and the General-style coaches will appear in the 16000-series. We have yet to see the plan for the short Madison cars (9500-style) because no sets have yet been made — the last one to appear was the Wabash Fallen Flags No. 1 set in 1986. The add-on diner cars made recently for the 9500-series Madison sets have been given 19000-series numbers. Many passenger cars do not carry their catalogue number. One interesting piece of trivia regarding passenger cars: only one carries a "BLT" date (the 16040 Badlands car)!

All passenger cars have come in sets or have been issued as add-ons to sets. Only two straggler General-style baggage cars appeared in other freight sets. Most sets were only sold separately (no set box). This is true for all the long aluminum cars, and for most of the short Madison cars.

The number of distinct passenger sets is actually quite limited — only 31 have been made in regular production since 1973. Three train club sets (two T C A and one T T O S) are described in Volume II, first edition.

PASSENGER CAR LISTINGS

491 NORFOLK AND WESTERN: See 7203.

577 NORFOLK AND WESTERN: See 9562.

578 NORFOLK AND WESTERN: See 9563.

579 NORFOLK AND WESTERN: See 9564.

580 NORFOLK AND WESTERN: See 9565.

581 NORFOLK AND WESTERN: See 9566.

582 NORFOLK AND WESTERN: See 9567.

0511 ST. LOUIS: 1981, 9500-style baggage car; T C A; see Volume II, first edition.

1973, 1974, 1975 T C A: Short O27 streamlined observation, coach, and coach; Bicentennial Specials; see Volume II, first edition.

9100 AMTRAK: 1989; see 19100.

9101 AMTRAK: 1989; see 19101.

9102 AMTRAK: 1989; see 19102.

9103 AMTRAK: 1989; see 19103.

9104 AMTRAK: 1989; see 19104.

GD VG EXC MT

9105 AMTRAK: 1989; see 19105.

9106 AMTRAK: 1989; see 19106.

9109 SANTA FE: 1991; see 19109.

9110 SANTA FE: 1991; see 19110.

9111 SANTA FE: 1991; see 19111.

9112 SANTA FE: 1991; see 19112.

9113 SANTA FE: 1991; see 19113.

LAKE SHORE LIMITED, 1976-1977

The following seven passenger cars made up the Amtrak Lake Shore Limited, modern Lionel's first regular reissue of the short O27 streamlined passenger cars since 1966. The first four cars (6403-6406) made up the 1663 boxed set, along with the 8664 Alco diesel. This is one of the few occasions Fundimensions placed a passenger set in its Traditional Line. The remaining three cars (6410-6412) were separate-sale add-ons to the set in 1977. All the cars are illuminated and have two operating couplers, except the observation car, which has one. Numbers in blue are centered on the lower body under the windows. The cars use the plastic Type IV wood-beam passenger trucks. The window stripes lack the silhouettes of the later Silver Spike set. All the cars are silver-painted with the red, white and blue Amtrak arrow logos and strips between the windows. This set and later Amtrak sets were good sellers because of the large number of Amtrak collectors. At the time, Lionel may have had plans to make other O27 passenger sets in the 6400-series, and created this number sequence to distinguish them from the larger passenger cars in the 9500-series. But this is the only passenger set with 6400-series numbers.

6403 AMTRAK: 1976-77, short O27 streamlined vista dome; silver with red and blue window stripes. This car and 6404, 6405 and 6406 were part of the 1663 Lake Shore Limited set.

15   20   45   65

6404 AMTRAK: 1976-77, short O27 streamlined Pullman; matches 6403. See Lake Shore Limited description preceding 6403.   15   20   45   65

6405 AMTRAK: 1976-77, short O27 streamlined Pullman; matches 6403. See Lake Shore Limited description preceding 6403.   15   20   45   65

6406 AMTRAK: 1976-77, short O27 streamlined observation; matches 6403. See Lake Shore Limited description preceding 6403.   15   20   45   65

6410 AMTRAK: 1977, short O27 streamlined Pullman; matches 6403. This and the 6411 and 6412 cars were offered as separate-sale items to expand the Lake Shore Limited set. See description preceding 6403.   10   15   30   50

6411 AMTRAK: 1977, short O27 streamlined Pullman; matches 6403. See Lake Shore Limited description preceding 6403.   10   15   30   50

6412 AMTRAK: 1977, short O27 streamlined vista dome; matches 6403. See Lake Shore Limited description preceding 6403.   —   —   30   50

QUICKSILVER EXPRESS, 1982-1983

The next three entries comprise a surprisingly handsome Traditional Line set called the Texas and Pacific Quicksilver Express,

the second regularly-catalogued modern era appearance of the short O27 streamlined passenger cars. Unlike the Lake Shore Limited, no later add-ons for this set were produced, a pity because the deep blue and silver sides and silver roofs on these cars are among the better color schemes made by Lionel. Collectors seemed to agree, and the set is somewhat hard to find now. The three cars (7200-7202) came in a boxed set (1253) with the 8268/8269 powered/dummy T & P Alco diesels. All the cars are illuminated (no silhouettes on the window strips), have silver lettering and stripes, and two operating couplers, except the observation car which has only one. Each car uses the plastic Type IV wood-beam passenger trucks.

7200 QUICKSILVER: 1982-83, short O27 streamlined Pullman; blue and silver; illuminated. Part of 1253 Quicksilver Express.   —   25   35   50

7201 QUICKSILVER: 1982-83, short O27 streamlined vista dome; matches 7200. See Quicksilver Express description preceding 7200.   —   25   35   50

7202 QUICKSILVER: 1982-83, short O27 streamlined observation; matches 7200. See Quicksilver Express description preceding 7200.   —   25   35   50

7203 NORFOLK AND WESTERN: 1982, long extruded aluminum dining car; uncatalogued; "491" is the number on the car, not 7203; add-on to Powhatan Arrow set; matches 9562. Announced in 1982 Fall Collector Center brochure. Quite hard to find. See Powhatan Arrow description preceding 9562 entry.   —   —   275   400

7204 SOUTHERN PACIFIC: 1982, long extruded aluminum dining car; uncatalogued; no number on car; add-on to Southern Pacific Daylight set of 1982; matches 9589. Very hard to find. See Southern Pacific Daylight description preceding 9589 entry. Appeared in 1982 Fall Collector Center brochure.   —   —   275   400

7205 DENVER: 1982, 9500-style combine; T C A; see Volume II, first edition.

7206 LOUISVILLE: 1983, 9500-style coach; T C A; see Volume II, first edition.

7207 NEW YORK CENTRAL: 1983, long extruded aluminum dining car; uncatalogued; add-on to the Twentieth Century Limited set; matches 9594. See Twentieth Century Limited set description preceding 9594 entry. Appeared in 1983 Fall collector Center brochure.   —   —   175   300

7208 PENNSYLVANIA: 1983, long extruded aluminum dining car; uncatalogued; "JOHN HANCOCK"; add-on to Pennsylvania Congressional Limited set of 1979; matches 9569 through 9575. See Congressional Limited set description preceding 9570 entry. Appeared in 1983 Fall Collector Center brochure.   —   —   175   250

7210 UNION PACIFIC: 1984, long extruded aluminum dining car. Part of Union Pacific Overland set. See set description preceding 9546 entry. Unlike other diner cars, this one was catalogued with the set.   —   —   125   225

7211 SOUTHERN PACIFIC: 1983, long extruded aluminum vista dome car; uncatalogued; no number on car; add-on to Southern Pacific Daylight set of 1982; matches 9589. Very hard to find. See Southern Pacific Daylight description preceding 9589 entry. Appeared in 1983 Fall Collector Center brochure.   —   —   300   400

B. Greenberg photograph

...eral-style passenger cars. The top two shelves show the B&O General set from 1983. The bottom shelves show old-style coaches from other General ...ts.

...*shelf:* 8315 B&O 4-4-0 General locomotive (see Steam Locomotive chapter for listing); 7215 Baltimore and Ohio.

...*nd shelf:* 7216 Baltimore and Ohio; 7217 Baltimore and Ohio.

...*rd shelf:* 9552 Western & Atlantic; 9560 Rock Island & Peoria.

...*om shelf:* 16010 Virginia & Truckee, from the 1988 Service Station Special set.

	GD	VG	EXC	MT

7212 PITTSBURGH: 1984, 9500-style coach; T C A; see Volume II, first edition.

BALTIMORE AND OHIO, 1983-1984

This General-style Traditional Line set (1351) was catalogued in 1983 and 1984 with the 8315 General locomotive and the three following cars: 7215, 7216 and 7217. General-type old-time passenger sets have usually been brisk sellers, and this set was no exception. Each car had bright blue sides with white trim round the windows and doors, white lettering and numbers, black roof, plastic arch bar trucks and two operating couplers. Each is also illuminated with window silhouettes.

7215 BALTIMORE AND OHIO: 1983-84, General-style coach; blue sides; black roof; white window striping and lettering. Part of 1351 Baltimore and Ohio set with 7216 and 7217.

		30	50
—	—	30	50

7216 BALTIMORE AND OHIO: 1983, General-style coach; matches 7215. See set description preceding 7215.

—	—	30	50

See Factory Errors and Prototypes chapter in Volume II, first edition.

7217 BALTIMORE AND OHIO: 1983, General-style baggage car; large multicolor eagle electrocal on side; matches 7215. See set description preceding 7215.

—	—	30	50

ILLINOIS CENTRAL "CITY OF NEW ORLEANS", 1985, 1987

The following six entries comprise a set of six long extruded aluminum cars known as the "City of New Orleans" set. Intended to go with the 8580/8581/8582 Illinois Central F-3 diesels, this was a separate-sale only set (no set box). The cars were all bright brown with a broad orange stripe on the lower body and yellow highlight stripes. Yellow "ILLINOIS CENTRAL" lettering is centered above the windows, and brown name and numbers are on the orange stripe below the windows. Like all long aluminum passenger cars, these are illuminated (except the baggage car) with window silhouettes and have the Type VII die-cast O Gauge four-wheel passenger trucks. This set did not sell as well as the other long aluminum passenger sets, possibly because collectors

A sampling of Pullmans from Lionels fabulous long extruded aluminum passenger car sets.   R. Kaptur Collection; B. Greenberg photogr:
Top shelf: Two versions of the 9588 Burlington vista dome. The car on the right is a factory error with no lettering above the windows.
Second shelf: 9575 Pennsylvania from the "Congressional Limited"; 580 (9565) Norfolk and Western from the "Powhatan Arrow."
Third shelf: 9549 Union Pacific from the "Overland Limited"; 9597 New York Central from the "20th Century Limited."
Bottom shelf: 7223 Illinois Central from the "City of New Orleans"; 9104 Amtrak (see listing 19104).

	GD	VG	EXC	MT

had reached some saturation after top-of-the-line sets were issued in each of the previous six years. This set may well have the most unusually named cars yet made by Lionel. It was catalogued in 1985 and in 1987, but was also available in 1986.

7220 ILLINOIS CENTRAL: 1985-87, long extruded aluminum baggage car; smooth-sided medium brown body (although pictured in dark brown in catalogue, production pieces are lighter in shade); orange and gold striping; gold "ILLINOIS CENTRAL" above windows; brown "RAILWAY EXPRESS AGENCY" and "BAGGAGE" lettering; not illuminated (the other cars in the set are); die-cast O Gauge four-wheel passenger trucks; operating couplers. Part of City of New Orleans set, whose components were all offered for separate-sale. See set description above.
— — 75 100

7221 ILLINOIS CENTRAL: 1985-87, long extruded aluminum combine; "LAKE PONTCHARTRAIN"; matches 7220. See City of New Orleans set description preceding 7220 entry.
— — 75 100

7222 ILLINOIS CENTRAL: 1985-87, long extruded aluminum passenger coach; "KING COAL"; matches 7221. See City of New Orleans set description preceding 7220 entry.
— — 75 120

7223 ILLINOIS CENTRAL: 1985-87, long extruded aluminum passenger coach; "BANANA ROAD"; matches 7221. See City of New Orleans set description preceding 7220 entry.
— — 75 120

7224 ILLINOIS CENTRAL: 1985-87, long extruded aluminum dining car; "GENERAL BEAUREGARD"; matches 7221. See City of New Orleans set description preceding 7220 entry.
— — 75 120

7225 ILLINOIS CENTRAL: 1985-87, long extruded aluminum observation car; "MEMPHIS"; red rear lights; lighted rear "City of New Orleans" drumhead; otherwise matches 7221. See City of New Orleans set description preceding 7220 entry.
— — 75 120

WABASH FALLEN FLAGS SERIES NO. 1, 1986-1987

Wabash's "Bluebird" paint schemes have always been favorites among prototype and model railroaders, and so it was in 1986 when this first set in the new Fallen Flags series was released. That, and the fact that it was the first short Madison-style set released since the Chessie in 1980, meant that this set sold very well and is now quite difficult to obtain. The set (separate-sale only, no set box) included the next six Madison-style 9500-series cars and was headed by a very handsome 4-6-2 Pacific steam locomotive, another reason for the set's popularity. Each car was dark blue with gold stripes and lettering and a black roof. The last three were lettered for cities along the Wabash route. Each car was illuminated with window silhouettes (except the baggage) and each had Type VIII six-wheel die-cast passenger trucks with operating couplers. This remains the only passenger set released

he Milwaukee Special passenger set, the first modern era passenger set from 1973.
p shelf: 9500 City of Milwaukee Pullman; 9501 City of Aberdeen Pullman.
cond shelf: 9502 President Washington observation; 9503 City of Chicago Pullman.
ttom shelf: 9504 City of Tacoma Pullman; 9506 City of Seattle Pullman.

F. Stem Collection; B. Greenberg photograph

GD   VG   EXC   MT

o date in either of Lionel's Specialty Collector series honoring the reat United States railroads — the Fallen Flag series, and the arlier Famous American Railroad series.

7227 WABASH: 1986-87, 9500-style dining car; dark blue body; old lettering; gold stripes; black roof; lights; passenger silhouet-es; three short stacks atop roof; die-cast six-wheel trucks. Part f Fallen Flags Series No. 1, whose components were all sold eparately. See Wabash set description above.

— — 75 100

7228 WABASH: 1986-87, 9500-style baggage car; matches 7227. See Wabash set description preceding 7227 entry.

— — 75 100

7229 WABASH: 1986-87, 9500-style combine; matches 7227. See Wabash set description preceding 7227 entry.

— — 75 100

7230 WABASH: 1986-87, 9500-style Pullman coach; "CITY OF ERU"; matches 7227. See Wabash set description preceding 7227 entry.

— — 75 100

7231 WABASH: 1986-87, 9500-style Pullman coach; "CITY OF DANVILLE"; matches 7227. See Wabash set description preced-ng 7227 entry.

— — 75 100

7232 WABASH: 1986-87, 9500-style observation car; "CITY OF WABASH"; matches 7227. See Wabash set description preceding 7227 entry.

— — 75 100

AMERICAN EXPRESS GENERAL SET, 1986

An uncatalogued special set for American Express in 1986 (1608) featured the following two General-type coach and baggage cars, neaded by the 8630 General locomotive, and included the 6587 latcar with horses and the 7312 stock car. This set was very

similar to the separate-sale General set released by Lionel in 1978, except it was boxed and included the stock car. Many of Lionel's old-style General passenger cars have come in sets with freight cars, which mirrored the practice on real railroads during the 19th century. Both the passenger cars were yellow with tuscan roof and lettering, illuminated, and had Type V plastic arch bar trucks with operating couplers. This limited-edition uncatalogued set is now quite hard to find.

7241 WESTERN & ATLANTIC: 1986, uncatalogued; General-style passenger coach; pale translucent yellow body; tus-can roof and lettering; illuminated; plastic arch bar trucks; operat-ing couplers. Part of uncatalogued American Express set 1608. T. Taylor Collection. — — 30 50

7242 WESTERN & ATLANTIC: 1986, General-style bag-gage car; uncatalogued; matches 7241. Also part of uncatalogued American Express General set 1608. See set description preced-ing 7241 entry. T. Taylor Collection. — — 30 50

A NOTE ON THE LIGHTING PROBLEMS OF THE 9500-SERIES PASSENGER CARS

By Henry Edmunds

When Lionel first made the 9500-series passenger cars in 1973, the firm found it had a problem with translucence of the plastic when the cars were lighted. If the cars were left unlined, the light would glow through the roofs and sides, creating an unsightly "blob" of light instead of the lighted window effect Lionel wanted. One early attempt to fix the problem involved painting the tops of the light bulbs with heat-resistant silver paint. That did not work because it cut the light down too much.

To solve this problem as inexpensively as possible, Lionel designed a cardboard roof liner which would come down a little way over

The remainder of The Milwaukee Special passenger set, all later add-ons to the set.
A. Rudman, F. Stem Collection; B. Greenberg photo
Top shelf: 9506 United States Mail combine; 9511 City of Minneapolis Pullman, a special coupon car.
Middle shelf: 9522 American Railway Express & Baggage, hard to find; 19003 Dining Car, purchased in 1988.
Bottom shelf: 9527 Roosevelt Campaign Special.

the sides inside the car and completely shade the roof. Overall, this "fix" worked well, except when the liner slid down to cover the windows, in which case the purchaser would have to laboriously pry open the roof pieces to push the liner back up to the roof.

Overall, Lionel's 9500 passenger cars show four different schemes for shading the light in these cars, as follows:

1. No cardboard roof liner present.
2. Unfinished plain cardboard liner.
3. White finished cardboard liner.
4. Unfinished yellow cardboard liner extending down the sides of the car with holes for the windows.

THE MILWAUKEE ROAD "MILWAUKEE SPECIAL", 1973-1976

This set was the first entry by the fledgling Lionel/Fundimensions group into the passenger set arena. The cars, a new style for Lionel, were based on the postwar Madison cars, but because the dies for the postwar versions had been lost, the modern cars were not quite a match and are quite a bit shorter. Still, they are excellent models. Their first appearance was with the 9500, 9502, and 9503 making up the Milwaukee Special set (1387), with the 8305 4-4-2 Milwaukee steam engine in 1973. This boxed set was followed in 1974 by three Pullmans (9501, 9504 and 9505), by the 9506 combo in 1975, and by the 9522 baggage car in late 1975. Two unusual set components added later were the 9511 Pullman car available only through a special coupon offer, and a 9527 Presidential Campaign observation car from 1976. Finally, a 19003 diner car was released in 1988. Unfortunately, this last car does not entirely match the orange of the earlier cars, but it does have operating couplers unlike its counterparts. In all, 11 Milwaukee cars were made.

GD VG EXC MT

The cars in this set are orange with maroon roofs (painted flat or glossy maroon) and are illuminated with white plastic window strips (no silhouettes). They have gold and black "THE MILWAUKEE ROAD" lettering centered above the windows and the name of the car centered below, with car numbers in gold near the ends. The names on the coaches are the principal cities on the Milwaukee Road routes. Each has plastic Type IV wood-beam passenger trucks and body-mounted dummy couplers (except the 19003 diner). The dummy couplers are the principal operating objection to the set.

9500 THE MILWAUKEE ROAD: 1973, 9500-style Pullman; "CITY OF MILWAUKEE"; flat orange; flat maroon roof fastened with tabs through floor; illuminated. Part of 1387 Milwaukee Special set. First in a new modern series of passenger cars based on a shortened version of the postwar heavyweight Madison passenger car. See set description above.
15 25 40 60

9501 THE MILWAUKEE ROAD: 1974, 9500-style Pullman; "CITY OF ABERDEEN"; add-on to Milwaukee Special set; matches 9500. See set description preceding 9500 entry. Mint condition requires bonus coupon described on box.
(A) Flat orange sides; flat maroon roof. 15 25 30 40
(B) Shiny orange sides; shiny maroon roof.
15 25 35 45

9502 THE MILWAUKEE ROAD: 1973, 9500-style observation; "PRESIDENT WASHINGTON"; matches 9500. Part of 1387 Milwaukee Special set. See set description preceding 9500 entry.
15 25 40 60

9503 THE MILWAUKEE ROAD: 1973, 9500-style Pullman; "CITY OF CHICAGO"; matches 9500. Part of 1387 Milwaukee Special set. See set description preceding 9500 entry.
15 25 40 60

9507 Pennsylvania.

	GD	VG	EXC	MT

9504 THE MILWAUKEE ROAD: 1974, 9500-style Pullman; "CITY OF TACOMA"; add-on to Milwaukee Special set. See set description preceding 9500 entry. Mint condition requires bonus coupon described on box.

(A) Roof fastened with tabs through floor.

	15	25	30	40

(B) Roof fastened through windows.

	15	25	30	40

9505 THE MILWAUKEE ROAD: 1974, 9500-style Pullman; "CITY OF SEATTLE"; add-on to Milwaukee Special set. See set description preceding 9500 entry.

(A) Tabs through floor hold roof.

	15	25	30	40

(B) Tabs through windows.

	15	25	30	40

9506 THE MILWAUKEE ROAD: 1975-1976, 9500-style baggage combine; "UNITED STATES MAIL/RAILWAY POST OFFICE"; add-on to Milwaukee Special set. See set description preceding 9500 entry. Announced in a late 1974 center brochure but released in 1975.

	12	15	25	40

PENNSYLVANIA "BROADWAY LIMITED", 1974-1976

The success of the new-style 9500-series passenger cars in the Milwaukee set naturally meant Lionel would go back for more. The Broadway Limited set (1487) came out in 1974 with the 9507, 9508 and 9509 cars pulled by the 8304 Pennsylvania steam locomotive in a boxed set. The set was listed, but not illustrated, in 1975. Four separate-sale cars followed in 1975 (9510 combination and the 9513, 9514 and 9515 Pullmans). The rare 9521 baggage car appeared in a late 1975 brochure and the 1976 catalogue, and a 9528 Campaign Special version of the observation car was listed in a late 1976 brochure (along with Milwaukee and B & O cars similarly decorated). As with those other two sets, a diner car (19002) was released in the late 1980s. Ten Broadway Limited cars were made in all.

All the cars in the Broadway Limited set are decorated in the classic Pennsylvania tuscan with black roofs. Gold lettering "PENNSYLVANIA" is below the windows. Like their Milwaukee predecessors, each is illuminated and has four-wheel Type IV wood-beam passenger trucks with dummy couplers attached directly to the body. Only the recent 19002 diner has operating couplers. Once again the car names designate major stops on P R R's network.

9507 PENNSYLVANIA: 1974-75, 9500-style Pullman; "CITY OF/MANHATTAN"; tuscan body with black roof; gold lettering; illuminated. Part of 1487 Broadway Limited set.

	15	20	40	60

9508 PENNSYLVANIA: 1974-75, 9500-style Pullman; "CITY OF PHILADELPHIA"; matches 9507. Part of 1487 Broadway Limited set. See set description preceding 9507 entry.

	15	20	40	60

	GD	VG	EXC	MT

9509 PENNSYLVANIA: 1974-75, 9500-style observation; "PRESIDENT ADAMS"; matches 9507. Part of 1487 Broadway Limited set. See set description preceding 9507 entry.

	20	30	50	75

9510 PENNSYLVANIA: 1975, 9500-style baggage-mail- coach combine; illuminated; "UNITED STATES MAIL RAILWAY POST OFFICE" in gold heat-stamped letters; add-on to the Broadway Limited set; matches 9507. See set description preceding 9507 entry. Announced in a late 1974 dealer flyer and released in 1975.

	10	15	30	50

9511 THE MILWAUKEE ROAD: 1974, 9500-style Pullman; uncatalogued; "CITY OF MINNEAPOLIS"; special coupon car; add-on to the Milwaukee Special set; matches 9500. See set description preceding 9500 entry.

	15	25	30	50

9512 SUMMERDALE JUNCTION: 1974, 9500-style coach; T T O S; see Volume II, first edition.

9513 PENNSYLVANIA: 1975, 9500-style Pullman; "PENN SQUARE"; add-on to the Broadway Limited set; matches 9507. See set description preceding 9507 entry.

	15	25	30	50

9514 PENNSYLVANIA: 1975, 9500-style Pullman; "TIMES SQUARE"; add-on to the Broadway Limited set; matches 9507. See set description preceding 9507 entry.

	15	25	30	50

9515 PENNSYLVANIA: 1975, 9500-style Pullman; "WASHINGTON CIRCLE"; add-on to the Broadway Limited set; matches 9507. See set description preceding 9507 entry.

	15	25	30	50

BALTIMORE AND OHIO "CAPITOL LIMITED", 1975-1976

This set was the third in Lionel's successful 9500-series Madison car trains, following the Milwaukee Special and Pennsylvania "Broadway Limited". It followed the same formula: an 8304 B & O Pacific steam locomotive pulled a set of three cars (9517, 9518 and 9519) in a top-of-the-line Traditional set (1587) released in 1975. A baggage car (9523) was released in a special late 1975 announcement with the baggage cars for the other two sets. And in 1976 three more Pullmans (9516, 9521 and 9525) were added to the set. Just like the earlier two sets, a Campaign observation car (9529) appeared in late 1976 and the 19010 diner car appeared in 1989, thirteen years after the last car in the set was produced. In all, nine B & O Capitol Limited cars have been made. It is interesting to note that Lionel titled the set "Capital Limited" in the 1975 catalogue. The set is referred to both ways.

These handsome cars were again diminished by the use of dummy body-mounted couplers, as on the earlier sets. Happily, this set marked the final use of such couplers. Beginning with the Southern Crescent Limited in 1977, truck- mounted operating couplers were used for all subsequent 9500- style cars. The cars in the Capitol Limited are dark blue with gray roofs and broad gray stripes through the windows. Each has yellow lettering, yellow accent stripes, and a yellow capitol dome logo to the right of the windows. "BALTIMORE AND OHIO" is centered above the windows and the car name centered below. Each car is illuminated with translucent window strips and has Type IV plastic wood-beam passenger trucks. The 19010 diner car has operating couplers.

A representative sampling of coaches from Lionels colorful 9500 passenger cars. All came in sets.
R. Kaptur, F. Stem Collections; B. Greenberg phot
Top shelf: 9503 The Milwaukee Road from the Milwaukee Special; 9514 Pennsylvania from "The Broadway Limited."
Second shelf: 9525 Baltimore and Ohio from "The Capitol Limited"; 9532 Southern from the "Crescent Limited".
Third shelf: 9539 Jersey Central's "Blue Comet"; 9583 Chessie from the Chessie Steam Special.
Bottom shelf: 9556 The Alton Limited; 7230 Wabash from the first Fallen Flags set.

	GD	VG	EXC	MT

9516 BALTIMORE AND OHIO: 1976, 9500-style Pullman; "MOUNTAIN TOP"; add-on to the Capitol Limited set; matches 9517. See set description above. **10 15 25 40**

9517 BALTIMORE AND OHIO: 1975, 9500-style coach; "CAPITAL CITY"; blue body; gray windows; yellow stripes; gray roof; illuminated. Part of 1587 Capitol Limited set. See set description preceding 9516 entry. **20 25 40 60**

9518 BALTIMORE AND OHIO: 1975, 9500-style observation; "NATIONAL VIEW"; illuminated; matches 9517. Part of 1587 Capitol Limited set. See set description preceding 9516 entry. **20 25 40 60**

9517 Baltimore and Ohio

9519 BALTIMORE AND OHIO: 1975, 9500-style baggage combine; "UNITED STATES MAIL"; illuminated; matches 9517. **20 25 40 6**

9520 PHOENIX: 1975, 9500-style combine; T T O S; se Volume II, first edition.

9521 PENNSYLVANIA: 1975-76, 9500-style double-door bag gage; illuminated; add-on to Broadway Limited set. See se description preceding 9507. Hard to find. Announced in late 197 dealer brochure and catalogued in 1976. **40 50 100 12**

9522 THE MILWAUKEE ROAD: 1975-76, 9500-styl double-door baggage car; illuminated; add-on to the Milwauke Special set. See set description preceding 9500 entry. Hard t find. Announced in late 1975 dealer brochure and catalogued i 1976. **40 50 100 12**

9523 BALTIMORE AND OHIO: 1975-76, 9500-style double door baggage car; "AMERICAN RAILWAY EXPRESS"; i luminated; add-on to the Capitol Limited set; matches 9517. Har to find. See set description preceding 9516 entry. Announced i late 1975 dealer brochure and catalogued in 1976. **40 50 60 8**

B. *Greenberg photograph*

Campaign Specials created in 1976 as add-ons to earlier passenger sets.
shelf: **9527 The Milwaukee Road.**
om shelf: **9529 Baltimore and Ohio; 9528 Pennsylvania.**

	GD	VG	EXC	MT

9524 BALTIMORE AND OHIO: 1976, 9500-style Pullman; "MARGRET CORBIN"; illuminated; add-on to Capitol Limited set; matches 9517. See set description preceding 9516 entry.

15   20   30   50

9525 BALTIMORE AND OHIO: 1976, 9500-style Pullman; "EMERALD BROOK"; add-on to Capitol Limited set; matches 9517. See set description preceding 9516 entry.

15   20   30   50

9526 SNOWBIRD: 1976, 9500-style observation; T T O S; see Volume II, first edition.

THE "CAMPAIGN SPECIALS"

The following three observation cars (one each for the Milwaukee, Pennsylvania and B & O sets) were the subjects of an unusual Lionel promotion in late 1976, prompted both by the Bicentennial spirit and an overstock of observation cars for the sets. The cars were issued in special "Campaign" boxes and supplied with bunting, campaign posters and a flag for the rear platform. In this manner, a user could run a "whistle-stop" campaign train the way the Presidential candidates did in the 1940s and 1950s. (Note, the election losers do not have their own cars!) A Milwaukee observation car was decorated for Roosevelt, a Pennsylvania car for Truman, and a B & O for Eisenhower. An added feature of the cars is that they came without attached couplers, although a small bag containing the couplers was enclosed in the box. Mint condition on these cars requires the two small envelopes, one containing the couplers and the other containing flag, pole, and small instruction sheet. I. D. Smith comment.

9527 THE MILWAUKEE ROAD: 1976, 9500-style campaign observation; uncatalogued; "ROOSEVELT"; red, white and blue bunting on car sides; small flag on rear platform; illuminated; add-on to Milwaukee Special set. See set description preceding 9500 entry. This and the next two cars were announced only in a 1976 dealer brochure.   20   40   50   65

	GD	VG	EXC	MT

9528 PENNSYLVANIA: 1976, 9500-style campaign observation; uncatalogued; "TRUMAN"; illuminated; add-on the Broadway Limited set; matches 9507. See set 9507 entry. Announced in late 1975 dealer brochure.   20   40   60   75

9529 BALTIMORE AND OHIO: 1976, 9500-style campaign observation; uncatalogued; "EISENHOWER"; illuminated; add-on to the Capitol Limited set; matches 9517. See set description preceding 9516 entry. Announced in late 1976 dealer brochure.

20   40   55   60

SOUTHERN RAILROAD "CRESCENT LIMITED" (OR "SOUTHERN CRESCENT"), 1977-1978

Lionel was clearly on a roll by 1977 with its 9500-style Madison cars. It made two significant changes when this set was released in 1977. First, Lionel altered the marketing scheme — no longer would these trains be Traditional Line cars issued together in a set box, but would be made as Collector Line separate-sale sets from this point on. That is, all the pieces would be considered part of the set, but would all be sold separately. Second, it corrected a persistent operator complaint by installing operating couplers in place of the undesirable dummy couplers used earlier.

Once again, the decorating scheme used on the Southern Crescent cars was a big hit among collectors. Each is a dark green with light green window strip and gold lettering and accent stripes. "CRESCENT LIMITED" is in gold centered above the windows with the car name centered below. Names famous in southern history, such as Robert E. Lee, Stonewall Jackson and P. G. T. Beauregard, were used on the coaches. All the cars are illuminated with translucent window strips and have Type IV plastic wood-beam passenger trucks.

All five of the following entries (9530 through 9534) were released in 1977 as separate-sale components of the set, along with the 8702 Southern 4-6-4 Hudson, another major step in upgrading these Madison-style sets. The set was catalogued again in 1978 and the 19001 diner car added in 1987.

GD   VG   EXC   MT

9530 CRESCENT LIMITED: 1977-78, 9500-style baggage; "JOEL CHANDLER HARRIS"; dark green body and roof; light apple green window stripe; gold edge striping and gold lettering; four-wheel wood-beam plastic trucks with operating truck-mounted couplers. (Previous cars in the 9500 heavyweight series had non-operating body-mounted couplers.) Part of the Southern "Crescent Limited" set, whose components were all sold separately. See set description above.   **15   20   30   50**

9531 CRESCENT LIMITED: 1977-78, 9500-style combination; "ANDREW PICKENS"; matches 9530. Part of the Southern "Crescent Limited" set, whose components were all sold separately. See set description above 9530 entry.   **15   20   30   50**

9532 CRESCENT LIMITED: 1977-78, 9500-style Pullman; "P. G. T./BEAUREGARD"; matches 9530. Part of the Southern "Crescent Limited" set, whose components were all sold separately. See set description above 9530 entry.   **15   20   30   50**

9533 CRESCENT LIMITED: 1977-78, 9500-style Pullman; "STONEWALL/JACKSON"; matches 9530. Part of the Southern "Crescent Limited" set, whose components were all sold separately. See set description above 9530 entry.   **15   20   30   50**

See Factory Errors and Prototypes chapter in Volume II, first edition.

9534 CRESCENT LIMITED: 1977-78, 9500-style observation; "ROBERT E. LEE"; matches 9530. Part of the Southern "Crescent Limited" set, whose components were all sold separately. See set description above 9530 entry.   **15   20   30   50**

See Factory Errors and Prototypes chapter in Volume II, first edition.

9535 COLUMBUS: 1977, 9500-style Pullman; T T O S; see Volume II, first edition.

JERSEY CENTRAL'S "THE BLUE COMET", 1978-1980

By the time this set was released, the old adage that bright-colored passenger train sets always sell had been proven conclusively. The Blue Comet set, whose distinguishing feature is the new six-wheel die-cast passenger trucks introduced with it, has been a great collector favorite right from the start. Its popularity can also be traced to fond memories of the original Standard Gauge and O Gauge Blue Comet sets produced by Lionel in the 1930s, both of which are nearly impossible to find today.

The modern Blue Comet continued Lionel's policy of bright graphics on the passenger cars. Each car is a deep blue with darker blue roof, cream white window strip and gold lettering, and gold highlight stripes. "THE BLUE COMET" is in widely-spaced words above the windows with the car names (named after actual comets) centered below the windows. A significant innovation on this set was the introduction of the Type VIII six-wheel die-cast passenger truck and operating couplers. This truck is used on all later issues of the 9500- series passenger cars. All the Blue Comet cars are illuminated with translucent window strips.

Following the marketing scheme of the Southern Crescent, all five cars of the Comet set (9536 through 9540) were offered for

GD   VG   EXC   MT

separate-sale only, in conjunction with the 8801 Blue Comet 4-6-4 Hudson. The 19000 diner car was added in 1987. The set was catalogued from 1978 through 1980.

9536 THE BLUE COMET: 1978-80, 9500-style baggage; "BARNARD"; blue unpainted plastic sides; dark blue roof; cream stripe through windows; gold lettering; gold stripes above and below windows; full detailed undercarriage; illuminated; die-cast six-wheel trucks; two disc couplers. Part of Blue Comet set, whose components were all sold separately. See set description above.
15   20   30   50

9537 THE BLUE COMET: 1978-80, 9500-style combination; "HALLEY"; matches 9536. Part of Blue Comet set, whose components were all sold separately. See set description preceding 9536 entry.   **15   20   30   50**

9538 THE BLUE COMET: 1978-80, 9500-style Pullman; "FAYE"; matches 9536. Part of Blue Comet set, whose components were all sold separately. See set description preceding 9536 entry.   **15   20   30   60**

9539 THE BLUE COMET: 1978-80, 9500-style Pullman; "WESTPHAL"; matches 9536. Part of Blue Comet set, whose components were all sold separately. See set description preceding 9536 entry.   **15   20   30   60**

9540 THE BLUE COMET: 1978-80, 9500-style observation; "TEMPEL"; matches 9536. Part of Blue Comet set, whose components were all sold separately. See set description preceding 9536 entry.   **10   15   30   50**

9541 SANTA FE: 1980-82, General- style baggage car; "RAILWAY EXPRESS AGENCY"; light tan body; cherry red roof and end platforms; black lettering and Santa Fe cross logo; not illuminated; plastic arch bar trucks; plastic wheels; dummy couplers. Part of 1053 The James Gang set. Lionel's General sets included both freight and passenger rolling stock.
—   —   20   30

9544 CHICAGO: 1980, 9500-style observation; T C A; see Volume II, first edition.

UNION PACIFIC "OVERLAND LIMITED", 1984

The Overland Limited set of yellow, red and gray long aluminum passenger cars joined an impressive 1984 offering of Collector Line equipment. This was the sixth F-3 powered aluminum passenger set offered in six years, and the paint quality problems encountered with the N Y C set in 1983, as well as the color matching problems with this set, resulted in relatively poor sales for this set, compared to earlier Lionel passenger sets. Collectors should be mindful that Lionel's operation was in Mexico at the time this set was produced.

The set (again separate-sale only, no box) consisted of the following five entries and the 7210 dining car (it is not clear why the diner is not numbered in the 9500-series with the rest of the set, since they were all made at the same time). The consist was pulled by the 8480/8481/8482 F-3 diesels, an impressive train when the color-matching is right.

Each car sports bright yellow sides, red lettering and highlight stripes, gray roofs and ends, and Type VII die-cast O Gauge passenger trucks with operating couplers. All except the baggage car are illuminated with silhouetted window strips.

	GD	VG	EXC	MT

9545 UNION PACIFIC: 1984, long extruded aluminum baggage car; yellow smooth-sided body; red striping and lettering; gray roof and ends. Part of the "Overland Limited" passenger set, whose components were all sold separately. See set description above. — — 75 100

9546 UNION PACIFIC: 1984, long extruded aluminum combine; illuminated; silhouettes in windows; otherwise matches 9545. Part of the Union Pacific "Overland Limited" set, whose components were all sold separately. See set description preceding 9545 entry. — — 75 100

9547 UNION PACIFIC: 1984, long extruded aluminum observation car; red taillights on rear; illuminated "Overland Limited" drumhead; otherwise matches 9546. Part of the "Overland Limited" set, whose components were all sold separately. See set description preceding 9545 entry. There have been vehement complaints from collectors that the yellow color on this car is much darker than the other cars in the set, and the doors do not match the body color. Numerous examples observed validate these complaints. — — 75 100

9548 UNION PACIFIC: 1984, long extruded aluminum passenger coach; "PLACID BAY"; "9548" is not on the car; matches 9546. Part of the "Overland Limited" set, whose components were all sold separately. See set description preceding 9545 entry. — — 75 100

9549 UNION PACIFIC: 1984, long extruded aluminum passenger coach; "OCEAN SUNSET"; "9549" is not on the car; matches 9546. Part of the "Overland Limited" set, whose components were all sold separately. See set description preceding 9545 entry. — — 75 100

"THE GENERAL", 1977-1980

Lionel made an exciting announcement in 1977 — the General locomotive and its 1860s-style freight and passenger cars would be revived after a wait of fifteen years, since the postwar version ceased production. The 1977 set, whose components were all sold separately only, was the first of seven similar sets, at various levels of quality, made over the next twelve years. The following two passenger coaches were lettered for the Western and Atlantic (like their 8701 locomotive) and were painted yellow with tuscan roofs, lettering and trim. The cars had Type V plastic arch bar trucks with operating couplers, and they were illuminated with translucent window strips. The set also included the 9553 flatcar with fences. The engine was catalogued in 1977 with the cars appearing in a year-end brochure. The full set was catalogued in 1978, 1979, and 1980.

9551 WESTERN & ATLANTIC: 1977-80, General-style baggage car; yellow body; tuscan platforms and roof; tuscan lettering; black stacks and ventilators; multicolor eagle logo; plastic arch bar trucks. Part of General set from 1977, whose components were all sold separately. First announced in a late 1977 flyer, then catalogued in 1978-80. — 15 30 50

9552 WESTERN & ATLANTIC: 1977-80, General-style coach; matches 9551. Part of General set from 1977, whose components were all sold separately. First announced in a late 1977 flyer, then catalogued in 1978-80. — 15 30 50

CHICAGO & ALTON "THE ALTON LIMITED", 1981

	GD	VG	EXC	MT

The following five entries (9554 through 9558) make up the separate-sale Alton Limited set, with the 8101 Chicago and Alton Hudson steam locomotive. The die-cast tender with the locomotive was the big news of this set, but the exceptionally colorful Alton paint scheme on the cars also contributed to this set's popularity. Each car is a deep maroon with a bright red window strip and silver roof. Gold lettering "THE ALTON LIMITED" highlight stripes and Type VIII die-cast six-wheel trucks complete the detail on these elegant cars. Each car is also illuminated with translucent window strips. A hard-to-find dining car (9599) was released in 1987. The "Red Train," as this set is also called, has become very difficult to obtain.

9554 THE ALTON LIMITED: 1981, 9500-series heavyweight-style baggage; "ARMSTRONG"; dark maroon body; silver roof; red window striping; gold lettering and highlight stripes; die-cast six-wheel passenger trucks. Part of the Alton Limited set, whose components were all sold separately. See set description above. — — 40 60

9555 THE ALTON LIMITED: 1981, 9500-style combine; "MISSOURI"; matches 9554. Part of Alton Limited set, whose components were all sold separately. See set description preceding 9554 entry. — — 40 60

9556 THE ALTON LIMITED: 1981, 9500-style coach; "WILSON"; matches 9554. Part of the Alton Limited set, whose components were all sold separately. See set description preceding 9554 entry. — — 50 80

9557 THE ALTON LIMITED: 1981, 9500-style coach; "WEBSTER GROVES"; matches 9554. Part of Alton Limited set, whose components were all sold separately. See set description preceding 9554 entry. — — 50 80

9558 THE ALTON LIMITED: 1981, 9500-style observation; "CHICAGO"; matches 9554. Part of Alton Limited set, whose components were all sold separately. See set description preceding 9554 entry. — — 50 80

ROCK ISLAND & PEORIA GENERAL SET, 1981-1982

The next three entries comprised a handsome General set released in 1981 with the chrome-plated 8004 General locomotive. This set differed from the earlier General sets in two ways: 1) it is considered a Collector, not a Traditional, set, and 2) it has three passenger coaches rather than one or two. This formula was repeated later with the B & O and Virginia Truckee sets. The cars are painted yellow-gold with tuscan roofs, lettering and trim. Each is illuminated and sports Type V arch bar trucks.

9559 ROCK ISLAND & PEORIA: 1981-82, General-style combine; light gold-painted body; tuscan roof, platforms, trim and lettering; multicolor big sky logo; black stacks and ventilators; illuminated; plastic arch bar trucks. Part of the Rock Island & Peoria set, whose components were all only available as separate-sale. See set description above. — — 35 50

9560 ROCK ISLAND & PEORIA: 1981-82, General-style coach; matches 9559. Part of Rock Island & Peoria General set, whose components were only available separately. See set description preceding 9559 entry. — — 35 50

	GD	VG	EXC	MT

9561 ROCK ISLAND & PEORIA: 1981-82, General- style coach; matches 9559. Part of Rock Island & Peoria General set, whose components were only available separately. See set description preceding 9559 entry. — — 35 50

NORFOLK AND WESTERN "POWHATAN ARROW", 1981

Collectors sat up and took notice when this set was released in 1981. It was enough that the beautiful 4-8-4 Norfolk in and Western bullet-nose "J" steam locomotive returned to the Lionel line after a twenty-year absence. But the long extruded aluminum cars in the set also marked two unique firsts: the first time the long cars had been painted (in maroon, gold and black, no less), and the long aluminum combine car made its debut with this set. Each car has a script "Powhatan Arrow" nameplate in gold, die-cast Type VII O Gauge passenger trucks, and all are illuminated with window silhouettes except the baggage car. A 9567 vista dome was added in late 1981 and a 7203 diner car was added in 1982. One unique feature about these cars: each carries a prototypical three- digit number — the catalogue numbers are not on the cars. As before, all components of this set were offered for separate-sale only. Many collectors consider this the most handsome passenger set Lionel (prewar, postwar, or modern era) has ever made, although the Southern Pacific "Daylight" will give it a run. In any case, this set is very hard to obtain.

9562 NORFOLK AND WESTERN: 1981, long extruded aluminum baggage; "Powhatan Arrow" in gold script; first painted extruded aluminum passenger car made by Lionel; black roof; maroon sides; gold striping and lettering; catalogue number is stamped on the boxes, not the cars; "577" is on the car. Part of the Powhatan Arrow set, whose components were all sold separately. See set description preceding 9562 entry. — — 90 125

9563 NORFOLK AND WESTERN: 1981, long extruded aluminum combine; "578" is the number on the car, not 9563; matches 9562. Part of Powhatan Arrow set, whose components were all sold separately. See set description preceding 9562 entry. — — 90 125

9564 NORFOLK AND WESTERN: 1981, long extruded aluminum coach; "579" is the number on the car, not 9564; matches 9562. Part of Powhatan Arrow set, whose components were all sold separately. See set description preceding 9562 entry. — — 110 150

9565 NORFOLK AND WESTERN: 1981, long extruded aluminum coach; "580" is the number on the car, not 9565; matches 9562. Part of Powhatan Arrow set, whose components were all sold separately. See set description preceding 9562 entry. — — 110 150

9566 NORFOLK AND WESTERN: 1981, long extruded aluminum observation; "581" is the number on the car, not 9566; matches 9562. Part of Powhatan Arrow set, whose components were all sold separately. See set description preceding 9562 entry. — — 90 125

9567 NORFOLK AND WESTERN: 1981, long extruded aluminum vista dome; uncatalogued; "582" is number on car, not 9567; matches 9562; add-on to Powhatan Arrow set. Appeared in the 1981 Fall Collector Center brochure. See set description preceding 9562 entry. — — 425 575

	GD	VG	EXC	MT

PENNSYLVANIA "CONGRESSIONAL LIMITED", 1979

This set was the first reissue of the long extruded aluminum cars since 1966, and they were long-awaited. Modern Lionel's versions were polished aluminum rather than flat, and as it would turn out, the modern company would issue many more cars for a given set than postwar Lionel did. In addition, modern Lionel has created four new body styles of the car (combine, diner, full vista dome and vista/observation). This first set (consisting of the 9570 through 9574 cars) was a curiosity in that, unlike later sets, it was not catalogued with a particular engine. In fact, the 8952-8953 P R R F-3 diesels with which it was intended to run did not match at all; the F-3s were Brunswick green! Collector pressure forced Lionel to make the 8970-8971 F-3 diesel combination in tuscan to match the stripes on the cars. These appeared in the same late 1979 brochure which announced the add-on 9575 Pullman for the set. The 9569 combine car appeared in the 1981 Fall Collector Center brochure, and the set was completed with the 7208 diner released in 1983. In reality the set looks good with the 8753 GG-1 electric or the 8551 EP-5 electric as well. It did not matter in the long run — there was enough pent-up demand for the long cars that they were a guaranteed success.

The eight cars in this set are ribbed-sided bodies similar to postwar production, with tuscan/maroon stripes and gold lettering. The names on four of the cars reprise the four- car Congressional Limited set produced by postwar Lionel. Note that Fundimensions changed to smooth-sided versions of these cars for the New York Central set in 1983, ostensibly to improve the painting process. Lionel Trains, Inc. returned to fluted-sided cars for 1989's Amtrak set.

All the modern Congressional Limited cars are illuminated with window silhouettes (except the baggage) and have Type VII die-cast O Gauge passenger trucks. As usual, the set was separate-sale only.

9569 PENNSYLVANIA: 1981, long extruded aluminum combine car; uncatalogued; "PAUL REVERE"; matches 9571; add-on to Congressional Limited set. See set description above. Although earlier numerically, this car was not part of the set initially. Appeared in 1981 Fall Collector Center brochure. — — 125 150

9570 PENNSYLVANIA: 1979, small door long extruded aluminum baggage car; "RAILWAY EXPRESS AGENCY"; mirror polished aluminum. Part of Pennsylvania Congressional Limited set, but without maroon stripes. Set components were offered for separate-sale only. See set description preceding 9569 entry. — 100 125 150

9571 PENNSYLVANIA: 1979, long extruded aluminum Pullman; "WILLIAM PENN"; mirror polished aluminum; iridescent maroon stripes; spring-loaded lamp receptacle; rerun of 1950s' 2543, but 2543 had flat-finished aluminum and brown stripes. Part of Congressional Limited set, whose components were only offered for separate-sale. See set description preceding 9569 entry. — 90 140 175

9572 PENNSYLVANIA: 1979, long extruded aluminum Pullman; "MOLLY PITCHER"; matches 9571. Part of Congressional Limited set, whose components were only offered for separate-sale. See set description preceding 9569 entry. — 100 140 175

The colorful Special Chessie Steam Special set. The diner is hard to find.
Top shelf: **9581 baggage car; 9582 combine.**
Middle shelf: **9583 coach; 9584 coach.**
Bottom shelf: **9586 diner car; 9585 observation.**

M. Solly Collection; B. Greenberg photograph

	GD	VG	EXC	MT

9573 PENNSYLVANIA: 1979, long extruded aluminum vista dome; "BETSY ROSS"; matches 9571. Part of Congressional Limited set, whose components were only offered for separate-sale. See set description preceding 9569 entry.
— 90 125 150

9574 PENNSYLVANIA: 1979, long extruded aluminum observation; "ALEXANDER HAMILTON"; "Lionel Limited" on back door inside of protective gate; matches 9571. Part of Congressional Limited set, whose components were only offered for separate-sale. See set description preceding 9569 entry.
— 90 125 150

9575 PENNSYLVANIA: 1979, long extruded aluminum Pullman car; uncatalogued; "THOMAS A. EDISON"; matches 9571; add-on to Congressional Limited set. See set description preceding 9569 entry. Appeared in late 1979 dealer brochure.
— — 135 175

BURLINGTON "TEXAS ZEPHYR", 1980

This stunning polished aluminum set followed the success of the Congressional Limited the year before. This time the matching chrome-plated F-3 diesels (8054/8055) were catalogued with the cars and together made quite an astounding set. The first five cars (9576 through 9580) were in the 1980 catalogue, while another vista dome (9588) was released late in 1980. As such, this is the only long passenger set with two vista domes and to date, it does not have a combine or diner.

These cars are also unique in that they do not have name stripes or other color decoration — simply black block lettering stamped in the smooth areas of the sides. However, all the cars except the baggage are illuminated with silhouette window strips, and all the cars have the Type VII die-cast O Gauge passenger trucks. The set was separate-sale only.

9576 BURLINGTON: 1980, long extruded aluminum baggage; "SILVER POUCH"; four-wheel O Gauge die-cast passenger trucks, 16" long, for O Gauge track. Only available for separate-sale. Part of the Burlington Texas Zephyr set, whose components were all sold separately. See set description above.
— — 70 100

9577 BURLINGTON: 1980, long extruded aluminum coach; "SILVER HALTER"; matches 9576. Part of the Burlington Texas Zephyr set, whose components were all sold separately. See set description preceding 9576 entry.
— — 80 110

9578 BURLINGTON: 1980, long extruded aluminum coach; "SILVER GLADIOLA"; matches 9576. Part of the Burlington Texas Zephyr set, whose components were all sold separately. See set description preceding 9576 entry.
— — 80 110

9579 BURLINGTON: 1980, long extruded aluminum vista dome; "SILVER KETTLE"; matches 9576. Part of the Burlington Texas Zephyr set, whose components were all sold separately. See set description preceding 9576 entry.
— — 80 110

9580 BURLINGTON: 1980, long extruded aluminum observation; "SILVER VERANDA"; matches 9576. Part of the Burlington Texas Zephyr set, whose components were all sold separately. See set description preceding 9576 entry.
— — 80 110

CHESSIE STEAM SPECIAL, 1980

This set, consisting of the next six entries, is the most elaborately decorated of the 9500-series Madison car sets and, along with the Alton set, the most popular. The first five cars (9581-9585) were released initially in the 1980 catalogue, accompanied by the magnificent 8003 Chessie Berkshire steam locomotive. The engine is one reason the set was so popular. A limited-run diner car (9586) was issued in 1986 and is somewhat hard to find.

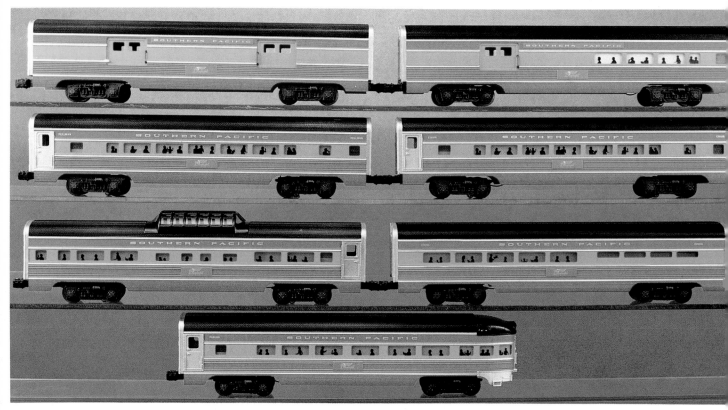

The **Southern Pacific Daylight set**, with its engines. The most expensive set made by modern Lionel.
Top shelf: **9589** baggage car; **9590** combo car.
Second shelf: **9591** Pullman; **9592** Pullman.
Third shelf: **7211** vista dome; **7204** diner. Two later additions and now very hard to find.
Bottom shelf: **9593** observation car.

R. Kaptur Collection; B. Greenberg photo

	GD	VG	EXC	MT

Another reason for the set's popularity is the bright color scheme on the cars. Each is painted bright yellow with a light gray roof and bright red-orange stripe (Lionel called it "vermilion") over the windows. The only lettering on the cars are the numbers in dark blue centered under the windows and a Steam Special logo at one end. The train was modeled after the real Steam Special which toured the country in the 1970s.

All the cars are illuminated with translucent window strips and have Type VIII die-cast six-wheel passenger trucks. The set is separate-sale only.

9581 CHESSIE: 1980, baggage car; yellow sides; gray roof; blue ends and lettering; vermilion stripe on sides. Part of Chessie Steam Special set, whose components were all sold separately. See set description above. — — 60 80

9582 CHESSIE: 1980, 9500-style combine; matches 9581. Part of Chessie Steam Special set, whose components were all sold separately. See set description preceding 9581 entry.
— — 60 80

9583 CHESSIE: 1980, 9500-style coach; matches 9581. Part of Chessie Steam Special set, whose components were all sold separately. See set description preceding 9581 entry.
— — 60 80

9584 CHESSIE: 1980, 9500-style coach; matches 9581. Part of Chessie Steam Special set, whose components were all sold separately. See set description preceding 9581 entry.
— — 60 80

9585 CHESSIE: 1980, 9500-style observation; matches 9581. Part of Chessie Steam Special set, whose components were all sold separately. See set description preceding 9581 entry.
— — 60 80

9586 CHESSIE: 1986, 9500-style diner car; add-on to Chessie Steam Special set; matches 9581-9585 above. See set description preceding 9581 entry. Sold as part of 1986 year-end Stocking Stuffer package; already hard to find. — — 110 125

9588 BURLINGTON: 1980, long extruded aluminum vista dome; uncatalogued; "SILVER DOME"; add-on to Burlington Texas Zephyr set; matches 9576. See set description preceding 9576 entry. Announced in 1980 Fall Collector Center brochure.
— — 110 150

See Factory Errors and Prototypes chapter in Volume II, first edition.

SOUTHERN PACIFIC "DAYLIGHT", 1982-1983

The "Daylight" has the distinction, so far at least, of being the single most valuable set produced by modern Lionel. It is certainly the most colorful. It also has the distinction of being the only set with three different engines designed to pull it — the 8260/8261/8262 F-3 diesel combination, the magnificent 8307 Gs4 streamlined steam locomotive, and the 18007 Gs2 steam locomo-

GD   VG   EXC   MT

tive all decorated in the red and orange Daylight scheme. The reasons for the scarcity and value are not hard to understand. All of the diesel and steam locomotives are scarce and very expensive, especially the 8307 engine. In addition, the B-unit for the F-3s (8261), the vista dome car (7211) and the dining car (7204) produced as add- ons to the set were made in very limited quantities and are very difficult to find. As if that were not enough, the release of the 18007 locomotive in 1991 means there are now three engines available to pull the one set of passenger cars. Your wallet better be filled if you plan to purchase this one.

There is no question the color scheme of this set is absolutely stunning: each car is painted bright red with a central orange stripe and black roof. The ends, doors, lettering and highlight stripes are silver. A "Daylight" script nameplate is affixed in the lower center. There are no numbers on the cars. This set features the fluted long extruded aluminum car bodies, and the painting complexity probably prompted Lionel to try the smooth-sided cars on its next set — the New York Central. The Daylight cars are illuminated with window silhouettes (except the baggage car) and have the usual Type VII die-cast O Gauge passenger trucks. And as usual, the set was separate-sale only.

The five cars following (9589 through 9593) were the first to appear in 1982, with the 8260-8262 F-3 AA combination. The 8261 F-3 B-unit and 7204 diner car were added in a 1982 Fall Collector Center brochure. Both are rare. The 8307 Gs4 steam locomotive was announced amid great fanfare in an early 1983 Collector brochure. And another scarce add-on, the 7211 vista dome, appeared in the Fall 1983 Collector Center brochure. Collectors thought that was the end of it, until the 19107 full vista dome car appeared in the 1990 Stocking Stuffers brochure, and the 18007 Gs2 steam locomotive made a dramatic appearance in the 1991 catalogue, and this one has RailSounds. Note: The Gs2 and Gs4 differ in their boiler front and running light arrangements.

9589 SOUTHERN PACIFIC: 1982-83, long extruded aluminum baggage; distinctive red, orange, silver and black "Daylight" colors; no number on car. Part of Southern Pacific Daylight set, whose components were all sold separately. See set description above.   —   —   100   125

9590 SOUTHERN PACIFIC: 1982-83, long extruded aluminum combo; no number on car; matches 9589. Part of Southern Pacific Daylight set, whose components were all sold separately. See set description preceding 9589 entry.
—   —   100   125

9591 SOUTHERN PACIFIC: 1982-83, long extruded aluminum Pullman; no number on car; matches 9589. Part of Southern Pacific Daylight set, whose components were all sold separately. See set description preceding 9589 entry.
(A) Usual silver ends   —   —   100   125

(B) Orange-painted ends as shown in 1982 catalogue. We do not know if only one or two cars in the set have this characteristic, or if a small set run was made. Reader comments invited. R. Burton Collection.   —   —   —   NRS

9592 SOUTHERN PACIFIC: 1982-83, long extruded aluminum Pullman; no number on car; matches 9589. Part of Southern Pacific Daylight set, whose components were all sold separately. See set description preceding 9589 entry.
—   —   100   125

9593 SOUTHERN PACIFIC: 1982-83, long extruded aluminum observation; no number on car; matches 9589. Part of

9599 Chicago and Alton diner car.

GD   VG   EXC   MT

Southern Pacific Daylight set, whose components were all sold separately. See set description preceding 9589 entry.
—   —   100   125

NEW YORK CENTRAL "TWENTIETH CENTURY LIMITED", 1983-1984

The Twentieth Century Limited was the fifth set of long extruded aluminum passenger cars in five years, and it became apparent by 1983 that collectors were having some difficulty bearing the great expense of these sets. In addition, Lionel's dark gray color scheme, although prototypical, lent itself to paint chipping and annoying fingerprints. As a result, this set and the Union Pacific and Illinois Central sets which followed did not sell as briskly as the earlier sets, and none of them could compete with the brilliant graphics of the Southern Pacific Daylight or the Norfolk and Western Powhatan Arrow.

Still, this set (modeled after the N Y C's New York-to-Chicago run, one of the most famous trains of all time) has one unique feature — the smooth-sided bodies of the passenger cars had replaced the fluted ridges of the earlier versions in order to improve the printing process. Also, the 8370/8371/8372 F-3 ABA diesel combination with which the set was catalogued is among the better looking of the F-3 diesels.

Five cars were released in the initial 1983 offering (9594 through 9598). Each is a two-tone gray with white lettering and stripes, and black roof. Each is illuminated (except the baggage) with window silhouettes and comes with the Type VII die-cast O Gauge trucks. Some cars (the 9596-9597 Pullmans and the 9598 observation) have no numbers, while the combo, baggage and diner cars do. The only add-on to this set was the 7207 diner car announced in the Fall 1983 Collector Center brochure. The set has no vista dome car.

The set (separate-sale only, as usual) was catalogued again in 1984, behind the 783 Hudson with which this set looks very good (given a few extra dollars to spend)!

9594 NEW YORK CENTRAL: 1983-84, double-door long extruded aluminum baggage; painted gray with white lettering and black roof; gray ends; four-wheel O Gauge die-cast passenger trucks; operating couplers. We have had reports that the smooth-sided cars in this and subsequent series have paint which can chip easily if mishandled. In addition, the dark gray color of the paint on these cars shows fingerprints easily, and these prints, once present, are hard to remove. Part of the Twentieth Century Limited set, whose components were all sold separately. See set description above.   —   —   100   125

9595 NEW YORK CENTRAL: 1983-84, long extruded aluminum combine; matches 9594. Part of the Twentieth Century

	GD	VG	EXC	MT

Limited set, whose components were all sold separately. See set description preceding 9594 entry. — — **115 150**

9596 NEW YORK CENTRAL: 1983-84, long extruded aluminum coach; "WAYNE COUNTY"; no number on car; matches 9594. Part of the Twentieth Century Limited set, whose components were all sold separately. See set description preceding 9594 entry. — — **115 150**

9597 NEW YORK CENTRAL: 1983-84, long extruded aluminum coach; "HUDSON RIVER"; no number on car; matches 9594. Part of the Twentieth Century Limited set, whose components were all sold separately. See set description preceding 9594 entry. — — **115 150**

9598 NEW YORK CENTRAL: 1983-84, long extruded aluminum observation; "MANHATTAN ISLAND"; illuminated drumhead with Twentieth Century Limited logo; no number on car; matches 9594. Part of the Twentieth Century Limited set, whose components were all sold separately. See set description preceding 9594 entry. — — **100 125**

9599 THE ALTON LIMITED: 1987, 9500-style dining car; add-on to Alton Limited set; matches 9554-9558. See set description preceding 9554 entry. Sold as part of 1986 year-end Stocking Stuffer package; already hard to find.

— — — **90**

THE "PENNSY" SET, 1987-1988

This set, which really has no name, consists of the 16000 through 16003 O27 short streamlined car. It is the first appearance of this style since the Quicksilver Express in 1982, and the first foray of Richard Kughn's new Lionel Trains, Inc. into the world of passenger sets. Although not one of Lionel's better graphics efforts (the lettering is blurred and not well spaced or centered), the set has sold reasonably well.

The first four cars (two coaches, a vista dome and an observation) came out in 1987, followed by a 16009 combo in 1988, a 16022 baggage in 1989, and a 16031 diner in 1990. Each car is classic P R R tuscan with gold lettering and a black roof. All are illuminated with window silhouettes (although not shown that way in the 1987 catalogue), and each has Type IV plastic wood-beam passenger trucks and operating couplers. The set (separate-sale only, no set box) was catalogued with the 18602 Pennsy 4-4-2 Columbia steam engine in 1987 and with a nice-looking pair of Pennsy Alco diesels in 1988 (18901-18902).

Note, this and all future O27 passenger sets (the short O27 streamline cars and the General-type coaches) will be numbered in the 16000-series in Lionel's new five-digit system.

16000 PENNSYLVANIA: 1987-88, 2400-style short streamlined O27 vista dome; revival of 2400-style cars not seen since Quicksilver Express cars of 1982; tuscan-painted body; gold lettering and number; black unpainted roof; illuminated; wood-beam four-wheel passenger trucks; operating couplers. Part of "Pennsy" passenger set, whose components were all sold separately. See set description above. — — **20 25**
See Factory Errors and Prototypes chapter in Volume II, first edition.

16001 PENNSYLVANIA: 1987-88, 2400-style short streamlined O27 passenger coach; matches 16000. Part of "Pennsy" passenger set, whose components were all sold separately. See set description preceding 16000 entry. — — **20 25**

16002 PENNSYLVANIA: 1987-88, 2400-style short streamlined O27 passenger coach; matches 16000. Part of "Pennsy" passenger set, whose components were all sold separately. See set description preceding 16000 entry. — — **20 25**

16003 PENNSYLVANIA: 1987-88, 2400-style short streamlined O27 observation; does not have red marker lights on end; matches 16000. Part of "Pennsy" passenger set, whose components were all sold separately. See set description preceding 16000 entry. — — **20 25**

16009 PENNSYLVANIA: 1988, 2400-style short streamlined O27 combine; made as an add-on for "Pennsy" passenger cars introduced in 1987; matches 16000. See set description preceding 16000 entry. — — **25**

VIRGINIA & TRUCKEE "DRY GULCH" SERVICE STATION SPECIAL, 1988

The next three entries (16010 through 16012) comprise the unusual and handsome "Dry Gulch Line" Service Station Special set for 1988 (11706). The set came boxed with the 18702 General-style engine in maroon and gold. The General-style coaches are yellow with a gray roof and green stripe above the windows. Each has white lettering and numbers, plastic Type V arch bar trucks with operating couplers, and each is illuminated with translucent window strips. Each car was also boxed within the set box. The set was similar to the Rock Island and B & O sets of the early 1980s.

16010 VIRGINIA & TRUCKEE: 1988, General-style coach; uncatalogued; yellow sides; gray roof; green stripe; white lettering, illuminated; plastic arch bar trucks. Part of 11706 "Dry Gulch" Service Station Special set. See set description above.
(A) Small lettering; matches 16011 and 16012.

— — — **40**

(B) Large lettering; does not match other cars. J. Strock and B. Trigg Collections. **NRS**

16011 VIRGINIA & TRUCKEE: 1988, General-style coach; uncatalogued; matches 16010. Part of 11706 "Dry Gulch" Service Station Special set. See set description preceding 16010 entry.

— — — **40**

16012 VIRGINIA & TRUCKEE: 1988, General-style baggage/combine; uncatalogued; "U. S. MAIL" and "WELLS FARGO"; matches 16010. Part of 11706 "Dry Gulch" Service Station Special set. See set description preceeding 16010 entry.

— — — **40**

AMTRAK "SILVER SPIKE", 1988-1989

Following its first entry into the passenger field with the 1987 Pennsy set, LTI came out with an excellent boxed Traditional Line set (11707) in Amtrak colors called the "Silver Spike". The following three O27 streamlined cars made up the set along with the 8903-8904 Alco AA diesel combination. In this respect, it looked very similar to the Lake Shore Limited set from 1976, except the Silver Spike set has window silhouettes, and the red/blue arrow logo is not painted on a white background as it was on the earlier set. Each car is silver-painted with the red and blue Amtrak arrow strips around the windows. The cars have blue and white lettering, Type IV plastic wood-beam passenger trucks with operating couplers, and each is illuminated with the window silhouettes.

R. Kaptur, R. LaVoie Collections; B. Greenberg photograph

popular New York Central set of O27 streamlined passenger cars from 1989.

shelf: 16016 New York Central; 16017 Lake Michigan.

nd shelf: 16018 Chicagoland; 16019 La Salle.

d shelf: 16020 Kankakee; 16021 Fort Dearborn, a diner car was added in 1991.

om shelf: 16002 Pennsylvania; 16023 Amtrak. Two recent O27 streamlined coaches.

	GD	VG	EXC	MT

Add-ons to the set were a 16023 coach in 1989, a 16033 baggage in 1990, and a 16048 diner car in 1991.

16013 AMTRAK: 1988-89, 2400-style short streamlined O27 combine; silver-painted body; red, white and blue Amtrak striping and logo; passenger silhouettes in windows; illuminated; plastic O27 passenger trucks; operating couplers. Part of 11707 Silver Spike passenger set. See set description above.

— — — 35

16014 AMTRAK: 1989, 2400-style short streamlined O27 vista dome; matches 16013. Part of 11707 Silver Spike set. See set description preceding 16013 entry. — — — 35

16015 AMTRAK: 1989, 2400-style short streamlined O27 observation; matches 16013. Part of 11707 Silver Spike set. See set description preceding 16013 entry. — — — 35

New York Central Passenger Set, 1989

By 1989, Lionel was in a groove in its production of the short O27 streamlined passenger cars. This set, like 1987's Pennsy, really

	GD	VG	EXC	MT

has no name and all components were offered for separate-sale only. It has been a surprisingly good seller, with many New York Central fans hungry for reasonably priced trains. Instead of waiting for add-ons, Lionel this time released six cars at the same time (baggage, combo, two coaches, vista dome and observation — 16016 through 16021). Each is painted in the usual N Y C two-tone gray with black roof and white lettering "NEW YORK CENTRAL" above the windows and name and numbers below. Each is illuminated with window silhouettes and has the Type IV plastic wood-beam passenger trucks with operating couplers. The only add-on to this set was the 16041 diner car from 1991. The set was catalogued with the 18606 Atlantic steam locomotive, which has had some operating problems. See the Steam Locomotive chapter for details.

Reader George Romich sent us an interesting note on this set. It seems it is a nearly exact match for a 1950s era Marx N Y C passenger set, among the few Marx sets made with interior lighting. When Marx was in the train business it usually spent time remaking what Lionel produced. It is nice to see Lionel returning the favor!

	GD	VG	EXC	MT

16016 NEW YORK CENTRAL: 1989, short O27 streamlined baggage; gray body; light gray central stripe; black roof; white lettering; illuminated; plastic O27 passenger trucks; operating couplers. Part of separate-sale N Y C passenger set. See set description above. — — — 25

16017 NEW YORK CENTRAL: 1989, short O27 streamlined combine car; "LAKE MICHIGAN"; matches 16016. Note silhouettes in baggage door! Part of separate-sale N Y C passenger set. See set description preceding 16016 entry. — — — 25

16018 NEW YORK CENTRAL: 1989, short O27 streamlined coach; "CHICAGOLAND"; matches 16016. Part of separate-sale N Y C passenger set. See set description preceding 16016 entry. — — — 25

16019 NEW YORK CENTRAL: 1989, short O27 streamlined vista dome; "LASALLE"; matches 16016. Part of separate-sale N Y C passenger set. See set description preceding 16016 entry. — — — 25

16020 NEW YORK CENTRAL: 1989, short O27 streamlined coach; "KANKAKEE"; matches 16016. Part of separate-sale N Y C passenger set. See set description preceding 16016 entry. — — — 25

16021 NEW YORK CENTRAL: 1989, short O27 streamlined observation; "FORT DEARBORN"; matches 16016. Part of separate-sale N Y C passenger set. See set description preceding 16016 entry. — — — 25

16022 PENNSYLVANIA: 1989, short O27 streamlined baggage car; add-on to the "Pennsy" passenger set from 1897; matches 16000. See set description preceding 16000 entry. — — — 22

16023 AMTRAK: 1989, short O27 streamlined coach; add-on to the 11707 Amtrak Silver Spike set of 1988; matches 16013. See set description preceding 16013 entry. — — — 25 See Factory Errors and Prototypes chapter in Volume II, first edition.

LIONEL LINES
"GREAT LAKES EXPRESS"
SERVICE STATION SPECIAL SET, 1990

This unique short O27 streamline passenger set was a big seller for LTI. It featured the following four passenger cars and, more impressively, a handsome light gray 18611 2-6-4 Atlantic Lionel Lines steam locomotive. Another unique item about the set is that the cars have Type VI die-cast O27 passenger trucks, not the plastic Type IV wood-beam trucks that had been used in previous modern era cars. Ironically, the original postwar 2400-series cars used these die-cast trucks, so Lionel has come full circle.

The Great Lakes Express cars are forest green with gray roofs, white lettering and yellow highlight stripes and window trim. Only four cars were included (should we expect more?), each lettered for cities in Michigan important to modern Lionel's operation. "LIONEL LINES" is above the windows and name and numbers below. All the cars are illuminated with window silhouettes. This boxed Traditional Line set (all Service Station Specials are considered Traditional Line) carries a 11712 set number. As a Service Station set announced in a separate flyer, all these cars are considered uncatalogued.

	GD	VG	EXC	MT

16027 LIONEL LINES: 1990, short O27 streamlined combo car; uncatalogued; "MT. CLEMENS"; forest green body; gray roof; white lettering; yellow stripes and window frames; illuminated window silhouettes; die-cast Type VII O27 passenger trucks; operating couplers. Part of "Great Lakes Express" Service Station Special set 11712. See set description above. — — — 35

16028 LIONEL LINES: 1990, short O27 streamlined coach; uncatalogued; "DETROIT"; matches 16027. Part of "Great Lakes Express" Service Station Special set 11712. See set description preceding 16027 entry. — — — 35

16029 LIONEL LINES: 1990, short O27 streamlined coach; uncatalogued; "LANSING"; matches 16027. Part of "Great Lakes Express" Service Station Special set 11712. See set description preceding 16027 entry. — — — 35

16030 LIONEL LINES: 1990, short O27 streamlined observation; uncatalogued; "CHESTERFIELD"; matches 16027. Part of "Great Lakes Express" Service Station Special set 11712. See set description preceding 16027 entry. — — — 35

16031 PENNSYLVANIA: 1990, short O27 streamlined diner; add-on to "Pennsy" passenger set of 1987; matches 16000. See set description preceding 16000 entry. — — — 25

16033 AMTRAK: 1990, short O27 streamlined baggage car; illuminated; add-on to 11707 Silver Spike set of 1988; matches 16013. See set description preceding 16013 entry. — — — 25

NORTHERN PACIFIC
PASSENGER SET, 1990-1991

This is the fifth set in four years following the short O27 streamline passenger set formula, with which LTI has obviously become quite comfortable. Similar to the N Y C set the year before, this no-name set of six cars (16034 through 16039) was only available separately. They are intended to be pulled by the 18609 2-6-4 Northern Pacific steam locomotive offered the same year. An unusual feature is that none of these cars have names — only "NORTHERN PACIFIC" above the windows in white and the red and black Monad ("ying-yang") logo at the lower center.

The set cars are quite attractive — forest green upper body and roof, light (lime) green lower body and white stripe between the two. Each car is illuminated with window silhouettes and has plastic versions of the O27 passenger truck — this is a new style truck which has been designated Type XIII. The set has been popular. It is the first time ever that Lionel has made a passenger set lettered for the Northern Pacific. The set was catalogued again in 1991.

16034 NORTHERN PACIFIC: 1990-91, short O27 streamlined baggage car; forest green body and roof; lime green lower body; white lettering and stripe; Monad logo; illuminated; plastic Type XIII O27 passenger trucks (a new style truck) with operating couplers. Part of separate-sale only Northern Pacific passenger set. See set description above. — — — 25

16035 NORTHERN PACIFIC: 1990-91, short O27 streamlined combo car; matches 16034. Part of separate-sale only Northern Pacific passenger set. See set description preceding 16034 entry. — — — 25

	GD	VG	EXC	MT

16036 NORTHERN PACIFIC: 1990-91, short O27 streamlined coach; matches 16034. Part of separate-sale only Northern Pacific passenger set. See set description preceding 16034 entry. — — — 25

16037 NORTHERN PACIFIC: 1990-91, short O27 streamlined vista dome; matches 16034. Part of separate-sale only Northern Pacific passenger set. See set description preceding 16034 entry. — — — 25

16038 NORTHERN PACIFIC: 1990-91, short O27 streamlined coach; matches 16034. Part of separate-sale only Northern Pacific passenger set. See set description preceding 16034 entry. — — — 25

16039 NORTHERN PACIFIC: 1990-91, short O27 streamlined observation; matches 16034. Part of separate-sale only Northern Pacific passenger set. See set description preceding 16034 entry. — — — 25

16040 SOUTHERN PACIFIC: 1990-91, General-style baggage/combo car; orange body; gray ends, roof and trim; white lettering "SOUTHERN PACIFIC" above windows; illuminated; ASF strong-arm trucks; "BLT 1-90 LIONEL". This is the only passenger car to have these trucks and to carry a built date. One of only two passenger cars not in a set with other similar cars (the other is the 9541 Santa Fe). This car (Lionel called it a "payroll car") came in the 11714 Badlands Express set. — — — 30

16041 NEW YORK CENTRAL: 1991, short O27 streamlined diner car; add-on to N Y C passenger set from 1989; matches 16016. See set description preceding 16016 entry. — — — 27

THE ILLINOIS CENTRAL PASSENGER SET, 1991

LTI continued its set formula for the short O27 streamlined passenger cars with this set released in 1991, the sixth such set in five years. The cars in this no-name set also have no names of their own, just "ILLINOIS CENTRAL" in yellow above the windows and numbers below. The set is intended to be pulled by the 18620 Illinois Central 2-6-2 steam locomotive also released in 1991. It is, in effect, the little brother of the F-3-powered Illinois Central "City of New Orleans" set made in 1985.

As before, the set is separate-sale only. Each car has a brown body with orange window stripe. The stripe is separated from the brown areas with yellow accent stripes. Each has yellow lettering and all are illuminated with window silhouettes, except the baggage car. The cars ride on the new Type XIII plastic O27 passenger trucks.

16042 ILLINOIS CENTRAL*: 1991, short O27 streamlined baggage car; brown body with orange central stripe; brown and orange areas separated by yellow accent stripes; yellow lettering "ILLINOIS CENTRAL" above windows and number centered below; not illuminated; Type XIII plastic O27 passenger trucks. Part of separate-sale only Illinois Central passenger set. See set description above. — — — 28

16043 ILLINOIS CENTRAL*: 1991, short O27 streamlined combo car; illuminated with window silhouettes; otherwise matches 16042. Part of separate-sale only Illinois Central passenger set. See set description preceding 16042 entry. — — — 28

16044 ILLINOIS CENTRAL*: 1991, short O27 streamlined passenger car; illuminated with window silhouettes; otherwise matches 16042. Part of separate-sale only Illinois Central passenger set. See set description preceding 16042 entry. — — — 28

16045 ILLINOIS CENTRAL*: 1991, short O27 streamlined vista dome car; illuminated with window silhouettes; otherwise matches 16042. Part of separate-sale only Illinois Central passenger set. See set description preceding 16042 entry. — — — 28

16046 ILLINOIS CENTRAL*: 1991, short O27 streamlined passenger car; illuminated with window silhouettes; otherwise matches 16042. Part of separate-sale only Illinois Central passenger set. See set description preceding 16042 entry. — — — 28

16047 ILLINOIS CENTRAL*: 1991, short O27 streamlined observation car; illuminated with window silhouettes; otherwise matches 16042. Part of separate-sale only Illinois Central passenger set. See set description preceding 16042 entry. — — — 28

16048 AMTRAK*: 1991, short O27 streamlined diner car; add-on to the 11707 Amtrak Silver Spike set of 1988; matches 16013. See set description preceding 16013 entry. — — — 26

17879 VALLEY FORGE: 1989, 9500-style dining car; T C A; see Volume II, first edition.

17883 ATLANTA: 1990, General-style passenger car; T C A; see Volume II, first edition.

19000 THE BLUE COMET: 1987, 9500-style diner car; uncatalogued; "GIACOBINI"; made as a match for the 9536-40 Blue Comet passenger cars of 1978-79. Part of "Happy Lionel Holidays" year-end package for 1987. See Blue Comet set description preceding 9536 entry. — — — 85
See Factory Errors and Prototypes chapter in Volume II, first edition.

19001 SOUTHERN CRESCENT: 1987, 9500-style dining car; uncatalogued; made as a match for 9530-9534 Southern Crescent passenger cars from 1977-78, including the older four-wheel trucks. Announced in 1987 year-end package. See Southern Crescent set description preceding 9530 entry. — — — 85

19002 PENNSYLVANIA: 1988, 9500-style dining car; uncatalogued; matches Pennsylvania "Broadway Limited" cars produced from 1974-76, except this car has Type IV wood-beam trucks with operating couplers. See Broadway Limited set description preceding 9507 entry. Announced in a 1988 holiday brochure. — — — 50

19003 THE MILWAUKEE ROAD: 1988, 9500-style dining car; uncatalogued; matches Milwaukee Special cars produced from 1973-76, except this car includes Type IV trucks with operating couplers. See Milwaukee Special set description preceding the 9500 entry. Announced in 1988 holiday brochure. — — — 50

19010 BALTIMORE AND OHIO: 1989, 9500-style dining car; uncatalogued; matches B & O "Capitol Limited" set produced in 1975, except this car has operating couplers. See Capitol

GD   VG   EXC   MT

Limited set description preceding 9516 entry. Appeared in late 1989 Holiday Collection brochure.   —   —   —   50

THE MADISON CARS, 1991

The following four cars comprised a long-awaited remake of the famous heavyweight "Madison" passenger car sets produced in 1941-42 and 1946-50. Lionel Trains, Inc. chose the 50th anniversary of their first appearance to unveil a brand new model of these classic passenger cars so prominent on the American railroads in the early part of this century.

The original prewar and postwar Lionel sets are near-legend in the Lionel hobby today, and finding them for sale now in good condition is a difficult proposition. This pent-up demand, as well as competitive pressures from other manufacturers to produce longer scale-length passenger cars, led Lionel to recreate the legend.

The Modern Madison cars are about 3 inches longer (15 inches) than their short Madison cousins which had served Lionel's passenger car demand so well from 1973 to 1987. The 1991 set is made of heavy phenolic plastic, simulating the Bakelite plastic from which the postwar cars were made and which made each of them a real "heavyweight." Each car is a handsome tuscan with white lettering and die-cast six-wheel trucks. The modern set does include some interesting differences: passenger silhouettes in the windows, spring-loaded swinging doors, and most interestingly, the modern set has the Sager Place observation car which was pictured but never made in the postwar era.

Each car is illuminated with two operating couplers, and each is named for a location significant to the history of the Lionel Corporation. All were sold separately, not in a set. The cars are pictured, as they often were in the postwar catalogues, right behind the scale New York Central Hudson.

19015 LIONEL LINES*: 1991, long Madison coach; "IRVINGTON"; new model of the long heavyweight passenger cars prominent on the real railroads in the 1920s and made originally by Lionel in the 1940s; tuscan-painted body 15 inches long made of heavy phenolic plastic to simulate the Bakelite plastic used to make the 1940s originals; white lettering; "9015" is the number on the car; illuminated with window silhouettes; spring-loaded swinging doors; die-cast six-wheel trucks; two operating couplers. Remake of postwar 2625. Part of separate-sale Madison car set. See set description above. Irvington is the northern New Jersey town in which the Lionel Corporation factory was located.
—   —   —   140

19016 LIONEL LINES*: 1991, long Madison coach; "MADISON"; "9016" is the number on the car; otherwise matches 19015. Part of separate-sale Madison car set. See set description preceding 19015 entry. Madison is the New York City street on which Joshua Lionel Cowen's family lived, and which was the home of one of the most important Lionel dealers — Madison Hardware.
—   —   —   140

19017 LIONEL LINES*: 1991, long Madison coach; "MANHATTAN"; "9017" is the number on the car; otherwise matches 19015. Part of separate-sale Madison car set. See set description preceding 19015 entry. The Lionel Corporation headquarters was located in Manhattan.
—   —   —   140

GD   VG   EXC   MT

19018 LIONEL LINES*: 1991, long Madison observation car; "SAGER PLACE"; "9018" is the number on the car; metal rear platform; illuminated drumhead; no coupler on rear truck; otherwise matches 19015. Part of separate sale Madison Car set. See set description preceding 19015 entry. The original postwar Sager Place observation car (2626) was pictured in the 1946 advance catalogue but was never made. Sager Place is the Irvington, New Jersey street where the old Lionel factory was located.
—   —   —   140

AMTRAK PASSENGER SET, 1989

Amtrak collectors were rewarded in 1989 with this magnificent set of seven, long, extruded aluminum passenger cars. The set has several interesting firsts: it is the first passenger set, large or small, specifically designated to be pulled by a GG-1 (in this case the Amtrak 18303), and this set is the first to make use of the realistic full vista dome car. As it happens, the set also has a small vista dome car. The car bodies here mark Lionel's return to fluted sides on its long aluminum cars, and only the central window strip is decorated in the red, white and blue Amtrak arrow scheme. Only six cars were catalogued in 1989 — the full vista dome car was announced in a year-end holiday brochure. But as a separate-sale Collector set it did not matter — everything was released at essentially the same time. There is no lettering except a white "Amtrak" on the window strip and a separate plate with black four-digit numbers (the "1" is dropped from the numbers on the cars). All the cars are illuminated with window silhouettes (except the baggage car) and have the Type VII die-cast O gauge passenger trucks.

19100 AMTRAK: 1989, long extruded aluminum double- door baggage car; unpainted polished aluminum with red, white and blue Amtrak arrow window strip; "9100" number plate; illuminated; die-cast O Gauge passenger trucks with operating couplers. Part of separate-sale Amtrak passenger set. See set description above.
—   —   —   150

19101 AMTRAK: 1989, long extruded aluminum combo car; "9101" number plate; matches 19100. Part of separate-sale Amtrak passenger set. See set description preceding 19100 entry.
—   —   —   150

19102 AMTRAK: 1989, long extruded aluminum coach; "9102" number plate; matches 19100. Part of separate- sale Amtrak passenger set. See set description preceding 19100 entry.
—   —   —   150

19103 AMTRAK: 1989, long extruded aluminum vista dome; "9103" number plate; matches 19100. Part of separate-sale Amtrak passenger set. See set description preceding 19100 entry.
—   —   —   150

19104 AMTRAK: 1989, long extruded aluminum dining car; "9104" number plate; matches 19100. Part of separate-sale Amtrak passenger set. See set description preceding 19100 entry.
—   —   —   150

19105 AMTRAK: 1989, long extruded aluminum full vista dome car; uncatalogued; illuminated; new body style for Lionel's long aluminum cars; features a vista dome nearly the full length of the car, rather than about ⅓ the length as on regular vista domes; car also has an altered side window pattern and large vents on one side; "9105" number plate. Otherwise matches paint

Note: The *full vista dome car* (or "Big Dome") only made its debut in Lionel land in 1989, but the real railroads had used them since the 1950s. Some are still in use today. The Budd Company built 24 of them for the Santa Fe Railroad for use on the Super Chief and El Capitan. Budd built more for the Great Northern, and Southern Pacific built their own for the "Daylight" runs. Pullman Standard built big domes for the Milwaukee Road's "Hiawatha," and these eventually landed with the Canadian National. The full dome cars today were purchased by Amtrak from the Santa Fe. W. Meyer comments.

	GD	VG	EXC	MT

scheme of Amtrak passenger set. See set description preceding 19100 entry. Pictured in the 1989 holiday brochure.
— — — **140**

19106 AMTRAK: 1989, long extruded aluminum observation; "9106" number plate; matches 19100. Part of separate-sale Amtrak passenger set. See set description preceding 19100 entry.
— — — **150**

19107 SOUTHERN PACIFIC: 1990, long extruded aluminum full vista dome car; uncatalogued; illuminated; add-on for Southern Pacific "Daylight" set from 1982; color scheme matches 9589 through 9593. See set description preceding the 9589 entry. Announced in the 1990 Stocking Stuffer brochure.
— — — **95**

SANTA FE PASSENGER SET, 1991

Yet another stunning long extruded aluminum passenger set appeared in the 1991 catalogue, another set which exhibits LTI's penchant for introducing new features and variations whenever they can. This set resurrects the famous Santa Fe F-3 diesels (18100 through 18102) — this time with RailSounds — which have proven such reliable favorites over the years. The passenger cars bring back the big Santa Fe liners last seen in 1961. But modern Lionel has solved the problems with the troublesome name strips of the earlier set by using simple nameplates attached directly to the car sides. Each car has a "SANTA FE" nameplate above the windows in black, and a number nameplate in black

below. As with the Amtrak set, the numberplates drop the "1" from the car number.

There are three unusual features which distinguish this set. First, the cars are a combination of the fluted and smooth-sided aluminum cars used earlier in the modern era. The sides are fluted while the roof is smooth. Second, Lionel has applied attractive silver paint to the sides of the Type VII die-cast O Gauge trucks used for these cars. Earlier aluminum passenger cars had black-sided trucks. Lastly, LTI created yet another new body style — a combination vista-observation car.

The five separate-sale cars announced in 1991 (19109 through 19113) are all illuminated (except the baggage) with window silhouettes.

19109 SANTA FE: 1991, long extruded aluminum double-door baggage car; unpainted polished aluminum body; fluted sides; smooth roof; no decoration other than "SANTA FE" nameplate in black lettering above the windows, with a small numberplate (reading "9109" dropping the "1") below the window; not illuminated, but both other cars in the set are; silver-painted die-cast O Gauge passenger trucks with operating couplers. Part of separate-sale Santa Fe passenger set. See set description.
— — — **100**

19110 SANTA FE: 1991, long extruded aluminum combo car; illuminated; "9110" number plate; matches 19109. Part of separate-sale Santa Fe passenger set. See set description preceding 19109 entry.
— — — **100**

19111 SANTA FE: 1991, long extruded aluminum diner car; illuminated; "9111" numberplate; matches 19109. Part of separate-sale Santa Fe passenger set. See set description preceding 19109 entry.
— — — **100**

19112 SANTA FE: 1991, long extruded aluminum coach; illuminated; "9112" numberplate; matches 19109. Part of separate-sale Santa Fe passenger set. See set description preceding 19109 entry.
— — — **100**

19113 SANTA FE: 1991, long extruded aluminum vista-observation; illuminated; "9113" numberplate; new combined vista dome-observation car body style, otherwise matches 19109. Part of separate-sale Santa Fe passenger set. See set description preceding 19109 entry.
— — — **100**

R • CHAPTER 15 • EFRIGERATOR CARS

THE 9800 REFRIGERATOR CAR SERIES

*I*t is hard to imagine why the 9800-series refrigerator cars have not commanded more attention among collectors than they have. These cars, commonly referred to as "reefers," represent the creativity of Fundimensions at its best. Longer than their boxcar counterparts, these cars are made entirely of stout plastic pieces which are extremely well detailed with wood-sided scribing on the sides and interior floors. The bottoms of the cars have realistic air tank details, and the plug doors open and close (although with peril to the plastic door guides on some versions).

Most importantly, the 9800-series gave Fundimensions a chance to show off its capabilities with graphics. Colorful electrocals grace the sides of these cars, advertising just about every conceivable product in food and drink. These include some strange choices for refrigeration: Bazooka bubble gum, Cheerios, and Old Dutch cleanser, among others! Meat packing plants, juice companies and breweries have advertised their wares on these cars. The situation is reminiscent of the late 19th century on American railroads, where for quite some time American companies would hire out space on railroad boxcars to advertise their wares. It was not unusual for a boxcar on a New York Central train of those years to advertise Lydia Pinkham's Patented Vegetable Elixir while carrying machine tools! In this Guide, such Lionel cars used to advertise products are identified as "Billboard" reefers.

The numbering system of these cars has been a little odd, too. The 9800 refrigerator cars were introduced in 1973 at the same time the 9800 Standard O series was produced. Since the Standard O series began with the 9801 Baltimore and Ohio, the refrigerator cars started with the 9850 Budweiser. In the early 1980s, the 9800 refrigerator cars used numbers in the lower half of the numbering system, most recently with

the Favorite Spirits cars, which are numbered in the 9820s, '30s, and '40s. Some cars were also numbered in the 7500-series. Production of reefers has continued in the Lionel Trains, Inc. five-digit numbering era with the 19500-series.

There are an astonishing number of sub-series within the refrigerator car series, so much so that we could not break them up into logical subheadings because of the extent of the overlap. There is literally something for everybody, and it can be great fun building a collection of the various types, most of which are not hard to find.

Among the most prominent is the sixteen Favorite Spirits series. These cars read somewhat like a Who's-Who of the liquor industry, and were obviously intended for an adult collector audience. These are among the most handsome of the reefer cars. Some command slightly higher premiums than others:

9827	Cutty Sark	9840	Fleischmann's
9828	J & B	9841	Calvert
9829	Dewars	9842	Seagram's gin
9830	Johnnie Walker	9843	Tanqueray
9834	Southern Comfort	9844	Sambuca Romana
9835	Jim Beam	9845	Baileys
9836	Old Grand-Dad	9846	Seagram's vodka
9837	Wild Turkey	9847	Wolfschmidt

If one is inclined to lower-proof beverages, there is the Beer car series. Readers interested in this set should be aware that there are three Standard O reefer cars (9802 Miller, 9807 Stroh's and 9825 Schaefer) which can be grouped with them, although the larger Standard O cars may not look quite right in a train with the smaller cars. And watch out, beer car collectors; Lionel sneaked that last Budweiser car in there in 1989 — it came in an uncatalogued Anheuser-Busch set and

---

* Asterisk found in listings indicates that the information within that listing was derived from Lionel catalogue only.

s hard to find:

9850	Budweiser	9866	Coors
9851	Schlitz	9871	Carling Black
9852	Miller		Label
9856	Old Milwaukee	9874	Miller Lite
9859	Pabst	16223	Budweiser
9862	Hamm's		

For the more conservative, there is a set which could be called the Non-Alcoholic Beverage series:

9814	Perrier		
9831	Pepsi	9879	Hills Bros. Coffee
9861	Tropicana orange juice	9885	Lipton Tea

Hungry? There is the Favorite Food freight consisting of six billboard reefers numbered in the 7500-series (by 1981 Lionel was running out of 9800-series numbers). These cars were actually intended to be run together in the separate-sale Favorite Food set headed by the 8160 Burger King GP-20 and the 6449 Wendy's caboose. For obvious reasons, this set is often mislabeled the "Fast" Food freight:

7509	Kentucky Fried chicken	7512	Arthur Treacher's
7510	Red Lobster	7513	Bonanza
7511	Pizza Hut	7514	Taco Bell

If you have a sweeter tooth, there is the Candy series:

9813	Ruffles	9867	Hershey's
9816	Brachs	9878	Good and Plenty
9817	Bazooka	9883	Oreo Cookies
9853	Cracker Jack	9884	Fritos
9854	Baby Ruth	9886	Mounds
9858	Butterfinger		

Then there is a group of billboard reefers which represents American enterprise at its best, or could perhaps be called the Kitchen Products series:

9812	Arm & Hammer	9870	Old Dutch Cleanser
9832	Cheerios	9873	Ralston Purina
9833	Vlasic	9875	Atlantic&Pacific
9855	Swift's	9877	Gerber
9860	Gold Medal	9881	Rath Packing

Of course, many of the other reefers could fit into that category, too. The 9873 is a nice match for the 9262 Ralston Purina hopper, and both are quite hard to find.

Another interesting aspect of the billboard reefers is that Lionel is required to print the small "circle R" patent registration mark (®) on cars advertising corporate products, as well as in the catalogue descriptions. This has led to many fun variations, with some cars having the mark and others missing it.

With all its "billboarding" in this series, Lionel did not forget the railroad realists. Such collectors prefer cars modeled after real prototypes, and these cars fit that bill:

9811	Pacific Fruit Express	9880	Santa Fe
9818	Western Maryland	9882	N Y R B
9819	Western Fruit	9887	Fruit Growers
9863	Railway Express Agency	9888	Green Bay Western
9869	Santa Fe	19500	Milwaukee
9872	Pacific Fruit Express	19505	Great Northern
9876	Central Vermont	19511	Western Maryland
		19520	C S X

These refrigerator cars are standard reefers, not "billboard" types. Because of their realistic appearance, and also since most were included only in limited sets, these cars generally demand a premium over the regular-issue billboard reefers.

One other series of reefers is worth particular mention. Between 1981 and 1985 Lionel produced special uncatalogued reefers for the annual Toy Fair in New York. These, like the Toy Fair boxcars produced in other years, were made in very limited quantities and are quite difficult to find. For those of you who like the challenge, here is the list (also see the Boxcar chapter):

1981:	0512
1982:	7519
1983:	7521
1984:	7523
1985:	7524

There is a terrific collector story behind the production of the 9853 Cracker Jack car in 1973 and 1974. The first cars produced were a dark caramel color, as portrayed in the 1973 catalogue. However, a few cars were made at the beginning of the production run with white sides, and collectors scrambled to acquire them. In 1974 these collectors were surprised to see the car pictured in white in the catalogue, and soon a flood of white 9853 cars hit the market. The expected situation became completely reversed; the caramel car is now regarded as the scarcer car, while the white car is readily available. Lionel apparently had other adventures with this car — there are versions missing the "circle R" registration marks and rare white cars with a faint "chalk white" border around the lettering, nearly invisible against the white sides. This is a prime example of the unpredictability of the collector marketplace.

The colorful reefer cars represent a fine opportunity for the beginning collector because most of them are readily available, some at real bargain prices. Only a few of the 9800-series refrigerator cars are scarce, mostly those in Collector sets. Only a relatively few reefers were included in sets; and given their low price, it is surprising Lionel has always considered them "Collector" cars. These cars look great when they are placed in a long string behind a modern set of diesels. They add color to a collection and offer many chances for specialization. In recent years Lionel has been phasing down the production of the 9800-series reefers in favor of the woodside variety, though one or two continue to be released each year.

9800-Series Reefer Body Types

The 9800-style refrigerator car is an all-plastic car with the roof and ends made of one piece and the bottom and sides made of another. The sides are distinguished by vertically scribed slats. The two pieces attach at the ends by screws. The oldest body type is more of a carry-over from postwar production than its successors, which had more and more detail eliminated in an attempt to simplify construction.

The Type I body features two metal door guides and a metal channel which runs the length of the car bottom and is attached by a single screw to the car body. In turn, the trucks are attached to the channel. The little metal control door and lithographed control gauge panel which were at the lower left of postwar production are missing, but three ice hatches are molded into the roof, and machinery doors underneath the ladders on each side of the body are wider than the ladders, as on the postwar cars. This style was used only on the first ten reefers (9850-9860) produced in 1973-1974. In reality, the 9800-series are only partially based on the two principal postwar reefers (the 6572 R E A and the 6672 Santa Fe). The modern reefers have detailed wood-scribed side pieces, unlike the postwar cars which had smooth steel-plated and riveted sides like the 6464-series. But the wonderfully detailed underframe, roof and ends were carried forward from postwar into the 9800-series reefers.

The Type II body is similar, but there are only two ice hatches at diagonal corners of the roof. Machinery doors are the same width as the ladders on the sides.

The Type III body retains the two ice hatches and the Type II machinery doors, but the door guides become snap-in plastic pieces, and the metal channel under the car is eliminated. Instead of the channel, the trucks are secured directly to the car body by a plastic or metal rivet. The change

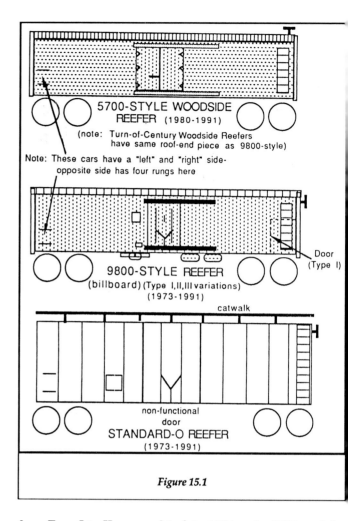

Figure 15.1

9800-SERIES REEFER BODY STYLES
By Donald J. Mitarotonda

TYPE I: 1973-1974
Two metal door guides.
Two metal bars running underneath frame, secured in center by one Phillips-head screw.
Trucks secured to metal.
Doors, underneath the ladders on each side of the body, are wider than the ladders.
Roof has three ice hatches, third ice hatch in one corner.

TYPE II: 1974-1976
Same as Type I, but doors underneath the ladders are the same width as the ladders; roof has two ice hatches in opposing corners.

TYPE III: 1976-Present
Two plastic door guides.
No metal bars underneath frame.
Trucks secured to the frame with a plastic pin.
Doors underneath the ladders are the same width as the ladders.
Roof has two ice hatches in opposing corners.

Figure 15.2

---

from Type I to II occurred in late 1974-early 1975, and the Type II style persisted into 1976. After 1976, Lionel moved to Type III, which is by far the most common, and is in use through the present day. Several cars vary through all the body styles.

It should be noted that the 7600 Bicentennial cars and the 7700 Tobacco Road cars are constructed quite similarly, except that the doors are sliding boxcar-style instead of refrigerator plug-door style.

THE STANDARD O-SERIES REEFERS

In 1973 Fundimensions introduced a line of full-scale box and refrigerator cars known as the Standard O series. These cars, reportedly based upon Pola designs made by the Rivarossi firm in Europe, were also the cars first equipped with the excellent Standard O sprung trucks. Although the cars were extremely well made, they did not meet the sales expectations of Fundimensions and did not persist for very long. Recently, the genre has been revived for rolling stock to match the 8406 Scale Hudson and other Collector Line limited sets. During the LTI era, many more handsome Standard O box and refrigerator cars have been produced, along with scale flatcars, ACF center-flow hoppers, scale wood-sided cabooses, and gondolas. This would seem to indicate that the reason the cars did not sell well in the 1973-1975 period was because Fundimensions had not produced true scale locomotives and cabooses to match them in an operating train. With the reissue of the Hudson and the creation of the scale SD-40 diesel and the scale cabooses, that situation has changed. It is possible that these cars will undergo a rebirth of popularity and the original issues will increase in value. An odd feature of the Standard O reefers is the molded-in door, which does not operate.

The availability of the Standard O cars varies considerably. Common cars such as the 9803 Johnson's Wax boxcar and the 9809 Clark reefer are easy to acquire at good prices. On the other hand, some cars such as the 9807 Stroh's reefer and the 9806 Rock Island boxcar are very hard to find. The New York Central (N Y R B) box and refrigerator cars command some attention, as do the box and refrigerator cars made available in a direct-mail campaign from Lionel in 1986. Behind the right engine, these cars make a very impressive train on a large layout. Their construction details are excellent, as well. The beginning collector may have a difficult time acquiring some of these cars, but a few representative samples would be good additions to anyone's collection.

The recent 17302 Santa Fe Standard O reefer marks a unique first for Lionel — it is the first Standard O car (of any type) with Lionel's new model of the "End-of-Train Device" (ETD) blinking light, which has been replacing cabooses on modern railroads for the last decade or so. As such, it is at the end of the first Lionel freight set ever made without a caboose.

THE 5700
TURN-OF-THE-CENTURY REEFERS

In 1980 Fundimensions tried something it had never tried before — a realistic "weathered" paint job. The firm issued eight cars which it called its "Turn of the Century" refrigerator cars. These cars (5700-5707) were modeled after wood-sided prototypes which were common on American railroads around 1910. The cars used 9800-series roof and end pieces, but the pieces which formed the sides and bottoms were new — horizontal wood scribing on the sides, extremely realistic riveting, and a scribed undercarriage. New doors were molded, with exceptional hinge and latch details. The cars also had true-to-life markings, and a special weatherbeaten treatment for the paint which is readily visible when the doors are opened to reveal the real color of the paint and plastic. These cars were also equipped with Standard O trucks; they represented Fundimensions' construction practices at its best.

Probably because the weathered look was so dramatically non-Lionel, the cars did not sell very well. And after only eight cars were produced, the series was discontinued in favor of the wood-sided reefer series, which sold much better. Turn-of-the-Century reefers are still readily available, making them highly desirable items if the collector favors their realistic look. The Oppenheimer, Budweiser, and Lindsay Brothers cars require a slight premium over the other

five, but none are really scarce. These eight cars look great in a train pulled by a postwar 675 or 2025 Pennsylvania K-4 steam locomotive, followed by an all-metal postwar 2457 Pennsylvania N5 caboose. They make a fine, high-quality set for the beginner's collection, and in future years they may appreciate in value because of their realistic appearance.

THE WOOD-SIDED REEFERS

In 1982 Fundimensions again tried to introduce a new series of refrigerator cars based upon an old-time theme, and this time the firm was much more successful with sales. The wood-sided reefers began with the 5708 Armour car and, in the first three years, four new cars in the series were produced each year. Three were made for 1985, but they were very dull in appearance and did not sell well, so they were carried over into the next year. These cars use the same highly detailed, horizontally scribed sides, bottom pieces and doors used on the Turn-of-the-Century reefers, but without the weathering process. The roof and end pieces are entirely new. The ends are scribed vertically and the roof is scribed across its width. Four ice hatches are present in the corners of the roof, and the wood scribing has been given a skillfully grained look. The brakewheel is atop the roof end rather than on the end itself. Although true to the prototype, this feature can be annoying when the collector puts the car back in its box, because the brakewheel always catches on the box divider. In recent production, the brakewheel has been shipped taped to the bottom to prevent damage. The 5700-series cars are equipped with the less expensive but realistic plastic arch bar trucks.

In 1987 Lionel hinted it was ending the series with three five-digit-numbered cars. This proved a case of semantics, because the style was restarted immediately the next year with two handsome cars in a new "Famous Inventor" series which continues today. The new series uses the same body as the 5700-style cars, except with Symington-Wayne trucks. The new cars shifted to ASF strong-arm trucks starting in 1990. Here is the list as of mid-1991 (Lionel has been releasing two per year in this set):

19506 Thomas Newcomen
19507 Thomas Edison
19508 Leonardo DaVinci
19509 Alexander Graham Bell
19512 Wright Brothers
19513 Ben Franklin
19522 Guglielmo Marconi
19523 Robert Goddard

The wood-sided reefers have sold very well as a class, and most are readily available to the beginning collector. The 5709 Railway Express is a little harder to find than most of the others, but only one of these reefers is truly rare: the 5712 Lionel Lines wood-sided reefer of 1983. This car jumped in value almost overnight and is nearly impossible to acquire. The 5720 Great Northern, a very attractive dark green car, was not made in great quantity and is also quite scarce. The Famous Inventor cars have been selling reasonably well.

Operationally, the wood-sided reefers can look very good when pulled behind any old-style steam engine, even the "General" engines. The new center-cab transfer cabooses have just the right old-fashioned look for a set of these cars. Most have been produced in prototypical orange, yellow and tuscan colors, so a train of these cars provides a realistic look lacking in the 9800-series, matched only by the Turn-of-the-Century reefers.

THE MILK CARS

Last but definitely not least are three excellent operating reefer cars offered in the modern era — the 9220 Borden in 1983, the 19802 Carnation of 1987, and the 19810 Bosco of 1988. These are operating milk cars based on the tradition of those millions of 3462 and 3662 cars made in the postwar era.

The modern cars are really hybrids of boxcar and refrigerator car features. They have metal frames and simulated steel-plated sides with excellent rivet detail like the Classic boxcar. In fact, they have more rivet detailing than nearly all modern boxcars. But they are also long cars with fine-scribed roof and end pieces like the wood-sided reefers. The door is a style unique to the milk cars, with spring-loaded split panels to allow the little man inside to stay hidden before surprising an unsuspecting youngster.

The internal mechanism, which allows milk cans to slide down a chute from the top hatch, stand upright, and be pushed out by the solenoid-activated man, is essentially the same as the postwar models. Another unique aspect of the modern cars is that they use older postwar bar-end trucks to hold the sliding-shoe power pickup needed to activate them. Cans and matching platforms are supplied with the milk cars. All have been good sellers, despite the somewhat steep price, and the paint schemes and handsome graphics of the new ones put the plain white postwar version to shame. It is curious to imagine these cars interesting today's children just as they did their parents 30 years before.

REFRIGERATOR CAR LISTINGS

	GD	VD	EXC	MT

0104 WHEAT THINS: 1984, reefer; see Volume II, first edition.

0124 OREO: 1984, reefer; see Volume II, first edition.

0512 TOY FAIR: 1981, reefer; uncatalogued; white sides; glossy blue roof and ends; white door; blue and red lettering; Fundimensions "F" logo to right of door; MPC and Craftmaster logos; Symington-Wayne trucks; "BLT 1-81". This car was the first reefer released by Lionel in its uncatalogued special Toy Fair Series. Boxcars had previously been used for the series, and after a run of reefers, Lionel returned to Toy Fair boxcars in 1986. Like all Toy Fair cars, this one is hard to find. It is not clear why the car bears this unusual number. — — 125 150

	GD	VD	EXC	MT

3764 KAHN'S: 1981, reefer; L O T S; see Volume II, first edition.

5700 OPPENHEIMER CASING CO.: 1981, Turn-of-the-Century wood-sided reefer; medium green weathered paint; black lettering; red and black logo; Standard O sprung trucks; no "BLT" date. First in the Turn-of-the-Century series, all of which were offered for separate-sale, not in sets. The series consists of the 5700-5707 cars. — — 25 45

5701 DAIRYMEN'S LEAGUE: 1981, Turn-of-the-Century wood-sided reefer; off-white weathered paint; black roof and ends; blue lettering and "MILK" logo; Standard O sprung trucks; no "BLT" date. — — 20 25

5702 NATIONAL DAIRY DESPATCH: 1981, Turn-of-the-Century wood-sided reefer; silver-gray body; red and silver weathered paint; dark red roof and ends; black lettering "UNIVERSAL/CARLOADING &/DISTRIBUTING/COMPANY"; number under- and over-scored; Standard O sprung trucks; no "BLT" date. — — 20 25

5703 NORTH AMERICAN DESPATCH: 1981, Turn-of-the-Century wood-sided reefer; weathered light yellow body; dark brown roof and ends; black lettering "FRIGICAR"; number under- and over-scored; Standard O sprung trucks; no "BLT" date. — — 20 25

5704 BUDWEISER: 1981-82, Turn-of-the-Century wood-sided reefer; dark green weathered paint scheme on body; number under- and over-scored; white lettering; Standard O sprung trucks; "BLT 1-81". This car is a little scarcer than the others in this group because of interest from beer car collectors. C. Rohlfing comment. — — 45 55

5705 BALL GLASS JARS: 1981-82, Turn-of-the-Century wood-sided reefer; yellow weathered paint scheme on body; brown roof and ends; blue bottle logo on door; blue lettering; Standard O sprung trucks; "BLT 1-81". Car is pictured all brown in the 1981-82 catalogues, but was made with yellow sides; brown prototypes may exist. — — 25 30

5706 LINDSAY BROS.: 1981-82, Turn-of-the-Century wood-sided reefer; tuscan-maroon weathered paint scheme on body; yellow lettering "CHICAGO/MILWAUKEE/AND/SAINT PAUL"; Standard O sprung trucks; "BLT 1-81". — — 25 30

5707 AMERICAN REFRIGERATOR TRANSIT CO.: 1981-82, Turn-of-the-Century wood-sided reefer; yellow weathered paint scheme on body; brown roof and ends; black lettering; number under- and over-scored; red, white and blue shield logo; Standard O sprung trucks; "BLT 1-81". Last of the Turn-of-the-Century weathered reefer cars. — — 20 25

5708 ARMOUR REFRIGERATOR LINE: 1982-83, wood-sided reefer; yellow sides; tuscan roof and ends; blue lettering; yellow and blue Armour logo; brakewheel on top, not on sides as on earlier cars; plastic arch bar trucks; "BLT 1-81". Car is a new wood-sided reefer style with sides based on 5700-5707 cars, but new roof and end design with detailed slat scribing. — — 17 20

5709 RAILWAY EXPRESS AGENCY: 1982-83, wood-sided reefer; green-painted body; yellow lettering; red and white diamond R E A electrocal; top brakewheel; plastic arch bar trucks; "BLT 1-82". Somewhat scarcer than the other early wood-sided reefers, because collectors use this car in passenger trains. — — 30 45

realistic Turn-of-the-Century refrigerator cars.

shelf: **5700** Oppenheimer Casing Co.; **5701** Dairymen's League.
nd shelf: **5702** National Dairy Despatch; **5703** North American Despatch.
d shelf: **5704** Budweiser; **5705** Ball Glass Jars.
om shelf: **5706** Lindsay Bros.; **5707** American Refrigerator Transit Co.

	GD	VD	EXC	MT

5710 CANADIAN PACIFIC RAILWAY: 1982-83, wood-sided reefer; tuscan body; white lettering; number under- and over-scored; top brakewheel; plastic arch bar trucks; "BLT 1-82". — — 17 20

5711 COMMERCIAL EXPRESS FAST FREIGHT LINE: 1982-83, wood-sided reefer; light caramel body; brown roof and ends; black lettering; red "C.X." scroll logo with car number in white; top brakewheel; plastic arch bar trucks; "BLT 1-82". — — 17 20

5712 LIONEL ELECTRIC TRAINS: 1982, wood-sided reefer; uncatalogued; bright orange body; bright blue roof and ends; blue doors; blue and white "LIONEL" electrocal; blue lettering; top brakewheel; plastic arch bar trucks; "BLT 1-82". Very hard to find; the price of this car has increased dramatically since it was first introduced, since it was the beginning of a very popular "Lionel Lines" separate-sale set for which new components are still being released. Appeared in a 1982 Fall Collector special brochure. — 175 200 300

	GD	VD	EXC	MT

5713 COTTON BELT ROUTE: 1983-84, wood-sided reefer; yellow sides; brown roof and ends; brown "COTTON/ BELT-/ROUTE" logo to right of door; brown lettering "ST. LOUIS/SOUTHWESTERN/REFRIGERATOR/DESPATCH"; top brakewheel; plastic arch bar trucks; "BLT 1-82". — — 15 20

5714 MICHIGAN CENTRAL: 1983-84, wood-sided reefer; white sides; brown roof and ends; black lettering; N Y C oval logo in black; top brakewheel; plastic arch bar trucks; "BLT 1-83". — — 15 20

5715 SANTA FE: 1983-84, wood-sided reefer; orange sides; tuscan roof and ends (shown as dark blue in the 1983 catalogue, but not produced that way); black lettering; black and white Santa Fe cross logo to left of door; top brakewheel; plastic arch bar trucks; "BLT 1-83". — — 20 25

5716 CENTRAL VERMONT: 1983-84, wood-sided reefer; silver-gray sides; black roof and ends; black and green lettering

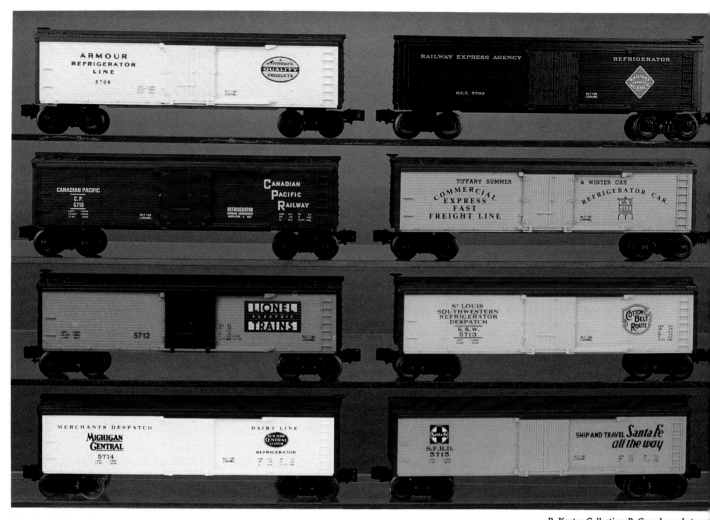

R. Kaptur Collection; B. Greenberg photogra

Wood-sided reefers, new in 1982. Note the modified roof end piece.
Top shelf: **5708** Armour Refrigerator Line; **5709** Railway Express Agency.
Second shelf: **5710** Canadian Pacific Railway; **5711** Commercial Express Fast Freight Line.
Third shelf: **5712** Lionel Electric Trains, an extremely rare car; **5713** Cotton Belt Route.
Bottom shelf: **5714** Michigan Central; **5715** Santa Fe.

	GD	VD	EXC	MT

"VERMONT/MILK" and "GREEN/MOUNTAIN/ROUTE"; top brakewheel; plastic arch bar trucks; "BLT 1-83".

| | — | — | 15 | 20 |

5718 LIONEL: 1983; see 9849.

5719 CANADIAN NATIONAL: 1984, wood-sided reefer; gray body; dark red lettering and maple leaf logo; number under- and over-scored; top brakewheel; plastic arch bar trucks; "BLT 1-84".

| | — | — | 15 | 20 |

5720 GREAT NORTHERN: 1984, wood-sided reefer; dark green body; gold lettering; red, white and black Great Northern goat logo; top brakewheel; plastic arch bar trucks; "BLT 1-84". This car was originally scheduled for production in Mexico just prior to Lionel's move back to Mt. Clemens, Michigan. Production problems prevented the Mexican run, so a few hundred were hurriedly run off in the United States. Many United States dealers were lucky to receive one or two of these cars, if any at all. As a result, this car is very difficult to find. C. Lang comment.

| | — | — | 85 | 125 |

	GD	VD	EXC	MT

5721 SOO LINE: 1984, wood-sided reefer; orange sides; brown roof and ends; black "V.R.T.X" lettering; black and white SOO Line logo; top brakewheel; plastic arch bar trucks; "BLT 1-84".

| | — | — | 15 | 20 |

5722 NICKEL PLATE ROAD: 1984, wood-sided reefer; yellow sides; brown roof and ends; black lettering; number under- and over-scored; top brakewheel; plastic arch bar trucks; "BLT 1-84".

| | — | — | 15 | 20 |

5730 STRASBURG RAILROAD: 1985-86, wood-sided reefer; tuscan body; yellow-gold lettering and numbering; top brakewheel; plastic arch bar trucks; "BLT 1-85". Popular in the Pennsylvania area because of association with Strasburg tourist railroad.

| | — | — | 15 | 20 |

5731 LOUISVILLE & NASHVILLE: 1985-86, wood-sided reefer; tuscan body; white lettering and numbering; number under- and over-scored; top brakewheel; plastic arch bar trucks; "BLT 1-85".

| | — | — | 12 | 15 |

R. Kaptur Collection; B. Greenberg photograph

Wood-sided reefers from 1984, and two hard-to-find specials.
Top shelf: 5716 Central Vermont; 5719 Canadian National.
Second shelf: 5720 Great Northern; 5721 Soo Line.
Third shelf: 5722 Nickel Plate Road; 5732 Central Railroad of New Jersey.
Bottom shelf: 6230 Erie Lackawanna Standard O reefer; 6700 Pacific Express, an operating ice car (see listing in boxcar chapter). Both cars are hard to find.

	GD	VD	EXC	MT

5732 CENTRAL RAILROAD OF NEW JERSEY: 1985-86, wood-sided reefer; maroon-wine body; white lettering; red and white bull's eye logo; top brakewheel; plastic arch bar trucks; "BLT 1-85". (Yes, this is the precursor to the Jersey Central.)
— — **20** **30**

5734 RAILWAY EXPRESS AGENCY: 1985, wood-sided reefer; T C A; see Volume II, first edition.

6230 ERIE LACKAWANNA: 1986, Standard O reefer; uncatalogued; orange sides; black ends; silver-painted roof; black lettering and diamond-E logo; Standard O trucks; "BLT 1-86". Part of special direct-mail Lionel offer associated with the B & A Hudson. Difficult to find. — — **135** **155**

6700 PACIFIC FRUIT EXPRESS: 1982; see Boxcar chapter.

7502 LIONEL 75TH ANNIVERSARY: 1975-76, 9800-style reefer; multicolor electrocals depicting significant Lionel innovations; yellow body; blue roof and ends; Symington-Wayne trucks; no "BLT" date. Part of 1585 75th Anniversary Special set. For

details on Lionel's 75th Anniversary Special set, refer to the Boxcar chapter. — **10** **15** **20**

7503 LIONEL 75TH ANNIVERSARY: 1975-76, 9800-style reefer; multicolor electrocals showing Lionel's most famous engines; orange body; brown roof and ends; Symington-Wayne trucks; no "BLT" date. Part of 1585 75th Anniversary Special set.
— **10** **15** **20**

7507 LIONEL 75TH ANNIVERSARY: 1975-76, 9800-style reefer; electrocals featuring various Lionel corporate logos; white body; blue roof and ends; Symington-Wayne trucks; no "BLT" date. Part of 1585 75th Anniversary Special set.
— **10** **15** **20**

7509 KENTUCKY FRIED CHICKEN: 1981-82, 9800-style reefer; red sides; tuscan roof and ends; white lettering; Colonel Sanders electrocal; Symington-Wayne trucks; "BLT 1-81". From Favorite Food freight set, available only as separate-sale.
— — **15** **20**

7510 RED LOBSTER: 1981-82, 9800-style reefer; white sides; black roof and ends; red lettering; lobster electrocal;

Three colorful reefers from Lionel's 75th Anniversary set and five Favorite Food reefers.
Top shelf: 7502 Lionel; 7503 Lionel.
Second shelf: 7507 Lionel; 7509 Kentucky Fried Chicken.
Third shelf: 7510 Red Lobster; 7511 Pizza Hut.
Bottom shelf: 7512 Arthur Treacher's Seafood; 7513 Bonanza International, Inc.

F. Stem Collection; B. Greenberg photograph

	GD	VD	EXC	MT

Symington-Wayne trucks; "BLT 1-81". From Favorite Food freight set, available only as separate-sale.

| | | — | — | 20 | 30 |

7511 PIZZA HUT: 1981-82, 9800-style reefer; white sides; red roof and ends; red lettering; hut electrocal; Symington-Wayne trucks; "BLT 1-81". From Favorite Food freight, available only as separate-sale.

— — 20 25

7512 ARTHUR TREACHER'S SEAFOOD: 1982, 9800-style reefer; yellow sides; green roof and ends; green lettering; Symington-Wayne trucks; "BLT 1-82". Part of Favorite Food series, available only as separate-sale. Catalogued as 9827, but made as 7512.

— — 20 25

7513 BONANZA INTERNATIONAL, INC: 1982, 9800-style reefer; white sides; red roof and ends; red and black lettering; Bonanza electrocal to right of door; Symington-Wayne trucks; "BLT 1-82". Part of Favorite Food series, available only as separate-sale. Catalogued as 9829, but made as 7513.

— — 20 25

	GD	VD	EXC	MT

7514 TACO BELL: 1982, 9800-style reefer; white sides; brown roof and ends; brown lettering; multicolor Taco Bell electrocal to right of door; Symington-Wayne trucks; "BLT 1-82". Part of Favorite Food series, available only as separate-sale. Catalogued as 9830, but made as 7514. — — 20 25

7519 TOY FAIR: 1982, reefer, 9800-series reefer body; white sides; red roof and ends; red doors; red, white and blue logos; Fundimensions "F" to left of door; Lionel, MPC and Craftmaster logos to right of door; gold "TOY FAIR 1982" lettering; Symington-Wayne trucks; "BLT 1-82". — — 150 175

7521 TOY FAIR: 1983, reefer, 9800-series reefer body; white sides; dark blue roof and ends; red doors; old-fashioned "TOY FAIR" script and gold edging to left of door; Fundimensions and MPC logos to right of door; Symington-Wayne trucks; no built date. — — 150 175

7523 TOY FAIR: 1984, 9800-series reefer; white sides; dark red roof and ends; dark blue doors; red and blue lettering; "1984" and "TOY FAIR" logos to left of door; General Mills toy division logos to right of door; Symington-Wayne trucks; "BLT 1-84". — — 150 175

Billboard reefers and four of the earliest Standard O reefers.
Top shelf: 7514 Taco Bell; 9220 Bordon, one of Lionel's new operating milk cars.
Second shelf: 9802 Miller High Life; 9805 Grand Trunk Western. These two cars inaugurated the Standard O series in 1973.
Third shelf: 9807 Stroh's Bohemian Beer; 9809 Clark.
Bottom shelf: 9811 Pacific Fruit Express from Famous American Railroad Set No. 2; 9812 Arm & Hammer.

R. Kaptur and F. Stem Collections; B. Greenberg photograph

	GD	VD	EXC	MT

7524 TOY FAIR: 1985, 9800-series reefer; light brown sides; dark brown roof and ends; brown lettering; varied red and blue Fundimensions logos; Symington-Wayne trucks; large "BUILT 1985 LIONEL" oval logo. This was the last Fundimensions-produced Toy Fair car and the last reefer in the series. L. Caponi comment and Collection. — — 175 200

9220 BORDEN: 1983-86, operating refrigerated milk car; white body; brown roof and ends; brown door; black lettering; yellow and black Elsie cow logo to right of door; stamped-metal frame supports operating mechanism; came with gray and white milk can platform and plastic weighted milk cans; car has postwar bar-end metal trucks because sliding shoe is needed to operate car. This and later 19800-series milk cars are a combination of boxcar-type steel plate riveted sides with reefer-type roof and ends. This car was catalogued in 1983 and 1984, but not produced until 1985! — — 90 100

9800 GRAND TRUNK WESTERN: See 9805.

9802 MILLER HIGH LIFE: 1973-75, Standard O reefer; white body; red lettering and logo; Standard O trucks; has "1-73" but no "BLT". This car, with the 9805 reefer and two boxcars, inaugurated the Standard O series of Lionel rolling stock in 1973. 15 20 30 40
See Factory Errors and Prototypes chapter in Volume II, first edition.

9805 GRAND TRUNK WESTERN: 1973-75, Standard O reefer; silver-painted gray body; black lettering; large "GT" logo to right; number under- and over-scored; Standard O trucks; "BLT 1-73". One of the first Standard O cars released by Lionel. A "9800" Grand Trunk Standard O reefer was pictured in an early 1973 brochure, but the car was made as the 9805. T. Wagner comment. 15 20 30 40

9807 STROH'S BOHEMIAN BEER: 1974-76, Standard O reefer; red-painted red body; gold and white lettering; gold

Standard O and billboard reefers.
Top shelf: 9813 Ruffles Brand; 9814 Perrier.
Second shelf: 9815 N Y R B; 9816 Brachs.
Third shelf: 9817 Bazooka Bubble Gum; 9819 Western Fruit Express.
Bottom shelf: 9818 Western Maryland; 9825 Schaefer.

R. Kaptur, A. Rudman, and F. Stem Collections; B. Greenberg photograph

	GD	VD	EXC	MT
"Stroh's" script logo; Standard O trucks; "BLT 1-74". Somewhat hard to find.	40	50	80	125

9809 CLARK: 1975-76, Standard O reefer; red-painted red body; blue lettering; orange and blue Clark bar logo to right; Standard O trucks; "BLT 1-75".

	GD	VD	EXC	MT
(A) Medium red-painted body.	15	20	25	40
(B) Dark red-painted body.	15	20	25	40

9811 PACIFIC FRUIT EXPRESS: 1980, reefer; yellow-painted yellow plastic body and doors; tuscan-painted tuscan plastic roof; black lettering; gold FARR Series 2 diamond insignia; red, white and blue Union Pacific shield; blue Southern Pacific circle logo; Symington-Wayne trucks; "BLT 1-80". Part of Famous American Railroad Series No. 2 whose components were all sold separately. — — **25 35**

9812 ARM & HAMMER: 1980, billboard reefer; yellow sides; red roof and ends; black lettering; yellow and red Baking Soda box electrocal to right; blue, white and red Arm & Hammer logo to left; Symington-Wayne trucks; "BLT 1-80". — — **15 20**

9813 RUFFLES BRAND: 1980, billboard reefer; blue roof and ends; red and blue logo; multicolor electrocal of chips bags; red lettering; Symington-Wayne trucks; "BLT 1-80".
(A) Light blue sides. Samson and G. Rogers Collections.
— — **10 20**
(B) White sides; very difficult to find. G. Halverson comment.
NRS

9814 PERRIER: 1980, billboard reefer; dark Brunswick green sides; light yellow ends and roof; "Perrier" electrocal to right of door; mountain spring electrocal to left of door shows a Perrier bottle bubbling from beneath the earth; bottle logo is a stick-in decal; Symington-Wayne trucks; "BLT 1-80".
— — **20 25**

See Factory Errors and Prototypes chapter in Volume II, first edition.

9815 N Y R B: 1984-85, (New York Central) Standard O reefer; orange body; tuscan roof and catwalk; blue lettering; "EARLY BIRD" logo; number under- and over-scored; Standard O trucks;

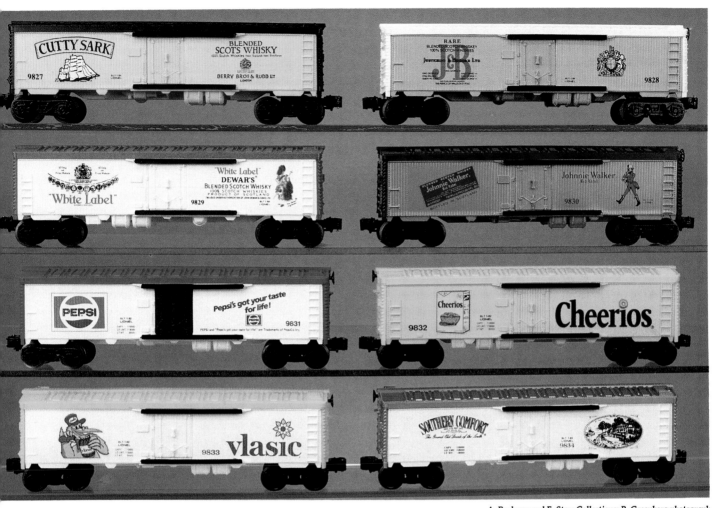

A. Rudman and F. Stem Collections; B. Greenberg photograph

...e first of the "Favorite Spirit" reefers.
...p shelf: 9827 Cutty Sark; 9828 J & B.
...cond shelf: 9829 White Label; 9830 Johnnie Walker Red Label.
...ird shelf: 9831 Pepsi; 9832 Cheerios.
...ttom shelf: 9833 Vlasic; 9834 Southern Comfort.

	GD	VD	EXC	MT

"BLT 1-85". Pictured in the 1984 catalogue but not made until the next year. F. Cieri and C. Rohlfing Collections.

| | — | — | 70 | 90 |

9816 BRACHS: 1980, billboard reefer; candy series; white sides; tuscan roof and ends; magenta doors; magenta, tuscan and white lettering and candy box logo; Symington-Wayne trucks; "BLT 1-80".

| | — | — | 15 | 20 |

9817 BAZOOKA BUBBLE GUM: 1980, billboard reefer; candy series; white sides; blue door; red and blue Bazooka electrocal; red and blue gum pack to right; Symington-Wayne trucks; "BLT 1-80".

(A) Orange-red roof and ends.

| | — | — | 10 | 20 |

(B) Orange roof and ends. C. Rohlfing Collection.

| | — | — | 15 | 20 |

9818 WESTERN MARYLAND: 1980, reefer; orange-red sides; Standard O trucks; "BLT 1-80". Part of 1070 Royal Limited set; see also 19511.

(A) Brown roof and ends; black lettering. R. and R. Hunley and M. Blacet Collections.

| | — | — | 25 | 35 |

(B) Black roof, ends and lettering.

| | | | | **NRS** |

	GD	VD	EXC	MT

(C) Brown roof, ends and lettering. The existence of this car has been questioned. Further reader comments requested. D. Griggs Collection.

| | | | | **NRS** |

9819 WESTERN FRUIT EXPRESS: 1981, reefer; yellow sides and ends; black lettering; Great Northern goat logo; number under- and over-scored; gold FARR Series 3 diamond insignia; Symington-Wayne trucks; "BLT 1-81". Part of Famous American Railroad Series No. 3, whose components were all sold separately.

| | — | — | 25 | 35 |

9825 SCHAEFER: 1976-77, Standard O reefer; white body; red lettering and roof; black catwalk; yellow, black and red beer stein logos to left; red Schaefer logo to right; electrocals are not well done on this car; Standard O trucks; "BLT 1-75".

| | 20 | 30 | 55 | 70 |

9827 ARTHUR TREACHER'S SEAFOOD: 1982; see 7512.

9827 CUTTY SARK: 1984, billboard reefer; Favorite Spirits series; yellow sides and doors; black roof and ends; black lettering; black and white sailing ship electrocal; Symington-Wayne trucks; "BLT 1-84".

| | — | — | 15 | 20 |

Some of the best-looking "Favorite Spirit" reefers.
Top shelf: 9835 Jim Beam; 9826 Old Grand-Dad.
Second shelf: 9837 Wild Turkey; 9840 Fleischmann's Distilled Dry Gin.
Third shelf: 9841 Calvert Gin; 9842 Seagram's Extra Dry Gin.
Bottom shelf: 9843 Tanqueray; 9844 Sambuca Romana.

A. Rudman Collection; B. Greenberg photograph

	GD	VD	EXC	MT

9828 J & B: 1984, billboard reefer; Favorite Spirits series; yellow-green sides and doors; white roof and ends; red and black lettering; detailed multicolor herald electrocal to right; Symington-Wayne trucks; "BLT 1-84". — — **15 20**

9829 BONANZA INTERNATIONAL, INC: 1982; see 7513.

9829 WHITE LABEL: 1984, billboard reefer; Favorite Spirits series; white sides and doors; red roof and ends; red and black lettering; orange and gold bagpiper electrocal; Symington-Wayne trucks; "BLT 1-84". — — **15 20**

9830 JOHNNIE WALKER RED LABEL: 1984, billboard reefer; Favorite Spirits series; yellow-gold sides and doors; maroon roof and ends; maroon lettering; maroon rectangular logo with gold lettering; red, blue and yellow Johnnie Walker electrocal; Symington-Wayne trucks; "BLT 1-84". — — **15 20** See Factory Errors and Prototypes chapter in Volume II, first edition

9830 TACO BELL: 1982; see 7514.

9831 PEPSI: 1982, billboard reefer; white sides; light blue ends and roof; dark blue door; red, white and blue Pepsi electrocal; Symington-Wayne trucks; "BLT 1-82". Compare to the 7800 Pepsi boxcar. — — **30 40**

9832 CHEERIOS: 1982, billboard reefer; yellow body; black lettering; Cheerios box electrocal; Symington-Wayne trucks; "BLT 1-82". — — **15 25**

9833 VLASIC: 1982, billboard reefer; white sides; yellow roof and ends; green lettering; Vlasic bird electrocal; Symington-Wayne trucks; "BLT 1-82". — — **15 20**

9834 SOUTHERN COMFORT: 1983-84, billboard reefer; Favorite Spirits series; white body; gold roof and ends; black lettering; black oval Southern mansion electrocal; Symington-Wayne trucks; "BLT 1-83". — — **20 30**

9835 JIM BEAM: 1983-84, billboard reefer; Favorite Spirits series; white sides; red roof and ends; red and black lettering; red, gold and black ribbon logo to right of door; Symington-Wayne trucks; "BLT 1-83". — — **20 30**

Billboard reefers and two of the confusing Cracker Jack cars.

Top shelf: 9845 Baileys Original Irish Cream; 9846 Seagram's Imported Vodka.

Second shelf: 9847 Wolfschmidt Genuine Vodka; 9850 Anheuser-Busch Budweiser, the first of Lionel's billboard reefers.

Third shelf: 9851 Schlitz; 9852 Miller High Life.

Bottom shelf: Two variations of the 9853 Cracker Jack. These are both standard production versions (camel and white sides). Several rare and confusing variations exist having to do with the border around the words "Cracker Jack".

R. Kaptur, R. LaVoie and A. Rudman Collections; B. Greenberg photograph

	GD	VD	EXC	MT

9836 OLD GRAND-DAD: 1983-84, billboard reefer; Favorite Spirits series; orange body; gold roof and ends; black-edged gold and brown lettering; orange, white and black electrocal to right of door; Symington-Wayne trucks; "BLT 1-83".
— — 20 30

9837 WILD TURKEY: 1983-84, billboard reefer; Favorite Spirits series; pale/straw yellow body; dark brown roof and ends; dark brown "WILD/TURKEY" lettering; turkey electrocal to right of door; Symington-Wayne trucks; "BLT 1-83".
— — 20 30

9840 FLEISCHMANN'S GIN: 1985, billboard reefer; Favorite Spirits series; light yellow sides and doors; maroon roof and ends; dark blue and dark orange lettering; blue and gold eagle electrocal; Symington-Wayne trucks; "BLT 1-85".
— — 15 20

9841 CALVERT GIN: 1985, billboard reefer; Favorite Spirits series; dark blue body; silver roof and ends; silver lettering; red and silver herald electrocal; Symington-Wayne trucks; "BLT 1-85".
— — 15 20

9842 SEAGRAM'S EXTRA DRY GIN: 1985, billboard reefer; Favorite Spirits series; cream sides; dark blue roof and ends; dark blue and red lettering; dark blue and cream shield electrocal; Symington-Wayne trucks; "BLT 1-85".
— — 15 20

9843 TANQUERAY: 1985, billboard reefer; Favorite Spirits series; white sides; dark green roof and ends; red and black lettering; red and black oval "T" electrocal; Symington-Wayne trucks; "BLT 1-85".
— — 15 20

9844 SAMBUCA ROMANA: 1986, billboard reefer; Favorite Spirits series; very dark blue sides; silver-gray roof and ends; silver and black coliseum logo; gray, silver and white lettering; Symington-Wayne trucks; "BLT 1-86".
— — 15 20

9845 BAILEYS ORIGINAL IRISH CREAM: 1986, billboard reefer; Favorite Spirits series; dark pea green sides; maroon roof and ends; orange, brown and gold electrocal; orange, black and white lettering; Symington-Wayne trucks; "BLT 1-86".
— — 20 25

	GD	VD	EXC	MT

9846 SEAGRAM'S IMPORTED VODKA: 1986, billboard reefer; Favorite Spirits series; dark gray sides; black roof and ends; red and silver logo; silver lettering; Symington-Wayne trucks; "BLT 1-86".

| | — | — | 15 | 20 |

> **Note:** *One significant note about the "Electrocal" decal application process is that the adherence of the electrocal to a glossy-painted body removes the glossy sheen, leaving a flat-painted appearance in the area adjacent. This is particularly noticeable on the 9847 and other dark glossy-painted cars in the Favorite Spirits series.*

9847 WOLFSCHMIDT GENUINE VODKA: 1986, billboard reefer; Favorite Spirits series; dark green sides; gold roof and ends; red, gold and white logo; white and gold lettering; Symington-Wayne trucks; "BLT 1-86".

| | — | — | 15 | 20 |

9849 LIONEL: 1983, reefer; uncatalogued; bright "Lionel"-orange body; orange doors; blue roof and ends; very large circular old-fashioned "LIONEL" logo in red, white and blue to the right of the door; Lionel "lion" electrocal to the left of the door; Symington-Wayne trucks. The number to the immediate right of the lion is portrayed as 5718 in the 1983 Collector Center brochure, but 9849 is the number of the production models. Considered part of a continuing separate-sale Lionel Lines set, whose components were offered beginning in 1982. This car and others in this series may have been prompted by the unauthorized repainting and sale of Lionel rolling stock in similar fashion by a small New England firm. R. LaVoie and C. Lang comments.

| | — | — | 50 | 70 |

9850 ANHEUSER BUSCH BUDWEISER: 1973-75, billboard reefer; beer series; Type I white body and door; red and black lettering; red and yellow Anheuser-Busch A-Eagle logo to right of door; Symington-Wayne trucks; "BLT 1-73".

(A) Light red roof and ends.	7	9	20	25
(B) Medium red roof and ends.	7	9	20	25
(C) Dark red roof and ends.	7	9	20	25
(D) Same as (A), but large period after "BEER CAR" at lower right.	12	15	30	40
(E) Same as (A), but Type II body.	7	9	20	25

9851 SCHLITZ: 1973-77, billboard reefer; beer series; white body and door; brown lettering "The Beer that made/Milwaukee Famous"; yellow, brown and blue Schlitz logo to left; Symington-Wayne trucks; "BLT 1-73".
(A) Type I body; shiny brown roof and ends.

| | 6 | 8 | 15 | 25 |

(B) Type II body with dull brown roof and ends. This is probably the version which appeared in the 1762 Wabash Cannonball set in 1977.

| | 6 | 8 | 15 | 25 |

9852 MILLER HIGH LIFE: 1973-77, billboard reefer; beer series; white body and door; black lettering; Miller electrocal to right in black, red and yellow; Symington-Wayne trucks; "BLT 1-73".
(A) Type I body; shiny brown roof and ends.

| | 5 | 10 | 15 | 25 |

(B) Type II body with dull brown roof and ends. This is probably the version which appeared in the 1664 Illinois Central freight set in 1976-77.

| | 5 | 10 | 15 | 25 |

(C) Same as (B), but Type III body. Reader confirmation requested.

| | | | | NRS |

	GD	VD	EXC	MT

9853 CRACKER JACK: 1973-75, billboard reefer; candy series; Type I body, except (I); brown roof and ends, except (H); red "Cracker/Jack" logo; blue lettering; blue sailor figure; Symington-Wayne trucks; "BLT 1-73". Among the first billboard reefers released, this car has more variations than any other reefer. There are two principal body colors (white and caramel), and important variations exist on the presence or absence of a border around the words "Cracker/Jack". The production history of this car has been quite difficult to establish — further reader comments are requested.
(A) Type I white body and door; faint chalk white" border around "Cracker/Jack" and blue sailor, almost invisible against white sides. This was probably a factory error made when the Cracker Jack electrocals were changed from no-border to white borders. It may have been produced when Lionel purged the molding machines in preparation for the caramel car runs. "Circle R" registration mark. Rare. D. Coletta Collection.

| | — | 80 | 100 | 125 |

(B) Same as (A), but black border around "Cracker/Jack". We would like to know more details on this car relative to (A).

| | | | | NRS |

(C) Type I light caramel body; dark caramel door; white border around "Cracker/Jack"; "circle R" registration mark. This version and (D) were run in 1974, after the white cars. C. Rohlfing, F. Salvatore, R. LaVoie and L. Stever Collections.

| | 20 | 25 | 30 | 35 |

(D) Same as (C), except medium caramel body and door. This is the standard production caramel version.

| | 15 | 20 | 25 | 30 |

(E) Same as (C) (caramel body), except no border around "Cracker/Jack". This was the first production run, in 1973. Reportedly less than 50 were made, probably before the main run of caramel cars.

| | 80 | 100 | 125 | 150 |

(F) Same as (A) (white body), but no border around "Cracker/Jack". This is the standard white version of the car run later in 1973 and early 1974.

| | 5 | 7 | 15 | 20 |

(G) Same as (F), except no registration mark.

| | 5 | 7 | 15 | 20 |

(H) Same as (F), except Type II body. Probably 1974 production. G. Halverson comment.

| | | | | NRS |

(I) Same as (F), except "Cracker" in blue and "Jack" in red, not both in red as on other cars; slight blue spot under "Jack". Further sightings requested. R. P. Bryan Collection.

| | | | | NRS |

9854 BABY RUTH: 1973-76, billboard reefer; candy series; Type I white body and door; red roof and ends; blue lettering; large red "Baby Ruth" logo; Symington-Wayne trucks; no "BLT" date.

(A) Small "circle R" registration mark.	6	10	15	20
(B) Same as (A), but with no registration mark.	—	20	30	45
(C) Same as (B), but with Type II body.	10	15	20	30
(D) Same as (A), but Type II body. C. Rohlfing Collection.	6	10	15	20
(E) Same as (A), but darker red roof and lettering.	6	10	15	20

9855 SWIFT REFRIGERATOR LINE: 1973-77, billboard reefer; silver body and door; black roof and ends; black lettering; red "Swift's/Premium" logo; Symington-Wayne trucks; "BLT 1-73". Some variations were reported with no "BLT" date or "BLT 1-7". These are probably cases of paint flaking, which has happened to other cars. This car appeared in the 1764 Heartland set, and was also sold separately.

More billboard reefers.
Top shelf: **9854 Curtiss Baby Ruth; 9855 Swift Refrigerator Line.**
Second shelf: **9856 Old Milwaukee; 9858 Curtiss Butterfinger.**
Third shelf: **9859 Pabst; 9860 Gold Medal Flour.**
Bottom shelf: **Two variations of the 9861 Tropicana Pure Orange Juice. Left has a flat green roof; right has a glossy green roof.**

R. Kaptur and R. LaVoie Collections; B. Greenberg photograph

	GD	VD	EXC	MT
(A) Type I body.	10	15	20	30
(B) Type II body.	10	15	20	30
(C) Type III body.				NRS

9856 OLD MILWAUKEE: 1975-76, billboard reefer; beer series; red body and door; gold roof and ends; white and black lettering; gold scroll flourish; Symington-Wayne trucks; "BLT 1-75".

	GD	VD	EXC	MT
(A) Type II body.	8	10	15	25
(B) Type III body.				NRS

9858 CURTISS BUTTERFINGER: 1974-76, billboard reefer; candy series; orange body and door; white and blue lettering; white border around "curtiss/Butterfinger"; candy bar electrocal to right; Symington-Wayne trucks; "BLT 2-73". F. Salvatore and C. Rohlfing Collections.

	GD	VD	EXC	MT
(A) Type I body; flat blue roof and ends.	6	8	20	25
(B) Blue gloss roof.	6	8	20	25
(C) Same as (B), but Type II body.	6	8	20	25
(D) Same as (B), but Type III body.				NRS
(E) Same as (B), but Type I body, postwar trucks. Further sightings requested. C. O'Dell Collection.				NRS

9859 PABST: 1974-75, billboard reefer; beer series; Type I white body and door; medium blue roof; blue and red lettering; red and blue Pabst Blue Ribbon logo to left; Symington-Wayne trucks; "BLT 2-73".

	GD	VD	EXC	MT
(A) Type I body.	6	10	15	25
(B) Type II body.	6	10	15	25

9860 GOLD MEDAL FLOUR: 1973-76, billboard reefer; bright orange roof and ends; white body and door; black lettering; orange and gold logos; Symington-Wayne trucks; "BLT 2-73". This is reportedly the version found in separate-sale boxes. A regular production version of this reefer was given to selected General Mills salespersons for outstanding sales efforts in 1973-74. It was accompanied by a special wood base and track section for display. W. W. Smith III Collection and comment.

	GD	VD	EXC	MT
(A) Type I body.	6	8	15	20
(B) Same as (A), but dull dark orange. This version was probably produced for the 1974 Grand National set. It may also have been sold separately. Reader comments requested.	6	8	15	20
(C) Same as (A), but Type II body.	6	8	15	20

W. Smith III Collection and comments

A regular production 9860 Gold Medal reefer was given to General Mills' salesman for special sales efforts. The award car was shipped from General Mills and was accompanied by a letter and a special base with a section and a half of late O27 track with wood-grained ties.

The following is excerpted from the letter which accompanied the car.

"Dear Gold Medal Man:

Gold Medal has been sold in volume ever since it won the Miller's International Exposition in 1880. And 1973-74 was no exception to volume selling...

Gold Medal wants you to have this Lionel railroad car to serve as a rewarding reminder of the volume selling job you did in 1973-74..."

	GD	VD	EXC	MT
(D) Same as (A), but Type III body. Confirmed as existing. G. Halverson comment.				NRS
(E) Type II body; dull orange roof; postwar trucks. Further sighting requested. C. O'Dell Collection.				NRS

9861 TROPICANA PURE ORANGE JUICE: 1975-77, billboard reefer; white body and door; green and orange lettering; Symington-Wayne trucks; "BLT 1-75". Came with the 1560 North American Express set in 1975, and was catalogued separately the next two years.

(A) Type II body; flat green roof and ends.				
	12	15	25	35
(B) Same as (A), but with Type III body; glossy green roof and ends; opaque white body and door.	10	12	20	25
(C) Type III body; translucent white body and door.				
	10	12	20	25

9862 HAMM'S: 1975-76, billboard reefer; beer series; blue body and door; white roof and ends; red and white lettering; Symington-Wayne trucks; "BLT 1-75".

(A) Type II body.	10	12	20	25
(B) Type III body.				NRS

9863 RAILWAY EXPRESS AGENCY: 1974-76, reefer; Type II green body and door; gold lettering; red and white R E A decal; Symington-Wayne trucks; "BLT 1-74". Came in the uncatalogued 1450 Rio Grande Service Station Special set in 1974, then catalogued the next two years.

(A) No electrocals (rubber stamped).	15	20	35	45
(B) Same as (A), but with electrocals.	10	15	30	40
(C) Same as (B); light green roof; with electrocals (gray mold).				
	10	15	30	40
(D) Same as (B), but with Type III body.				
	10	15	30	40

9864 T C A SEATTLE: 1974, reefer; see Volume II, first edition.

	GD	VD	EXC	MT

9866 COORS: 1976-77, billboard reefer; beer series; Type III white body; brown roof; white doors; black and dark yellow lettering; multicolor Coors Colorado logo; Symington-Wayne trucks; "BLT 1-76".

(A) No "R" registration mark.	10	15	25	35
(B) Low "R" registration mark.	12	20	30	40
(C) High "R" registration mark.	12	20	30	40
(D) Low "R" registration mark touching the "s" in "Coors" logo. Hard to find.	40	50	60	75

9867 HERSHEY'S: 1976-77, billboard reefer; candy series; Type III chocolate brown body; silver roof and ends; silver doors; maroon and silver lettering; Symington-Wayne trucks; no "BLT" date. C. Rohlfing Collection.

	10	15	20	40

9868 T T O S OKLAHOMA: 1980, reefer; see Volume II, first edition.

9869 SANTA FE: 1976, reefer; uncatalogued; Type III white body; brown roof and ends; brown door; black lettering and cross logo; Standard O trucks; "BLT 1-76". Part of 1672 Northern Pacific Service Station Special set in 1976, whose components were the first regular O-scale cars to be equipped with the Standard O sprung trucks. Reportedly 5,000 made. C. Lang comment.

	15	25	35	50

9870 OLD DUTCH CLEANSER: 1977-80, billboard reefer; Type III yellow body; red roof and ends; red door; blue lettering; red, blue and white Old Dutch cleaning lady electrocal; white "Old Dutch/Cleanser" logo outlined in red; registration mark; red and white Purex oval logo; Symington-Wayne trucks; "BLT 1-77". M. Blacet Collection.

	6	8	15	20

9871 CARLING BLACK LABEL BEER: 1977-80, billboard reefer; beer series; Type III dark red body; black roof and ends; dark red door; white, gold and black lettering and electrocal; Symington-Wayne trucks; "BLT 1-77".

	10	12	20	25

9872 PACIFIC FRUIT EXPRESS: 1977-79, reefer; Type III orange body; silver roof and ends; orange door; black lettering with white boldface "P", "F", and "E"; Union Pacific and Southern Pacific logos at upper left; Symington-Wayne trucks; "BLT 1-77".

	10	12	25	35

9873 RALSTON PURINA: 1978, billboard reefer; Type III body; blue plastic ends and roof painted blue; white plastic sides painted white; elaborate Ralston Purina checkerboard electrocal in red, white and blue on car side states "Car Used 1945-64"; Symington-Wayne trucks; "BLT 1-78".

	10	12	20	30

See Factory Error and Prototypes chapter in Volume II, first edition.

9874 LITE: 1978-79, billboard reefer; beer series; Type III body; blue plastic roof and ends painted blue; white plastic sides painted white; white doors painted gold; gold and blue "A FINE PILSNER/BEER" electrocal; dark blue "Lite"; Symington-Wayne trucks; "BLT 1-78".

	10	12	25	35

9875 ATLANTIC & PACIFIC: 1978-79, billboard reefer; mustard sides; brown-painted roof and ends; red and black A & P electrocal; red and black lettering; Symington-Wayne trucks; "BLT 1-78".

	6	8	20	25

9876 CENTRAL VERMONT: 1978, reefer; gray sides painted silver; black plastic roof and ends painted black; green lettering; silver door; Standard O trucks; "BLT 1-78". Part of 1867 Milwaukee Limited freight set.

	—	—	30	40

9877 GERBER: 1979-80, billboard reefer; medium blue-painted sides and door; dark blue-painted roof and ends;

R. Kaptur, R. LaVoie, and M. Solly Collections; B. Greenberg photograph

me of the most colorful reefers.
ɔ shelf: 9862 Hamm's; 9863 Railway Express Agency.
ʃond shelf: Two variations of the 9866 Coors. The variation is in the position of the circle-R registration marks.
ird shelf: 9867 Hershey's; 9869 Santa Fe.
ttom shelf: 9870 Old Dutch Cleanser; 9871 Carling Black Label Beer.

	GD	VD	EXC	MT

well-known Gerber baby shown on black and white electrocal; white lettering; Symington-Wayne trucks; "BLT 1-79".

	10	20	30	45

9878 GOOD AND PLENTY: 1979, billboard reefer; candy series; white-painted sides; magenta-painted roof and ends; Good and Plenty box black and magenta electrocal; black lettering; Symington-Wayne trucks; "BLT 1-79". **6   8   15   20**

9879 KRAFT PHILADELPHIA CREAM CHEESE: 1979, billboard reefer; originally shown in 1979 advance catalogue with gray sides, dark blue roof and ends, and blue and white Kraft Philadelphia Cream Cheese electrocal. After the prototype (now in the Lionel archives) was made, the Kraft Company withdrew its permission to use the name and logo, and the number was reassigned to the Hills Bros. car (next entry).

Not Manufactured

9879 HILLS BROS: 1979-80, billboard reefer; red-painted sides; yellow-painted roof and ends; yellow and red coffee can electrocal; white and yellow lettering; Symington-Wayne trucks; "BLT 1-79". **6   8   15   20**

	GD	VD	EXC	MT

9880 SANTA FE: 1979, billboard reefer; orange-painted sides; tuscan-painted roof and ends; black and white cross logo; black "SHIP AND TRAVEL Santa Fe/all the way" lettering; gold FARR Series 1 diamond insignia; Symington-Wayne trucks; "BLT 1-79". From Santa Fe Famous American Railroad Series No. 1, whose components were all offered only for separate-sale.

	20	25	35	50

9881 THE RATH PACKING CO.: 1979, billboard reefer; uncatalogued; yellow sides; tuscan roof and ends; black, yellow and white Rath electrocal; Standard O trucks; "BLT 1-79". Available only as part of set No. 1970, The Southern Pacific Limited. The set and the car were announced in the 1979 advance catalogue, but when the set became a quick sell-out it was removed from the regular catalogue. **—   —   30   40**

9882 N Y R B: 1979, (New York Central) reefer; dark orange-painted sides; tuscan-painted roof and ends; Early Bird Service electrocal; black lettering; number under- and over-scored; Standard O trucks; "BLT 1-79". From set No. 1971, The Quaker City Limited. **—   20   30   40**

Some later billboard reefers as the 9800 series drew to a close.

R. Kaptur, R. LaVoie and A. Rudman Collections; B. Greenberg photograph

Top shelf: 9872 Pacific Fruit Express; 9873 Ralston Purina.
Second shelf: 9874 Lite; 9875 Atlantic & Pacific.
Third shelf: 9876 Central Vermont; 9877 Gerber.
Bottom shelf: 9878 Good and Plenty; 9879 Hills Bros.

	GD	VD	EXC	MT

9883 OREO CHOCOLATE SANDWICH COOKIES: 1979, billboard reefer; candy series; gray sides; blue-painted roof and ends; blue and red Oreo cookie package electrocal and Nabisco logo; dark blue lettering; Symington-Wayne trucks; "BLT 1-79".

	10	20	35	50

9884 FRITOS BRAND CORN CHIPS: 1981-82, billboard reefer; yellow-orange sides; red roof and ends; dark red doors; red Fritos logo electrocal; red lettering; Symington-Wayne trucks; "BLT 1-81".

	—	8	15	20

9885 LIPTON 100 TEA BAGS: 1981-82, billboard reefer; split deep red and yellow sides; dark red door; dark brown roof and ends; brown, white and yellow lettering; Symington-Wayne trucks; "BLT 1-81".

	—	8	15	20

9886 DARK CHOCOLATE MOUNDS: 1981-82, billboard reefer; candy series; white sides; red roof and ends; brown-maroon doors; brown and red Mounds package electrocal; brown and red lettering; Symington-Wayne trucks; "BLT 1-81".

	—	8	15	20

9887 FRUIT GROWERS EXPRESS: 1983, reefer; yellow sides; dark green roof and ends; black lettering; Standard O trucks; FARR Series 4 diamond insignia; "BLT 1-83". Part of

	GD	VD	EXC	MT

Famous American Railroad Series No. 4, whose components were all sold separately.

	—	—	35	45

9888 GREEN BAY & WESTERN: 1983, reefer; gray sides; red roof and ends; black lettering; Standard O trucks; "BLT 1-83". Part of 1361 Gold Coast Limited set. Catalogue showed car with white sides.

	—	—	50	70

16223 BUDWEISER: 1989, billboard reefer; uncatalogued; 9800-type white body; red roof and ends; red and black lettering; large "BUDWEISER" logo to left; Eagle-A logo to right; "ANHEUSER-BUSCH/BEER CAR" around eagle; Symington-Wayne trucks; "BLT 1-89". There is no number on the car. 16223 is Lionel's internal catalogue number; came in 11775 uncatalogued Anheuser-Busch set. Similar to, but not the same as, 9850.

	—	—	—	50

17300 CANADIAN PACIFIC RAILWAY: 1989, Standard O reefer; tuscan body and doors; white lettering; number under- and over-scored; "CANADIAN/PACIFIC/RAILWAY" in large letters to right; Standard O trucks; "BLT 1-89". Part of 11710 C P Rail set.

	—	—	—	55

W. Dyson, R. Kaptur, R. LaVoie and A. Rudman Collections; B. Greenberg photograph

e last of the 9800-series reefers, from 1980-83.

p shelf: 9880 Santa Fe from Famous American Railroad Set No. 1; 9881 The Rath Packing Co. from Southern Pacific Limited set.
ond shelf: 9882 N Y R B, from the Quaker City Limited set; 9883 Oreo Chocolate Sandwich Cookies.
ird shelf: 9884 Fritos Brand Corn Chips; 9885 Lipton 100 Tea Bags.
ttom shelf: 9886 Dark Chocolate Mounds; 9887 Fruit Growers Express, from Famous American Railroad Set No. 4.

	GD	VD	EXC	MT

17301 CONRAIL: 1987, Standard O reefer; medium blue body; white lettering and Conrail wheel logo; black catwalk; Standard O trucks; "BLT 1-87". Part of 11700 Conrail Limited set.

— — 40 50

17302 SANTA FE: 1990, Standard O reefer; yellow body; black roof and ends; black lettering and large black cross logo "Ship and Travel/SANTA FE/ — all the way"; blinking yellow ETD light on brakewheel side powered from roller pickup snapped on one Standard O truck; "BLT 1-90". This is the first Standard O series car with an End-of-Train Device (ETD), the first ETD in a Collector set, the first Collector freight set without a caboose, and one of the first cars for which a power pickup technique was devised for the Standard O trucks. Came only in 11713 Santa Fe Dash-8 set.

— — — 75

19324 DELAWARE & HUDSON*: 1991, reefer; yellow body and roof; black ends; blue lettering and large D&H shield logo to right of door; Standard O trucks; "BLT 1-91". Part of 11719 Coastal Freight Service Station Special set for 1991. This is an unusual number for a reefer car.

— — — 30

	GD	VD	EXC	MT

19500 UNION REFRIGERATOR TRANSIT LINES: 1987, reefer; 9800-series body; yellow sides; brown roof and ends; black lettering; number under- and over-scored; red and white rectangular "THE/MILWAUKEE/ROAD" logo; Standard O trucks; "BLT 1-87". Part of Milwaukee Fallen Flags set No. 2, whose components were only sold separately.

— — — 35

19502 NORTH WESTERN REFRIGERATOR LINE COMPANY: 1987, (Chicago & North Western) wood-sided reefer; Brunswick green lower sides, doors and roof; yellow upper sides; dark green lettering; number under- and over-scored; red, yellow and green North Western decal logo; plastic arch bar trucks; "BLT 1-87".

— — — 30

19503 MAINE POTATOES: 1987, (Bangor and Aroostook) wood-sided reefer; blue lower sides; white upper sides; red roof, ends and doors; contrasting blue and white lettering; "BANGOR AND/AROOSTOOK" logos; brown potato logo; plastic arch bar trucks; "BLT 1-87".

— — — 35

19504 NORTHERN PACIFIC: 1987, wood-sided reefer; yellow sides and doors; bright red-orange roof and ends; black letter-

R. Kaptur, R. LaVoie and A. Rudman Collections; B. Greenberg photograph

Lionel now issues its Standard O reefers in the 17300 series and its regular reefers in the 19500 series.
Top shelf: 17300 Canadian Pacific Railway; 17301 Conrail.
Second shelf: 17302 Santa Fe with blinking yellow ETD light; 19500 Milwaukee Road.
Third shelf: 19502 Chicago & North Western Refrigerator Line Company; 19503 Bangor & Aroostook (Maine Potatoes).
Bottom shelf: 19504 Northern Pacific; 19505 Great Northern.

	GD	VD	EXC	MT

ing; number under- and over-scored; red and white Monad logo decal; plastic arch bar trucks. Watch for peeling decals.

— — — 30

19505 GREAT NORTHERN: 1988, reefer; green and orange Great Northern paint and striping scheme; green and white lettering; Standard O trucks; "BLT 1-88". Part of Fallen Flags set No. 3, whose components were all sold separately.

— — — 45

19506 THOMAS NEWCOMEN: 1988, wood-sided reefer; Famous Inventor series; white sides and doors; bright red roof and ends; black lettering and steam engine electrocal; "THOMAS NEWCOMEN/1663 – 1729/INVENTOR OF THE/STEAM ENGINE"; plastic arch bar trucks; "BLT 1-88". First car in the new "Famous Inventor" series of wood-sided reefers.

— — — 25

	GD	VD	EXC	MT

19507 THOMAS EDISON: 1988, wood-sided reefer; Famous Inventor series; light tan sides and doors; dark brown roof and ends; black and white phonograph electrocal; black-, white- and flesh-colored Edison figure electrocal; "PHONOGRAPH—1877"; "THOMAS ALVA EDISON/1847 1976 1931"; black, white and gold electric lamp electrocal "ELECTRIC/LAMP –| 1880"; plastic arch bar trucks; "BLT 1-88".

— — — 25

19508 LEONARDO DA VINCI: 1989, wood-sided reefer; Famous Inventor series; pale straw yellow sides; gold roof and ends (catalogue shows brown roof); black lettering; "LEONARDO da VINCI/1452 – 1519/PAINTER—SCIENTIST/INVENTOR"; Mona Lisa electrocal to left of door; Symington-Wayne trucks; "BLT 1-89".

— — — 20

19509 ALEXANDER GRAHAM BELL: 1989, wood-sided reefer; Famous Inventor series; light blue sides; dark blue roof and ends; black lettering; "Alexander Graham Bell/1847 – 1922" to

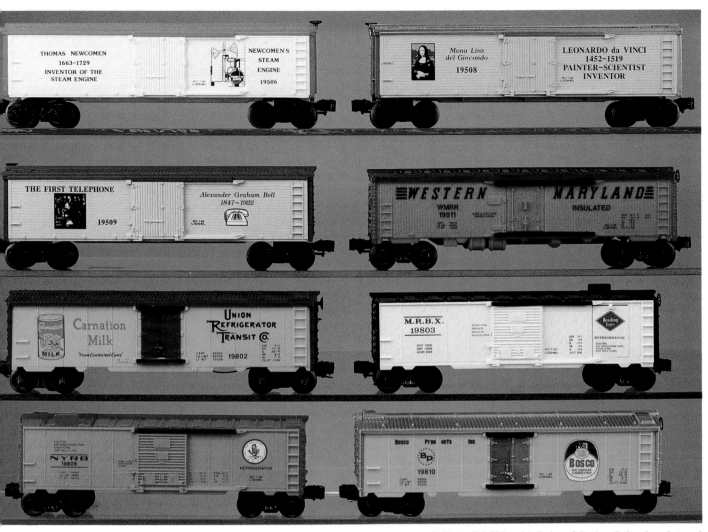

R. Kaptur, R. LaVoie and A. Rudman Collections; B. Greenberg photograph

e first in a new series of wood-sided reefers honoring "Famous Inventors." The two ice cars are really combination refrigerator/boxcar design.

o shelf: **19506** Thomas Newcomen; **19508** Leonardo Da Vinci.

ond shelf: **19509** Alexander Graham Bell; **19511** Western Maryland, from the Fallen Flags set.

ird shelf: **19802** Carnation operating milk car; **19803** Reading Lines operating ice car (see boxcar chapter for listing).

tom shelf: **19808** N Y R B, an operating ice car (see boxcar chapter for listing); **19810** Bosco operating milk car.

	GD	VD	EXC	MT

right of door; electrocal of Bell with the first phone to left side; Symington-Wayne trucks; "BLT 1-89". — — — **20**

19511 WESTERN MARYLAND: 1989, reefer; orange sides; brown roof; red ends; black lettering; large "WESTERN MARYLAND" logo across top of car; Standard O trucks; "BLT 1-89". Part of W M Fallen Flags Series No. 4, whose components were all sold separately. Very similar to earlier 9818, which matches this set perfectly. — — — **30**

19512 WRIGHT BROTHERS: 1990, wood-sided reefer; Famous Inventor series; light gray/off-white sides; green roof and ends; black lettering; "KITTY HAWK 1903" to right of door with Wright Flyer electrocal; "WILBUR WRIGHT/1867 – 1912/OR-VILLE WRIGHT/1871-1948" in black to left; ASF strong-arm trucks; "BLT 1-90". — — — **21**

19513 BEN FRANKLIN: 1990, wood-sided reefer; Famous Inventor series; tan sides; red roof and ends; black lettering; "BEN

	GD	VD	EXC	MT

FRANKLIN/1706 – 1790" at right; electrocal of Franklin to left; "INVENTOR—PUBLISHER—STATESMAN"; 1990 was the 200th anniversary of Franklin's death; ASF strong-arm trucks; "BLT 1-90". — — — **21**

> **Note:** *A packaged set of three wood-sided reefers, "The Old Glory" series, was a surprising uncatalogued late-1989 Lionel release. The three cars (19516-19518) depicted significant events in United States history. They came together in red, white and blue star-studded "Old Glory" set box. Note the sequence of door colors on the three cars. The doors used are Classic boxcar-style.*

19516 GEORGE WASHINGTON: 1989, 1991, wood-sided reefer; from Old Glory series; white sides; silver roof and ends; red

Top shelf: **Box used for The Old Glory Series; 19516 George Washington.**
Bottom shelf: **19517 Civil War; 19518 Man on the Moon.**

B. Greenberg photograph

	GD	VD	EXC	MT

door; electrocal of Washington crossing the Delaware at left; thirteen-star flag to right; blue lettering "When in the Course of human events..."; Symington-Wayne trucks; "BLT 1-89". Part of three-car Old Glory set 19599, announced in late 1989 flyer and catalogued in 1991. — — — 22

19517 CIVIL WAR: 1989, 1991, wood-sided reefer; from Old Glory series; white sides; silver roof and ends; white door; electrocal of Union and Confederate caps and artillery to left; 35-star flag to right; blue lettering; "Four score and seven years ago..."; Symington-Wayne trucks; "BLT 1-89". Part of three-car Old Glory set 19599, announced in a late 1989 flyer and catalogued in 1991. — — — 22

19518 MAN ON THE MOON: 1989, 1991, wood-sided reefer; from Old Glory series; white sides; silver roof and ends; blue door; electrocal of Armstrong on the moon to left; 50-star flag to right; blue lettering "That's one small step for man..."; Symington-Wayne trucks; "BLT 1-89". Part of three-car Old Glory set 19599, announced in a late 1989 flyer and catalogued in 1991. — — — 22

19520 C S X*: 1991, reefer; yellow sides; black roof and ends; black "C&O" and "CSX" lettering; ASF strong-arm trucks; "BLT 1-91". — — — 23

19522 GUGLIELMO MARCONI: 1991, wood-sided reefer; Famous Inventor series; silver sides; black roof, ends and door; black lettering "GUGLIELMO MARCONI/1874 – 1937/INVENTOR" to left; "HIS WIRELESS TELEGRAPH SAVED LIVES AT

	GD	VD	EXC	MT

SEA" to right with electrocal of ship avoiding iceburg using radio; ASF strong-arm trucks; "BLT 1-91". — — — 25

19523 ROBERT GODDARD: 1991, wood-sided reefer; Famous Inventor series; white sides and door; red roof and ends; red lettering "THE MAN BEHIND EVERY ROCKET THAT FLIES" with rocket electrocal to left; "ROBERT GODDARD/1882 – 1945/ROCKET SCIENTIST" to right in red; ASF strong-arm trucks; "BLT 1-91". — — — 25

19802 UNION REFRIGERATOR TRANSIT: 1987, operating milk car with platform; yellow sides; brown roof, ends and doors; red, yellow and black Carnation can logo and lettering; black ornate "UNION REFRIGERATED TRANSIT CO." lettering; white man pushes weighted plastic cans out door onto platform with gray base and steps and white railings; postwar bar-end die-cast trucks with sliding shoes for power pickup; special sheet of decals included to decorate cans. Similar to Bosco operating milk car of postwar years, this car has been a "hot" seller.
— — — 100

19803 M. R. B. X: 1987; see Boxcar chapter.

19808 N Y R B: 1988; see Boxcar chapter.

19810 BOSCO PRODUCTS INC: 1988, operating milk car with platform; bright yellow sides; silver-painted roof, ends and doors; brown, white, red and black Bosco electrocal; dark brown "Bosco Products Inc." lettering; gray and white platform; seven gray plastic milk cans with self-stick Bosco labels; postwar die-cast bar-end trucks with sliding shoes for power pickup. Reissue of postwar 3672. — — — 90

S EARCHLIGHT CAR S

The searchlight car certainly ranks as one of Lionel's most recognizable and popular action cars. The modern Lionel searchlight car is modeled after the 6822 "Night Crew" postwar searchlight car, except that the rubber man of the postwar model is missing from the recent versions.

There are two types of searchlight cars. The first is patterned after the postwar 6822, and uses a standard flatcar body (long Type II, mold 6511-2 — see the Flatcar chapter) with a superstructure attached which closely resembles the one used on the track maintenance cars. The structure even has "TRACK MAINTENANCE" embossed on it. Instead of the extension platform used on the maintenance cars, a metal yoke with a bulb socket and plastic lens hood is placed on the superstructure, wired to a roller pickup on the trucks.

The second searchlight car type did not appear until 1989, when Lionel Trains, Inc. revived the depressed-center extension searchlight car last seen in 1959 on the 3650. This one uses a standard depressed-center flatcar with a plastic generator on one side and a removable searchlight on the other, held in place by a magnet. In between is a cable reel with wire allowing the light to be placed up to four feet from the car.

Postwar had a third style of searchlight car which was the same as the second style just discussed, except that a vibrator motor caused the searchlight hood to rotate, albeit noisily, as the train ran. This is actually the most popular of postwar searchlight cars. It is yet to be seen if modern Lionel will revive it, too.

The first Fundimensions searchlight car enjoyed a long life, the tuscan 9302 Louisville and Nashville car with a gray superstructure and black light hood. This car ran from 1973 through 1978, a long time for a Lionel train. The earliest models had an MPC logo on the car side; they are less common than the car without the logo. There is another scarce version of the car with white lettering instead of yellow.

In 1979, the 9302 was replaced by an attractive 9312 Conrail car with a blue flatcar base. The car was pictured with an orange superstructure in the 1979 advance catalogue, but the pictures in all the regular catalogues showed the superstructure as gray. As it turned out, the car was made both ways, in apparently equal quantities, although regional variations in availability exist. The Conrail car was produced through 1983.

After producing only two versions of the car over its first thirteen years, Fundimensions and LTI have greatly expanded their searchlight car production in the last seven years.

A black and gray C N W, which came only in the Northern Freight Flyer set, appeared in 1983. Reading and U. S. Marines cars followed, as did another handsome black and gray New York Central model for the Yard Chief set.

Changing ownership and number systems in 1987, LTI started putting out one or two searchlight cars each year — Canadian National, Southern, and Lehigh Valley cars were issued. Many, like the Lehigh and 1989's Rio Grande, were released only in sets and are somewhat hard to find. Even the company's own Lionel Railroader Club got into the act with a scarce special issue.

In keeping with its continued expansion and diversification of the Lionel Lines, LTI revived the depressed-center extension searchlight car in 1989 with the 16615 in Lionel Lines colors. New York Central and Western Pacific versions followed. Lionel Trains, Inc. appears determined to offer one of each type every year in the future.

So, until a few years ago, the modern era searchlight cars offered little incentive to collectors because there were only a few varieties, and those were quite numerous. The situation has changed, however. The recent cars create a handsome and collectable group, with several of them relatively scarce and desirable (the 6522 C N W, 6529 N Y C, 9345 Reading, 16608 Lehigh Valley, 16616 Rio Grande, and particularly the 16803 Lionel Railroader Club).

---

* *Asterick found in listings indicates that the information within that listing was derived from Lionel catalogue only.*

A collection of Lionel's fun searchlight cars.
Top shelf: **6526 U S Marines; 6529 N Y C.**
Second shelf: **9302 L&N; 9312 Conrail.**
Third shelf: **9345 Reading; 16606 Southern.**
Bottom shelf **16608 Lehigh Valley; 16625 N Y C depressed-center version with removable searchlight.**

R. Kaptur, R. LaVoie, and M. Solly Collections; B. Greenberg photograph

SEARCHLIGHT CAR LISTINGS

	GD	VG	EXC	MT

6522 CHICAGO & NORTH WESTERN: 1983-85, searchlight car; gray body; red-orange superstructure; black searchlight hood; white lettering; Symington-Wayne trucks. Part of 1354 Northern Freight Flyer set.   — — 25 30

6526 U S: 1984-85, (Marines) searchlight car; camouflage-painted olive drab flatcar, superstructure and searchlight hood; Symington-Wayne trucks with one fixed coupler; "BLT 1-84". Matches 5726 U. S. Marines bunk car and 8485 U. S. Marines diesel switcher, all sold separately, not in a set. Came with sheet of decals to be applied to car by purchaser, although some examples have been found in sealed boxes with decals already applied by the factory. C. Rohlfing comment.   — — 15 20

	GD	VG	EXC	MT

6529 N Y C: 1985-86, searchlight car; black flatcar body; white lettering; gray superstructure; black lens hood; Symington-Wayne trucks with one dummy coupler; "BLT 1-85". Only available in the 1502 Yard Chief switcher set. Car was catalogued as 9247, but made as 6529.   — — 20 25

9247: See 6529.

9302 L & N: 1973-78, (Louisville & Nashville) searchlight car; brown body; gray superstructure with mold 6812-5; black searchlight hood; yellow lettering on flatcar base; superstructure embossed "TRACK MAINTENANCE" and has two shovels, wire, control panel, and oxygen tanks molded in; Symington-Wayne trucks with disc couplers; "BLT 1-72". The searchlight is not a part of the superstructure as such, but is fastened to the superstructure by a circular metal fastener and is not intended to be removed. D. Griggs Collection.
(A) MPC logo.   8 10 15 20
(B) No MPC logo.   6 8 12 17

16615 Lionel Lines; 16803 Railroader Club (see Volume II, first edition).   *M. Solly Collection; B. Greenberg photograph*

	GD	VG	EXC	MT

(C) All white lettering. Beware of chemically altered fakes.
— — **50 65**

9312 C R: 1979-83, searchlight car; blue body; white lettering and wheel logo; black searchlight hood; gray or orange plastic superstructure; mold "No. 3520-12", with box embossed "TRACK MAINTENANCE" and tools, wire, control panel and oxygen tanks molded in; "BLT 1-78". Announced in a late 1978 Accessory Center dealer brochure and catalogued for separate-sale from 1979 through 1983.
(A) Unpainted gray superstructure; plastic rivet holding trucks. Nordby observation.
— **10 15 20**
(B) Unpainted orange superstructure; metal rivet holding trucks. C. Rohlfing and Nordby observations. This version was shown only in the 1979 advance catalogue. Apparently, both versions were produced in about the same numbers, but there were distinct regional differences in distribution which led collectors to believe that the orange superstructure version was scarce. It carries only a small premium over the gray superstructure version. R. LaVoie and Bryan Smith observations.
— **12 20 25**

9345 READING: 1984-85, searchlight car; dark green flatcar body with yellow lettering; cream superstructure with black and white Reading diamond-shaped pressure-sensitive decal on both sides; black searchlight hood; Symington-Wayne trucks; "BLT 1-84".
— — **20 25**

16601 CANADIAN NATIONAL: 1988, searchlight car; maroon flatcar body and searchlight hood; light gray superstructure; Symington-Wayne trucks.
— — — **25**

16606 SOUTHERN: 1987, searchlight car; green flatcar base; white lettering; light gray superstructure; black searchlight hood; Symington-Wayne trucks; "BLT 1-87". Except for its trucks, this car matches the rolling stock in 11704 Southern Freight Runner Service Station set. However, the searchlight car was not sold with the set.
— — — **20**

16608 LEHIGH VALLEY: 1987, searchlight car; black flatcar body; white lettering; light gray superstructure; silver searchlight hood; Symington-Wayne trucks; "BLT 1-87". Came only in Black Diamond set 11702. Note: the previous edition of this Guide erroneously listed this car as 16603.
— — **30 40**

16615 LIONEL LINES: 1989, extended searchlight car; first in a series of new depressed-center searchlight cars (reissues of postwar 3650) in which the light can be moved and repositioned up to four feet from the car; black short depressed-center flatcar body with white lettering; light gray generator housing; black searchlight hood; green cable reel with hand crank to unwind wire; Symington-Wayne trucks; "BLT 1-89".
— — — **25**

16616 RIO GRANDE: 1989, searchlight car; uncatalogued; pale yellow flatcar body; medium gray superstructure; black searchlight hood; black lettering; die-cast arch bar trucks with unusual raised rivet holding trucks to body; "BLT 1-89". Part of 11758 Desert King Service Station Special set for 1989.
— — — **28**

16625 N Y C: 1990, extended searchlight car; similar to 16615; light brown/tuscan depressed-center flatcar body; white lettering; orange generator housing; light gray searchlight hood with blue lens; light tan cable reel with wire and hand crank; ASF strong-arm trucks; "BLT 1-90".
— — — **28**

16626 C S X: 1990, searchlight car; dark green flatcar body and searchlight hood; yellow lettering; light gray supestructure; ASF strong-arm trucks; "BLT 1-90". Came only in 11717 C S X freight set, the top-of-the-line Traditional set of 1990. M. Daniels Collection.
— — — **24**

16637 WESTERN PACIFIC*: 1991, extended searchlight car; brown body; yellow lettering; light gray generator housing; black searchlight hood; orange cable reel with wire and hand crank; ASF strong-arm trucks; "BLT 1-91".
— — — **32**

16803 RAILROADER CLUB: 1990, searchlight car; see Volume II, first edition.

T ANK CARS AND VAT CARS

CHAPTER 17

TANK CARS

*A*s of a few years ago, Lionel had revived all the major tank car styles used in the postwar years, including long one-dome tanks with dome catwalks, short one-dome tanks without dome catwalks, two-dome tankers and three-dome tankers. The last style to be revived, the 6465-type two-dome tank car, emerged in Shell markings in 1983. It is not too surprising that Lionel paid a great deal of attention to tank cars, even though in the real railroad world these cars are far more common in refinery areas than they are in other parts of the country. After all, one of the largest sales markets for toy trains is the East Coast, where tankers are rather common.

What was surprising was that until 1990, modern Lionel had not developed its own original versions of tank cars. On real railroads, tank cars exist in astonishing variety, and other scale model firms have issued many more tank car styles than Lionel. The ice was broken in 1990 when Lionel Trains, Inc. at last announced two brand-new long tankers based on the G A T X "Uni-body" construction in which tank, dome and ends are cast in one piece. These are considered Standard O tank cars — the first issued by Lionel — intended to go with other recent scale-length rolling stock and engines such as the Hudson and SD-40. These new cars have sold well, and we can expect many more road names in this new style, which should help to revitalize Lionel's tank car line.

As a result, Lionel now has five types of tank cars in its line. Only a few of the two-dome tankers have been made, and the first did not appear until 1983, even though the car was very common in postwar, as the 6465 Sunoco. The three-dome tank car has seen a bit more variety, and these include nice steam-valve details on the domes. The long single-dome tank car with a metal platform around the dome and a metal ladder, derived from the postwar 6315, has become the predominant tanker style in the modern Lionel line. Twenty-nine regular-issue cars have appeared in this style, many in sets, and there

is every reason to believe production of this handsome car will continue indefinitely. The fifth style is a short (6¾ inches vs 8¼ inches for the long version) single-dome tank car modeled after the postwar 6015. These cars are made for inexpensive sets and do not come with the metal platform handrails and ladders of their longer big brothers. Oddly enough, although they are longer and in greater demand, the long single-dome cars and the triple-dome cars have plastic frames (albeit well detailed) for the most part, while the shorter one- and two-dome tank cars frequently appeared on stamped-metal frames!

The modern era Lionel tank cars begin in early 1970 with the interesting 9150 Gulf single-dome tank car, the first versions of which used leftover plastic postwar AAR trucks. These trucks had open axle ends, an uncoupling disc attached to a spring steel strip, and a black plastic knuckle rivet — all characteristics of late postwar production of the AAR truck, which was later modified heavily by Fundimensions. This particular tank car illustrated another problem, perhaps one which reflected inexperience. Before the advent of the Tampo decorating process in early 1973, the tank cars had to be decorated by a silk-screening process, in which ink is forced through a nylon screen made from a photograph. This process (which is required to conform to the rounded tank surface) had been used on postwar tank cars. Many early examples of the 9150 have lettering and logos which are badly blurred. Fundimensions soon corrected the problem and applied silk-screening to the 9250 Waterpoxy three-dome tank car as well.

The construction differences between the modern era Lionel cars and those made in the postwar era are more or less minor. The postwar cars had their brakewheels on a raised shaft; in Fundimensions production, they are mounted directly on the frame without the shaft. The 9250 Waterpoxy three-dome tank car had several interesting varieties. The earliest version of the 9250 came with leftover bar-end metal postwar trucks and a brakewheel on a raised shaft; possibly it was made in Hillside, not Mount Clemens. Soon, the car came with regular issue Symington-Wayne trucks. Later produc-

---

* *Asterisk found in listings indicates that the information within that listing was derived from Lionel catalogue only.*

tion of the 9250 featured lettering and coloring which was much brighter than its predecessors. In addition, where these had come in a large Type I box, this last version was shoe-horned into a small Type I box.

The three-dome tank car has had many successors since the 9250. It has come in Sunoco, DuPont, Bakelite, Gulf, Magnolia, B & O, Southern, and many other real railroad and corporate names. Strangely, there are not too many variations of these cars, and none of the three-dome tank cars are especially rare. The hardest ones to acquire are the ones in limited sets, such as the black 9138 Sunoco and the 9313 Gulf.

Two different tank ends are found on the single-dome tank cars. The first type was used up to the 9153 Chevron tank car in 1974; this tank car end had "Lionel" lettering and the "circle-L" logo just above the wire railing, as did all the postwar single-dome tank cars. The second type omits this lettering.

There is another curious tank car available; it is found inside a boxcar! This car-within-a-car was issued for the Lionel Collectors' Club of America as the 97330 Airco. Many collectors have taken the tank out of the boxcar body (which was the 9733) and added a frame, railings and a platform to create a 97330 Airco tank car to match the boxcar. This curious arrangement has not been duplicated since.

Another unusual situation occurred with two nearly identical yellow Shell single-dome tank cars. Fundimensions issued the 9151 Shell tank car in 1972 with a yellow body, red lettering and yellow ends. Apparently, somebody thought the car looked a little too plain, because in the next production year the car's number was changed to 9152, the lettering became a little more bold, and the ends were made black instead of yellow. As a result, the all-yellow 9151 is a great deal more difficult to find than many collectors believe.

Some innovative decorating schemes have made their debuts with the single-dome tank car. In 1975 Fundimensions surprised collectors with its 9154 Borden tank car which featured a shiny, simulated chrome-plated body. Black lettering and black ends gave it an extremely formal look which was popular with many collectors. This example was soon followed by others in Gulf, Sunoco, Texaco, and Mobilgas markings. In 1978 Fundimensions hit the jackpot with an unusual and fanciful car which won a great following for its bright decoration. This was the 9278 Life Savers tank car; the body of the car was covered by an incredibly bright pressure-sensitive decal to make the car look like a large roll of multicolored Life Savers candy rolling down the tracks. This car sold so well that Fundimensions next issued a single-dome tank car which looked like a Tootsie Roll candy package.

Another candy tanker was scheduled for production but was deleted after the catalogue came out in early 1980. This was the Stick-O-Pep tank car, which would have been similar to the Life Savers tank car except for stripes in pink, black and white. Although the car was never produced, the decals were in fact printed, and some have gotten into circulation. The collector should know that any such car is a product of decal application outside the factory rather than actual production. It is not clear why the car was withdrawn, especially in view of the huge success of the Life Savers car. Perhaps the candy company withdrew its permission to use its trademark very late in the production cycle. That did, in fact, happen with the

9879 Kraft Philadelphia Cream Cheese refrigerator car, for which a few prototypes exist in the Mt. Clemens archives. The 9879 number was hurriedly reassigned to the Hills Brothers car.

The short all-plastic single-dome tank car has been made in Mobilgas (two colors), Firestone, Alaska and Sunoco markings. The yellow 9050 Sunoco is a little harder to find than all the others, probably because it was the first and an exact remake of the postwar yellow 6015 car, right down to the old metal frame. Thereafter, they came with plastic frames until quite recently, when a 16111 Alaska was outfitted with the metal frame once again. These small tank cars do not attract too much collector attention (except perhaps for the 9050 Sunoco tank car), and are usually easy to find at inexpensive prices.

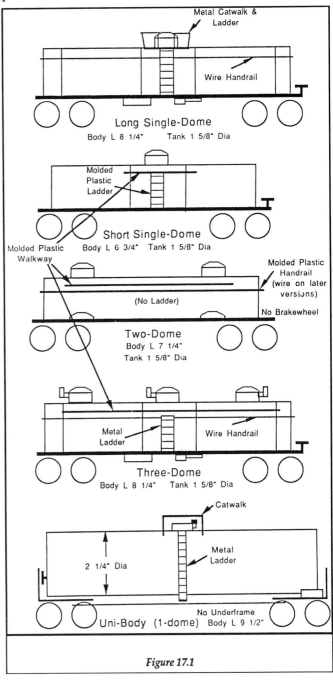

Figure 17.1

The two-dome tank car modeled upon the omnipresent postwar 6465 Sunoco tank car was a recent addition to the modern era Lionel line in Shell and Gulf markings. It illustrates a curious phenomenon reported by many dealers in its Shell configuration — yellow cars and locomotives do not, as a rule, sell very well. Nobody seems to know why this is so, unless it is because the public does not perceive yellow as a prototypical color and therefore judges the rolling stock as unrealistic.

Lionel has, however, revitalized the two-dome tank car in the last few years, and the four produced by LTI since 1986 feature a nice touch not present on the Fundimensions pieces — wire handrails. As on other rolling stock, the MPC logo appears on earlier tank cars (before 1972-1973) and disappears thereafter.

Although very few of the modern era Lionel tank cars are true rarities, they are certainly colorful, and a good collection can be built at relatively modest cost. The tank cars from the Collector sets, such as the 9277 Cities Service, the 9331 Union 76, and the 6305 British Columbia, show excellent potential for appreciation in value because of their limited production.

The most difficult tank cars to find would have to be the 9278 Life Savers and two recent very limited production special issues, the 16106 Mopar and the 17885 Artrain cars. Most likely, the new unibody tank cars will also be in demand after a time.

VAT CARS

The Lionel vat car is a curious but attractive creation. A metal frame is the basis for a low-slung open framework car with a roof supported by girder work on the sides and ends. Within this open framework are four round vats anchored to the car base. The roof has simulated hatches atop each of the vats. The first Fundimensions vat car to emerge was the Heinz pickle car in 1974. Like its postwar predecessor, this car has several variations, including unmarked vats as an interesting factory error. This car was followed by a Libby pineapple vat car in 1975 and a Mogen-David wine car in 1977.

Four other vat cars have been produced since the first three, but these may indicate a new direction for the vat cars. In 1983 an extremely handsome Budweiser beer vat car was produced in red, white and silver markings. It was such a good seller that it was followed by a blue and white Miller Lite beer vat car and a dark maroon Dr. Pepper version. A surprise (and uncatalogued) addition to the vat car line was 1990's re-release of the Budweiser vat (numbered 16625) in different colors than its 9193 predecessor. The 16625 is intended as an add-on to the uncatalogued 1989 Anheuser-Busch set. These four cars may mean that Lionel plans on marketing future vat cars in beer and soda pop markings, a strategy which would create an interesting series of cars for collectors.

TANK AND VAT CAR LISTINGS

	GD	VG	EXC	MT

303 STAUFFER CHEMICAL: 1985, single-dome tank car; L O T S; see Volume II, first edition.

0782 LIONEL RAILROADER CLUB: 1985, single-dome tank car; see Volume II, first edition.

6108 MICRORACERS: 1989; see 16108.

6300 CORN PRODUCTS: 1981-82, three-dome tank car; dark yellow body; black lettering; black-painted lower third of tank; metal ladders; wire handrails; Symington-Wayne trucks; "BLT 1-81". From 1154 Reading Yard King set. Somewhat hard to find. **12 15 25 35**

6301 GULF: 1981-82, single-dome tank car; white body with large orange "Gulf" letters; black number and capacity data; black-painted lower third of tank; black metal dome, walkway and ladders; wire handrails; Symington-Wayne trucks; "BLT 1-81". **— — 20 25**

6302 QUAKER STATE: 1981-82, three-dome tank car; medium green body; white lettering; black frame; wire handrails and ladders; Symington-Wayne trucks; "BLT 1-81". **— 20 30 40**

6304 GREAT NORTHERN: 1981, single-dome tank car; dark green body; yellow lettering; black, red and white Great Northern goat logo; gold FARR Series 3 diamond insignia; black metal dome walkway and ladders; wire handrails; Symington-Wayne trucks; "BLT 1-81". From Great Northern Famous American Railroads Series No. 3, whose components were only available for separate-sale. **— 35 50 65**

6305 BRITISH COLUMBIA RAILWAY: 1981, single-dome tank car; light green body; yellow and white flower logo; white lettering; black metal dome walkway and ladders; wire handrails; Standard O trucks; "BLT 1-81". From 1158 Maple Leaf Limited set. **— 40 50 65**

6306 SOUTHERN: 1983, single-dome tank car; silver body; black lettering; S R logo to right; gold FARR Series 4 diamond insignia; black metal dome walkway and ladders; wire handrails; Standard O trucks; "BLT 1-83". From Southern Famous American Railroad Series No. 4, whose components were all sold separately. **— — 45 60**

6307 PENNSYLVANIA: 1984-85, single-dome tank car; deep wine/maroon tank; black frame; black dome top; white lettering; gold FARR Series 5 diamond insignia; black metal ladders; black dome catwalk; Standard O trucks; "BLT 1-84". Has become a big favorite with collectors because of its attractive color scheme and logos. From P R R Famous American Railroad Series No. 5, whose components were all sold separately. **— — 50 65**

6308 ALASKA RAILROAD: 1982-83, short single-dome tank car; dark blue body; black plastic frame; yellow lettering and Eskimo logo; Symington-Wayne trucks; one operating and one dummy coupler; "BLT 1-82". Separate-sale item in 1982. Appeared in 9195 rolling stock assortment in 1983. **— — 25 30**

6310 SHELL: 1983-84, two-dome tank car; yellow body; red lettering and Shell logo to right; black stamped-metal frame; Symington-Wayne trucks; one operating and one dummy coupler; "BLT 1-83". Separate-sale item. First Fundimensions revival of postwar 6465-style two-dome tank car. **— — 15 20**

Handsome tank cars from the early 1980s.
Top shelf: 6301 Gulf; 6300 Corn Products.
Second shelf: 6302 Quaker State; 6304 Great Northern.
Third shelf: 6305 British Columbia Railway; 6306 Southern.
Bottom shelf: 6307 Pennsylvania; 6308 Alaska Railroad.

W. Dyson Collection; B. Schwab photograph

	GD	VG	EXC	MT

6312 CHESAPEAKE & OHIO: 1984-85, two-dome tank car; 6465-style; dark blue body; yellow lettering; stamped-metal frame; Symington-Wayne trucks; one operating and one dummy coupler; "BLT1-84". Part of 1402 Chessie System set.

— — **20 30**

6313 LIONEL LINES: 1984, single-dome tank car; uncatalogued; bright orange body; blue tank ends and dome cover; red, white and blue circular Lionel logo at left and "LIONEL / LINES" in dark blue at right; metal ladder and dome walkway; wire handrails; Symington-Wayne trucks; "BLT 1-84". Appeared in 1984 spring brochure. Expected to be in demand since it is considered part of Lionel Lines set, whose components were issued beginning in 1982. Limited production. — — **40 55**

6314 BALTIMORE & OHIO: 1986, three-dome tank car; dark blue body; yellow lettering and capitol logo; metal ladders; wire handrails; Symington-Wayne trucks; one operating and one dummy coupler; "BLT 1-86". Part of 1652 B & O freight set.

— — **35 50**

6315 T C A PITTSBURGH: 1972, single-dome tank car; see Volume II, first edition.

6317 GULF OIL CORPORATION: 1984-85, two-dome tank car; 6465-style; unpainted white tank body; orange lettering; orange and white Gulf logo; stamped-metal frame; Symington-Wayne trucks; one operating and one dummy coupler; "BLT 1-84". Separate-sale item, not in a set. — — **15 20**

6323 VIRGINIA CHEMICALS: 1986, single-dome tank car; L C C A; see Volume II, first edition.

6357 FRISCO: 1983, single-dome tank car; black body; white lettering and Frisco shield; yellow tank cover; black metal dome walkway and ladders; wire handrails; Standard O trucks; "BLT 1-83". Only available as part of 1361 Gold Coast Limited set.

— — **50 65**

9036 MOBILGAS: 1978-81, short single-dome tank car; white plastic body with red lettering; black ends; one brakewheel; Symington-Wayne trucks; one operating and one dummy coupler; metal wheels. Part of 1866 Great Plains Express set in 1978-79,

More tank cars.

W. Dyson Collection; B. Schwab photograph

Top shelf: **6310** Shell; **6312** Chesapeake & Ohio.
Second shelf: **6313** Lionel Lines; **6314** Baltimore & Ohio.
Third shelf: **6317** Gulf Oil Corporation; **6357** Frisco.
Bottom shelf: **9039** Mobilgas; **9050** Sunoco, the earliest modern tank car.

	GD	VG	EXC	MT
1050 New Englander set in 1980-81, and 1865/1052 Chesapeake Flyer set.	2	4	6	12

9039 MOBILGAS: 1978, 1980, short single-dome tank car; red plastic body; black ends; white lettering and Mobil "Flying Horse" logo to right; black plastic frame; one brakewheel; Symington-Wayne trucks; metal wheels; one operating and one dummy coupler; "BLT 1-78". This car was offered only in several rolling stock assortments between 1978 and 1980, and appeared in a 1978 dealer brochure. It was intended for the 1051 Texas and Pacific diesel set of 1980, but that set was never made. Unlike three other cars in the set (boxcar, caboose and flatcar) which were never made, this car actually exists.

	GD	VG	EXC	MT
	5	8	10	15

9050 SUNOCO: 1970-71, short single-dome tank car; yellow body; blue lettering (except (E); Sunoco "arrow" logo, MPC logo; metal frame; no "BLT" date. Appeared in the 1085 Santa Fe twin diesel set, and for separate-sale in 1970.

	GD	VG	EXC	MT
(A) Yellow-orange body; AAR trucks; one operating and one dummy coupler; medium orange-yellow background in Sunoco logo.	7	10	20	25
(B) Same as (A), but medium yellow body; Symington-Wayne trucks; one operating and one dummy coupler.	4	5	10	20
(C) Same as (B), but dark yellow body.	4	5	10	20
(D) Same as (B), but light yellow body; light orange-yellow background in Sunoco logo.	4	5	10	20
(E) Same as (B), but with green lettering. G. Halverson Collection.	—	—	30	60

9051 FIRESTONE: 1974-75, 1978, short single-dome tank car; black plastic frame; one operating and one dummy coupler; Symington-Wayne trucks; "BLT 1-74"; no MPC logo. Separate-sale item in 1974-75, and came in a 1978 rolling stock assortment.

(A) Unpainted shiny white body; light blue lettering.

	GD	VG	EXC	MT
	5	8	15	20

W. Dyson, R. Kaptur, R. LaVoie, A. Rudman, M. Solly, and F. Stem Collections; B. Schwab photograph

Lionel's vat cars.
Top shelf: **9106 Miller Lite Beer; 9107 Dr Pepper.**
Second shelf: **9128 Heinz; 9132 Libby's Crushed Pineapple.**
Bottom shelf: **9146 Mogen David Wine; 9193 Budweiser.**

	GD	VG	EXC	MT
(B) Painted flat white body; blue lettering.	5	8	15	20

9106 MILLER LITE BEER: 1984-85, vat car; dark blue body and roof; white lettering; four white vats with red, gold and blue Miller logo; metal chassis; Symington-Wayne trucks; "BLT 1-84".

	GD	VG	EXC	MT
	—	—	15	20

9107 DR PEPPER: 1986-87, vat car; medium red body and roof; orange vats; white lettering on car; white "DR/PEPPER" logo on vats; metal chassis; plastic AAR trucks; "BLT 1-85". Separate-sale item, not in a set.

	—	—	15	20

9128 HEINZ: 1974-76, vat car; red roof; gray sides; red lettering on frame; Symington-Wayne trucks; "BLT 1-74".
(A) Medium yellow vats; green lettering.

	6	8	15	20
(B) Light yellow vats; green lettering.

| | 6 | 8 | 15 | 20 |
(C) Light yellow vats; light turquoise lettering.

| | 12 | 15 | 20 | 25 |
(D) Medium yellow vats; turquoise lettering.

| | 12 | 15 | 20 | 25 |

See Factory Errors and Prototypes chapter in Volume II, first edition.

9132 LIBBY'S CRUSHED PINEAPPLE: 1975-77, vat car; green roof; gray sides; yellow vats; red and brown lettering on vats; green lettering on frame; Symington-Wayne trucks; "BLT 1-75". This car first appeared in the 1579 Milwaukee Road Service Station Special set in 1975, then was catalogued the next two years. Some examples came in boxes marked "Dole's Pineapple" instead of "Libby's". Paper stickers correcting the error were

pasted over the box description. This is probably a printer's error, not an indication that a Dole's car was planned.

	6	10	15	20

9138 SUNOCO: 1978, three-dome tank car; uncatalogued; black body; white lettering; yellow and red Sunoco decal to right; black plastic frame; brakewheel; wire handrails; metal ladders; Standard O trucks; "BLT 1-78". Part of 1868 Minneapolis and St. Louis Service Station Special set. 15 20 35 45

9146 MOGEN DAVID WINE: 1977-81, vat car; silver roof; blue sides; tan vats; blue vat lettering; white frame lettering; Symington-Wayne trucks; "BLT 1-77".
(A) Light tan vents; lighter blue frame; Type V box.

| | 8 | 10 | 15 | 20 |
(B) Medium tan vats; dark blue frame; Type VI box. F. Mace Collection. 10 12 20 25

9147 TEXACO: 1977-78, single-dome tank car; chrome body; black end and dome covers; red and black lettering; large green and red Texaco star to right; black metal dome walkway and ladders; wire handrails; Symington-Wayne trucks; "BLT 1-77". 10 15 20 40

9148 DUPONT: 1977-81, three-dome tank car; cream-yellow body, Cascade green-painted lower third of tank; black lettering; red logo; wire handrails; metal ladders; Symington-Wayne trucks; "BLT 1-76". 6 10 20 25

9150 GULF: 1970-71, single-dome tank car; white unpainted plastic body; black and orange lettering and logo; black metal dome walkway and ladders; wire handrails; Symington-Wayne trucks except (A); "BLT 1-70"; MPC logo. Typically, many ex-

A selection of tank cars from the 1970s.
Top shelf: 9051 Firestone; 9138 Sunoco.
Second shelf: 9147 Texaco; 9148 Dupont.
Third shelf: 9150 Gulf; 9151 Shell.
Bottom shelf: Two versions of the 9152 Shell tank car. The car on the left is painted a slightly lighter yellow.

W. Dyson Collection; B. Schwab photograph

	GD	VG	EXC	MT

amples of this car have fuzzy, ill-defined markings. Slight premium for well-marked example. Car is shown orange in the 1971 catalogue, but was made white.
(A) 1970; early production; black silk-screened lettering; orange silk-screened Gulf logo; plastic frame with low brakewheel; left-over late postwar AAR trucks. R. LaVoie Collection.

	15	20	30	35

(B) Same as (A), but Symington-Wayne trucks.

	10	15	20	30

(C) Same as (B), but darker orange Gulf logo. P. Piker Collection.

	10	15	20	30

9151 SHELL: 1972, single-dome tank car; yellow body, ends and dome cover; red lettering; red seashell logo to right; black metal dome walkway and ladders; wire handrails; Symington-Wayne trucks; "BLT 1-72"; MPC logo. Came in the 1186 Cross Country Express set and for separate-sale.

	10	15	25	30

9152 SHELL: 1973-76, single-dome tank car; yellow body similar to 9151 except for black ends and dome cover; red lettering (bolder and darker than on 9151); Symington-Wayne trucks; "BLT 2-73"; no MPC logo. This car came in the 1388 Golden State Arrow set and was also offered for separate-sale. Early production had postwar-style tank ends with "L" in a circle, as on the postwar 6315. Later production did not have this circle. G. Halverson comment. Same comment applies to next entry.
(A) Light yellow body.

	6	10	20	25

(B) Medium yellow body.

	6	10	20	25

9153 CHEVRON: 1974-76, single-dome tank car; silver body; blue ends and dome cover; blue lettering; red, white, blue and black Chevron logo; black metal dome walkway and ladders; wire handrails; Symington-Wayne trucks; "BLT 1-74"; no MPC logo. Came in the 1584 N & W Spirit of America set, and for separate-sale.
(A) Light blue and red decals.

	6	8	15	30

(B) Dark blue and orange decals.

	6	8	15	30

Bright chromed tankers and variations on an early one.
Top shelf: 9153 Chevron; 9154 Borden.
Second shelf: 9156 Mobilgas; 9159 Sunoco.
Third shelf: 9189 Gulf; 9250(A) Waterpoxy, note the bar-end trucks and tall brake wheel post.
Bottom shelf: Two more versions of the 9250 Waterpoxy, (C) and (D). The car on the left is painted white.

W. Dyson Collection; B. Schwab photograph

	GD	VG	EXC	MT

9154 BORDEN: 1975-76, single-dome tank car; chrome body; black ends and dome cover; black lettering; yellow Borden flower decal; black metal dome walkway and ladders; wire handrails; Symington-Wayne trucks; "BLT 1-75"; no MPC logo. This was the first Fundimensions tank car to feature a chromed finish.
    10   20   30   40

9155 MONSANTO: 1975, single-dome tank car; L C C A; see Volume II, first edition.

9156 MOBILGAS: 1976-77, single-dome tank car; chrome tank body; black ends and dome cover; red and blue lettering and logo; red "Flying Horse" logo; black metal dome walkway and ladders; wire handrails; Symington-Wayne trucks; "BLT 1-76".
    10   20   30   40

9159 SUNOCO: 1976, single-dome tank car; chrome body; blue ends and dome cover; blue lettering; red and yellow arrow decal to right; black metal dome walkway and ladders; wire handrails; Symington-Wayne trucks; "BLT 1-76". Came only in 1665 Empire State Express set.
    20   25   40   60

9189 GULF: 1977, single-dome tank car; chrome body; black ends and dome cover; blue lettering; blue, white and orange Gulf decal; black metal dome walkway and ladders; wire handrails; Symington-Wayne trucks; "BLT 1-77". Came only in 1765 Rocky Mountain Special set.
    20   25   35   45

9193 BUDWEISER: 1983-84, vat car; silver roof; red sides; red and white vats; red vat "bow-tie" lettering; white frame lettering; Symington-Wayne trucks; "BLT 1-83". Separate-sale item which was a good seller. C. Rohlfing and L. Caponi comments.
    —   10   15   20

9250 WATERPOXY: 1970-71, three-dome tank car; white body; blue and green lettering; metal ladder; wire handrails; "BLT 7-70"; MPC logo. One sample observed came in Type I box dated July 1971. T. Rollo comment. Appeared in the 1971, but not the 1970 catalogue.
(A) Postwar die-cast bar-end trucks with tabs; one old-type raised brakewheel stand; unpainted white plastic; as a result lettering is dull. This car may have been manufactured at the old Lionel

Tankers from 1978-80. A few are hard to find.
Top shelf: 9277 Cities Service; 9278 Life Savers, the hardest of all tank cars to find.
Second shelf: 9279 Magnolia; 9313 Gulf.
Third shelf: 9321 Santa Fe; 9324 Tootsie Roll.
Bottom shelf: 9327 Bakelite Plastics; 9331 Union 76.

W. Dyson Collection; B. Schwab photograph

	GD	VG	EXC	MT

Hillside, New Jersey plant before the firm moved to Mt. Clemens, Michigan. E. Whyte Collection.
7   15   25   50

(B) Same as (A), but Symington-Wayne trucks; plastic brakewheel mounted directly to frame.   **6   10   20   30**
(C) Same as (B), but white-painted translucent tank and ends; much brighter green and blue lettering than (A) or (B); Symington-Wayne trucks. Came in smaller Type I box with black "9250 / G. M. C. X. / TANK CAR" stamped in black on ends. Probably later production. R. LaVoie Collection.   **6   10   20   30**

(D) Same as (B), but dark blue frame instead of black; similar to frame color variations of 6560 crane car. Further sightings requested. M. Sabatelle comment.   **NRS**

9277 CITIES SERVICE: 1978, single-dome tank car; dark green body and dome; black plastic frame; white lettering; one brakewheel; black metal ladders and dome walkway; wire handrails; Standard O trucks; "BLT 1-78". Part of Milwaukee Limited set.   **15   25   40   50**

	GD	VG	EXC	MT

9278 LIFE SAVERS: 1978-79, single-dome tank car; extraordinarily bright pressure-sensitive decal around tank body showing five flavors; chrome-plated tank and dome; black metal dome walkway and ladders; wire handrails; one brakewheel; Symington-Wayne trucks. Separate-sale item only. Good seller and hard to find recently.   **30   50   80   100**

9279 MAGNOLIA: 1978-79, three-dome tank car; white plastic body painted white; large black "MA/GNO/LIA" lettering; black plastic frame; black ends; black lower third of tank; shiny wire handrails; black metal ladders; Symington-Wayne trucks; "BLT 1-78".   **8   15   20   25**

9313 GULF: 1979, three-dome tank car; black plastic painted shiny black; white lettering; orange and black Gulf logo; shiny wire handrails; black metal ladders; one brakewheel; Standard O trucks; "BLT 1-79". Part of set No. 1970, the Southern Pacific Limited.   **—   30   45   55**

9321 SANTA FE: 1979, single-dome tank car; silver-painted body; black "A.T.S.F." lettering; black plastic frame; black and white Santa Fe cross decal; gold FARR Series 1 diamond insignia;

Some interesting large tankers. Note dome cap colors.
Top shelf: 9334 Humble; 9344 Citgo.
Second shelf: 9353 Crystal Car Line; 9354 Pennzoil.
Third shelf: 9367 Union Pacific; 9369 Sinclair.
Bottom shelf: 9373 Getty; 9386 The Pure Oil Company.

W. Dyson Collection; B. Schwab photograph

	GD	VG	EXC	MT

metal dome walkways and ladders; wire handrails; Symington-Wayne trucks; "BLT 1-79". Part of Santa Fe Famous American Railroad Series No. 1, whose components were all sold separately.

| | 15 | 20 | 30 | 40 |

9324 TOOTSIE ROLL: 1979-81, single-dome tank car; white dome and ends with red stripe; brown center tank section; white lettering; black metal dome walkway and metal ladders; wire handrails; Symington-Wayne trucks; "BLT 1-79". Follow-up to the successful Life Savers car. Separate-sale only.

| | 10 | 20 | 35 | 45 |

9327 BAKELITE: 1980, three-dome tank car; white upper body; red lower third of tank body; red lettering; red and white "UNION/CARBIDE" logo; wire handrail; metal ladders; Symington-Wayne trucks; "BLT 1-80".

| | — | 10 | 15 | 20 |

9331 UNION 76: 1979, single-dome tank car; glossy dark blue body; orange lettering and "76/UNION" logo; black metal dome

walkway and metal ladders; wire handrails; Standard O trucks; "BLT 1-79". From set No. 1971, the Quaker City Limited.

| | 20 | 30 | 40 | 60 |

9334 HUMBLE: 1979, single-dome tank car; silver-painted tank; red Humble logo and blue lettering; black ends and dome cover; black metal dome walkway and ladders; wire handrails; Symington-Wayne trucks; "BLT 1-79".

| | 6 | 10 | 20 | 30 |

9344 CITGO: 1980, three-dome tank car; white body; black lower third of tank; blue lettering; red and blue "CITGO" logo; wire handrails; metal ladder; Standard O trucks; "BLT 1-80". From the 1070 Royal Limited set.

| | 10 | 20 | 35 | 50 |

9347 NIAGARA FALLS: 1979, three-dome tank car; T T O S; see Volume II, first edition.

9353 CRYSTAL CAR LINE: 1980, three-dome tank car; red body; white lettering; black lower third of tank body; wire handrails; metal ladders; Symington-Wayne trucks; "BLT 1-80".

| | — | — | 15 | 25 |

The most recent Lionel tank car production.
Top shelf: 16102 Southern; 16103 Lehigh Valley.
Second shelf: 16104 Santa Fe; 16107 Sunoco.
Third shelf: 16111 Alaska Railroad.
Bottom shelf: 19600 Milwaukee Road; 19601 North American.

W. Dyson Collection; B. Schwab photograph

	GD	VG	EXC	MT

9354 PENNZOIL: 1980, single-dome tank car; chrome-finished; bright yellow and black logo to right; black lettering; black ends and dome cover; black metal dome walkway and ladders; wire handrails; Symington-Wayne trucks; "BLT 1-80".

— 15 20 30

9356 LIFE SAVERS STIK-O-PEP: 1980, single-dome tank car; planned for 1980 release and shown in the Toy Fair catalogue of that year, but pulled from production at the last minute for unknown reasons; our guess is withdrawal of corporate permission or the demand of a royalty. The pressure-sensitive decals for the car had been contracted and already made; presumably, all such decals would have been stored or destroyed after production was canceled. However, one surviving set of decals has been found and applied to a chrome-plated tank car after the original decorations had been removed, leaving just the chromed tank body. It is not known how many of these decals have survived, but any 9356 tank car in existence was definitely produced outside the factory. F. Fisher Collection. Reader comments invited.

Not Manufactured

9367 UNION PACIFIC: 1980, single-dome tank car; silver-painted tank body; black ends and dome cover; black lettering; gold FARR Series 2 diamond insignia; black metal dome walkway and ladders; wire handrails; Symington-Wayne trucks; "BLT 1-80". Part of U P Famous American Railroad Series No. 2, whose components were available only as separate-sale.
(A) Red, white and blue Union Pacific shield decal to right.

— 20 30 40

(B) Same as (A), but Union Pacific shield is smaller and darker colored and is an electrocal rather than a decal. This was probably a running change implemented because the decals had a tendency to peel. L. Lefebvre Collection.

— 25 35 50

9369 SINCLAIR: 1980, single-dome tank car; medium green tank; white lettering and dinosaur logo to left; black metal dome walkway and ladders; wire handrails; Standard O trucks; "BLT 1-80". From 1071 Mid-Atlantic set. 20 30 45 60

9373 GETTY: 1980-81, single-dome tank car; white body; red dome cap; red and orange logo; black lettering; black metal dome walkway and ladders; wire handrails; Symington-Wayne trucks; "BLT 1-80". From 1072 Cross Country Express set. This car was

	GD	VG	EXC	MT

shown with a white dome cap in the 1980 and 1981 catalogues, but pictured correctly (i.e., as made) in a 1983 Montgomery Ward catalogue, where presumably an actual set was photographed.

— 25 40 50

9386 THE PURE OIL COMPANY: 1981, single-dome tank car; cream tank body; blue ends and dome cover; dark blue lettering and logo; black metal dome walkway and ladders; wire handrails; Standard O trucks; "BLT 1-81". From 1160 Great Lakes Limited set. — 25 40 50

16102 SOUTHERN: 1987, three-dome tank car; uncatalogued; dark green tank body; black frame; gold lettering and Southern herald; chromed handrail; metal ladder; Standard O trucks; "BLT 1-87". Part of 11704 Southern Freight Runner Service Station Special set. — — — 35

16103 LEHIGH VALLEY: 1988, two-dome tank car; unpainted gray body; black lettering and number; red flag logo; stamped steel frame; Symington-Wayne trucks; "BLT 1-88". Separate-sale item, but matches 11702 Black Diamond set from 1987. This was the first time modern Lionel used wire handrails on the two-dome tank car. — — 15 20

16104 SANTA FE: 1989, two-dome tank car; black body; white lettering; bar code to right; stamped-metal frame; wire handrails; Symington Wayne trucks; "BLT 1-89". Separate-sale only, not in a set. — — — 20

16105 RIO GRANDE: 1989, three-dome tank car; uncatalogued; silver-painted body; black lettering; black plastic frame; wire handrails; Standard O trucks; "BLT 1-89". Available only in 11758 Desert King Rio Grande Service Station Special set. — — — 40

16106 MOPAR EXPRESS: 1988, three-dome tank car; uncatalogued; white body; red and blue lettering; blue stripes; no number on car; Symington-Wayne trucks; "BLT 1-88". Offered only as part of uncatalogued 11757 Mopar Express set in 1988. Set was the same as Mopar set from 1987, except this car was added the following year. Reportedly only 600 made. F. Blackwell comment. L. Bohn Collection. — — — 80

16107 SUNOCO: 1990, two-dome tank car; black body; white lettering; Sunoco yellow and red arrow logo to left; black stamped-metal frame; wire handrails; ASF strong-arm trucks; "BLT 1-90". Separate-sale only, not in a set. — — — 18

16108 MICRORACERS: 1989, short single-dome tank car; uncatalogued; yellow body; black lettering "RACING FUEL/LPC"; number "6108" on car; plastic frame; Symington-Wayne trucks; "BLT 1-89". The "C" in "RACING" is misaligned to the rest of the word. Part of uncatalogued 11771 Microracers set made for K-Mart. R. Walle comment. — — — 25

16109 BALTIMORE & OHIO*: 1991, single-dome tank car; black body; white lettering and capitol dome logo; car has end lettering; number under- and over-scored; black metal dome walkway and ladders; wire handrails; stamped-metal frame; Standard O trucks; "BLT 1-91". Part of 11719 Coastal Freight Service Station Special set. — — — 35

16111 ALASKA RAILROAD: 1990, short single-dome tank car; unpainted white plastic body; dark blue lettering and Eskimo logo; stamped-metal frame; Symington-Wayne trucks; "BLT 1-89". Came with 16999 rolling stock assortment. All the pieces in this assortment say "BLT 1-89", but were issued in 1990 with Symington-Wayne trucks, while most regular issue rolling stock in 1990 had the new ASF strong-arm trucks. Lionel may have

used this means to sell off excess Symington-Wayne trucks and Traditional Line pieces for a 1989 set that was never made.

— — — 15

16112 DOWX: 1990, three-dome tank car; yellow body; blue lettering; wire handrails; metal ladder; Dow logo to right; plastic frame; ASF strong-arm trucks; "BLT 1-90". Available only in 11717 C S X freight set. M. Daniels Collection.

— — — 25

16113 DIAMOND SHAMROCK*: 1991, two-dome tank car; white body; black lettering; black and red "d" logo; black stamped-metal frame; wire handrails; ASF strong-arm trucks; "BLT 1-91". Separate-sale only, not in a set. — — — 18

16114 HOOKER*: 1991, short single-dome tank car; black body; yellow lettering; "HOOKER/NIAGARA FALLS,NY"; ASF strong-arm trucks; "BLT 1-91". Part of 11720 Santa Fe Special set. — — — 15

16225 BUDWEISER: 1990, vat car; uncatalogued; gray frame; black roof; white lettering on car; white vats with gray wood-slat appearance; Anheuser A-eagle logo on each vat; ASF strong-arm trucks; "BLT 1-90". Intended as an add-on to the uncatalogued Budweiser set from 1989. Available only from an Anheuser-Busch gift catalogue. Reportedly less than 2500 made. J. D'Introno Collection. — — — 70

17873 ASHLAND: 1988, three-dome tank car; L C C A; see Volume II, first edition.

17877 KATY: 1989, single-dome tank car; T T O S; see Volume II, first edition.

17885 ARTRAIN: 1990, single-dome tank car; uncatalogued; bright medium blue body; white lettering and "Artrain" logo to left side; black metal dome walkway and ladders; wire handrails; Standard O trucks; "BLT 1-90". Artrain is a mobile art museum, based in Michigan, which transports art exhibits around the United States. This car could only be obtained via a 1990 fundraiser by Artrain, in which it was offered in return for donations to the museum. Reportedly less than 1000 were made. This is the second Artrain car after the special 9486 Michigan 150th Anniversary car issued in the same fashion in 1986-87. Both cars are all Lionel-produced. Artrain plans future releases of more rolling stock. — — — 90

17900 SANTA FE: 1990, single-dome Standard O unibody tank car; entirely new tank car style produced by LTI in late 1990, based on GATX (General American Transportation) unibody design, where tank body, ends and dome are a one-piece casting. The tank is longer (9½") and of larger diameter than any previous Lionel tank car. This car is also unique in that there is no full-length chassis frame — the tank ends rest on short platforms attached directly to the Standard O trucks; remainder of the tank is unsupported. Railings, brakewheel and red warning placard on end platforms; dome walkway and metal ladder; detailed dome valves and hatch; underbody drain; black tank body with large white "Santa Fe" letters to left; bar code and chemical data to right; "BLT 1-90". First Standard O tank car issued by Lionel. Offered for separate-sale only, not in a set. This car goes well with the Standard O Dash-8 set issued earlier in 1990.

— — — 60

17901 CHEVRON: 1990, single-dome Standard O unibody tank car; cream/light tan body; red, white, blue and black Chevron logo to left; black lettering, railings, brakewheel and warning placards on end platforms; metal dome walkway and ladder; detailed dome valves and hatch; underbody drain; Standard O

	GD	VG	EXC	MT

trucks; "BLT 1-90". Offered for separate-sale only, not in a set. See 17900 listing for background. — — — **60**

17902 NEW JERSEY ZINC*: 1991, single-dome Standard O tank unibody tank car; white and blue body; blue lower portion of tank; blue and white lettering; "TiO2 SLURRY" and "NJZ"; detailed capacity data; white-painted dome walkway; black metal ladder; railings, brakewheel and warning placard on end platforms; detailed dome valves and hatch; underbody drain; Standard O trucks; "BLT 1-91". Offered for separate sale only, not in a set. See 17900 entry for background. — — — **55**

17903 CONOCO*: 1991, single-dome Standard O tank unibody tank car; white body; black and red lettering; large red "Conoco" logo; white-painted dome walkway; black metal ladder; railings, brakewheel and warning placard on end platforms; detailed dome valves and hatch; underbody drain; Standard O trucks; "BLT 1-91". Offered for separate-sale only, not in a set. See 17900 entry for background. — — — **55**

19600 MILWAUKEE ROAD: 1987, single-dome tank car; dull orange-painted body; black lower third of tank; black dome cover and ends with white lettering; black lettering on tank body; red and white rectangular Milwaukee logo at right; black metal

dome walkway and ladders; wire handrails; Standard O trucks; "BLT 1-87". Part of Milwaukee Fallen Flags set No. 2, whose components were all offered for separate-sale. This is one of the first regular-issue tank cars to have end lettering. — — — **35**

19601 NORTH AMERICAN: 1989, single-dome tank car; silver-painted body; black "MARK 20"; black, red and blue North American decal; black metal dome walkway and ladders; wire handrails; Standard O trucks. Part of Western Maryland Fallen Flags Series No. 4, whose components were only available separately. — — — **45**

19602 JOHNSON*: 1991, single-dome tank car; silver-painted body; red and black "JOHNSON" logo; black lettering; black metal dome walkway and ladders; wire handrails; Standard O trucks. Part of Frisco Fallen Flags Series No. 5, whose components were only sold separately. — — — **35**

38356 DOWX: 1987, three-dome tank car; L O T S; see Volume II, first edition.

97330 AIRCO: 1979, single-dome tank car; L C C A; found inside 9733 L C C A boxcar; see Volume II, first edition.

T · CHAPTER 18 · S
T RUCK S

Throughout this book, the descriptions of the rolling stock issued by modern era Lionel may include phrases such as "Type IX body" or "Standard O Trucks." In an effort to make clear what is meant by such classifications, we often preface the particular chapter with descriptions of body, railing, or other variations which apply to the cars in those chapters alone. However, it is important to recognize construction variations which affect the whole range of modern era production, even though they may not have a dramatic effect upon value. The collector will soon see that these universal variations have their own stories to tell.

One good example of the intricacies of the manufacturing process occurred rather early in Fundimensions' history. The couplers on rolling stock made by Fundimensions and its successors work by a snap-in plastic armature with a metal base which, when pulled down by the magnet on a remote uncoupler track, opens the coupler knuckle and uncouples the car. Postwar Lionel used several different assemblies which would be too costly in today's train world. Therefore, Fundimensions experimented considerably with its uncoupling armatures. We think the company at first tried to glue a flat metal disc onto the plastic surface of the armature shank where it was molded into a rounded end, although we have not been able to confirm this. Then a metal bar was glued into a recess cut into the bottom of the armature shank.

A short time later, someone at the factory came up with an idea which has no doubt saved thousands of dollars for the firm. Fundimensions changed the mold of the downward shaft of the armature so that there was a hole running down the shaft tube. Then the workers placed a simple large, chrome-headed thumb tack into the hole! This solution has worked so well that it is standard practice on even the most expensive trains made by modern era Lionel. Operationally, it is just as good as the reliable metal flap on the old postwar bar-end metal magnetic trucks — and it is a great deal cheaper.

This chapter classifies three areas which cut across all of modern era Lionel's production of rolling stock: the types of trucks, the types of coupler armatures, and the types of wheelsets. For other areas particular to the type of car, see the individual chapters.

TYPES OF TRUCKS

The *plastic* trucks used by modern era Lionel are made of Delrin, a low-friction plastic patented by the duPont Corporation. The side frames of these trucks have a gloss and an oily feel. They are much more flexible and far less brittle than the styrene plastic used in postwar production. Modern era trucks have small holes molded part way into the side frames; these are the bearings for the wheel sets, which have their wheels permanently fixed to the axles. The needle point end of the axles fit into the holes and rotate within them as the car rolls. The wear characteristics of the bearings appear to be excellent, since Delrin has a self-lubrication quality to it. Since the rolling surfaces of the wheels are angled to allow for a differential action around curved track, modern era trucks have performed much better than their postwar equivalents. In addition, the knuckle springs in the couplers are integral to the knuckle instead of a separate metal spring, which often became dislodged in postwar trucks. Since the modern springs are plastic, the couplers should be stored in the open position to allow it to retain its memory and not to stretch.

The *metal* trucks used by modern era Lionel also show advances over their postwar counterparts. In 1973 the firm produced a marvelously well-detailed truck for its scale Standard O Series. This die-cast truck features a bolster bar suspended from the truck frame by actual functional springs, just like the prototype. It has been used on many other non-Standard O cars because of its high quality. Lionel has also produced a well-detailed six-wheel passenger truck in metal; it, too, has been used on steam locomotive tenders, crane cars, and other pieces of rolling stock. In late 1986

Lionel, Inc. introduced a beautifully detailed die-cast arch bar truck for its revivals of the wood-sided cabooses.

TYPE I: AAR TRUCKS WITH TIMKEN BEARINGS —
These trucks are carry-over pieces from late postwar production, except that the side frames are made of Delrin plastic rather than styrene. The detail on these trucks tends to be grainy and rather blurred; apparently, the postwar die used to make them was worn badly. For that reason, these trucks are found only on stock issued from 1970 through early 1972, particularly some of the 9200-series boxcars and the early large hopper cars. All of these trucks are of the later, open-axle style (the ends of the axles are visible from the bottom).

Type IIB Symington-Wayne freight car truck.

B. Schwab photograph

TYPE II: SYMINGTON-WAYNE TRUCKS —
Formerly known as Bettendorf, these plastic trucks were by far the most common ones on modern era Lionel rolling stock up to 1990. Some previous Greenberg Guides (along with the entire train fraternity) called these trucks Bettendorf types. That is an error. In November 1964, an advertisement appeared in the trade magazine *Modern Railroads* for the Symington-Wayne Company of Chicago. This ad clearly showed that the truck Fundimensions and its successors have used for their models is the Symington-Wayne high-speed XL-70 truck. The next issue of the magazine contained a feature article on these trucks. We are indebted to Mr. Thomas Hawley of Lansing, Michigan, for sending us this information and to Texas collector Cliff Lang, who first advised us of this error. There are several variations of these trucks. Most variations have to do with the rear projection at the top of the truck, but there are other variations in coupler shank height to compensate for the differing fastening points on various rolling stock. All variations may be found with either a coupler shank which angles downward, or a coupler shank which comes straight out from the truck frame.

TYPE II A: The top of the truck sideframe is smooth when viewed from the side. There is a small, flat, square-shaped tab at the rear of the truck.

TYPE II B: Identical to Type II A, except that the top of the truck sideframe is not smooth; it has a projection with five rivets.

TYPE II C: Large, rounded projection on the truck rear with a flat punched hole; smooth truck sideframe.

TYPE II D: Identical to Type II C, except that the truck sideframe has the five-rivet projection.

TYPE II E: Rounded projection on the truck rear, but much smaller than Types II C or D. The hole at the rear of the projection is raised by a peg-like structure; smooth truck side frame.

TYPE II F: Identical to Type II E, but has the five-rivet projection on the truck sideframe.

TYPE II G: Medium-sized block-like square projection on truck rear, much more massive than Types II A and B; longer, self-centering coupler shanks; smooth truck side frames. This truck can be found most often on bay window cabooses. There may be a version with the five-rivet projection, but confirmation is needed.

TYPE II H: Identical to Types II A, C or E, but coupler is a non-operating solid plastic piece; used on inexpensive production. There may be a version with the five-rivet projection, but confirmation is needed. Note that the top surfaces of the non-operating couplers are hollowed out, while the operating ones are solid.

TYPE III: STANDARD O SPRUNG TRUCKS —
Many collectors regard these trucks as the finest ever made by Lionel, postwar or modern era. Except for the Delrin coupler armature which includes the steel disk, they are entirely die-cast. Later versions have small Delrin wheel bearings inserted into the side frames. The trucks fasten to their cars with a small screw and a fiber collar. The bolster bar running across the truck is suspended from the truck side frames by two tiny coil springs on each side; these springs actually are functional. The truck is close in design to the standard freight trucks used by the Association of American Railroads for many years. Like the prototypes, the construction is open, with most of the wheel surfaces showing. Lionel has used this truck on most of its Collector Series freight cars.

Type III Standard O sprung truck.

B. Schwab photograph

TYPE III A Standard Type III, as described above.

TYPE III B Introduced around 1984-85, this variation has small Delrin-plastic inserts placed in the wheel bearing holes in the side frames, to improve wear characteristics. The Type IIIA trucks must be lubricated occasionally under heavy use, but Type IIIB trucks do not.

TYPE III C Same as Type IIIB except mold number "9550-050" has been added to underside of truck bolster. A nearly-invisible inscription on the bolster interior reads "Made in China". Also, the Delrin knuckle has been replaced with a die-cast knuckle and separate spring, similar to postwar practice. This change occurred in 1989.

TYPE III D In 1990, Lionel finally managed to adapt this fine truck for a power pickup. This is a snap-in assembly with a spring-loaded roller and a rather fragil copper strip spanning both axles to provide a ground.

TYPE IV: WOOD-BEAM PASSENGER TRUCKS —
These plastic trucks have been used on the early 9500-series short Madison passenger cars and the short 6400-series Amtrak O27 streamlined passenger cars. Their latest use has been on the O27 New York Central passenger cars issued for separate-sale in 1989. They are modeled after the old wooden-beam trucks used on United States railroads in the 19th Century. Like all passenger car trucks, its distinguishing feature is a long coupler shank. It is curious that Lionel would use such an old-fashioned truck on relatively modern passenger cars, but so it goes.

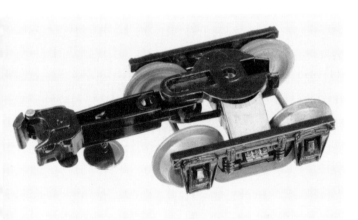

pe IV Wood-beam passenger truck.   *B. Schwab photograph*

TYPE V: PLASTIC ARCH BAR TRUCKS — These
plastic open-type trucks are a carry-over from the "General" style trucks used by postwar Lionel in the late 1950s for its Civil War locomotive, tenders and passenger coaches. They were also used on the Fundimensions revival of those cars, and lately they have been used for the new bunk and tool car series and the wood-sided reefer series. They are more sturdy than their forebears, thanks to the Delrin plastic formula, but they are more fragile than other modern era Lionel trucks. The center part of the sideframe on this truck, with its two molded springs, closely resembles the Type I AAR trucks.

TYPE VI: DIE-CAST O27 PASSENGER TRUCKS —
These die-cast trucks are carry-overs from the original metal trucks used on the postwar O27 streamlined passenger cars, beginning with the 2400-series in the late 1940s. These trucks feature long coupler shanks, two molded springs, and a small air cylinder. Ironically, Fundimensions bypassed these trucks when it revived the O27 passenger cars, but the firm then reissued them for use on certain pieces such as the 9307 animated gondola, the four-truck depressed-center flatcar and certain bay window cabooses. A plastic version of this truck (see Type XIII) appeared in 1990.

Type VI Die-cast O27 passenger truck.   *B. Schwab photograph*

TYPE VII: DIE-CAST O GAUGE PASSENGER TRUCKS —
When Fundimensions revived the extruded aluminum passenger cars with the Congressional Limited cars in 1979, the firm also revived the original trucks. These well-detailed four-wheel die-cast trucks feature very long coupler shanks which are made self-centering by a hairspring where they meet the truck frame. Also prominent are four simulated springs and a large air cylinder. They have been used in all aluminum O Gauge passenger cars produced since then, but nowhere else.

Type V Plastic arch bar truck.   *B. Schwab photograph*

Type VII Die-cast O Gauge truck.   *B. Schwab photograph*

TYPE VIII: DIE-CAST SIX-WHEEL PASSENGER TRUCKS

— Fundimensions introduced an entirely new passenger truck upon issuing its Blue Comet set in 1978. The truck side frames are die-cast, as is the coupler and its shank. As with the O Gauge four-wheel trucks, the couplers are made self-centering by means of a hairspring. These trucks have been used on the Blue Comet, Chessie Steam Special, Chicago and Alton, and Wabash passenger cars, as well as the six-wheel tenders on most deluxe steam engines since then and most of the newer crane cars. It has one operating weakness: the axles are fastened to the trucks by slide-in plastic bearings which may come loose if not periodically checked.

Type VIII Die-cast six-wheel passenger truck.   *B. Schwab photograph*

TYPE IX: DIE-CAST ARCH BAR TRUCKS

— When Lionel put out a brochure for a special direct-mail-order Hudson and series of freight cars in late 1986, most of the freight cars had Standard O trucks. But the two wood-sided cabooses, excellent revivals of the prewar New York Central semi-scale caboose, had an entirely new truck — a highly realistic die-cast arch bar truck. These trucks have the same good open-style construction as the Standard O trucks, but no operating springs. Thus, they were adapted immediately for a roller carriage for illumination, while the firm spent several years deciding how to do so with the Standard O sprung trucks. So far, arch bar trucks have been put onto all wood-sided cabooses

and the Pennsylvania N5C caboose which matches the bronze GG-1 of 1987. Expect these excellent trucks to be placed on many more cars in the future.

Type IX Die-cast arch bar truck.   *B. Schwab photogr*

TYPE X: ASF STRONG-ARM TRUCKS

— 1990 marked the first time in seventeen years that Lionel had changed the plastic trucks in its regular Traditional Line rolling stock. This truck was announced in the 1989 catalogue, but the company did not begin installing it on the rolling stock until 1990. Collectors (having long objected to the looks of the rather obscure Symington-Wayne trucks) approved of the more realistic-looking side frames on these trucks, which can be recognized by three prominent molded-in springs. The design is based on the American Steel Foundry prototype. Structurally, the truck is not significantly different than the Symington-Wayne, but the coupler shank appears to have a bit more material. Lionel has applied the "Strong-Arm" descriptor to the coupler on this truck, implying it will not inadvertently open as often as the couplers on the Symington-Wayne did.

Type X ASF strong-arm truck.   *B. Schwab photograp*

TYPE XI: **DIE-CAST LONG-DISTANCE TENDER TRUCKS** — These appeared first on the 18006 Reading T-1 tender in 1989, the 18009 Mohawk tender in 1990 and on the 18011 Chessie T-1 tender in 1991. The enormously detailed six-wheel metal side frames feature two small molded brakepads around each wheel and four round holes in the side frames between the wheels. They are large, scale length, and quite open in appearance, befitting their status on the longest steam locomotive tenders Lionel has ever made. As with several other new truck styles introduced recently, we should expect to see more of this handsome truck.

TYPE XII: **BAR-END TRUCKS** — These die-cast trucks are carryovers from postwar Lionel production. The truck takes its name from the semi-circular end of the bolster bar which protrudes from the side frames just above the springs. Lionel will sometimes refer to this truck as "Betterdorf" type. They are used on isolated modern era pieces: operating cattle and horse cars, where they are used to support the sliding-shoe power pickup needed to operate them; and the revivals of the 2466 tenders, which are so constructed as to require this type of truck.

B. Schwab photograph

pe XII Bar-end truck.

TYPE XIII: **PLASTIC O27 PASSENGER TRUCKS** — These are essentially plastic versions of the Type VI die-cast

B. Schwab photograph

e XIII Plastic O27 passenger truck.

O27 passenger trucks. But unlike the Type VI trucks these were actually used on modern era steamlined O27 passenger cars. They first appeared on the Northern Pacific O27 streamlined passenger cars in 1990.

TYPE XIV: **DIE-CAST LEAF-SPRING TRUCKS** — A new-style truck quite similar to the Type IX arch bar trucks except it has closed side frames rather than the open construction of Type IX. The wheel bearings and leaf spring at the center are also more prominent on this truck. This new truck first appeared on the 18000 B-6 tender in 1989 and later came with the tender on the 18611 Lionel Lines locomotive from the 1990 Service Station set.

B. Schwab photograph

Type XIV Die-cast leaf-spring truck.

TYPE XV: **DIE-CAST "CENTURY" TENDER TRUCKS** — Another long six-wheel die-cast truck in the style of the Type XI T-1 tender truck. It is very similar to the Type XI truck except the round holes on that truck are oval -shaped on the century version, and the journal boxes read "Timken". This truck has appeared only once in the modern era to date, but what a one it was — 1990s revival of the 700E scale Hudson, the 5340 New York Central, a fine model of the great locomotive which pulled the "Twentieth Century Limited."

TYPES OF COUPLER ARMATURES

From the beginning, Fundimensions and its successors have used a detachable armature for all its trucks. This offers operating advantages over the older postwar arrangement, since the operator can often cure a stubborn coupler which refuses to close properly by simply exchanging armatures. These armatures, made of Delrin plastic, came with a metal uncoupling disk and are designed to plug into two holes in the coupler shanks and can be removed by simply prying them out with one's fingernail. They feature a small tab projection for manual uncoupling. Variations involve the uncoupling shaft protruding downward from the armature.

TYPE I: A small, flat metal disc is simply glued onto the flared bottom of the armature shaft. Confirmation of this is requested.

TYPE II: A metal bar is inserted into a recess cut into the flared bottom of the armature shaft. This variety is found most often on cars equipped with the AAR trucks with Timken bearings.

TYPE III: A flat-headed thumb tack with a blackened point is pressed into the armature shaft. This first appears in later 1970 production.

TYPE IV: A chrome-plated, large, round-headed thumb tack (or something like it) is pressed into the armature shaft. First appearing in late 1971 production, this variety is by far the most common.

TYPES OF WHEEL SETS

As previously mentioned, Fundimensions designed a new set of wheels for its rolling stock from the outset of its production. Regardless of type, these wheels feature angled rolling surfaces (known as "fast-angle") to provide for a differential action around curved track. This cuts drag and rolling resistance to a minimum. The wheels are integral with the axles, which have needlepoint bearings. Since Fundimensions and its successors have subcontracted for the production of these wheelsets (a much more common practice than one may think), there have been several different types of wheelsets used over the years. The differences are mostly found in the inside of the wheel surfaces. So far, we have identified the following eight varieties:

TYPE I: Blackened wheels and axles; deeply recessed inner wheel section with thick outer rim on inside surface stamped "LIONEL MPC"; four, large, round, raised metal projections near junction of wheel with axle; lettering is very hard to see on some examples because the die wore down with use. There is usually a casting mark between and just outside the circumference of two of the projections.

TYPE II: Same as Type I, except no "LIONEL MPC" lettering. These are clearly different from worn-die versions of Type I.

TYPE III: Blackened axles; shiny bronzed inner and outer surfaces; four less distinct (as opposed to Types I and II) flat metal projections near junction of wheel with axle. On some examples, there appears to be a manufacturer's mark which looks like a letter "F" extended to form a letter "C". The mark could also be a large "L" connected to a small "L" inside a slightly open rectangle.

TYPE IV: Blackened wheels and axles; no lettering; three barely visible small flat round projections near junction of wheel and axle.

TYPE V: Same as Type IV, but shiny chromed axles, no dots on inside wheel surfaces. Except for axles, Types IV and V are very difficult to distinguish.

TYPE VI: Heavy, light gray, pressed-powdered-iron wheel (which can suffer chipped flanges with abuse); solid inner surface with one slight indentation; shiny chromed axles. Cars equipped with these wheels roll better because their center of gravity is lower. These wheels are the most common in current use.

TYPE VII: Black plastic wheel and axle; deep inner recess; trucks used exclusively for inexpensive production; will not operate track-activated accessories using insulated rails.

TYPE VIII: Same as Type III, except has shiny chromed wheels and axles. A. Passman comment.

INDEX

Note: parenthesis around a page number indicates a photograph.

Item	Page	Item	Page	Item	Page	Item	Page
6567	211	7304	173, (171)	7803	114, (113)	8064	29, (24)
6573	254	7309	173, (171)	7806	114	8065	29
6574	211	7312	173	7807	115	8066	29, (25)
6575	217	7401	173, (171)	7808	173, (114)	8067	21
6576	211	7403	113	7809	115, (114)	8068	29, (33)
6579	211, (210)	7404	113, (171)	7810	115, (114)	8071	42, (42)
6582	217	7500	37, (35)	7811	115, (114)	8072	42
6585	217	7501	113	7812	173	8100	76, (79)
6587	217	7502	291, (292)	7813	115	8101	76, (78)
6593	211, (210)	7503	291, (292)	7814	115	8102	87
6670	211	7504	242, (242)	7815	115	8104	99
6700	113, 291, (291)	7505	113	7816	115	8111	46
6900	189, (189)	7506	113	7817	115	8140	88, (88)
6901	189, (189)	7507	291, (292)	7900	173	8141	88, (93)
6903	190, (189)	7508	192, (193)	7901	162, (161)	8142	89, (89)
6904	190, (189)	7509	291, (292)	7902	162, (161)	8150	57, (55)
6905	190, (189)	7510	291, (292)	7903	163	8151	42, (42)
6906	190, (189)	7511	292, (292)	7904	173, (161)	8152	42, (42)
6907	204, (203)	7512	292, (292)	7905	163	8153	46, (33)
6908	192, (193)	7513	292, (292)	7908	163	8154	46
6910	190, (190)	7514	292, (293)	7909	163	8155	37, (35)
6912	198	7515	107, (106)	7910	163, (161)	8156	37
6913	191	7517	107	7912	164, (162)	8157	49, (48)
6916	207, (206)	7518	107, (106)	7913	173, (161)	8158	29, (24)
6917	191, (190)	7519	292	7914	164, (165)	8159	29
6918	198, (196)	7520	114	7920	164	8160	29, (25)
6919	198	7521	292	7925	164	8161	59
6920	204, (203)	7522	107, (106)	7926	164, (161)	8162	42, (42)
6921	198	7523	292	7930	164, (161)	8163	42
6926	191	7524	293	7931	164, (161)	8164	14, (18)
7200	264	7525	114	7932	164	8182	46
7201	264	7530	107, (106)	8001	87	8200	42, 89, (40), (88)
7202	264	7600	192, (177)	8002	75, (77)	8201	42, (38)
7203	264	7601	177, (176)	8003	75, (77)	8203	42, 89, (90)
7204	264, (276)	7602	177, (176)	8004	75, 99, (80), (98)	8204	42, 89
7205	264	7603	178, (176)	8005	99	8206	50, 76, (78)
7206	264	7604	178, (176)	8006	75	8209	89, (89)
7207	264	7605	178, (176)	8007	87	8210	77, (81)
7208	264	7606	178, (176)	8008	87, (45)	8212	89
7210	264	7607	178, (177)	8010	45, (45)	8213	89
7211	264, (276)	7608	178, (177)	8014	76	8214	89
7212	265	7609	178, (177)	8020	20	8215	77, (82)
7215	265, (265)	7610	178, (177)	8021	20	8250	29
7216	265, (265)	7611	179, (177)	8022	20	8252	21
7217	265, (265)	7612	179, (177)	8025	21, (21)	8253	21
7220	266	7613	179, (177)	8030	28, (24)	8254	30
7221	266	7700	180	8031	28, (24)	8255	30
7222	266	7701	180	8040	87, (88)	8258	30, (29)
7223	266, (266)	7702	180	8041	87, (93)	8260	14, (14)
7224	266	7703	180	8042	87, (92)	8261	15, (18)
7225	266	7704	180	8043	87	8262	15, (14)
7227	267	7705	181	8050	37, (35)	8263	30
7228	267	7706	181	8051	37	8264	59, (59)
7229	267	7707	181	8054	14, (12)	8265	42, (39)
7230	267, (270)	7708	181	8055	14, (12)	8266	42, (29), (42)
7231	267	7709	181, (179)	8056	49, (48)	8268	21, (22)
7232	267	7710	181, (179)	8057	46, (46)	8269	22, (22)
7241	267	7711	181, (179)	8059	14, (18)	8272	53
7242	267	7712	181, (179)	8060	14, (18)	8300	57, 89
7301	173	7800	114, (113)	8061	37, (35)	8301	49, (49)
7302	173, (171)	7801	114, (113)	8062	14, 76, (12)	8302	53, 89, (53)
7303	173, (171)	7802	114, (113)	8063	42, (42)	8303	57, 89, (55), (92)

Note: parenthesis around a page number indicates a photograph.

Note: parenthesis around a page number indicates a photograph.

Item	Page	Item	Page	Item	Page	Item	Page
9001	164	9072	207	9154	317, (317)	9225	233, (232)
9010	242, (242)	9073	199, (200)	9155	317	9226	225, (224)
9011	243	9075	199	9156	317, (317)	9228	120, (120)
9012	243, (243)	9076	199	9157	218, (219)	9229	121, (120)
9013	244, (242)	9077	199	9158	218, (219)	9230	121, (120)
9014	217	9078	207	9159	317, (317)	9231	186, (185)
9015	244, (243)	9079	200, 245, (243)	9160	192, (193)	9232	219, (219)
9016	244, (243)	9080	200	9161	193, (193)	9233	219, (216)
9017	230	9085	208, (206)	9162	193, (193)	9234	219, (219)
9018	244	9090	167, (167)	9163	193, (193)	9235	211, (212)
9019	217	9100	50, 263	9164	193	9236	211
9020	217, (217)	9101	263	9165	193, (194)	9237	121
9021	207	9102	263	9166	200, (200)	9238	254, (255)
9022	218, (217)	9103	263	9167	193, (194)	9239	195, (195)
9023	218, (217)	9104	263, (266)	9168	193, (194)	9240	247, (245)
9024	218	9105	264	9169	200, (200)	9241	254, (255)
9025	207, 244, (206)	9106	264, 315, (315)	9170	194	9245	211
9026	218	9107	315, (315)	9171	200, (200)	9247	308
9027	207	9109	264	9172	201, (200)	9250	317, (317)
9029	218	9110	245, 264, (244)	9173	201	9259X	186
9030	230, (231)	9111	245, 264, (244)	9174	185, (185)	9260	247, (133), (247)
9031	230, (230)	9112	246, 264, (244)	9175	194, (194)	9261	247, (247)
9032	230, (231)	9113	246, 264, (244)	9176	194, (194)	9262	247, (247)
9033	231, (231)	9114	246, (244)	9177	185, (185)	9263	248, (247)
9034	245	9115	246, (244)	9178	201	9264	248, (247)
9035	164, (163)	9116	246, (244)	9179	208, (207)	9265	248, (247)
9036	313	9117	246, (245)	9180	194, (194)	9266	248, (247)
9037	164, (163)	9118	246	9181	194, (194)	9267	248, (247)
9038	245, (243)	9119	246, (245)	9182	194, (194)	9268	186, (185)
9039	314, (314)	9120	223, (223)	9183	195, (159), (195)	9269	186
9040	164, (163)	9121	218, (219)	9184	186, (185)	9270	196, (195)
9041	164, (163)	9122	223, (223)	9185	195, (195)	9271	186, (185)
9042	166, (163)	9123	102, (103)	9186	195, (195)	9272	186, (185)
9043	166, (163)	9124	218	9187	201, (200)	9273	187, (186)
9044	166	9125	102, (103)	9188	186, (185)	9274	187, (186)
9045	166	9126	103, (103)	9189	317, (317)	9276	201, 248, (248)
9046	166	9128	315, (315)	9193	317, (315)	9277	318, (318)
9047	166	9129	103, (104)	9200	117, (116)	9278	318, (318)
9048	166	9130	246, (245)	9201	118, (116)	9279	318, (318)
9049	166, 231	9131	231, (231)	9202	118, (116)	9280	174, (120)
9050	314, (314)	9132	315, (315)	9203	118, (116)	9281	104, (104)
9051	314, (316)	9133	224, (223), (245)	9204	118, (116)	9282	225, (224)
9052	167, (163)	9134	246, (245)	9205	118, (116)	9283	233
9053	167	9135	246, (245)	9206	118, (116)	9284	233, (232)
9054	167	9136	232, (231)	9207	118, (116)	9285	225, (224)
9055	231, (231)	9137	232	9208	118, (117)	9286	249, (248)
9057	198	9138	315, (316)	9209	119, (117)	9287	196, (195)
9058	198	9139	103, (104)	9210	119, (117)	9288	196, (195)
9059	199	9140	232, (231)	9211	119, (117)	9289	196
9060	199, (196)	9141	232, (232)	9212	224	9290	234, (232)
9061	199, (196)	9142	233	9213	247, (245)	9300	254, (255)
9062	199, (196)	9143	233, (232)	9214	119, (117)	9301	121, (120)
9063	199, (196)	9144	233, (232)	9215	119, (117)	9302	308, (308)
9064	199, (196)	9145	103, 168, (104)	9216	103, (104)	9303	255, (255)
9065	199, (200)	9146	315, (315)	9217	120, (117)	9304	255, (254)
9066	199	9147	315, (316)	9218	120, (117)	9305	174, 255
9067	207, (207)	9148	315, (316)	9219	120, (120)	9306	219, 255
9068	207, (207)	9149	224, (223)	9220	293, (293)	9307	234, (232)
9069	199	9150	315, (316)	9221	173, (172)	9308	121, (120)
9070	199, (200)	9151	316, (316)	9222	224, (223)	9309	187
9071	207	9152	316, (316)	9223	120, (120)	9310	255
		9153	316, (317)	9224	174, (172)	9311	255

Note: parenthesis around a page number indicates a photograph.

Note: parenthesis around a page number indicates a photograph.

Item	Page	Item	Page	Item	Page	Item	Page
9599	278	9728	175, (138)	9807	293, (293)	9875	300, (302)
9600	160, (157)	9729	140, (138)	9808	172, (170)	9876	300, (302)
9601	160, (157)	9730	141, (138)	9809	294, (293)	9877	300, (302)
9602	160, (157)	9731	141, (139)	9811	294, (293)	9878	301, (302)
9603	160, (157)	9732	141, (139)	9812	294, (293)	9879	301, (302)
9604	160, (157)	9733	141, (139)	9813	294, (294)	9880	301, (303)
9605	160, (157)	9734	141, (139)	9814	294, (294)	9881	301, (303)
9606	160, (157)	9735	141, (139)	9815	294, (294)	9882	301, (303)
9607	160, (157)	9737	141, (139)	9816	295, (294)	9883	302, (303)
9608	160, (158)	9738	142, (140)	9817	295, (294)	9884	302, (303)
9610	160, (158)	9739	142, (141)	9818	295, (294)	9885	302, (303)
9611	160	9740	143, (141)	9819	295, (294)	9886	302, (303)
9620	132	9742	143, (141)	9820	235, (233)	9887	302, (303)
9621	132, (133)	9743	143, (141)	9821	235, (233)	9888	302
9622	132, (133)	9744	144, (141)	9822	235, (233)	16000	278
9623	132, (133)	9745	144, (141)	9823	220, (216)	16001	278
9624	132, (133)	9747	144, (142)	9824	235, (234)	16002	278, (279)
9625	133, (133)	9748	144, (142)	9825	295, (294)	16003	278
9626	160, (158)	9749	145, (142)	9826	172, (170), (296)	16009	278
9627	160, (158)	9750	145, (142)	9827	295, (295)	16010	278, (265)
9628	160, (158)	9751	146, (142)	9828	296, (295)	16011	278
9629	160, (158)	9752	146, (142)	9829	296, (295)	16012	278
9660	160, (159)	9753	146, (143)	9830	296, (295)	16013	279
9661	160, (159)	9754	146, (143)	9831	296, (295)	16014	279
9662	160, (159)	9755	147, (143)	9832	296, (295)	16015	279
9663	160, (159)	9757	147, (143)	9833	296, (295)	16016	280, (279)
9664	160, (159)	9758	147, (143)	9834	296, (295)	16017	280, (279)
9665	160, (159)	9759	148, (143)	9835	296, (296)	16018	280, (279)
9666	160	9760	148, (144)	9836	297	16019	280, (279)
9667	160	9761	148, (144)	9837	297, (296)	16020	280, (279)
9668	160	9762	148, (144)	9840	297, (296)	16021	280, (279)
9669	160	9763	175, (144)	9841	297, (296)	16022	280
9670	161	9764	148, (144)	9842	297, (296)	16023	280, (279)
9671	161	9767	148, (144)	9843	297, (296)	16027	280
9672	161	9768	148, (145)	9844	297, (296)	16028	280
9678	161	9769	148, (145)	9845	297, (297)	16029	280
9700	135, (134)	9770	148, (145)	9846	298, (297)	16030	280
9701	135, (134)	9771	149, (145)	9847	298, (297)	16031	280
9702	136, (134)	9772	149, (145)	9849	298	16033	280
9703	136, (134)	9773	175, (145)	9850	298, (297)	16034	280
9704	136, (134)	9774	149, (146)	9851	298, (297)	16035	280
9705	136, (135)	9775	149, (146)	9852	298, (297)	16036	281
9706	137, 191, (135), (190)	9776	149, (140)	9853	298, (297)	16037	281
		9777	149, (146)	9854	298, (299)	16038	281
9707	175, (135)	9778	149, (146)	9855	298, (299)	16039	281
9708	137, (135)	9779	149, (146)	9856	299, (299)	16040	281
9709	138, (135)	9780	149, (146)	9858	299, (299)	16041	281
9710	138, (135)	9781	149, (147)	9859	299, (299)	16042	281
9711	139, (136)	9782	149, (147)	9860	299, (299), (300)	16043	281
9712	139, (136)	9783	149, (147)	9861	300, (299)	16044	281
9713	139, (136)	9784	150, (147)	9862	300, (301)	16045	281
9714	139, (136)	9785	150, (147)	9863	300, (301)	16046	281
9715	139, (136)	9786	150, (147)	9864	300	16047	281
9716	140, (136)	9787	150, (148)	9866	300, (301)	16048	281
9717	140, (137)	9788	150, (148)	9867	300, (301)	16102	321, (320)
9718	140, (137)	9789	150, (148)	9868	300	16103	321, (320)
9719	140, (137)	9800	293	9869	300, (301)	16104	321, (320)
9723	140, (137)	9801	171, (170)	9870	300, (301)	16105	321
9724	140, (137)	9802	293, (293)	9871	300, (301)	16106	321
9725	175, (137)	9803	171, (170)	9872	300, (302)	16107	321, (320)
9726	140, (138)	9805	293, (293)	9873	300, (302)	16108	321
9727	140, (138)	9806	172, (170)	9874	300, (302)	16109	321

Note: parenthesis around a page number indicates a photograph.

Note: parenthesis around a page number indicates a photograph.

Item	Page	Item	Page	Item	Page	Item	Page
18501	47	19100	282	19400	236, (234)	19808	156, 306,
18502	34, (29), (154)	19101	282	19401	236, (234)		(174), (305)
18503	47	19102	282	19402	212, (212)	19809	156, (174)
18504	34	19103	282	19403	236, (234)	19810	306, (305)
18551	23	19104	282	19404	226, (225)	19811	156
18552	44	19105	282	19405	212	19813	156, (174)
18600	96	19106	283	19408	236	19816	208
18601	96	19107	283	19409	222	19900	156
18602	96	19109	283	19410	236	19901	157, (156)
18604	96	19110	283	19500	303, (304)	19902	157
18605	96	19111	283	19502	303, (304)	19903	157, (156)
18606	96	19112	283	19503	303, (304)	19904	157, (156)
18607	96	19113	283	19504	303, (304)	19905	157, (156)
18608	96	19200	152, (152)	19505	304, (304)	19906	157, (156)
18609	96	19201	152, (152)	19506	304, (305)	19907	157
18610	97	19202	152, (152)	19507	304	19908	158, (156)
18611	97	19203	152, (152)	19508	304, (305)	19909	158
18612	97	19204	152, (151)	19509	304, (305)	19910	158
18613	97	19205	153, (151)	19510	175, (174)	19911	158
18614	97	19206	153, (151)	19511	305, (305)	19912	158
18615	97	19207	153, (151)	19512	305	19913	158
18616	97	19208	153, (151)	19513	305	19914	158
18617	97	19209	153, (151)	19515	175	25000	252, (243)
18618	97	19210	153, (151)	19516	305, (306)	33000	34
18620	97	19211	153, (151)	19517	306, (306)	33004	35
18700	97	19212	153, (153)	19518	306, (306)	33005	35
18702	100	19213	153, (153)	19519	175	38356	322
18704	97	19214	153, (153)	19520	306	80948	158
18705	97	19215	154, (153)	19522	306	81487	226
18706	97	19216	154, (153)	19523	306	97330	322
18707	97	19217	154, (153)	19600	322, (320)	118815	25
18716	100	19218	154, (153)	19601	322, (320)	121315	161
18800	34, (29)	19219	155, (154)	19602	322	298224	226, (242)
18801	39, (37)	19220	155, (154)	19651	111, (110)		
18802	34	19221	155, (154)	19652	111, (110)		
18803	24	19222	155, (154)	19653	111, (110)		
18804	24	19223	155, (154)	19654	111, (110)		
18805	24	19228	155	19655	111, (110)		
18806	44	19229	155	19656	111, (110)		
18807	24	19230	155	19657	111		
18808	44	19231	155	19658	111		
18809	24	19232	155	19700	191, (190)		
18810	44	19233	155	19701	197		
18811	44	19234	155	19702	197, (195)		
18812	34	19235	155	19703	191, (190)		
18813	45	19300	258, (258)	19704	191, (190)		
18814	24	19301	258, (258)	19705	191		
18815	25	19302	251, (250)	19706	191, (190)		
18900	63	19303	251, (250)	19707	208		
18901	23	19304	251, (250)	19708	188, (154)		
18902	23	19305	258, (258)	19709	208, (206)		
18903	23	19307	258, (258)	19710	191		
18904	23	19308	259, (258)	19712	197		
19000	281, (154)	19309	251, (250)	19800	175, (174)		
19001	281	19310	251	19801	175, (174)		
19002	281	19311	251	19802	306, (152), (305)		
19003	281, (268)	19312	252, (250)	19803	156, 306, (152),		
19010	281	19313	259, (258)		(305)		
19015	282	19315	259	19804	252, (251)		
19016	282	19316	252	19805	156, (152)		
19017	282	19317	252	19806	252, (251)		
19018	282	19324	303	19807	191, (190)		

Note: parenthesis around a page number indicates a photograph.